STATISTICAL
METHODS...

STATISTICAL
METHODS...

FREDERICK C. MILLS

Columbia University

THIRD EDITION

HOLT, RINEHART AND WINSTON

New York · Chicago · San Francisco
Toronto

2063600

PRINTED IN THE UNITED STATES OF AMERICA

6 7 8 9

To

D. C. M.

Preface to the Third Edition

The techniques of modern statistics permeate the research activities of social and natural scientists and the practices of private and public administrators. The simple methods of dealing with "classified facts respecting the condition . . . of the people of a state," which constituted "statistics" for our grandfathers, have grown into a comprehensive system of concepts and of related procedures for the advancement of knowledge and for dealing with the uncertainties that face men in the ordinary affairs of life. The growth of this discipline has extended, indeed, over centuries, but the advance has been greatly accelerated in recent decades.

In the Preface to the second edition of this book, published in 1938, I wrote "The postwar years have witnessed . . . the initiation of such another period of ferment and creative activity as that which, earlier, brought the great contributions of Karl Pearson and his associates. The older instruments of quantitative analysis have been refined . . .; methods of designing statistical experiments and formulating and testing hypotheses have been improved; statistical inference has been placed on a sounder foundation." The years that have passed since 1938 have brought no slackening in the tempo of advance. The mathematical and logical bases of statistics have been strengthened and broadened; the tools of statistical analysis have been sharpened. And the forces of growth are still strong.

In preparing the third edition of *Statistical Methods* I have sought to take account of the more important of recent developments that bear on the applications of statistics in the social sciences, in business administration, and in governmental affairs. I have extended and brought up to date examples of the uses of statistics in research and administration. I have tried to make the text a more effective instrument for instruction in the logic and methodology of modern statistics, and a more useful handbook for the practicing statistician. To these ends, the book has been re-worked from first to last. The structure of the opening descriptive sections (Chapters 2–5) has been modified only slightly, but the balance of the book has been substantially re-written. Sections have been added on several topics not treated in preceding editions.

The chief change in arrangement is in the early introduction of statistical inference. A foundation for this is laid in Chapter 6; the two following chapters deal at greater length with procedures for generalizing from sample statistics and for testing hypotheses. These topics are further developed in succeeding chapters. The emphasis thus given to inference is, I think, not only logically but pedagogically desirable. Processes of inference are the essence of modern statistics. The concepts that underlie these processes give coherence to an exposition of statistical procedures. Moreover, this aspect of statistics is the most stimulating to the student. Consideration of the doctrines of inference can lift statistics from the humdrum to the (sometimes even) glamorous, as a subject of instruction. An effective presentation of statistical inference can offer the student discipline in scientific method, and can provide an illuminating experience in the uses of applied logic. This subject should be introduced early and should, I venture, be the continuing thread that ties together the topics making up a course in statistics.

Subjects of special interest to economic and social scientists — index numbers and time series — are somewhat more fully treated in the present edition than in the preceding one. The chapters on index numbers now include a section on the measurement of productivity changes, a topic of special concern in an era of rapid technological advance. In handling time series, discussion of the more traditional methods of analysis is supplemented by an account of the fruitful techniques used by the National Bureau of Economic Research in the study of business cycles. The final chapter of the book is given to the art of sample surveys, a relatively new instrument of rich potential.

In the organization and presentation of subject matter I have had two objectives. I have sought to make the exposition intelligible to the non-mathematical reader — that is, to the reader whose formal mathematical training does not go beyond the elements of algebra and analytic geometry. While I have tried to set forth the nature of the theory that underlies specific procedures and to establish the logical bases of these procedures, I have not, in general, essayed to give mathematical proofs of the various theorems discussed. As Sir Ronald Fisher has said, this is "an age of technical cooperation." There must be division of labor between the tool-makers in statistics and the great body of students and practitioners who employ statistics in subject-matter fields and in administration. This book is directed to the needs of users. It is of course essential that users understand the assumptions on which particular procedures rest and the limitations attaching to particular instruments. I have attempted to make these assumptions and limitations clear.

My second objective in presentation has been to give a coherent discussion of statistical methods. The statistical approach embodies a fundamentally unified attitude toward the world of men, things, and events; it entails the application to diverse problems of a central body of principles. A vital element is lost if statistics be regarded as a bundle of unrelated procedures. I hope that I have succeeded in making this book an integrated whole.

This does not mean that there is but one proper order for the treatment of topics in the development of statistical principles. Individual teachers may well wish to modify, in detail, the order I have employed, or to select sections from the body of the book and the appendices for inclusion in a brief course of study. As I have indicated, I think it desirable that the student be introduced to the concepts of statistical inference at an early stage, after certain descriptive procedures have been covered. Thereafter, choice among the diverse techniques and applications of statistics may depend upon the background and interests of particular student groups. Variation in order and content of treatment is by no means inconsistent with coherence and continuity in the exposition of principles of statistical inquiry.

The list of references at the end of each chapter is designed to serve the needs of readers at different levels of statistical competence, and of varying interests. Most of the lists include elementary texts, intermediate texts, and treatises developing the mathematical foundations of statistics. Certain of the lists include, also, references to original memoirs of special importance and to research studies exemplifying applications of particular methods.

The obligations, both general and specific, that I have incurred in the preparation of this volume are numerous. The writer of any such book as this draws upon a body of knowledge built up through the efforts of many workers over many years. My indebtedness to these workers will be clear; it is acknowledged with pleasure. I am grateful, too, to representatives of public and private agencies who have been uniformly courteous and obliging in complying with requests for data and for information on procedures. Specifically, I would mention the Chief Statistician's Division of the American Telephone and Telegraph Company, the National Bureau of Economic Research, the Bureau of Labor Statistics, and the Bureau of the Census. The tables appended to this volume are drawn from various sources. My chief obligations here are to Sir Ronald Fisher of Cambridge University and his publishers, Messrs. Oliver and Boyd of Edinburgh and London; to Professor George W. Snedecor and the Iowa State College Press; to Professor Truman L. Kelley and the Harvard University Press; and to Dr. W. H. S. Stevens and the Bureau of Transport Economics and Statistics of the Interstate Commerce Commission. Generous help has been given me by members of my family — by William H. Mills and Robert L. Mills on specific points, by Dorothy C. Mills on the many tasks entailed in the making of a book. To them, and to others who have aided me with counsel and suggestion, I am deeply grateful. Finally, I must reaffirm my thanks to those who assisted me in various ways in the preparation of earlier editions.

Although I should like to believe that the text of this book is free of mistakes, typographical and other, I may not do so. I shall be obliged to readers who will inform me of errors they may detect.

F. C. M.

February, 1955.

Contents

CONTENTS

CHAPTER 1

On Statistics and Statistical Methods

This book deals with a mode of inquiry — a method of investigating social and natural processes and of providing bases for decisions in research and administration. Seen in detail, statistical techniques are numerous and varied, but in sum they constitute a unified, systematic, and logical approach to the study of the affairs of man and the order of nature. In their workaday applications they furnish investigators and administrators with succinct descriptive summaries of masses of observations. But we should miss the essence of this mode of inquiry if we saw it merely as a collection of techniques for summarizing experience, in the form of averages, standard deviations, coefficients of correlation, index numbers, trend lines, and seasonal and cyclical patterns. For its use does not end with the perhaps prosaic tasks of simple description. In broad as well as in narrow spheres it can provide a foundation for rational action when a choice must be made among alternative procedures. And, perhaps most important of all, in the statistical approach we have a means for the advancement of knowledge that seems to accord in fundamental ways with the nature of things in the world we are seeking to understand.

In their most significant aspect modern statistical techniques are procedures for the making of what Dewey has termed warranted assertions. Such assertions, when statistically based, may be estimates or generalizations that go beyond the sample of observations immediately studied; they may be decisions that accept or reject hypotheses. Inference, in these forms, is the heart of modern statistics. In the detailed development of methods of statistical inference we shall examine the nature and role of random samples; we shall be concerned with populations of persons, things, events, and measurements, and with means of estimating the attributes of such populations on the basis of samples drawn from them. We shall discuss techniques adapted to the testing of hypotheses.

These various methods, we have said, seem to accord with reality — with the ways of men and of nature in the world about us. To explore this subject in detail would take us beyond the direct concerns of the working statistician. And yet this working statistician may properly ask whether his techniques are adapted to the raw materials with which he deals. There is much evidence to indicate that they are, whether the statistician be dealing with the mass attributes of human beings or of other organic forms, or with the behavior of assemblages of physical entities. More than eighty years ago Clerk Maxwell wrote, ". . . our actual knowledge of concrete things is of an essentially statistical nature. . . . .Those uniformities which we observe in our experiments with quantities of matter containing millions of molecules are uniformities . . . arising from the slumping together of multitudes of cases each of which is by no means uniform with the others." The emphasis Maxwell here placed upon *aggregates*, as opposed to individuals, and upon uniformities in group behavior, is the emphasis that characterizes all statistical inquiry. For although omnipresent chance may shape the behavior of individuals, making it unpredictable, valid statements may still be made about aggregates.

Maxwell was concerned with molecular theory. The statistical view of nature that he first made explicit now shapes the approach of physical scientists in studies that go far beyond the field of molecular phenomena. Indeed, such a view is mandatory wherever an element of probability enters into our knowledge of the physical world — and there are few areas into which it does not enter. In the realms of organic nature and of human relations our present funds of useful knowledge rest largely upon conceptions of the same statistical character. Such knowledge deals with things that are individually indeterminate; the behavior of John Jones, the precise yield of corn in a given plot, the transmission of the quality represented by a particular gene, the price of wheat on a given day in a competitive market — these are individually unforeseeable and unpredictable. But when each of the entities of which we are speaking is combined with similar entities we have aggregates in which clear uniformities are discernible. It is with such uniformities in the behavior of aggregates, whether they be aggregates of molecules, of neutrons and protons, of genes, or of human beings, that statistical generalizations deal. Because these uniformities are nearly always imperfect, although definable and in some degree predictable, statistical generalizations are always couched in terms of probabilities. Statistical knowledge is thus imperfect, and always marked by uncertainty. But it is knowledge that is usable in the world of natural and human events.

Procedures by which such knowledge is established and extended are discussed in the pages that follow. They rest, at bottom, upon the rational and informed use of data of observation. Since accurate and relevant observations are the building blocks of statistical inquiry, a word is in order, in this introductory note, about the character of the data available to workers in the fields of human affairs with which this book deals. These data are numerous. They often fall short of specific needs, it is true, but they are more accurate and vastly more comprehensive than those that were available a short quarter century ago. For immediate purposes these data may be regarded as of two types — those acquired by random sampling, and those not so acquired.

In deriving the statistical generalizations we have spoken of the investigator seeks to employ randomly acquired data. What this means, in detail, we shall discuss later. Here we shall say, only, that sample data drawn from a stated population are randomly acquired when the sampling process gives each individual element of that population a definable probability of inclusion in the sample. Some of the data available to statisticians today have been obtained by procedures that yield truly random samples. Indeed, one of the most encouraging of recent developments in the improvement of social, economic, and business "intelligence" (using that word in its military sense) is the growing use of closely controlled survey techniques for obtaining random samples. This is true of a number of current compilations made by federal agencies. Private investigators, too, in increasing degree, design field studies to yield random samples adapted to specific purposes. When randomness is thus realized, the methods of generalization and of testing that will be described in the discussion of statistical inference are applicable.

But vast collections of data available for use in social, economic, and business research have not been randomly obtained. They may be nonrandom because of the way they were compiled. Statistical agencies, both governmental and private, sometimes gather statistics that are readily available rather than those that are desirable for the purpose in hand. (In fact, the truly desirable may be quite unavailable.) Or a given set of data may be nonrandom because of inevitable interdependence among successive observations, a condition usually true of statistics making up time series. In dealing with such nonrandom samples probability concepts, and modes of inquiry and generalization involving such concepts, do not apply, or apply only with important reservations. When these methods are misapplied, serious error may result. This is not to say that nonrandom observations are of no value. There is much information to be gleaned from such data, perhaps all the information needed for particular purposes. In some tasks purely descriptive statistics may play a pre-eminent role in providing brief and effective summaries of varied experience, and may serve as an indispensable aid to rational judgment. But the careful investigator will be scrupulous in limiting the uses to which nonrandom data are put, and cautious in generalizing from them.

These brief introductory remarks anticipate ideas and concepts that will be developed in the pages that follow, but they may serve a purpose in suggesting to the student of statistics something of the nature of the tools we shall be talking about, and of the method of inquiry these tools implement. It is a powerful method, widely applicable today in administration and research. Yet, as goes without saying, it is not all-powerful or all-sufficient. As cautionary aids in the application of the methods discussed in this book, two general points may be left in the mind of the reader.

We have spoken of statistical techniques as tools, or instruments, and the terms are appropriate. But it is obvious that tools must be used with judgment. In statistical work the investigator must have the benefit of guiding principles and rational concepts. For the statistician, as statistician, faces two occupational hazards — the danger that he will overemphasize the accumulation of data, and the danger that he will be overconcerned with techniques of manipulating data. The piling up of evidence, quantitative or otherwise, is not the object of investigation, nor does indiscriminate accumulation necessarily provide a basis for wise decisions. The warranted assertions that are sought in all inquiry are achieved through the rational use of evidence — the use of empirical data in making generalizations that go beyond the limits of observation, in testing hypotheses, in modifying hypotheses when they fail to accord with relevant observations. The play of reason in formulating theories is checked by reference to the data of observation; the accumulation and manipulation of such data are controlled and guided by reason.

The second general warning may sound equally obvious, but it is no less pertinent to the work of the statistician. Techniques can never be given priority over substantive knowledge of the field of inquiry, over what J. L. Henderson has spoken of as ". . . intimate, habitual, intuitive familiarity with things." Sharp tools may be grievously misused without this deep familiarity with reality in the area of investigation — and this statement applies with special force to the use of statistical techniques. If such techniques are to be well and wisely employed they must be adapted, with understanding, to the materials under study.

REFERENCES

Cohen, Morris R., "The Statistical View of Nature," *Journal of the American Statistical Association*, June 1936.

Kelley, Truman L., *Fundamentals of Statistics*, Chap. 1.

Kendall, M. G., "The Statistical Approach," *Economica*, May 1950.

Merz, J. T., *A History of European Thought in the Nineteenth Century*, Vol. II, Chap. 12, "The Statistical View of Nature."

Mills, F. C., "On Measurement in Economics," in *The Trend of Economics*, R. G. Tugwell, ed.

Royce, Josiah, "The Mechanical, the Historical and the Statistical," *Science*, April 17, 1914.

Wirth, L., ed., *Eleven Twenty Six: A Decade of Social Science Research*, section on "Quantification: the Quest for Precision."

The publishers and the dates of publication of the books named in chapter reference lists are given in the bibliography at the end of this volume.

Aspects of Graphic Presentation

Some Relevant Principles and Basic Procedures

The explanation of methods of condensing, analyzing, and interpreting quantitative observations must start with the discussion of some fundamental considerations that are mathematical rather than statistical in character. In doing so it is deemed advisable, even at the risk of treading quite familiar ground, to discuss certain simple mathematical conceptions to which constant reference will be made in later chapters.

Statistical analysis is concerned primarily with data based upon measurement, expressed either in pecuniary or physical units. The methods of coordinate geometry, developed first by the philosopher Descartes, greatly facilitate the manipulation and interpretation of such data. We briefly summarize some relevant principles of coordinate geometry.

Rectangular Coordinates. If two straight lines intersecting each other at right angles are drawn in a plane, it is possible to describe the location of any point in that plane with reference to the point of intersection of the two lines. We will call one of the lines (a vertical line) $Y'Y$, the other line (horizontal) $X'X$, and the point of intersection (or *origin*) O (see Fig. 2.1). If P be any point in the plane, we may draw the line PM, parallel to $Y'Y$ and intersecting $X'X$ at M, and the line PN, parallel to $X'X$ and intersecting $Y'Y$ at N. If we set OM equal to g units and ON equal to h units, g and h constitute the *coordinates* of P, describing its location with reference to the origin O. Thus, in Fig. 2.1, g equals 6 and h equals 5. The distance g along the x-axis is termed the *abscissa* of the point P, while the distance h along the y-axis is termed the *or-*

dinate of the point *P*. (It is a rule of notation always to give the abscissa first, followed by the ordinate.) The coordinates of any other point in the same plane may be determined in the same way. Conversely, any two real numbers determine a point in the plane, if one be taken as the abscissa and the other as the ordinate.

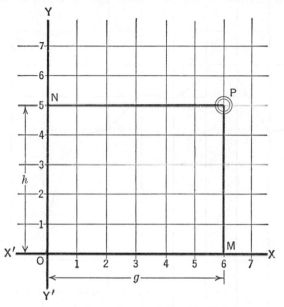

FIG. 2.1. Location of a Point with Reference to Rectangular Coordinates.

A point may lie either to the right or left or above or below the origin, *O*. It is conventional to designate as positive abscissas laid off to the right of the origin, and as negative abscissas laid off to the left of the origin, while ordinates are positive when laid off above the origin and negative when laid off below the origin. In general, the values to be dealt with in economic and social statistics lie in the upper right-hand quadrant, where both abscissa and ordinate are positive.

This conception of coordinates is fundamental in mathematics and of basic importance in statistical work. A very simple example will illustrate the utility of this device in representing economic observations. The figures presented in Table 2 1 may be employed.

These data may be represented graphically on the coordinate system, months being laid off along the *x*-axis and number of automobiles along the *y*-axis, as in the accompanying diagram (Fig. 2.2). In plotting the abscissas, December, 1953, is considered as located at the point of origin. The *x*-value of the entry for January.

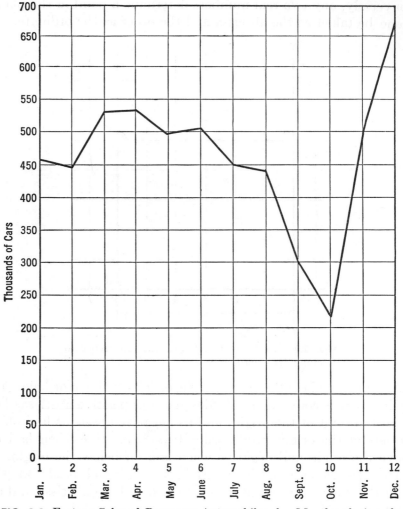

FIG. 2.2. Factory Sales of Passenger Automobiles, by Months, during the Year 1954.*

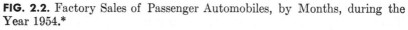

* Source: Automobile Manufacturers Association.

1954, is thus 1, of the February figure 2, etc. The coordinates of the point representing the number of cars sold in January, 1954, are 1 and 454,562; for February the values are 2 and 446,676. The coordinates for December are 12 and 669,778. The movement of automobile sales during the year may be more easily followed if the points are connected by a series of straight lines, as is done in the figure.

TABLE 2–1

Factory Sales of Passenger Automobiles in the United States, by Months, during the Year 1954 *

Month	Number of passenger cars sold
January	454,562
February	446,676
March	531,529
April	534,667
May	497,062
June	507,055
July	451,663
August	445,300
September	300,998
October	221,195
November	498,248
December	669,778

* Source: Automobile Manufacturers Association.

Functional Relationship. In the location of any point by means of coordinates, it has been pointed out, two values are involved; every point ties together and expresses a relation between two factors. In the above case these are months and number of passenger automobiles sold at factories. With the passage of time the volume of automobile sales changes, and the broken line shows the direction and magnitude of these changes. Both time and number of cars sold are *variables*, that is, they are quantities not of constant value but characterized by variations in value in the given discussion. Thus in Fig. 2.1 the abscissa has a fixed value of 6, while the ordinate has a fixed value of 5, but in Fig. 2.2 both abscissa and ordinate have varying values, the one varying from 1 to 12, the other from 221,195 to 669,778. The symbols x and y are, by convention, used to designate such variable quantities as these, the former in all cases representing the variable plotted along the horizontal axis, the latter representing the variable plotted along the vertical axis.[1]

Independent and dependent variables. In Fig. 2.2, which depicts

---

[1] It should be noted that letters at the end of the alphabet are used as symbols for *variables*, while letters at the beginning of the alphabet are used as symbols for *constants*, i.e., quantities the values of which do not change in the given discussion.

the changes taking place in automobile sales with the passage of time, it will be noted that the latter variable changes by an arbitrary unit, one month. Having made an independent change in the time factor we then determine the change in output taking place during the period thus arbitrarily chopped out. The variable which increases or decreases by increments arbitrarily determined is called the *independent variable*, and is generally plotted on the x-axis. The other variable is termed the *dependent variable*, and is plotted on the y-axis. This dependence may be real, in the sense that the values of the second variable are definitely determined by the values of the independent variable, or it may be purely a conventional dependence of the type described. Time, it should be noted, is always plotted as independent, when it constitutes one of the variables.

When two variables y and x are so related that the value of y is determined by a given value of x, y is said to be a function of x. The general expression for such a relationship is $y = f(x)$. Thus the speed at a given moment of a body falling in a vacuum is a function of the time it has been falling, the pressure of a given volume of gas is a function of its temperature, the increase of a given principal sum of money at a fixed rate of interest is a function of time. If the values of the independent variable be laid off on the x-axis of a rectilinear chart and the corresponding values of the function (i.e., the dependent variable) be laid off on the y-axis, a graphic representation of the function will be secured, in the form of a curve.[2] This concept of functional relationship is a very important one in statistical work. Some of the simpler functions may be briefly discussed.

The straight line. The simplest case of relationship between variables is that in which $y = x$. As an example, the relation between the age of a tree and the number of rings in its trunk may be cited. A tree 6 years old will have 6 rings, one 20 years old will have 20 rings, and so on. This relationship may be represented on a coordinate chart, several sample values of x and y being taken. When these points are plotted and a line drawn through them, we secure a straight line passing through the origin (see Fig. 2.3).

Similarly, any equation of the first degree (i.e., not involving xy, or powers of x or y other than the first) may be represented by a

---

[2] The general term "curve" is used to designate any line, straight or curved, when located with reference to a coordinate system.

straight line. The generalized equation can be reduced to the form $y = a + bx$, where a is a constant representing the distance from the origin to the point of intersection of the given line and the y-axis, and b is a constant representing the slope of the given line (that is, the tangent of the angle which the line makes with the horizontal). The constant term a is called the y-intercept. It is clear from the generalized equation of the straight line that when x has a value of zero, y will be equal to this constant term. In the example represented by Fig. 2.3 a is equal to 0, and b to 1. The location of a given line depends upon the signs of a and b as well as upon their magni-

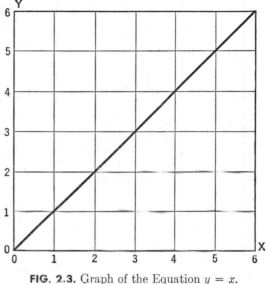

FIG. 2.3. Graph of the Equation $y = x$.

tudes. The practical problem involved in the determination of any straight line is that of finding the values of a and b from the data, a problem that will appear in various forms in the discussion of statistical methods.

These points may be illustrated by the plotting of a simple equation of the first degree. Thus, to construct the graph of the function, $y = 2 + 3x$, various values of x are assumed, and corresponding values of y are determined. These may be arranged in the form of a table:

x	y $(2 + 3x)$
-4	-10
-2	-4
0	2
2	8
4	14

Plotting these values and connecting the plotted points, the graph illustrated in Fig. 2.4 is secured. It will be noted that since this function is linear (that is, the graph takes the form of a straight line) any two of the points would have been sufficient to locate the line. The y-intercept is equal to the constant term 2, and the tangent of the angle that the given line makes with the horizontal (the slope of the line) is equal to 3, the coefficient of x. That this curve represents the equation is proved by the fact that the equation is satisfied by the coordinates of every point on the curve, and that every pair of values satisfying the equation is represented by a point on the curve. It is characteristic of a linear relationship that if one variable be increased by a constant amount, the corresponding increment of the other variable will be constant. In the above case as x grows by constant increments of 2, for example, the constant increment of the y-variable is 6. Series that increase in this way by constant increments are termed *arithmetic series*.

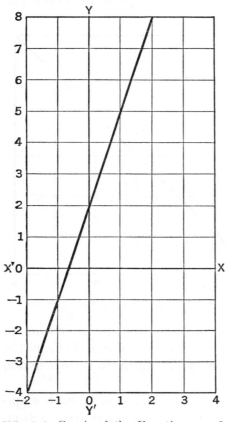

FIG. 2.4. Graph of the Equation $y = 2 + 3x$.

Many examples of linear relationship between variables are found in the physical sciences. An example from the economic world is found in the growth of money at simple interest, that is, interest which is not compounded. If we let r represent the rate of simple interest, x the number of years, and y the sum to which one dollar will amount at the end of x years, the equation of relationship is of the form

$$y = 1 + rx$$

Since in a given case r will be constant, this is of the simple linear type. In statistical work precise relationships of this type rarely if ever occur, but approximations to the straight line relationship are found constantly.

Nonlinear relationship. Nonlinear functions are of many types, of which only a few of the more common will be discussed here. The student should be familiar with the general characteristics of the chief nonperiodic curves, of which the parabolic and hyperbolic types, on the one hand, and the exponential type on the other, are the most important. Polynomials are mentioned as a more general form of rather wide utility. Of periodic functions the sine curve is briefly described, as a fundamental form.

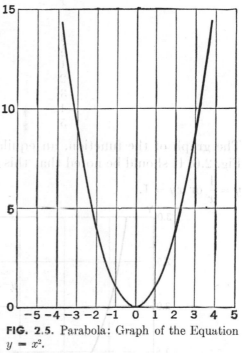

FIG. 2.5. Parabola: Graph of the Equation $y = x^2$.

Functional relationships of the parabolic or hyperbolic form are quite common in the physical sciences, and such curves are found to fit certain classes of social and economic data. The general equation, when there is no constant term, is of the form $y = ax^b$. The curve is *parabolic* when the exponent b is positive, and *hyperbolic* when b is negative. The two following examples will serve to illustrate these types:

Problem: To construct the graph of the function $y = x^2$.

x	y (x^2)
-5	25
-4	16
-3	9
-2	4
-1	1
0	0
1	1
2	4
3	9
4	16
5	25

The graph is shown in Fig. 2.5.

Problem: To construct the graph of the function $y = x^{-1}$, for positive values of x.

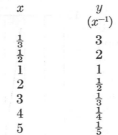

x	y (x^{-1})
$\frac{1}{3}$	3
$\frac{1}{2}$	2
1	1
2	$\frac{1}{2}$
3	$\frac{1}{3}$
4	$\frac{1}{4}$
5	$\frac{1}{5}$

The graph of the function, an equilateral hyperbola, is shown in Fig. 2.6. It should be noted that this equation may also be written $y = \dfrac{1}{x}$ or $xy = 1$.

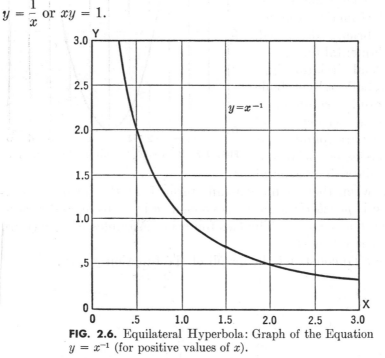

FIG. 2.6. Equilateral Hyperbola: Graph of the Equation $y = x^{-1}$ (for positive values of x).

It is characteristic of relationships of this type that as x changes in geometric progression, y also changes in geometric progression. Thus, in the example of the parabola given above ($y = x^2$), if we select the x values which form a geometric series,[3] the corresponding y values form a similar series:

[3] A geometric series is one each term of which is derived from the preceding term by the application of a constant multiplier.

x	1	2	4	8	16	32
y	1	4	16	64	256	1,024

Another class of functions is of the form represented by the equation $y = ab^x$. In equations of this type one of the variable quantities occurs as an exponent; graphs representing such equations are called *exponential curves*. The example that follows illustrates the type.

Problem: To construct the graph of the function $y = 2^x$, for positive values of x.

x	y (2^x)
0	1
1	2
2	4
3	8
4	16
5	32
6	64

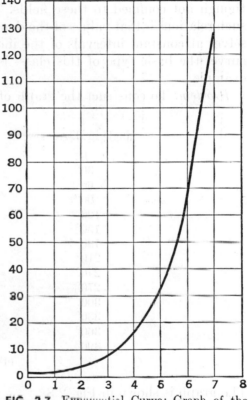

This graph is plotted in Fig. 2.7.

It has been noted that the relationship between two variables that increase by constant increments (constituting arithmetic series) may be represented by a straight line, and that the relationship between variables changing in geometric progression may be represented by either a parabola or a hyperbola. The exponential curve constitutes a hybrid type. It describes a relation in which one variable increases in arithmetic progression while the other increases in geometric progression. The figures given above illustrate this relationship.

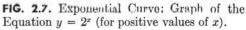

FIG. 2.7. Exponential Curve; Graph of the Equation $y = 2^x$ (for positive values of x).

Extensions of the simple linear form $y = a + bx$, employing higher powers of x, give *polynomial* expressions of the type

$$y = a + bx + cx^2 + dx^3 + \cdots$$

Here we have a polynomial in one variable; y is a function of x alone. In a relationship of this type a specific value of y is given by the sum of a finite number of terms, each of which consists of a power of x multiplied by a constant. (The constant a may be thought of as ax^o.) If y is a function of more than one variable, say of w, x, and z, we should have a polynomial in several variables. Both forms are extensively applied in statistical practice.

Periodic functions constitute another distinct type, a class represented notably by electrical and meteorological relations, though not confined to these fields. The characteristic feature of such relations is that values of the dependent variable repeat themselves at constant intervals of the independent variable. The sine curve, the basic type of this class, is illustrated in the following example.

Problem: To construct the graph of the function $y = \sin x$.

x (angle in degrees)	y ($\sin x$)
0°	.000
30°	.500
60°	.866
90°	1.000
120°	.866
150°	.500
180°	.000
210°	− .500
240°	− .866
270°	− 1.000
300°	− .866
330°	− .500
360°	.000
390°	.500
	etc.

The graph is shown in Fig. 2.8.

The full importance in statistical work of securing a mathematical expression for the relation between two variables cannot be demonstrated until the subject has been further developed. One fundamental object is the determination of physical or economic regularities underlying observed phenomena. More specifically, equations defining such a relation are used in estimating values of one variable from given values of the other. Examples throughout the book will serve to illustrate how these objects are attained.

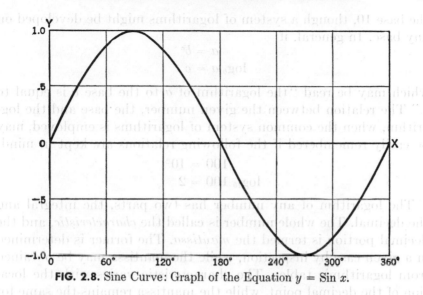

FIG. 2.8. Sine Curve: Graph of the Equation $y = \sin x$.

Logarithms and Their Use in Graphic Presentation. Logarithms, which play such an important part in general mathematical operations, are of equal importance in the manipulation of the raw materials of statistics. The characteristics of logarithms, and the methods by which they are employed to facilitate arithmetic processes, may be briefly reviewed. The detailed discussion is concerned only with the common system of logarithms of which the base is 10.

The nature of logarithms. Any positive number may be expressed as a power of 10. Thus

$$1,000 = 10 \times 10 \times 10 = 10^3$$
$$10,000 = 10 \times 10 \times 10 \times 10 = 10^4$$

In each case the *exponent* of 10 (the small number written above and to the right) indicates the number of times the figure 10 is repeated as a factor. For the integral powers of 10 the exponent is a whole number, but for other numbers the exponent will contain a fractional value. Thus 100 is equal to 10 raised to the power 2, or 10^2; 110 is equal to 10 raised to the power 2.04139, or $10^{2.04139}$.

The exponent of 10, or the index of the power to which 10 must be raised to equal a certain number, is called the *logarithm* of that number. The logarithm of 100 is 2, the logarithm of 110 is 2.04139, the logarithm of 998 is 2.99913. These figures all have reference to the base 10, though a system of logarithms might be developed on any base. In general, if

$$a = b^c$$
$$\log_b a = c$$

which may be read "the logarithm of a to the base b is equal to c." The relation between the given number, the base and the logarithm, when the common system of logarithms is employed, may be easily remembered if the following relations are kept in mind:

$$100 = 10^2$$
$$\log_{10} 100 = 2$$

The logarithm of any number has two parts, the integral and the decimal. The whole number is called the *characteristic*, and the decimal portion is termed the *mantissa*. The former is determined in a given case by inspection, while the mantissa may be obtained from logarithmic tables. The characteristic varies with the location of the decimal point, while the mantissa remains the same for any given combination of numbers. This fact is illustrated by the following figures:

$$
\begin{array}{lrl}
\log \text{ of } & 8{,}450 & = 3.92686 \\
\log \text{ of } & 845 & = 2.92686 \\
\log \text{ of } & 84.5 & = 1.92686 \\
\log \text{ of } & 8.45 & = 0.92686 \\
\log \text{ of } & 0.845 & = 9.92686 - 10 \\
\log \text{ of } & 0.0845 & = 8.92686 - 10 \\
\end{array}
$$

In finding the natural number to which a given logarithm corresponds (such natural numbers are termed *antilogarithms*), the mantissa determines the sequence of figures, while the whole number, or characteristic, determines the location of the decimal point. For example, in seeking the antilogarithm of 2.17609 it is found that the decimal .17609 follows the natural number 1500 in a table of logarithms. Since the characteristic is 2, the natural number desired must lie between 100 and 1,000, and must therefore be 150.

A brief study of the following figures, showing the progression of numbers corresponding to certain powers of 10, will help to fix in mind the relations between the multiples of 10 and their logarithms, and will enable the characteristic of a desired logarithm to be readily determined.

.0001	.001	.01	.1	1	10	100	1,000	10,000
10^{-4}	10^{-3}	10^{-2}	10^{-1}	10^0	10^1	10^2	10^3	10^4

The exponents of 10 in the lower row are the logarithms of the numbers in the upper row.

It should be noted that the logarithms of all numbers from 0 to 1 are negative. Thus the logarithm of 0.845 is $-1 + .92686$; this is written $9.92686 - 10$. In covering the range of all positive natural numbers from zero to infinity, logarithms traverse all positive and negative values. A negative natural number, therefore, can have neither a positive nor a negative logarithm.

The advantage of thus expressing numbers as powers of 10 lies in the fact that the ordinary arithmetic operations of multiplication, division, raising to powers, and extracting roots are greatly facilitated by this procedure.

To multiply numbers, add their logarithms. The sum of the logarithms of the factors is the logarithm of their product. In general terms:

$$a^b \times a^c = a^{(b+c)}$$

Specifically, putting $a = 10$, $b = 2$, $c = 3$:

$$10^2 \times 10^3 = (10 \times 10) \times (10 \times 10 \times 10) = 10^5 = 100,000$$
$$100 \times 1,000 \qquad\qquad\qquad\qquad\qquad\qquad = 100,000$$

To divide one number by another, subtract the logarithm of the latter from the logarithm of the former. The remainder is the logarithm of the desired quotient.

In general terms:

$$a^b \div a^c = a^{(b-c)}$$

Specifically, putting $a = 10$, $b = 5$, $c = 2$:

$$10^5 \div 10^2 = \frac{10 \times 10 \times 10 \times 10 \times 10}{10 \times 10} = 10^3 = 1,000$$
$$100,000 \div 100 \qquad\qquad\qquad\qquad\qquad\qquad = 1,000$$

To raise a given number to any power, multiply the logarithm of the number by the index of the power. The product is the logarithm of the desired power.

In general terms:

$$(a^b)^c = a^{bc}$$

Specifically, putting $a = 10$, $b = 3$, $c = 2$:

$$(10^3)^2 = (10 \times 10 \times 10) \times (10 \times 10 \times 10) = 10^6 = 1,000,000$$
$$1,000^2 \qquad\qquad\qquad\qquad\qquad\qquad\qquad\qquad = 1,000,000$$

To extract any root of a given number, divide the logarithm of the number by the index of the root. The quotient is the logarithm of the desired root.

In general terms:

$$\sqrt[b]{a^c} = a^{\left(\frac{c}{b}\right)}$$

Specifically, putting $a = 10$, $b = 3$, $c = 6$:

$$\sqrt[3]{10^6} = 10^{\frac{6}{3}} = 10^2 = 100$$
$$\sqrt[3]{1{,}000{,}000} = 100$$

In summary:

$$\log (a \times b) = \log a + \log b$$
$$\log (a \div b) = \log a - \log b$$
$$\log a^b = b \times \log a$$
$$\log \sqrt[b]{a} = \log a \div b$$

Logarithmic equations. The graphic representation of data by means of a system of rectangular coordinates has been described above and some of the advantages of this method have been outlined. For many purposes it is desirable to plot logarithms rather than the natural numbers themselves. This may result in bringing out significant relations more distinctly, or it may serve greatly to simplify and facilitate the manipulation of data. In particular, when it is possible through the use of logarithms to reduce a complex curve to the straight line form, a distinct gain has been made in the direction of simplicity of treatment and interpretation.

A linear equation, it will be recalled, is of the general form $y = a + bx$, where a and b are constants that measure, respectively, the y-intercept of the given line and the slope. The simplification of equations through the use of logarithms involves in all cases the substitution of $\log x$ or $\log y$, or both, for the x or y variables, thereby reducing an equation of a higher order to a simpler form. This process may be illustrated with reference to the equation $y = x^2$. When plotted on rectangular coordinates this equation gives a curve of the parabolic type (see Fig. 2.5). Reduced to logarithmic form this becomes $\log y = 2 \log x$. This equation, in which the variables are $\log y$ and $\log x$, is linear in form. It is plotted in Fig. 2.9, for positive values of $\log x$. To indicate the relations involved, natural numbers corresponding to the logarithms are given on scales to the right and at the top of the figure. The natural numbers appearing on the scales constitute geometric series, while their

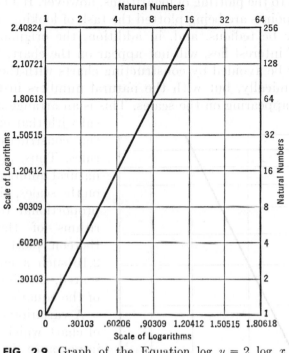

FIG. 2.9. Graph of the Equation log $y = 2$ log x
(logarithmic form of the equation $y = x^2$).

logarithms form arithmetic series. It will be noted that equal distances on the chart, vertical or horizontal, represent equal absolute increments on the scale of logarithms and equal percentage increments on the scale of natural numbers.

The equation $y = 5x^3$ can be reduced in the same way to log $y =$ log $5 + 3$ log x, a linear form. Similarly, all equations of the type $y = ax^b$, that is to say, all simple parabolas and hyperbolas, can be reduced to the straight line form log $y =$ log $a + b$ log x. Graphically this means plotting the logarithms of the y's against the logarithms of the x's.

A different problem is presented by an equation of the type $y = ab^x$, the graph of which is termed an exponential curve. Expressed in logarithmic form, we have log $y =$ log $a + x$ log b. This also is of the linear type, the two constants being log a and log b, while the variables are x and log y. If we plot the natural x's and the logs of the y's with such an equation, a straight line will be secured. A curve of this type is discussed and illustrated below.

Logarithmic and semilogarithmic charts. There are certain disadvantages to the plotting of logarithms, however. If a considerable number of points are being plotted the task of looking up the logarithms may be tedious, and, in addition, the original values, in which chief interest lies, will not appear on the chart. These difficulties may be avoided by constructing charts with the scales laid off logarithmically, but with the natural numbers instead of the logarithms appearing on the scales. This is an arrangement identical with that employed in the construction of slide rules. Thus, although the natural numbers are given on the scales, distances are proportional to the logarithms of the numbers thereon plotted. In Fig. 2.10 such a chart is presented, showing the graph of the equation $y = x^2$.

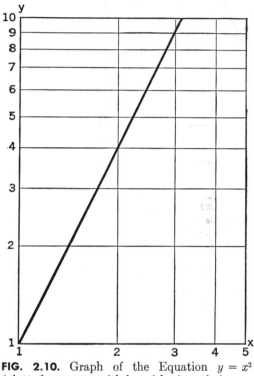

FIG. 2.10. Graph of the Equation $y = x^2$ (plotted on paper with logarithmic scales).

A variation of this type of chart which is of great importance in statistical work is one that is scaled arithmetically on the horizontal axis and logarithmically on the vertical axis. This is equivalent, of course, to plotting the x's on the natural scale and plotting the logarithms of the y's. As was pointed out above, such a combination of scales reduces a curve of the exponential type to a straight line. Plotting paper of this semilogarithmic or "ratio" type may be constructed with the aid of a slide rule or of logarithms, or may be purchased ready-made. It is of particular value in charting social and economic statistics when time is one of the variables, time being plotted on the arithmetic scale.

As an example of this type of curve the compound interest law may be used. If r be taken to represent the rate of interest, x the number of years, p the principal, and y the sum to which the principal amounts at the end of x years (interest being compounded annually), an equation is secured of the form

$$y = p(1 + r)^x$$

Expressed logarithmically this becomes

$$\log y = \log p + x \log (1 + r)$$

the equation to a straight line.

In Fig. 2.11 a curve representing the growth of $10 at compound interest at 6 percent is plotted on the natural scale. This is the graph of the exponential equation

$$y = 10(1 + .06)^x$$

y representing the total amount of principal and interest at the end of x years. Figure 2.12 shows the same data plotted on semilogarithmic paper, the exponential curve being reduced to a straight line.

The use of semilogarithmic paper is not confined to cases in which an exponential curve is straightened out, for the significance of many types of data is most effectively brought out

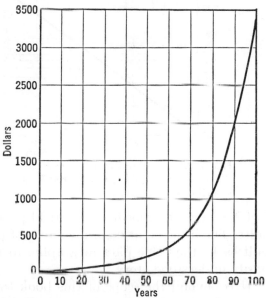

FIG. 2.11. The Compound Interest Law: Growth of $10.00 at Compound Interest at 6 Percent for 100 Years (plotted on arithmetic scale).

when charts of this type are used. These advantages are more fully explained below.

Types of Graphic Presentation

When the results of observations or statistical investigations have been secured in quantitative form, one of the first steps toward analysis and interpretation of the data is that of presenting these results graphically. Not only is such procedure of scientific value in paving the way for further investigation of relationships,

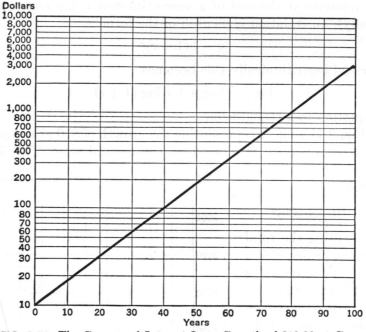

FIG. 2.12. The Compound Interest Law: Growth of $10.00 at Compound Interest at 6 Percent for 100 Years (plotted on semilogarithmic or ratio scale).

but it serves an immediate practical purpose in visualizing the results. The interpretation of a column of raw figures may be a difficult task; the same data in graphic form may tell a simple and easily understood story.

It is beyond the scope of this book to present any detailed account of the multiplicity of graphs employed by engineers and statisticians today. Certain of the more important principles of graphic presentation may be briefly explained, however, and some of the chief types of graphs in daily use may be illustrated. Other examples appear in later chapters of this book.

The selection of the type of chart to be employed in a given case will depend upon the character of the material to be plotted and the purpose to be served. While the data of a given problem may frequently be presented graphically in several different forms, there is generally one type of chart best adapted to that material. It may be true, also, that certain types would be quite inappropriate to the data in question. The selection of a type of chart to employ, therefore, must be made with the characteristics of the data clearly in mind. Perhaps more important is the *purpose* the given chart is designed to serve. Each of the many types of charts in common use is appropriate to certain specific purposes. It will bring out certain characteristics of the data or will emphasize certain relationships. There is no chart that is sovereign for all purposes. Until the purpose is clearly defined the best chart form cannot be selected. The following descriptions of a few standard types will facilitate the selection of an appropriate form.

The Plotting of Time Series. In the graphic presentation of a time series, primary interest attaches to the chronological varia-

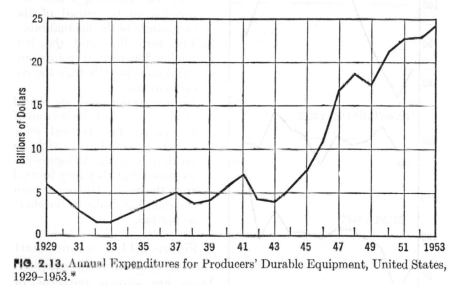

FIG. 2.13. Annual Expenditures for Producers' Durable Equipment, United States, 1929–1953.*

* Source Office of Business Economics, U.S. Department of Commerce.

tions in the values of the data — to the general trend and to fluctuations about the trend. If the purpose is to emphasize the *absolute* variations, the differences in absolute units between the values of the series at different times, a simple chart of the type illustrated in Fig. 2.13 will serve the purpose. This chart depicts total annual expenditures for producers' durable equipment in the United States during the period 1929–1953. Expenditures for such equipment are, of course, one of the major components of gross private domestic investment. Both scales are arithmetic. Points representing the various annual values are shown and, to facilitate interpretation, these points are connected by a series of straight lines. The chart traces clearly the drop in equipment purchases that came with the

1929 recession, the fluctuations of the following decade, and the rise to unprecedentedly high levels in the years following the war.

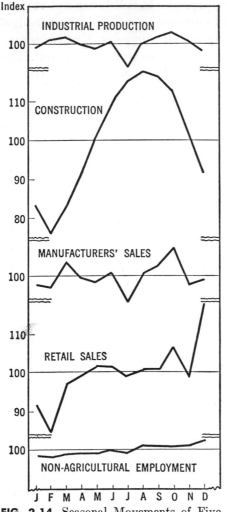

With respect to general make-up, the following points should be noted:

1. The title constitutes a clear description of the material plotted and indicates the period covered.
2. The vertical scale begins at the zero line, enabling a true impression to be gained of the magnitude of the fluctuations.
3. The zero line and the line joining the plotted points are ruled more heavily than the co-ordinate lines.
4. Figures for the scales are placed at the left and at the bottom of the chart. The vertical scale may be repeated at the right to facilitate reading. All figures are so placed that they may be read from the base as bottom or from the right hand edge of the chart as bottom.

FIG. 2.14. Seasonal Movements of Five Economic Indicators.*

* Chart reproduced by courtesy of the Federal Reserve Bank of Philadelphia from the May 1954 issue of the *Business Review* of that Bank.

Figure 2.14 is a line chart serving a different purpose. Here are shown patterns of seasonal variation in five basic economic series. The plotted indexes fluctuate about a base line of 100, which represents, for each series, an average annual value.[4] The sharp contrasts among seasonal rhythms in these five major fields are clearly revealed by the paralleling of graphs in this arrangement.

Advantages of the ratio chart. If *relative* rather than *absolute* variations are of chief concern, the chart employed should be of the semilogarithmic type, scaled logarithmically on the *y*-axis and

[4] The construction of index numbers of seasonal variation is discussed in Chapter 11.

arithmetically on the x-axis. In such a chart, as we have noted, equal percentage variations are represented by equal vertical distances, as opposed to the ordinary arithmetic type in which equal absolute variations are represented by equal vertical distances. The argument for the use of the semilogarithmic or ratio chart for the representation of time series is that, in general, the significance of a given change depends upon the magnitude of the base from which the change is measured. That is, an increase of 100 on a base of 100 is as significant as an increase of 10,000 on a base of 10,000.

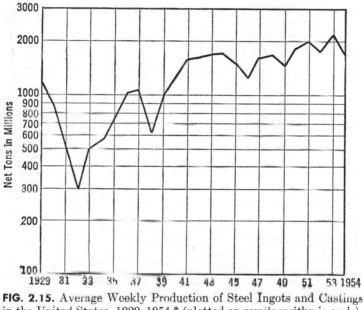

FIG. 2.15. Average Weekly Production of Steel Ingots and Castings in the United States, 1929–1954 * (plotted on semilogarithmic scale).

* Source: American Iron and Steel Institute.

In each case there is an increase of 100 percent. The absolute increase in the second case is 100 times that in the first case, and the two changes would show in this proportion on the arithmetic chart. They would show as of equal importance on the semilogarithmic chart.

Such a chart is presented in Fig. 2.15, which shows the course of steel production in the United States from 1929 to 1954. The absolute magnitudes are plotted, but the vertical scale is so constructed as to represent variations from year to year in proportion to their relative magnitude.

Certain distinctive advantages of the ratio or logarithmic ruling

are brought out by a comparison of Fig. 2.16 and Fig. 2.17. Here
are shown exports of the United States, from 1929 to 1953, to four
broad continental divisions. If the four series are to be presented on
a single chart, scaled arithmetically, a scale must be selected that
will include the largest item recorded, which is for $9,344,000,000

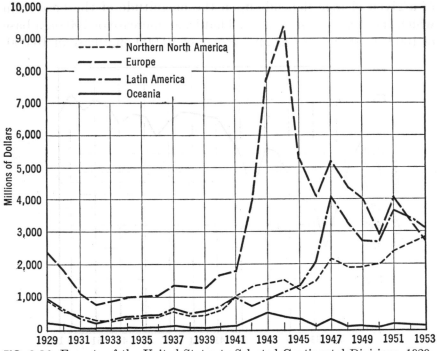

FIG. 2.16. Exports of the United States to Selected Continental Divisions, 1929–
1953.*

* Source: Bureau of the Census, U.S. Department of Commerce (summarized in the *Statistical Abstract
of the U.S.*, 1953 and the *Economic Almanac* of the National Industrial Conference Board, 1953–1954).

worth of exports to Europe, in 1944. Such a scale reduces the relative importance of all the smaller magnitudes. Fluctuations in exports to Europe during this period were much greater, in absolute
terms, than the fluctuations in trade with other divisions. Variations in trade with Oceania, at the other extreme, seem insignificant. If one is interested in relative variations such a picture is
quite misleading. When the data are plotted on the ratio scale, in
Fig. 2.17, the picture is placed in truer perspective. Movements at
the lower end of the scale are discernible, and the relative amplitudes of changes in the volume of exports to different divisions may

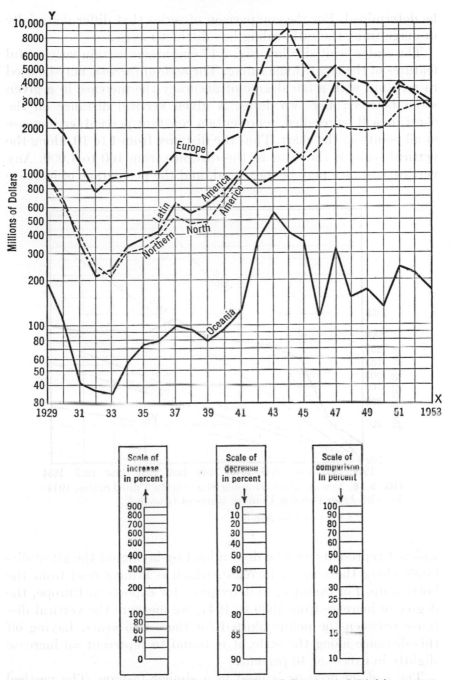

FIG. 2.17. Exports of the United States to Selected Continental Divisions, 1929–1953. Semilogarithmic Plotting, with Scales of Increase, Decrease, and Comparison.

be determined. For the comparison of series that differ materially in magnitude, the ratio ruling has distinct merits.

The scales printed below Fig. 2.17 emphasize certain very useful features of the logarithmic ruling. The *scale of increase* may be used to measure with a fair degree of accuracy the increase in a given series between any two dates. A given vertical distance on the chart, it will be recalled, represents a constant percentage increase at all points on the chart. Thus the distance from 1 to 10, along the vertical scale, is the same as the distance from 100 to 1,000. Any vertical distance may be measured, and the percentage of increase

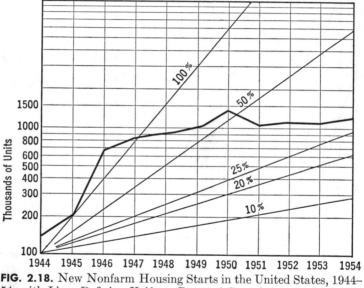

FIG. 2.18. New Nonfarm Housing Starts in the United States, 1944–54, with Lines Defining Uniform Rates of Growth.*

* Source: U.S. Bureau of Labor Statistics

which it represents may be determined by laying off the given distance along the scale of increase, which is always read from the bottom up. For example, to determine, for exports to Europe, the degree of increase from 1939 to 1941, we measure the vertical distance between the points plotted for these two years. Laying off this distance along the scale, it is found to represent an increase slightly in excess of 40 percent.

The *scale of decrease* is used in a similar fashion. The vertical distance between any two points is measured, and the percentage decrease which it represents is determined by laying off the given distance on the scale from the top downward. The arrows indicate the direction in which the various scales are to be read.

By means of the *scale of comparison* the percentage relation of one series to another at any time may be determined. For example, we may wish to know the percentage relation between exports to Northern North America and exports to Latin America in 1951. The vertical distance between the two plotted points is measured, and laid off on the scale of comparison, reading from the top downward. We find that exports to Northern North America in that year amounted to about 70 percent of exports to Latin America.

Scales of the type illustrated above may be readily constructed on a given chart by using the ratio ruling for the scale intervals. When a series of charts is prepared on semilogarithmic paper of a standard type it is convenient to construct such scales in a more permanent form, in the shape of special rulers.

A ratio chart is particularly useful when interest attaches to rates of growth (or decline) over a considerable period of time. In such a case, the reading of the chart is facilitated by the plotting of straight diagonal lines indicating uniform rates of change. These should radiate from a single point of origin. The procedure is illustrated in Fig. 2.18. Each of the several diagonal lines there shown indicates changes at a uniform annual rate. By reference to these lines the user of the chart may readily determine the approximate rate of growth of the plotted series between any two years.

The chief advantages of the semilogarithmic ruling in chart construction may be briefly summarized:

1. A curve of the exponential type becomes a straight line when plotted on a semilogarithmic chart. For example, a curve representing the growth of any sum of money at compound interest takes the form of a straight line when so plotted.
2. The graph will be a straight line so long as the *rate* of increase or decrease remains constant.
3. Equal relative changes are represented by lines having equal slopes. Thus two series increasing or decreasing at equal rates will be represented by parallel lines.
4. Comparison of the rates of change in two or more series is effected by comparison of the slopes of the plotted lines.
5. The semilogarithmic ruling permits the plotting of absolute magnitudes and the comparison of relative changes.
6. Comparison of series differing materially in the magnitude of individual items is possible with the semilogarithmic chart.
7. Percentages of change may be read and percentage relations between magnitudes determined directly from the chart.

The Use of Bar Charts for the Comparison of Magnitudes and of Relative Values. A simple column diagram may be useful in the comparison of aggregates, when attention is to be drawn to absolute differences. The eye readily distinguishes such differences as those represented in Fig. 2.19, showing total income payments to individuals in six New England states in 1952. The bars may be drawn vertically, as in the example just cited, or horizontally, as in Fig. 2.20. The latter diagram gives the ranking of ten leading

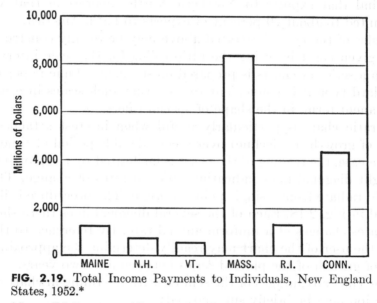

FIG. 2.19. Total Income Payments to Individuals, New England States, 1952.*

* Source: U.S. Department of Commerce.

cities of the United States, by population in 1950. The horizontal representation is particularly advantageous when the chart-maker wishes to present the data with the corresponding bars.

Columns may be employed effectively in setting forth, for comparison, the relative values of several time series for a stated period or date. Fig. 2.21 shows the standing of six elements of the price system in October, 1954, with reference to 1939 as base. The wide range of variation is well brought out by this presentation.

Further examples of column diagrams, as employed in the representation of frequency distributions, are contained in the next chapter. It is there shown how a frequency polygon or frequency curve may grow out of the simple bar diagram, when data of certain kinds are being handled. Such frequency curves constitute very important graphic types, but it will be appropriate to treat them in full at a later point.

Representation of Component Parts. Bar diagrams are well adapted to the showing of the component parts of a given aggregate. These parts may be given in absolute terms, as in Fig. 2.22. This particular illustration shows the same aggregate, the total investment funds of state and local governments in the United States

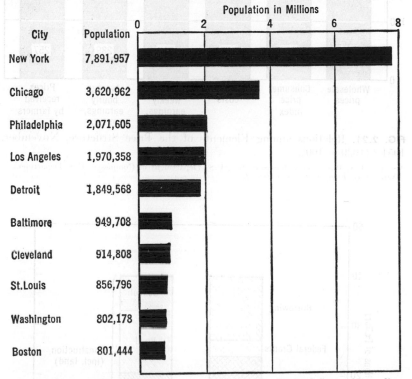

FIG. 2.20. Ranking of Ten Leading Cities of the United States according to Population as of April 1, 1950.*

* Source of data: Bureau of the Census, U.S. Department of Commerce (as presented in the *Economic Almanac*, National Industrial Conference Board, 1953–1954).

during the six-year period 1948–1953, broken up in two ways, to show the *sources* of these funds and the *uses* to which they have been put. In another form, exemplified by Fig. 2.23, the diagrams may show the percentage distribution of an aggregate among its parts at a given date, or at different times. This figure defines the changing industrial composition of the work force of the United States over the period 1870–1950.

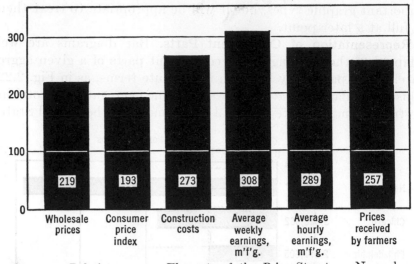

FIG. 2.21. Relations among Elements of the Price Structure, November, 1954 * (1939 = 100).

* Source: U.S. Bureau of Labor Statistics, U.S. Department of Commerce, U.S. Department of Agriculture, *Engineering News Record*.

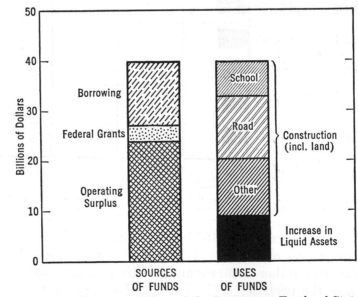

FIG. 2.22. Sources and Uses of the Investment Funds of State and Local Governments Aggregated for the Period 1948–1953.*

* Source of data: Office of Business Economics, U.S. Department of Commerce. Definitions of terms are given in "Private and Public Debt in 1953," by H. D. Osborne and J. A. Gorman, *Survey of Current Business*, October 1954, from which the chart is reproduced.

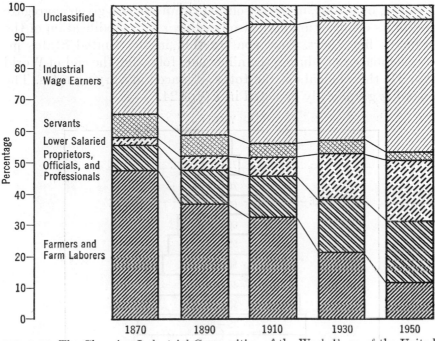

FIG. 2.23. The Changing Industrial Composition of the Work Force of the United States, 1870–1950.* Percentage Distribution in Each of Five Census Years.

* Source: "Industrial Classes in the United States, 1870 to 1950," by Tillman M. Sogge, *Journal of the American Statistical Association*, June, 1954. For the period 1870–1930, the aggregate to which the plotted percentages relate is the total of gainful workers; for 1950 the aggregate is the labor force of the country.

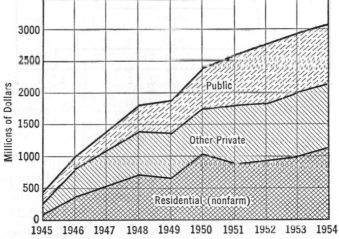

FIG. 2.24. Expenditures for New Construction in the United States, and Three Components Thereof. Monthly Averages, 1945–1954.*

* Source of data: Compiled by various federal agencies; published in *Economic Indicators* by the Joint Committee on the Economic Report.

Shifts, over time, in the absolute magnitude of a given aggregate and in its composition may also be shown by a modification of the ordinary line chart. New construction in the United States increased materially during the nine years following the end of World War II; the elements of the total advanced at varying rates. The record is graphically depicted in Fig. 2.24.

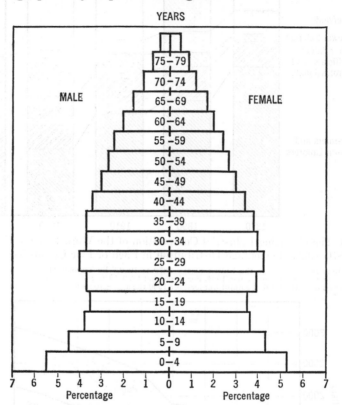

YEARS

MALE   FEMALE

75—79
70—74
65—69
60—64
55—59
50—54
45—49
40—44
35—39
30—34
25—29
20—24
15—19
10—14
5—9
0—4

7 6 5 4 3 2 1 0 1 2 3 4 5 6 7
   Percentage   Percentage

FIG. 2.25. Structure of the Population of the United States, 1950, Showing Percentage Composition by Age and Sex.*

* Source: Bureau of the Census, U.S. Department of Commerce.

Representation of Population Structure. A distinctive type of chart has been used to define the age structure of the population, by sexes. The characteristics of the population of the United States, in 1950, in these respects, are shown by Fig. 2.25. (Those 85 years old or over are not included.) These diagrams change their shape over time, of course, as age structure varies, but ordinarily these changes occur slowly. A picture of a violent alteration in both sex and age structure is given by Fig. 2.26. The ravages of

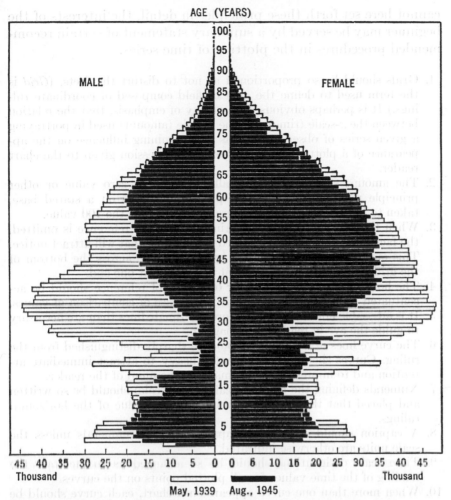

AGE (YEARS)

MALE

FEMALE

45 40 35 30 25 20 15 10 5 0   0 5 10 15 20 25 30 35 40 45
Thousand   Thousand

May, 1939   Aug., 1945

FIG. 2.26. Structure of the Population of Berlin, 1939 and 1945, Showing Composition by Age and Sex.*

* Source: *Statistische Praxis*, Monatszeitschrift des Statistischen Zentralamts, Berlin, October 1946.

war on the population of Berlin during the brief period of six years from 1939 to 1945 are here dramatically depicted.

Note on Procedures in Graphic Presentation. The various illustrations given above will serve as examples of the methods employed in the graphic representation of observations. Much, of course, has been left uncovered concerning the art of graphic portrayal. Principles of effective, pleasing, and honest design have been developed in recent decades, and progress has been made in the standardization of practices in chart making. Although we cannot here set forth these principles in detail, the interests of the beginner may be served by a summary statement of certain recommended procedures in the plotting of time series.

1. Grids should be so proportioned as not to distort the facts. (*Grid* is the term used to define the area or field composed of coordinate rulings.) It is perhaps obvious, but worthy of emphasis, that the relation between the *x*-scale (time) and the *y*-scale (amount) used in portraying a given series of observations has a determining influence on the appearance of a plotted curve, and on the impression given to the chart reader.

2. The amount scale should normally include the zero value or other principle point of reference. In plotting relatives on a stated base, taken to be 100, the point of reference is of course the 100 value.

3. When the zero value or other principle point of reference is omitted, the fact should be clearly indicated in a manner that will attract notice. This omission may be indicated by a wavy line across the bottom of the grid, or by means of a straight line waved at one end.

4. The horizontal axis, zero line, or other line of reference should be accentuated so as to indicate that it is the base of comparison of values.

5. It is advisable not to show any more coordinate lines than are necessary to guide the eye in reading the diagram.

6. The curve lines of a diagram should be sharply distinguished from the ruling. Curves should be sufficiently heavy to attract immediate attention and to impress a visual image on the mind of the reader.

7. Numerals defining the amount scale (the *y*-scale) should be so written and placed that they will clearly indicate the value of the horizontal rulings.

8. A caption should always accompany the scale numerals unless the scale units are otherwise indicated.

9. Time scale designations should be so arranged as to facilitate the reading of the time values for all plotted points on the curves.

10. When more than one curve appears on a chart, each curve should be clearly identified by an appropriate label or key.

11. The title of a diagram should be made as clear and complete as possible. The main title should give the reader a quick understanding of what the chart is about. Material serving to complement or supplement the main title should be placed in a subtitle.[5]

---

[5] For a detailed statement of principles of preferred practice in graphic presentation the reader should consult the manual on *Time Series Charts* prepared by the Committee on Standards for Graphic Presentation, which is published by the American Society of Mechanical Engineers, New York. These standards have the approval of the American Standards Association. See also Mudgett, Ref. 114, and Smart and Arnold, Ref. 144.

The eleven principles listed above are based on the recommendations of the Committee on Standards for Graphic Presentation. The wording has been modified in a few cases, since the recommendations have been lifted out of context.

REFERENCES

Allen, R. G. D., *Mathematical Analysis for Economists*, Chaps. 1, 2, 3, 9.

Committee on Graphics, "A Guide for Preparing Technical Illustrations for Publication and Projection," *American Standards Association*.

Committee on Standards for Graphic Presentation, "Time Series Charts, A Manual of Design and Construction," *American Standards Association*.

Croxton, F. E. and Cowden, D. J., *Applied General Statistics*, Chaps. 4–6.

Federal Reserve System, Board of Governors, *Charts on Money, Bank Credit, Money Rates and Business*, Washington, D.C. (monthly).

Fowler, C. B., Griffin, J. I., Cohen, J. B., Cropsey, J., Greenwald, W. I., and Sethur, F., *Economic Handbook: A Visual Survey*.

Goulden, C. H., *Methods of Statistical Analysis*, 2nd ed., Chap. 1.

Livingston, J. A., "Charts Should Tell a Story," *Journal of the American Statistical Association*, Sept. 1945.

Lutz, R. R., *Graphic Presentation Simplified*.

Mudgett, B. D., *Statistical Tables and Charts*.

Riggleman, J. R. and Frisbee, I. N., *Business Statistics*, 3rd ed., Chaps. 5, 6.

Smart, L. E. and Arnold, S., *Practical Rules for Graphic Presentation*.

Spear, Mary E., *Charting Statistics*.

Spurr, W. A., Kellogg, L. S. and Smith, J. H., *Business and Economic Statistics*, Chaps. 7–8.

Tintner, G., *Mathematics and Statistics for Economists*, Chaps. 1, 2.

Walker, Helen M., *Mathematics Essential for Elementary Statistics*, 2nd ed.

The publishers and the dates of publication of the books named in chapter reference lists are given in the bibliography at the end of this volume.

CHAPTER **3**

The Organization of Statistical
Data: Frequency Distributions

Our systematic discussion of statistical procedures opens here, with the investigator possessed of the body of observations that make up a sample. It is assumed that these observations relate to a quantity that may take different numerical values — that is, that we are dealing with a *variable*. The data may have been compiled in the first instance by the statistician himself,[1] or they may have been obtained from primary or secondary sources. Before generalizations or tests may be based upon these materials, organization of the observations is usually necessary.

Preliminary Considerations and Operations

At the outset we should distinguish between problems arising in the analysis of observations ordered in time and problems involved in the treatment of observations not so ordered, or for which the time order is not relevant to the object of inquiry. In studying a time series the primary object is to measure and analyze the chronological variations in the value of the variable. Thus one may study variations in sales over a period of years, fluctuations in the production of bituminous coal, changes in the level of wholesale prices, or the movements of national income from year to year. Quite different is the procedure in the study of such a problem as income distribution at a given time. Here we are desirous of knowing how many income recipients in the United States fall in each of a num-

---

[1] Practices employed in the field work of sampling, and some sampling principles, are treated in Chapter 19.

ber of income classes. The general problem of organization in this latter class of cases is to determine how many times each value of a variable is repeated and how these values are distributed. Data of this sort, when organized, constitute a *frequency series*, as opposed to the *time* or *historical series*. The methods appropriate to these two types of data differ fundamentally and will therefore be treated separately. In the present section we are concerned with the organization and preliminary treatment of data not arranged in order of time.

We may here recall the distinction drawn in Chapter 1 between statistical description and statistical inference. The present chapter and the two next following are concerned solely with problems of description. In the consideration of these problems, however, we should bear in mind their relation to the processes of inference that constitute the heart of statistical method. We shall open the discussion of these processes in Chapter 6. One minor but practical aspect of the distinction between description and inference should be noted here, since it bears upon the language and symbols we shall employ. We shall speak of a measure derived from a sample as a *statistic*. Such a statistic may be an end in itself, as a quantitative description of an attribute of the sample. More often the statistic is of use to us as a basis for an estimate of the corresponding attribute of the parent population. A measure defining such a population attribute is called a *parameter*. It is a useful general rule (although there are exceptions to it) to use Latin letters as symbols for statistics, Greek letters as symbols for parameters.

Raw data. When quantitative data of the type with which the statistician works are presented in a raw state they appear as masses of unorganized material, without form or structure. They may have been drawn from the records of family saving, or from the production or sales records of a business establishment; they may represent a miscellaneous collection of price quotations. If the data have been gathered by other agencies they may already have been arranged in the form of a general table, but this form may be entirely unsuited to the particular object in the mind of the investigator. The first task of the statistician is the organization of the figures in such a form that their significance, for the purpose in hand, may be appreciated, that comparison with masses of similar data may be facilitated, and that further analysis may be possible. Data, the results of *observation*, must be put into definite form and given coherent structure before the generalizations and tests that constitute the process of *inference* are possible.

The figures that follow, representing the earnings during a given week of 220 individuals engaged in piece work in textile manufacturing, will serve as an example of such data in their raw state.

Weekly Earnings of 220 Textile Workers

$49.85	$59.85	$44.40	$57.10	$44.70	$48.80	$44.55	$50.10
48.65	50.50	53.80	51.05	46.85	46.20	47.40	48.30
50.55	48.40	50.40	45.10	48.50	52.05	55.10	43.85
50.10	51.65	55.40	50.30	45.65	45.55	46.65	51.75
53.20	60.50	48.35	48.50	46.20	52.05	52.70	51.20
47.55	42.50	52.65	45.30	58.60	67.60	49.55	48.25
51.45	46.05	46.95	46.40	49.25	47.95	41.05	47.40
45.30	48.65	50.15	51.35	50.05	49.95	49.05	46.65
49.20	50.45	56.90	49.55	52.85	45.40	45.25	49.00
49.60	54.50	50.45	45.85	46.70	50.65	51.30	61.25
52.25	54.10	50.20	51.25	49.25	47.35	59.95	56.40
50.35	50.60	49.45	58.15	39.55	47.85	49.55	48.70
45.55	55.65	43.30	47.70	47.10	51.55	53.00	38.80
52.00	49.65	48.65	52.60	45.85	54.70	44.10	53.65
48.10	45.00	52.95	51.25	50.15	50.80	51.65	56.70
45.45	50.70	40.40	50.30	48.60	51.85	49.75	51.10
50.00	46.60	47.60	53.10	51.25	50.70	63.85	62.10
55.70	55.25	52.30	41.85	50.55	51.95	49.45	48.35
42.20	50.25	47.00	55.95	48.15	50.75	47.70	52.30
53.45	46.45	49.15	58.95	46.30	53.55	55.30	48.10
64.75	53.35	64.05	49.40	51.90	52.70	49.65	49.70
48.55	48.70	48.45	51.70	59.30	50.95	46.35	46.95
51.70	47.30	54.70	49.30	50.40	44.40	51.10	49.85
54.45	49.75	43.60	44.85	44.75	45.70	49.40	48.45
49.45	50.70	46.50	50.00	52.40	57.30	44.25	49.50
45.75	46.45	40.10	54.65	47.70	49.65	47.75	49.00
61.90	52.90	57.30	57.75	60.40	46.15	47.15	49.60
46.80	50.85	42.95	51.95				

The array. If these figures are arranged in order of magnitude something will have been done toward securing a coherent structure. The range covered and the general distribution throughout this range will then be clear, and the way will be prepared for further organization. When so arranged the *array* on page 43 is secured.

The Construction of Frequency Tables

General Features. While the array presents the figures in a shape much more suitable for study than is the haphazard distribution first shown, there is still something to be desired before the mind can readily grasp the full significance of the data. The factory manager may see that the smallest amount earned during the week was

Array: Weekly Earnings of 220 Textile Workers

$38.80	$45.55	$47.35	$48.70	$49.85	$50.75	$52.25	$55.30
39.55	45.65	47.40	48.70	49.85	50.80	52.30	55.40
40.10	45.70	47.40	48.80	49.95	50.85	52.30	55.65
40.40	45.75	47.55	49.00	50.00	50.95	52.40	55.70
41.05	45.85	47.60	49.00	50.00	51.05	52.60	55.95
41.85	45.85	47.70	49.05	50.05	51.10	52.65	56.40
42.20	46.05	47.70	49.15	50.10	51.10	52.70	56.70
42.50	46.15	47.70	49.20	50.10	51.20	52.70	56.90
42.95	46.20	47.75	49.25	50.15	51.25	52.85	57.10
43.30	46.20	47.85	49.25	50.15	51.25	52.90	57.30
43.60	46.30	47.95	49.30	50.20	51.25	52.95	57.30
43.85	46.35	48.10	49.40	50.25	51.30	53.00	57.75
44.10	46.40	48.10	49.40	50.30	51.35	53.10	58.15
44.25	46.45	48.15	49.45	50.30	51.45	53.20	58.60
44.40	46.45	48.25	49.45	50.35	51.55	53.35	58.95
44.40	46.50	48.30	49.45	50.40	51.65	53.45	59.30
44.55	46.60	48.35	49.50	50.40	51.65	53.55	59.85
44.70	46.65	48.35	49.55	50.45	51.70	53.65	59.95
44.75	46.65	48.40	49.55	50.45	51.70	53.80	60.40
44.85	46.70	48.45	49.55	50.50	51.75	54.10	60.50
45.00	46.80	48.45	49.60	50.55	51.85	54.45	61.25
45.10	46.85	48.50	49.60	50.55	51.90	54.50	61.90
45.25	46.95	48.50	49.65	50.60	51.95	54.65	62.10
45.30	46.95	48.55	49.65	50.65	51.95	54.70	63.85
45.30	47.00	48.60	49.65	50.70	52.00	54.70	64.05
45.40	47.10	48.65	49.70	50.70	52.05	55.10	64.75
45.45	47.15	48.65	49.75	50.70	52.05	55.25	67.60
45.55	47.30	48.65	49.75				

$38.80, that the largest amount earned was $67.60, and that most of the employees earned between $46.00 and $53.00, but this is still a vague description of the data. By a process of grouping, that is, by putting into common classes all individuals whose earnings fall within certain limits, a simplified and more compact presentation of the wage distribution may be obtained. Table 3-1 shows the results of this grouping process when the range of each class (the *class-interval*) is five dollars.

This table presents a condensed summary of the original figures, a summary which not only gives us the approximate range of the earnings, but shows, also, how the earnings of the 220 workers are distributed throughout this range. There has been a considerable loss of detail, it will be noted. From the table we may learn that there are 58 persons who earned, during the given week, between $43.00 and $48.00 (the class extends to but does not include $48.00), but we cannot learn how the earnings of the 58 individuals were distributed throughout this range of five dollars. All may have earned exactly $43.00, so far as we may know from the figures shown in the table. This loss of detail is an inevitable accompaniment of the condensation and simplification which the process of classification involves.

If the size of the class-interval be decreased the loss of detail is less pronounced, though the increase in the number of classes means a more cumbersome table and one that presents a more complex picture to the eye. Tables 3–2, 3–3, and 3–4 present the same data, classified with intervals of three dollars, two dollars, and one dollar.

TABLE 3–1

Frequency Distribution of Employees
(Classified on the basis of weekly earnings; class-interval = $5)

Weekly earnings	Number earning stated amount (frequency)
$38.00 to $42.99	9
43.00 to 47.99	58
48.00 to 52.99	110
53.00 to 57.99	28
58.00 to 62.99	11
63.00 to 67.99	4
	220

The four tables we have thus constructed represent four different degrees of condensation of the same data. Tables 3–1, 3–2, and 3–3 present the same general characteristics: a small number of cases in the extreme classes and a more or less regular increase in the frequencies as the center of each of the distributions is approached. The departure from regularity becomes greater the greater the number of classes. Table 3–4, in which the class-interval is one dollar, has 30 classes. In this table the distribution of cases throughout the range is irregular, with noticeable departures from symmetry. The structure of each of the other tables is orderly and approaches more closely a condition of symmetry. Each presents the wage data in condensed and compact form, so that one consulting the tables may learn of the size and distribution of weekly earnings in the factory in question much more readily than by reference to the chaotic collection of figures first shown. Such organized collections of data are termed *frequency distributions*, and their purpose, as the term implies, is to show in a condensed form the nature of the distribution of a variable quantity throughout the range covered by the values of the variable. The construction of

Frequency Distributions of Employees
(Classified on the basis of weekly earnings)

TABLE 3–2		TABLE 3–3		TABLE 3–4	
(Class-interval = $3)		(Class-interval = $2)		(Class-interval = $1)	
Weekly earnings	Fre-quency	Weekly earnings	Fre-quency	Weekly earnings	Fre-quency
$38.00 to $40.99	4	$38.00 to $39.99	2	$38.00 to $38.99	1
41.00 to 43.99	8	40.00 to 41.99	4	39.00 to 39.99	1
44.00 to 46.99	40	42.00 to 43.99	6	40.00 to 40.99	2
47.00 to 49.99	63	44.00 to 45.99	22	41.00 to 41.99	2
50.00 to 52.99	62	46.00 to 47.99	33	42.00 to 42.99	3
53.00 to 55.99	21	48.00 to 49.99	48	43.00 to 43.99	3
56.00 to 58.99	10	50.00 to 51.99	48	44.00 to 44.99	8
59.00 to 61.99	7	52.00 to 53.99	22	45.00 to 45.99	14
62.00 to 64.99	4	54.00 to 55.99	13	46.00 to 46.99	18
65.00 to 67.99	1	56.00 to 57.99	7	47.00 to 47.99	15
	220	58.00 to 59.99	6	48.00 to 48.99	20
		60.00 to 61.99	4	49.00 to 49.99	28
		62.00 to 63.99	2	50.00 to 50.99	28
		64.00 to 65.99	2	51.00 to 51.99	20
		66.00 to 67.99	1	52.00 to 52.99	14
			220	53.00 to 53.99	8
				54.00 to 54.99	6
				55.00 to 55.99	7
				56.00 to 56.99	3
				57.00 to 57.99	4
				58.00 to 58.99	3
				59.00 to 59.99	3
				60.00 to 60.99	2
				61.00 to 61.99	2
				62.00 to 62.99	1
				63.00 to 63.99	1
				64.00 to 64.99	2
				65.00 to 65.99	0
				66.00 to 66.99	0
				67.00 to 67.99	1
					220

such a table is the first step to be taken in the organization and analysis of quantitative data of the type represented above.

This general introduction to the subject of frequency tables has left untouched many important matters in connection with their construction. It remains to present a summary statement of these details. It will be clear that the first step here taken, the arrangement of the items in order of magnitude, is unnecessary in the actual construction of such a table. Having determined the upper and lower limits through an inspection of the data, one has but to decide on the number of classes desired, write the class-intervals

on an appropriate blank sheet, and proceed to tally the cases falling in each of the classes thus set off. When this process is completed the frequencies are computed and the totals arranged in tabular form of the type illustrated above. These simple operations involve decisions on a number of points, however.

Size of Class-Interval. In deciding upon the size of the class-interval (which is equivalent to deciding upon the number of classes) one fundamental consideration should be borne in mind, namely, that classes should be so arranged that there will be no material departure from an even distribution of cases within each class. This arrangement is necessary because, in interpreting the frequency table and in subsequent calculations based upon it, the mid-value of each class (the *class mark*) is taken to represent the values of all cases falling in that class. Thus, in basing calculations upon Table 3-3, it is assumed that the 33 cases falling between $46.00 and $48.00 may all be represented by the mid-value of that class, $47.00. This assumption will seldom be strictly valid. In the case just cited reference to the original figures will show that it is not a correct assumption. Absolute accuracy would only be obtained by having a class for every value represented in the original figures. Since condensation is necessary, an arrangement of classes should be secured which will minimize the error involved, without transgressing other requirements. Table 3-1 furnishes an example of class-intervals too wide for the material.

The requirement that has just been described clearly calls for a large number of classes. A second requirement, which ordinarily conflicts with this, is that the number of classes should be so determined that an orderly and regular sequence of frequencies is secured. If the classification is too narrow for the data, regularity will not be attained in this respect, and a table without structure or order will be secured. It is desirable, also, that the number of classes be limited in order that the data may be easily manipulated and their significance readily grasped.

A useful procedure for approximating a suitable class-interval has been suggested by H. A. Sturges (Ref. 154). Given a series of N items of which the *range* (the difference between the smallest item and the largest item) is known, a suitable class-interval i may be approximated from the formula

$$i = \frac{\text{Range}}{1 + 3.322 \log N}$$

The specific figure secured in a given instance is likely to be a fractional value, quite unsuited to actual use. An appropriate round number close to the theoretical value, may be chosen.[2] Thus, in the example cited above, with a range of $28.80 and N equal to 220, the use of a class-interval of $3.28 is indicated by the formula. The nearest round number, suitable with reference to other considerations as well, is $3.00. Table 3–2, in which this class-interval is employed, seems to conform most thoroughly to all the requirements we have set forth.

Location of Class Limits. The location of class limits is a matter of considerable importance, for attention to this matter will simplify tabulation and facilitate later calculation. Tabulation of data is easiest when class limits are integers and the class-interval itself is a whole number. Calculation of averages and other statistical measures is facilitated when the mid-values of classes are integers.

Some types of data show a tendency to cluster or concentrate about certain values on the scale along which they are distributed. This is illustrated by the following figures, which form part of a table showing business loans outstanding on the books of a comprehensive sample of member banks of the Federal Reserve System on November 20, 1946. The loans are distributed according to the rate of interest charged.

Interest rate (percent per annum)	Number of loans (in thousands)
2.1 to 2.9	13.7
3.0	31.8
3.1 to 3.9	13.2
4.0	117.2
4.1 to 4.9	26.6
5.0	141.1
5.1 to 5.9	3.6

Here is quite obvious bunching about the integers. The original classified data would show, also, a secondary concentration at each half of one percent. It is clear that in classifying measurements of this sort the midpoints of the various classes should fall at those values about which the observations are concentrated, and class limits must be located with this end in view. For in calculations

---

[2] The use of this formula rests on the assumption that the proper distribution into classes is given, for all numbers that are powers of 2, by a series of binomial coefficients. The relation of the terms in the binomial expansion to the theory of frequency distributions is discussed below, in Chapter 6.

based upon a frequency table the assumption is made that all the items in each class are concentrated at the midpoint of that class. Thus if a standard class-interval of one half of one percent were to be employed in classifying data of the type represented above, the classes should extend from $1\frac{3}{4}$ to (but not including) $2\frac{1}{4}$, $2\frac{1}{4}$ to $2\frac{3}{4}$, $2\frac{3}{4}$ to $3\frac{1}{4}$, rather than from 2 to $2\frac{1}{2}$, $2\frac{1}{2}$ to 3, etc.

Accuracy of observations and the definition of classes. In the construction of frequency tables it is essential that there be a clear definition of classes, so that there may be no uncertainty as to their range and no question as to the precise class in which a given case falls. A table with an arrangement similar to the following is sometimes encountered:

Class-interval	Frequency
0 to 10	3
10 to 20	8
20 to 30	15
30 to 40	6
40 to 50	2

In the absence of explanation, a question arises at once as to whether a case with a value of 10 would fall in the first or in the second class. It is highly desirable that the range of each class be indicated in some such way as the following, in order that this ambiguity may be avoided:

Class-interval	Frequency
0 to 9.9	3
10 to 19.9	8
20 to 29.9	15
30 to 39.9	6
40 to 49.9	2

This procedure solves the difficulty, however, only in case the observations are accurate to the nearest tenth. If the observations are accurate only to the nearest unit (that is, if the cases recorded as having a value of 10 actually lie between 9.5 and 10.5) a mere change in the description of the class range does not solve the problem of allocating a case at the class limit. In such a case an observation falling at a class boundary may be cut in two, one half being allocated to each of the adjacent classes.

Yule and Kendall lay down the useful principle that in fixing a class boundary the limit should be carried to a farther place in decimals, or a smaller fraction, than the values of the individual cases as originally recorded. Thus, in the preceding example, if observations were correct to the nearest tenth, it would mean that a value recorded as 9.9 actually lay between 9.85 and 9.95. In accurately describing the classes, therefore, the intervals should be given as 0 to 9.95, 9.95 to 19.95, etc. (Since the observations to be tabulated are recorded only to the first decimal place no ambiguity arises from the apparent overlapping of these class limits.) It should be noted that the values of the midpoints, or class marks, with these class limits, would be 4.95, 14.95, etc. In presenting and using the table as given above the real meaning of the class limits should be borne in mind. In all cases class boundaries must be fixed with reference to the accuracy of the observations, and exact class marks must be used to ensure accuracy in subsequent calculations.

The work of tabulation is simplified if, in designating a class, both limits are stated, as above. Errors are likely if only the lower limit of each class is given, or if the midpoint alone is designated. It is desirable, however, particularly if calculations are to be based upon the table, to include a separate column showing the values of the midpoints of the various classes.

Other requirements. Class-intervals should be uniform throughout the table in order that all classes may be comparable. Occasionally tables are published with varying class-intervals, so that on one section of the scale the number of items falling within a class having an interval of 5 is given, and on another section of the scale the number of items falling within a class having a range of 10 is given. Obviously, comparison of classes is impossible. It may be desirable to show in more detail the cases falling within certain ranges on the scale, but this end is best achieved by the construction of a supplementary table relating only to the cases falling within this restricted section. The utility of the main table is not lessened thereby.

Similar in nature is the requirement that there should be no indeterminate classes, that is, classes the ranges of which are not defined. Had all the individuals making $50.00 and over in the illustration of piece-work earnings been entered in a class with the designation "$50.00 and over," the upper limit of this class would have been quite uncertain. This fault in a table is a vital one when it is desired to base calculations upon the data contained in the table. When there are several extreme cases the inclusion of such classes is sometimes unavoidable, but when this is done the actual values of the cases included in such "open end" classes should be given in a footnote to the table.

The errors described in the two preceding paragraphs are exemplified in Table 3–5.

TABLE 3–5

Frequency Distribution of Rented Dwellings in Reno, Nevada, 1934*
(Classified on the basis of rental value)

Monthly rental	Number of dwellings in each class (frequency)
Under $10.00	327
$10.00 to $14.99	349
15.00 to 19.99	521
20.00 to 29.99	1,039
30.00 to 49.99	1,075
50.00 to 74.99	189
75.00 to 99.99	24
$100.00 and over	9
	3,533

* The table is taken from *Real Property Inventory, 1934. Summary and Sixty-Four Cities Combined*, Department of Commerce, Washington. Figures for 255 rented dwellings in Reno were not reported.

In this case the ranges of the two "open end" classes are not known. The ranges of the intermediate classes vary, being $5.00 for two classes, $10.00 for one class, $20.00 for one class, and $25.00 for two classes. The purposes of a special investigation may sometimes be served by the use of such a form, but a table of this type is poorly adapted to the requirements of statistical calculation.

A statistical table, in the form presented to users, should be adapted to the special purpose it is designed to serve. It is not enough that it should meet technical requirements of the kind outlined in the preceding pages. It should have an orderly structure and clear and unambiguous column headings and title; it should be self-sufficient and self-explanatory.

Graphic Representation of Frequency Distributions

Frequency distributions of the type illustrated above serve a very important statistical function in presenting a compact summary of data, and in preparing these data for further manipulation. Such distributions may be presented not only in tabular form, but graphically, utilizing the general principles of the coordinate system which were explained above. Many of the characteristic features of a frequency distribution are most clearly revealed when the graphic method is adopted.

Table 3–1, presenting the weekly earnings of 220 employees, with a class-interval of five dollars, is depicted graphically in Fig. 3.1. In this figure class-intervals are plotted along the x-axis and the corresponding class-frequencies along the y-axis, appropriate scales being selected. The fact should be noted that the scale of abscissas starts not with zero, but with $33. For convenience in presentation, that part of the scale extending from 0 to $33 is

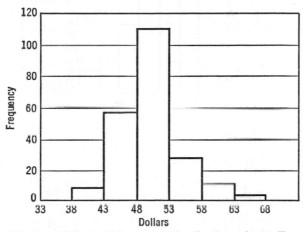

FIG. 3.1. Column Diagram: Distribution of 220 Employees Classified on the Basis of Weekly Earnings (Class-interval = $5.00).

omitted. The student should bear this in mind in seeking to secure a correct impression of the relations between the two variables plotted. In constructing such a figure, which is termed a *column diagram* or *histogram*, short horizontal lines are drawn connecting the points plotted to represent the upper and lower limits of each class-interval. In interpreting this diagram it should be noted that the areas of the different rectangles are proportional to the number of cases represented, the total area representing the entire 220 cases. This device thus presents to the eye a very clear picture of the distribution, showing quite unmistakably the relative number of workers falling in each of the wage classes.

The classes in this case are so large, however, that some violence is done to the facts. So many details are lost that a true conception of the disposition of the items is not given. Fig. 3.2 is a histogram depicting the distribution of cases when a class-interval of three dollars is used. In this case, with smaller steps, we approach more

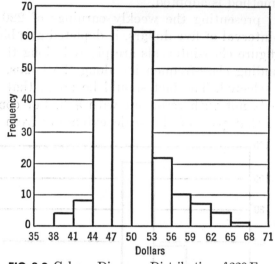

FIG. 3.2. Column Diagram: Distribution of 220 Employees Classified on the Basis of Weekly Earnings (Class-interval = $3.00).

closely an orderly and symmetrical distribution. The same is true of Fig. 3.3, which shows the distribution when the class-interval is two dollars. The distribution represented in Fig. 3.4 has a class-interval of one dollar which, as has been pointed out, is too narrow for the data, with the result that a somewhat irregular structure is

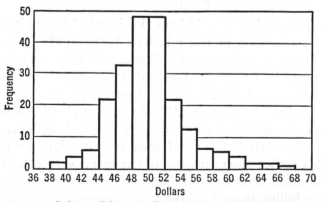

FIG. 3.3. Column Diagram: Distribution of 220 Employees Classified on the Basis of Weekly Earnings (Class-interval = $2.00).

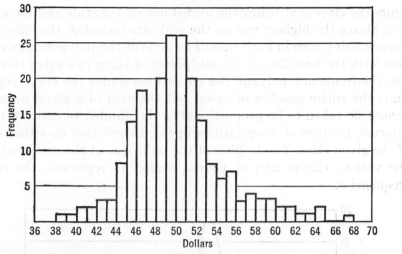

FIG. 3.4. Column Diagram: Distribution of 220 Employees Classified on the Basis of Weekly Earnings (Class-interval = $1.00).

secured. (It should be noted that the vertical scale is not the same in these four figures, so that comparison with respect to class frequencies is only possible by reference to the scale figures.)

Frequency polygons corresponding to the histograms of Figs. 3.1 and 3.4 are shown in Figs. 3.5 and 3.6. Each of these polygons has been constructed by plotting as abscissas the midpoints of the class-intervals, and as ordinates the class frequencies, the points thus secured being connected by a broken line. In completing such a

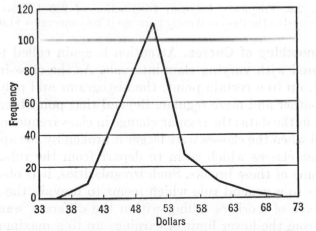

FIG. 3.5. Frequency Polygon: Distribution of 220 Employees Classified on the Basis of Weekly Earnings (Class-interval = $5.00).

figure the class next below the lowest one on the scale and the class next above the highest one on the scale are included, the class frequency being zero in each case. The ends of the polygon thus connect with the base line at the midpoints of these two extra classes. For the frequency polygon the entire area under the curve represents the entire number of cases, but the area of a given interval cannot be taken to be proportional to the number of cases in that interval, because of irregularities in the distribution on either side of the given class. The heights of the ordinates at the midpoints of the various classes are, of course, scaled to represent the class frequencies.

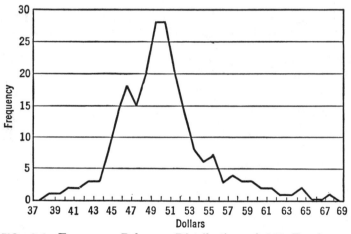

FIG. 3.6. Frequency Polygon: Distribution of 220 Employees Classified on the Basis of Weekly Earnings (Class-interval = $1.00).

The Smoothing of Curves. Attention is again called to the results secured with varying class-intervals. As the class-interval is decreased, up to a certain point, the histograms and polygons become smoother and more regular. Beyond that point breaks begin to appear in the data; the regular change in class frequencies which was found when the classes were larger is broken by the appearance of irregular classes which seem to depart from the rule. Fig. 3.4 reveals some of these breaks. Such irregularities, it is obvious, are exceptions to a general rule which seems to prevail, the rule that the numbers of workers falling within the different wage classes increase from the lower limit of earnings up to a maximum in the neighborhood of $50.00 and then decrease till, in the topmost class from $67.00 to $67.99, but one worker is found. Since all the 220 individuals are engaged in the same work, and since their earnings depend only upon their rapidity and skill, one would expect a quite regular increase and decrease. If we had figures not for one week only, but for 52 weeks, and took the average weekly earnings of each of the 220 workers for the year, we should expect greater regularity with the smaller class-intervals than is actually found, since the accidental fluctuations peculiar to one week alone would thus be eliminated. Or, if we had earnings during one week for 11,440 workers (52 times 220), the same result would be secured. Thus, if regularity and smoothness are to be secured, it is essential not only to decrease the size of the classes but also to increase the number of cases, in order that the accidental irregularities that affect a small number of observations may be eliminated. A refined classification with a small number of cases leads to the condition exemplified in Figs. 3.4 and 3.6. But such an increase in the number of cases is, in general, a practical impossibility. We wish, if possible, to develop a feasible method of approximating the distribution that would be secured with very small class-intervals and a very large number of cases. Such an approximation is possible through the device of curve smoothing. By this method we may secure a smooth *frequency curve* that lacks the irregularities occasioned by minor fluctuations.

Such a smooth frequency curve represents what is taken to be the true underlying distribution of the members of the population from which the sample was drawn. It was pointed out that areas in the frequency polygon are not proportional to the number of cases included, the cause lying in the irregularities of the data. In a smoothed frequency curve these irregularities have been eliminated, and the area between ordinates erected at given points on the scale of abscissas is assumed to be proportional to the theoretical frequency of cases between the given values. Moreover, a smooth progression having been established, frequencies for intermediate values not shown in the original table may be determined by interpolation.[3]

The data of Table 3–6 representing the distribution in 1918 of

---

[3] The limitations of practical statistical work are such that there must of necessity be many gaps in the data. The given values of the variables are not continuous. Interpolation is the process of estimating values of a variable quantity between given values, or of locating a point on a curve between given points. That interpolation is most accurate which leads to estimated values having the highest degree of consistency with the given values.

personal incomes below $4,000, will serve to exemplify the smoothing process.[4]

TABLE 3–6

Distribution of Income among Personal Income Recipients in 1918
(Including all personal incomes below $4,000)

Income class *	Number of persons †
$ 0 to $ 100	62,809
100 to 200	103,704
200 to 300	209,087
300 to 400	489,963
400 to 500	961,991
500 to 600	1,549,974
600 to 700	2,154,474
700 to 800	2,668,466
800 to 900	3,013,034
900 to 1,000	3,144,722
1,000 to 1,100	3,074,351
1,100 to 1,200	2,850,526
1,200 to 1,300	2,535,285
1,300 to 1,400	2,205,728
1,400 to 1,500	1,832,230
1,500 to 1,600	1,512,649
1,600 to 1,700	1,234,397
1,700 to 1,800	999,996
1,800 to 1,900	811,236
1,900 to 2,000	663,789
2,000 to 2,100	549,787
2,100 to 2,200	463,222
2,200 to 2,300	395,115
2,300 to 2,400	340,141
2,400 to 2,500	295,490
2,500 to 2,600	258,650
2,600 to 2,700	227,731
2,700 to 2,800	201,488
2,800 to 2,900	178,901
2,900 to 3,000	154,499
3,000 to 3,100	142,802
3,100 to 3,200	128,217
3,200 to 3,300	115,583
3,300 to 3,400	104,504
3,400 to 3,500	94,803
3,500 to 3,600	86,405
3,600 to 3,700	79,023
3,700 to 3,800	72,562
3,800 to 3,900	66,900
3,900 to 4,000	61,894

* The definition of classes used is equivalent to "$0 to and not including $100," etc. Thus an individual with an income of $100 would fall in the second class.

† Mitchell's report states "The numbers below are given to the nearest unit. It is not pretended that such arithmetic accuracy is anything more than technical."

[4] From Mitchell, King, Macaulay and Knauth, Ref. 108. The graduated income estimates are those of Frederick R. Macaulay.

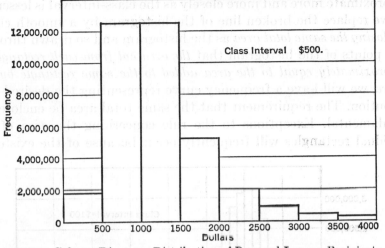

FIG. 3.7. Column Diagram: Distribution of Personal Income Recipients in the United States, 1918. Including All Recipients of Incomes Below $4,000 (Class-interval = $500).

Figures 3.7, 3.8, and 3.9 present column diagrams of these income data, grouped with class-intervals of $500, $200, and $100. As the class-interval is decreased the histograms become more regular and uniform, but our original data permit us to carry this process only to the point where the class-interval is $100. Our problem is to determine the underlying distribution which the data

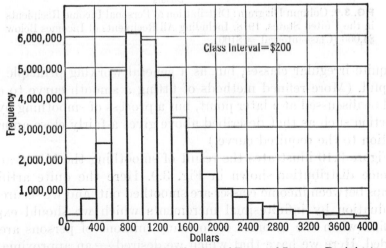

FIG. 3.8. Column Diagram: Distribution of Personal Income Recipients in the United States, 1918. Including All Recipients of Incomes Below $4,000 (Class-interval = $200).

approximate more and more closely as the class-interval is lessened. If we replace the broken line of the histogram by a smooth curve *enclosing the same total area* as the histogram and so drawn through the points of the histogram that *the area cut from each rectangle is approximately equal to the area added to the same rectangle by the curve,* we will have a frequency curve representing the desired distribution. The requirement that the same total area be enclosed is fundamental. Exceptions to the rule concerning the area of individual rectangles will frequently occur because of the existence

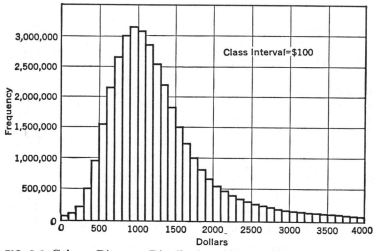

FIG. 3.9. Column Diagram: Distribution of Personal Income Recipients in the United States, 1918. Including All Recipients of Incomes Below $4,000 (Class-interval = $100).

of quite irregular classes, but as a general working principle it is helpful. (More refined methods of fitting a smooth curve to data will be discussed at a later point, but a process of smoothing by inspection such as that described above gives a fairly close approximation to the required curve.)

Figure 3.10 illustrates the result of smoothing the histogram of income distribution shown in Fig. 3.9. Here the quite artificial jumps between income classes are smoothed out, and we secure the graduation by infinitesimal increments which we should expect to find when the incomes of so many millions of persons are included. Here we have that which we desired — an approximation to the true underlying distribution, with the sharp breaks resulting from the method of classification eliminated.

Note on the contemporary distribution of income. The preceding detailed estimates of income distribution in the United States for 1918 serve well the immediate purpose — that of exemplifying the passage from a broken column diagram to the smooth curve approximating the distribution of incomes in the parent population. Macaulay's figures constitute, indeed, the most comprehensive set of graduated income estimates available. They do not, however, provide an accurate representation of income distribution in the United States today. The economic changes of the last thirty years

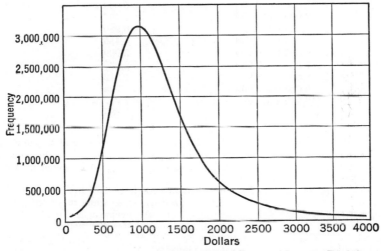

FIG. 3.10. Frequency Curve: Distribution of Personal Income Recipients in the United States, 1918. Including all Recipients of Incomes Below $4,000. (Derived from the column diagram with class-interval of $100.)

have brought major shifts in the division of income by size-classes. Estimates of income distribution in a more recent year, 1950, are given in Table 3–7.

In this discussion of curve smoothing we have been dealing with a major aspect of statistical work — the estimation of the attributes of a population. In particular, we have here been concerned with the manner in which the members of a population of income recipients are distributed, with reference to income size. The present quite preliminary approach to this problem, through the smoothing of an observational distribution, is essentially mechanical. But the problem is one that will enter into much of the subsequent discussion. The precise definition of the manner in which the values of a variable are distributed — the determination of the

TABLE 3–7

Distribution of Family Personal Income
by Families and Unattached Individuals, United States, 1950 *
(Incomes before deduction of income taxes)

Income class	Number of families and unattached individuals (in thousands)
Less than $1,000	3,704
$ 1,000 to 1,999	7,328
2,000 to 2,999	8,044
3,000 to 3,999	8,463
4,000 to 4,999	6,980
5,000 to 5,999	4,459
6,000 to 6,999	2,909
7,000 to 7,999	2,036
8,000 to 8,999	1,212
9,000 to 9,999	728
10,000 and over	2,727
Total	48,590

* Source: "Income Distribution in the United States," a supplement to the *Survey of Current Business*, Office of Business Economics, U.S. Department of Commerce, 1953. Table 3–7 is derived from the absolute and relative frequencies given in Appendix Tables 2 and 24 of this publication.

The estimates in Table 3–7 are based upon Federal income tax returns (projected from earlier years, since 1950 returns were not available when these estimates were prepared) and on sample field surveys of 1950 family income conducted by the Census Bureau and the Board of Governors of the Federal Reserve System. These returns were related to estimates of total family personal income made by the Office of Business Economics as a part of the national income accounts.

The reader will note that the income-receiving unit in Table 3–7 is the family. In preceding income tables in the text it was the individual income recipient. (In the Commerce Department definition, a "family" is a group of two or more related persons living in the same household. An "unattached individual" is a person living alone or with persons not related to him.) Table 3–7 differs, also, from the preceding text tables in that the entire range of incomes is included.

law of distribution prevailing in the case in question — is the objective of scientific work in many fields. Statistics as a scientific discipline has developed and strengthened as our knowledge of the sampling distributions of statistical characteristics has grown. With this we shall deal in greater detail at later points.

Continuous and Discrete Variables. The logical validity of the smoothing process is dependent on the nature of the data being manipulated. From this point of view frequency series of the type discussed above may be divided into two classes, those that relate to continuous variables and those that relate to discontinuous variables. A continuous variable is one that may take any numerical value within a specified range. When observations on such a variable are ranked in order of magnitude, successive values may differ by infinitesimal increments. A discontinuous variable takes only discrete values. Observations on such a variable, ranked in order, change in value only by definite amounts. The curve of underlying values does not rise smoothly, as for the continuous series, but by jumps.

The fact should be emphasized that in making this distinction we are speaking of the values as they would be found in the underlying universe of phenomena from which the actual bodies of material we study are drawn. Any given sample, whether representing continuous or discrete series, will be marked by breaks in the values of the variable. This will be true, in the case of a continuous series, because of the limitations of the instruments and senses we use in measuring. Thus if we measure the heights of individual persons, we may do so to the nearest inch, or perhaps to the nearest eighth or sixteenth of an inch. Yet if ten million men were arranged in order of height the differences between successive individuals would be much smaller than the smallest measurable interval. Height is a continuous variable, even though the observations that enter into a given sample are marked by discontinuity.

Quite different is the distribution of such a variable as interest or discount rates. If one were to secure 100 such quotations and rank them in the order of size the variations would be discontinuous, as in a sample of men whose heights are measured. But in the case of heights the underlying values, if they could be determined for a large population, would be marked by continuous variation, whereas, were an infinite number of discount rate quotations secured, there would still be breaks in the sequence. Discount rates increase or decrease by one quarter or one half of one percent, not by infinitesimal amounts. Such a series is termed discrete, or noncontinuous.

A good example of a discrete series, which also serves as an example of a J-shaped distribution, is provided by Table 3–8 (see Fig. 3.11). This is a classification of machine-tool makers, based upon the number of types of machine tools produced by each.

The series is, of course, discrete since the number of types of tools made by each producer is necessarily defined by an integer. The high degree of specialization in the industry is shown by the concentration of machine-tool makers at the lower end of the scale.

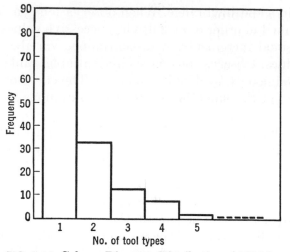

FIG. 3.11. Column Diagram: Distribution of 137 Machine Tool Builders, Classified by Number of Tool Types Produced.

More than half of the total number made but one style of machine tool.

The smoothing process provides a means of securing an approximation to the distribution of values as they would be found if a sample could be increased indefinitely in size. It is based upon the assumption that the irregularities found in the sample actually studied are accidental, and that the underlying values would show

TABLE 3–8

Classification of Membership of National Machine Tool Builders' Association according to Number of Types of Machine Tools Produced *

Types of tools Number	Number of manufacturers
1	80
2	33
3	13
4	8
5	2
More than five	1
	137

* From "Trends in Manhours Expended per Unit, Selected Machine Tools, 1939–1945." U.S. Bureau of Labor Statistics, June, 1947, p. 44.

continuous and unbroken variation. Obviously, therefore, it is only fully justified when applied to a continuous series. A histogram of human heights may be smoothed in order to secure a representation of the true underlying distribution in the population at large, and interpolation based upon this smoothing process is valid. But smoothing is quite illogical for a markedly discontinuous series. It would be meaningless to construct a smooth curve showing the distribution of discount rates for the purpose of securing the theoretical frequency of rates between 4.3675 percent and 4.3850 percent. In practical statistical work, however, it is frequently helpful to handle discrete series as though they were continuous, and in these cases the smoothing device may be employed. But in the interpretation and use of the smoothed curve the logical distinction between continuous and discontinuous variation should be kept in mind.

A U-shaped frequency distribution. In sharp contrast to the customary frequency distributions, in which frequencies increase to a maximum and then decline, is the type represented by the data in Table 3–9. In this distribution commodities are classified on

TABLE 3–9

Distribution of 206 Commodities Classified according to Frequency of Monthly Price Changes in Wholesale Markets, 1890–1925 [*]

Class limits Measure of frequency of change [†]	Number of commodities
.00– .10	45
.11– .20	25
.21– .30	16
.31– .40	19
.41– .50	14
.51– .60	7
.61– .70	6
.71– .80	15
.81– .90	15
.91–1.00	44
	206

* Excluding 1914–21

† The range of the first class in the above table (in actual values .00 to .105, the original measures being recorded to the second decimal place) is slightly greater than the range of any other class, and the range of the last class (in actual values .905 to 1.000) is slightly less than the range of any other class. The error introduced is negligible, however.

the basis of the frequency of price change, in wholesale markets. An index of frequency of change was constructed for each of 206 commodities for which average monthly prices were available for the period 1890–1925 (the disturbed years 1914–21 were omitted). The index was simply the ratio of the number of months in which prices changed (from the price of the preceding month) to the total number of months less one covered by a continuous price record. Thus for a record covering 120 successive months, the index would be 0 (0/119) for a commodity marked by no price changes; the

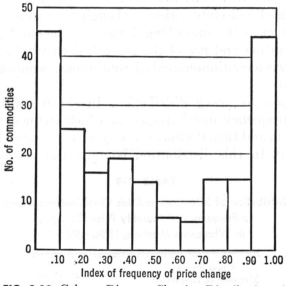

FIG. 3.12. Column Diagram Showing Distribution of Measures of Frequency of Price Changes, 1890–1925 (1914–1921 excluded).

index would be 1.00 (119/119) for a commodity for which the price changed every month.[5] The graphic representation of this distribution, in Fig. 3.12 reveals the remarkable clustering of commodities at the two extremes of the x-scale, with frequencies at a minimum near the median position on the scale. This rather rare distribution type has special interest for economists, in this case, for the light it throws on the movement of prices. High inflexibility and high flexibility were the two dominant types of price behavior in the period covered by this record.

[5] See Mills, Ref. 100, pp. 56–60, 379–81 for a fuller discussion.

Cumulative Arrangement of Statistical Data

For certain purposes it is desirable to arrange data cumulatively, rather than in exclusive classes of the type illustrated in the frequency tables presented above. The accompanying tables will illustrate some of the advantages of this arrangement.

In a study by Kurtz of the durability of telephone poles the results given in Table 3–10 were secured. The table shows that 1,150

TABLE 3–10

Frequency Distribution of 248,707 Telephone Poles, Classified according to Length of Life

Length of life (years)	Number of poles (frequency)
0– 0.9	1,150
1– 1.9	4,221
2– 2.9	10,692
3– 3.9	13,966
4– 4.9	16,633
5– 5.9	18,211
6– 6.9	19,011
7– 7.9	19,260
8– 8.9	20,909
9– 9.9	19,879
10–10.9	20,764
11–11.9	15,454
12–12.9	14,237
13–13.9	13,779
14–14.9	9,764
15–15.9	8,534
16–16.9	7,650
17–17.9	6,918
18–18.9	4,591
19–19.9	1,798
20–20.9	815
21–21.9	313
22–22.9	102
23–23.9	47

poles were scrapped during the first year of use, that 4,221 were scrapped after reaching the age of one year and before reaching the age of two years, and so on. This is simply a frequency table of the ordinary type. A much more significant arrangement for many purposes is secured when the figures are assembled cumulatively, as in Table 3–11.

TABLE 3–11

Cumulative Distribution of 248,707 Telephone Poles, Classified
according to Length of Life
(Cumulated upward with reference to life scale)

Length of life	Number of poles surviving (frequency)
Less than 1 year	1,150
" " 2 years	5,371
" " 3 "	16,063
" " 4 "	30,029
" " 5 "	46,662
" " 6 "	64,873
" " 7 "	83,884
" " 8 "	103,144
" " 9 "	124,053
" " 10 "	143,932
" " 11 "	164,696
" " 12 "	180,150
" " 13 "	194,387
" " 14 "	208,166
" " 15 "	217,930
" " 16 "	226,464
" " 17 "	234,123
" " 18 "	241,041
" " 19 "	245,632
" " 20 "	247,430
" " 21 "	248,245
" " 22 "	248,558
" " 23 "	248,660
" " 24 "	248,707

We should note that it is possible to cumulate a frequency series
in two different ways. From Table 3–11 we may determine readily
the number failing to attain any given age. It is often more convenient to reverse the process, so that the table will enable the
total number above any given value to be immediately determined.
When the telephone pole figures are thus *cumulated downward* Table
3–12 is secured.

Cumulative tables such as those given above have distinct advantages in the handling of many types of data. Life tables are
generally presented in this form. The scientific study of deprecia-
tion will lead to the construction of elaborate "mortality tables"
for various types of equipment, and these will be most useful in the
cumulative form. It is frequently desirable to reduce the frequencies to percentages, as in column (3) of Table 3–12. Cumulated

TABLE 3–12

Cumulative Distribution of 248,707 Telephone Poles, Classified
according to Length of Life
(Cumulated downward with reference to life scale)

(1) Length of life	(2) Number of poles surviving frequency	(3) Percent
0 and more	248,707	100.0
1 year " "	247,557	99.5
2 years " "	243,336	97.8
3 " " "	232,644	93.6
4 " " "	218,678	88.0
5 " " "	202,045	81.2
6 " " "	183,834	73.8
7 " " "	164,823	66.3
8 " " "	145,563	58.5
9 " " "	124,654	50.1
10 " " "	104,775	42.1
11 " " "	84,011	33.8
12 " " "	68,557	27.6
13 " " "	54,320	21.8
14 " " "	40,541	16.3
15 " " "	30,777	12.4
16 " " "	22,243	8.9
17 " " "	14,584	5.9
18 " " "	7,666	3.1
19 " " "	3,075	1.2
20 " " "	1,277	0.5
21 " " "	462	0.2
22 " " "	149	0.06
23 " " "	47	0.02
24 " " "	0	0.00

percentages are particularly helpful when frequency distributions
arc to be compared.

The Ogive, or Cumulative Frequency Curve. The general utility
of such cumulated data is limited by the classification system necessarily adopted in condensing the material. Unless we interpolate
mathematically we are limited to the points on the scale actually
noted in Tables 3–11 and 3–12. For this reason, a generalized cumulative curve similar to the smoothed frequency curve described
in the preceding section is desirable. If the values given in Table
3–11 be plotted on coordinate paper (the length of life in each case
as abscissa, and the corresponding number of poles as ordinate)
and a smooth curve drawn through the points thus plotted, the

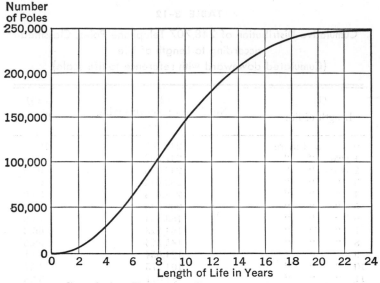

FIG. 3.13. Cumulative Frequency Curve: Distribution of Telephone Poles Classified according to Length of Life (cumulated upward).

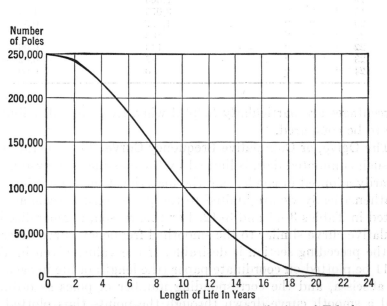

FIG. 3.14. Cumulative Frequency Curve: Distribution of Telephone Poles Classified according to Length of Life (cumulated downward).

cumulative frequency curve shown in Fig. 3.13 is secured. In Fig. 3.14 the data of Table 3–12 are plotted.

Such a curve constitutes one of the most effective and useful representations of a frequency series. It is obvious that the limitations of the particular class-interval adopted are in large part removed; the shape of the curve will be fundamentally the same, though the class-interval and number of classes may vary. Frequency curves of the usual type may not be compared unless the groupings are the same, but cumulative frequency curves are subject to no such restriction. Moreover, uneven class-intervals do not distort the *ogive*, or cumulative curve, as they do the ordinary frequency curve.

The cumulative curve is particularly well adapted to interpolation. Thus if it is desired to know the number of poles surviving less than $15\frac{1}{2}$ years, the value of the ordinate of the curve having $15\frac{1}{2}$ as abscissa may be approximated from Fig. 3.13. A value of 222,000 is secured. If the number surviving $8\frac{1}{2}$ years or more is desired, a similar estimate may be made from Fig. 3.14. The interpolated figure in this case is 135,000.

Another type of interpolation possible with such a curve is the determination of the number of cases falling within any given interval. One is not limited to the class-intervals marked out in the original tables. For instance, it may be desirable to know the number of poles surviving more than $10\frac{1}{2}$ but less than 15 years. Reading from the table or from the chart we find that 217,930 poles survived less than 15 years. Interpolating on the chart in the manner described above a figure of 154,000 is secured for the number surviving less than $10\frac{1}{2}$ years. Subtracting the latter figure from the former we have 63,930 as the number of poles falling within the $10\frac{1}{2}$ to 15 years interval. The figure is, of course, an approximation to the true value, as are all values secured through such smoothing and interpolation.

It should be noted that the ogive may be derived directly from the array, without the formation of a frequency table as an intermediate step. This curve, in fact, may be looked upon as merely a graphic representation of the array. It represents one of the simplest forms of statistical organization, as well as one of the most effective methods of manipulating quantitative data.

Relation between the ogive and the frequency curve. The ogive and the frequency curve are merely two different arrangements of precisely the same material, each arrangement having certain distinctive advantages. The characteristics of each may be more clearly apparent if the structural relationship between these two curves is understood. This relationship is graphically portrayed in Fig. 3.15.

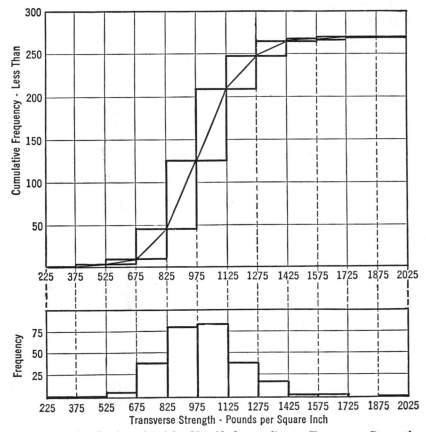

FIG. 3.15. Distribution of Bricks Classified according to Transverse Strength. Illustrating the Structural Relation between the Ogive and the Frequency Curve.

This figure is based upon the data in Table 3–13, showing the results of certain tests of the transverse strength of bricks. The upper part of Fig. 3.15 indicates the method by which the ogive is built up. Just as in the histogram, the area of each rectangle is proportional to the number of cases falling in the given class. Since the operation is a cumulative one, however, the base of each rectangle is the cumulated frequencies of all preceding classes. Thus

TABLE 3–13

Frequency Distribution of Bricks Classified
according to Transverse Strength *

Transverse strength (lbs. per sq. inch)	Number of bricks having strength within given limits (frequency)
225– 374.9	1
375– 524.9	1
525– 674.9	6
675– 824.9	38
825– 974.9	80
975–1124.9	83
1125–1274.9	39
1275–1424.9	17
1425–1574.9	2
1575–1724.9	2
1725–1874.9	0
1875–2024.9	1
Total	270

* The data are from the *A.S.T.M. Manual on Presentation of Data,* published by the American Society for Testing Materials, Philadelphia, 1933.

the y-value (frequency) of the first rectangle is 1, erected from 0 as a base, the y-value of the second class is 1, erected from 1 as a base, the y-value of the third class is 6, erected from 2 as a base, and so on. The slope of the curve connecting these rectangles is gradual at first when the frequencies are low, then steeper as the frequencies become greater, and finally tapers off as the frequencies decrease near the upper limit of the distribution.

When the various rectangles representing the class frequencies are dropped to the zero line as a common base, the x-values remaining the same throughout, the histogram or column diagram described in an earlier section is secured. From this the frequency polygon or smoothed frequency curve may be derived.

The Lorenz Curve. Another arrangement of cumulative frequencies is particularly useful in studying income distribution. The data recorded in Table 3–14, taken from the 1949 midyear report of the President's Council of Economic Advisors, will serve to exemplify the procedure.

This arrangement, in which the basis of classification (column 1) and the frequencies (columns 2 and 3) are in corresponding rela-

TABLE 3–14

Cumulative Distribution of Spending Units in the United States Ranked
according to Percentage of Total Money Income Received in 1948
before and after Deduction of Federal Income Tax *

Spending units † ranked by size of income	Cumulative percentage of total money income received	
(1)	(2) Before tax	(3) After tax
Lowest tenth	1	1
Second tenth	4	5
Third tenth	9	10
Fourth tenth	15	17
Fifth tenth	22	25
Sixth tenth	31	34
Seventh tenth	41	44
Eighth tenth	53	56
Ninth tenth	68	71
Highest tenth	100	100

* Based on data from the 1949 Survey of Consumer Finances, conducted for the Board
of Governors of the Federal Reserve System by the Survey Research Center of the
University of Michigan. The figures given are, of course, estimates. They are based
on a sample survey covering 3000 to 3500 spending units. For an account of the
methods used see the *Federal Reserve Bulletin*, June 1949.
† A spending unit consists of related persons who live together and pool their incomes
for their major items of expense.

tive terms, permits the type of graphic portrayal illustrated by
Fig. 3.16. An absolutely equal distribution of income, cumulatively
expressed, would be represented by a straight line inclined at an
angle of 45 degrees. One tenth of the number of spending units
would receive one tenth of the income, three tenths of the number
of spending units would receive three tenths of the income, etc.
The greater the departure from equality (the greater the concentration of income in upper income groups) the more widely will the
curve of cumulative relative frequencies depart from the line of
equal distribution. Effective comparison of degrees of concentration at different times or under different conditions is facilitated by
the use of such graphs as these, which are known as Lorenz curves.
Of the two distributions here compared, one relating to the distribution of income before deduction of Federal income taxes, one
to income distribution after taxes, the latter shows a closer approach to equality of distribution. This is, of course, the natural
result of the application of a graduated income tax.

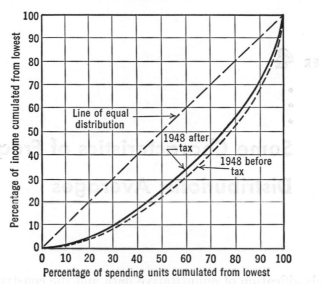

FIG. 3.16. Lorenz Curves Showing the Distribution of Income in the United States in 1948 before and after Deduction of Federal Income Tax.*

* As estimated by the Survey Research Center for the Board of Governors of the Federal Reserve System.

REFERENCES

Croxton, F. E. and Cowden, D. J., *Applied General Statistics*, Chap. 8.

Dixon, W. J. and Massey, F. J. Jr., *Introduction to Statistical Analysis*, Chap. 2.

Goulden, C. H., *Methods of Statistical Analysis*, 2nd ed., Chap. 2.

Kendall, M. G., *The Advanced Theory of Statistics*, 3rd ed., Vol. I, Chap. 1.

Riggleman, J. R. and Frisbee, I. N., *Business Statistics*, 3rd ed., Chap. 7.

Rosander, A. C., *Elementary Principles of Statistics*, Chap. 3.

Simpson, G. and Kafka, F., *Basic Statistics*, Chaps. 8, 9.

Spurr, W. A., Kellogg, L. S. and Smith, J. H., *Business and Economic Statistics*, Chap. 9.

Waugh, A. E., *Elements of Statistical Method*, 3rd ed., Chap. 3.

Wilks, S. S., *Elementary Statistical Analysis*, Chap. 2.

Yule, G. U. and Kendall, M. G., *An Introduction to the Theory of Statistics*, 14th ed., Chap. 4.

The publishers and the dates of publication of the books named in chapter reference lists are given in the bibliography at the end of this volume.

Some Characteristics of Frequency Distributions: Averages

The classification of quantitative data and the construction of a frequency distribution are a first stage in the task of organization and examination. By means of classification the underlying structure of the data may be revealed and the essential unity of a mass of material may be brought out. But this is only the beginning of the processes of description and inference. It remains to develop methods of measuring and expressing more concisely the significant characteristics of a body of data. For certain purposes the frequency distribution itself must be summarized and condensed, must be boiled down until its essence has been distilled into three or four significant figures.

If each frequency distribution constituted a novel and unique phenomenon, obeying a law peculiar to itself, the task of studying and describing such distributions would be a difficult one. Fortunately this is not so. Quantitative data in widely different fields, when assembled in frequency distributions, show certain common characteristics, obey certain general laws. Experience in one field, therefore, constitutes a guide to work in others. Uniformity in the behavior of masses of data makes possible the development of a generalized method of organizing, analyzing, and comparing measurements drawn from many fields of scientific study.

Examples of Frequency Distributions from Diverse Fields

This fact of a common law of arrangement running through the universe of quantitative facts may be brought home most effec-

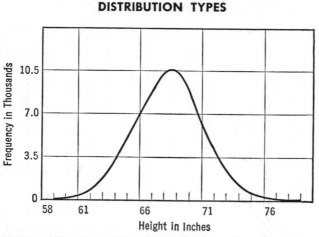

FIG. 4.1. Frequency Curve: Distribution of 67,995 Soldiers Classified by Height.

tively by a comparison of distributions illustrative of various types of data. The characteristics of the frequency distributions and of the frequency curves which follow should be noted, and the distributions compared.

TABLE 4–1

Distribution of Soldiers Classified by Height, 1943 *

Height in inches	Number of soldiers
60	136
61	340
62	748
63	1,632
64	3,204
65	5,576
66	8,227
67	9,791
68	10,675
69	9,519
70	7,343
71	5,100
72	3,060
73	1,428
74	680
75	272
76	136
77	68
Total	67,995

* Source: *Report No. 1–BM*, Army Service Forces, Office of Surgeon General, Medical Statistics Division, "Height and Weight Data for Men Inducted into the Army and for Rejected Men." Classification of inductees by height is based on the whole number of inches reported, disregarding any fractional parts of an inch.

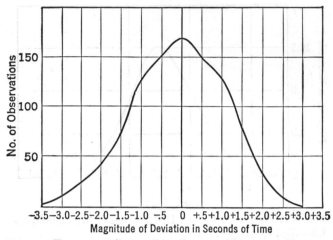

FIG. 4.2. Frequency Curve: Distribution of Errors of Observation in Astronomical Measurements.

The curve in Fig. 4.1 is based upon the data classified in Table 4–1, relating to the heights of a sample of 67,995 men inducted into the U.S. Army in 1943.

Figure 4.2 depicts a frequency curve based upon 1,000 observations made at Greenwich, of the right ascension of Polaris.[1] The

TABLE 4–2

Distribution of Errors of Observation in Astronomical Measurements
(1,000 observations of the Right Ascension of Polaris)

Magnitude of deviation, in seconds of time, from origin	Number of observations
− 3.5	2
− 3.0	12
− 2.5	25
− 2.0	43
− 1.5	74
− 1.0	126
− 0.5	150
0	168
0.5	148
1.0	129
1.5	78
2.0	33
2.5	10
3.0	2
	1,000

[1] From Whittaker and Robinson, Ref. 190.

values on the abscissa define deviations, in seconds of time, from an origin near the mean of all the observations. Frequencies of occurrence of given values on the x-scale are measured, of course, as ordinates on the y-scale. The distribution plotted in Fig. 4.2 is given in Table 4–2.

| 2 | 7 | 16 | 25 | 25 | 16 | 7 | 2 |

FIG. 4.3. Zone of Dispersion, Artillery Firing, Showing the Theoretical Percentage Distribution of Shots.

If a piece of artillery be accurately adjusted on a given target (a point) and 100 shots be fired, it will be found that the points of impact of the hundred shots will be dispersed about the target. No

TABLE 4–3

Distribution of 1,000 Shots from a Single Gun

Division	Number of shots recorded
1 (top)	1
2	4
3	10
4	89
5	190
6	212
7	204
8	193
9	79
10	16
11 (bottom)	2
	1,000

matter how accurate the piece or the adjustment only a small percentage of the shots will fall upon the exact point at which they were directed. The points of impact will be scattered about the target in a quite regular fashion, however. If a rectangle be so drawn as to include all the points of impact, and this rectangle (or *zone of dispersion*) be divided into eight equal parts, the distribution of shots within these sections will be as indicated in Fig. 4.3. (In any given case there are likely to be slight departures from this order, but in the long run this distribution will prevail.)

This general rule holds for all classes of guns. The more accurate the gun the smaller will be the zone of dispersion, but the distribu-

tion within this zone is theoretically the same in all cases. Rules
of fire used in artillery adjustment are based upon this fact.

The results of actual firing may be contrasted with this theoretical distribution. Table 4–3 presents a record of one thousand shots
fired from a battery gun at the middle of a stationary target 200
yards distant.[2] The target was divided by horizontal lines into
eleven equal divisions. These results are presented graphically in
Fig. 4.4.

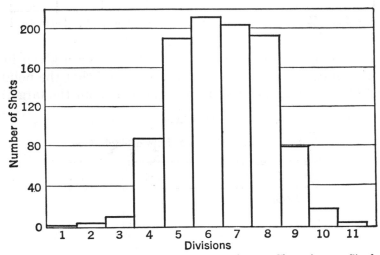

FIG. 4.4. Column Diagram: Distribution of 1,000 Shots from a Single
Gun.

The zone of dispersion being divided into eleven divisions instead of the eight referred to in describing the theoretical distribution, a direct comparison cannot be made. We have here, however,
the same general type of distribution found in the other examples
given. A tendency toward concentration in the lower half of the
target reflects a slight departure from symmetry.

When coins are tossed the distribution of heads and tails is assumed to be determined by pure chance. In a single experiment ten
coins were tossed 100 times. Table 4–4 shows the frequencies with
which given numbers of heads appeared. (The greatest number of
heads possible in a given throw under such conditions is, of course,
10; it is also possible that no heads should appear.) Figure 4.5
depicts the corresponding frequency distribution.

[2] From Merriman, Ref. 98.

TABLE 4–4

Distribution of Results in Coin Tossing Experiment
(Ten coins tossed 100 times)

Number of heads	Frequency of occurrence
10	0
9	1
8	4
7	7
6	23
5	30
4	20
3	9
2	5
1	1
0	0
	100

We find in these four widely different fields something approaching a uniform law of arrangement of quantitative data. Do economic data show the same general characteristics? If reference be made to examples given in Chapter 3, comparisons with the four preceding illustrations may be made. The frequency distributions referred to are those relating to weekly earnings of employees, the

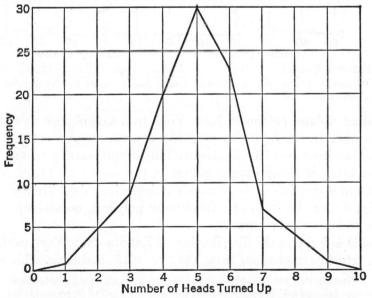

FIG. 4.5. Frequency Polygon: Distribution of Heads in a Coin Tossing Experiment.

length of life of telephone poles, and the size-distribution of income in the United States. (The curve of the 1918 distribution, it should be noted, would show a long tail extending far to the right if the incomes above $4000 were included.) Several additional examples of economic data may be given.

Figure 4.6 illustrates the order in which price variations are distributed. It is based upon a study made by W. C. Mitchell of 5,578 individual cases of change in the wholesale prices of commodities from one year to the next.[3] Thus, for example, the average price of

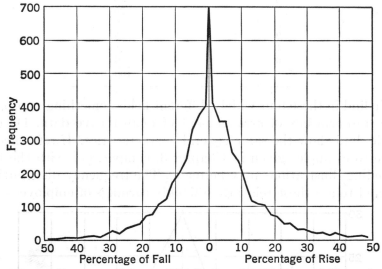

FIG. 4.6. Frequency Polygon: Distribution of 5,540 Cases of Change in Wholesale Prices of Commodities from One Year to the Next (after Mitchell).

middling upland cotton in New York in a given year was $0.115 per pound. In the following year the average price was $0.128 per pound, an increase of 11.3 percent. This would constitute one entry in the table of rising prices, falling in the class "10–11.9%." The entire table consists of 5,578 such entries. These data are presented in Fig. 4.6 in the form of a frequency polygon, no attempt being made to smooth the curve.

Table 4–5 shows the distribution of London-New York exchange rates (sterling exchange) from 1882 to 1913, inclusive. This was a

[3] From Mitchell, Ref. 106. The figure shows the price changes only within the range of a 51 percent fall and a 51 percent rise. One case of a price fall of 55 percent is not shown, and 37 cases of price increases ranging from 52 percent to 104 percent have not been included.

TABLE 4–5

Distribution of London-New York Exchange Rates as Recorded by Months during the Period 1882–1913

Class-interval	Frequency (number of months given rate prevailed)
$4.8275–$4.8324	1
4.8325– 4.8374	6
4.8375– 4.8424	11
4.8425– 4.8474	21
4.8475– 4.8524	23
4.8525– 4.8574	24
4.8575– 4.8624	25
4.8625– 4.8674	40
4.8675– 4.8724	45
4.8725– 4.8774	49
4.8775– 4.8824	35
4.8825– 4.8874	45
4.8875– 4.8924	33
4.8925– 4.8974	16
4.8975– 4.9024	8
4.9025– 4.9074	1
4.9075– 4.9124	1
	384

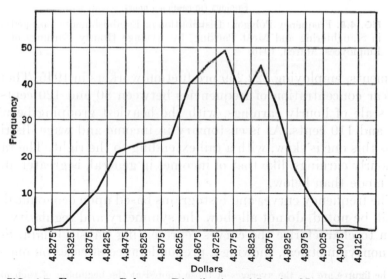

FIG. 4.7. Frequency Polygon: Distribution of London-New York Exchange Rates (as recorded over a period of 384 months).

period when both currencies were freely convertible into gold, at fixed ratios, with customary market forces operating to keep exchange rates between the two "gold points." Observations covering recent decades would show quite different characteristics. In the distribution shown graphically in Fig. 4.7 monthly rates have been classified according to the frequency of their occurrence over the 32 years of prewar experience.[4]

A distribution of slaughtering and meat-packing plants, classified according to the average hourly earnings of employees, is shown in Table 4–6 and graphically in Fig. 4.8. The data relate to 309 estab-

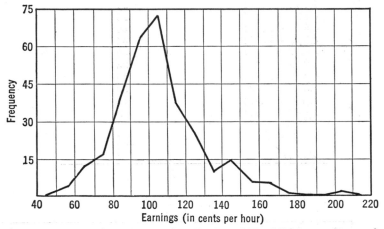

FIG. 4.8. Frequency Polygon: Distribution of Establishments Engaged in Slaughtering and Meat Packing, by Average Hourly Earnings of Employees, March, 1946.

lishments, employing 122,269 production workers in 1946. There is a clear concentration of frequencies between 80 and 120 cents on the scale of hourly earnings, with the heaviest grouping between 100 and 110 cents. As is customary in income and wage distributions this one is skew, with a tail extending to the right. The range of hourly earnings, like that of incomes in general, is greater above the mode than below.

The frequency curves and histograms based upon economic data, it will be noted, do not all show the symmetry and regularity that seem to characterize the curves representing physical data. Some are nonsymmetrical, showing a preponderance of cases on one side

---

[4] "The figures are . . . the averages of those quoted at the beginning of each month in the *Economist;* on and after July, 1886, the exchange is the 'telegraphic transfer,' before that date, 'short at interest.'" The data are taken from Peake, Ref. 125.

TABLE 4–6

Frequency Distribution of Establishments Engaged in Slaughtering
and Meat Packing, by Average Hourly Earnings of Employees
in March, 1946 *

Hourly Earnings Plant Average	Number of Reporting Establishments
50– 59.9 cents	4
60– 69.9 cents	12
70– 79.9 cents	17
80– 89.9 cents	41
90– 99.9 cents	63
100–109.9 cents	73
110–119.9 cents	37
120–129.9 cents	25
130–139.9 cents	10
140–149.9 cents	14
150–159.9 cents	6
160–169.9 cents	5
170–179.9 cents	1
180–189.9 cents	0
190–199.9 cents	0
200–209.9 cents	1
Total	309

* Reports cover any part of the pay period ending nearest March 15, 1946, on both full-time and part-time basis.

of the point of greatest concentration. In some there are breaks in the regularity of the increase or decrease of frequencies. But in spite of these differences there is obviously a family resemblance between the measurements drawn from the fields of economics, astronomy, anthropometry, ballistics, and pure chance.[5] Certain of the common characteristics may be noted.

Some General Characteristics. There is, in the first place, *variation* in the values of the measurements secured. Human heights vary, astronomical measurements of the same quantity differ, projectiles fired under conditions as nearly constant as it is humanly possible to make them fail to land at the same spot, incomes vary as between individuals, and hourly earnings vary from man to man and from plant to plant. The various observations or values

[5] Examples of more extreme deviations from standard types have been cited. Thus there are J-shaped distributions with maximum frequencies at one end of the scale of x-values; there are U-shaped distributions in which the concentrations of frequencies come at the tails rather than toward the center of the range of x-values. For distributions of these types the descriptive measures to be discussed in this and the following chapter lose some of their power and significance. But such distributions, although of special interest when they occur, are rare.

secured in a given case are distributed along a scale, between two extreme values.

The distribution of these values along the scale (the x-axis) is such that, moving from one extreme value towards the other, the number of cases found at successive points along the scale (the successive class frequencies) increases with more or less regularity up to a maximum, and then decreases in much the same way. In spite of variation, therefore, we find a *central tendency*, a massing of cases at certain points on the scale of values. This is the second notable characteristic that all the frequency distributions appear to possess in common.

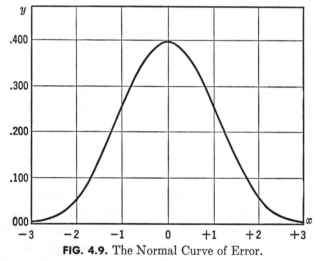

FIG. 4.9. The Normal Curve of Error.

If we measure, for each of the successive classes, the amount of deviation along the scale from the point of greatest concentration it will be noted that small deviations are much more frequent than large ones, that extreme deviations are rare, and that deviations on both sides of the point of concentration reach perfect (or almost perfect) equality in the examples taken from the physical sciences and from the field of pure chance, and approximate equality in the economic distributions. (Exceptions to this rule of approximate equality on the two sides of the point of greatest concentration are not infrequent, the example of income distribution being a striking case in point.)

Figure 4.9 is a graph of what is called the normal distribution. The traditional term for the curve is "normal curve of error." Its characteristics, and the nature of the scales used in its representation, will be discussed in greater detail in a later section. At this point it is presented merely as a basic type which some of the above examples approach closely, and from which others represent more or less pronounced deviations. Departures from this type, let it be emphasized, are numerous and significant, but as a basic form this normal curve of error is extremely important in statistical work. Its existence and our knowledge of its qualities are a main justification for the use of a generalized method of describing frequency distributions. Distributions of quantitative data vary, and their variations from each other and from certain standard types are of the greatest significance, but in spite of their variations a family resemblance runs through them all. Each new frequency distribution is not an isolated phenomenon, but a member of a large family. Accordingly, the task of describing a given distribution and generalizing from it may be approached with confidence in methods that have been found applicable in other cases.

Given this more or less common type, how may a given distribution be described and differentiated from others? Certain methods will have been suggested by the preceding discussion.

Descriptive Measures: General

The values of all the observations, it has been noted, are spread along a scale. The frequency distribution may be described by the selection of a single value on that scale which is thoroughly representative of the distribution as a whole. Since the frequencies vary, an obvious choice is the selection of that value which occurs the greatest number of times, or, in other words, that point on the scale at which the concentration is greatest. This value constitutes a *measure of the central tendency* of the distribution. Thus, one might find the income class in which the greatest number of families fall, and let the midpoint of that class (which is $3,500 in the distribution presented in Table 3–7) serve as the representative of the distribution. This most common value, it should be noted, is only one of several possible measures of the central tendency of a given distribution. All such measures are termed *averages*. They are sometimes spoken of as measures of *location*, since they locate the distribution, or important elements of it, on the x-scale.

A single representative value of this type has many uses but, by itself, it obviously leaves out many facts concerning the distribution. Of great importance is the character of the distribution about the average. Are the values of all tabulated cases closely concentrated, or is there pronounced dispersion over a wide range? The representative character of any average depends upon how closely the other values cling to it, upon the degree of concentration about the central tendency. The average, therefore, must be supplemented by a *measure of variation*, a measure of the "scatter" about the central value.

An adequate description should include also an account of the degree of symmetry of the distribution. It is highly important to know whether there are equal distributions of cases on the two sides of the point of greatest concentration, or whether the frequency curve is skewed to one side, as in the case of income distribution illustrated above. If the curve is not symmetrical the degree of a symmetry should be determined, and for this purpose *measures of skewness* have been developed.

Statisticians have employed, also, a measure of the degree of peakedness of frequency curves, derived by comparing given curves with the normal curve of error as a standard. It is obvious that the frequency polygon representing price changes from year to year (Fig. 4.6) would, if smoothed, yield a curve much more peaked than the normal curve, and this fact of pronounced concentration at the central value is highly significant. This characteristic of frequency curves is called *kurtosis*, or *peakedness*, or *excess*. The measurement of kurtosis, when suitable, constitutes the final step in the description of the frequency distribution.

When these various measures have been secured the task of statistical inquiry will be well under way. The chaotic assortment of data with which we started will have been reduced to workable form in the shape of a frequency table, and the essential facts that the table reveals will have been distilled into three or four significant measures. This process not only reveals the characteristics of the given distribution, but also facilitates comparison with similar distributions. For example, it is impossible to compare some tens of millions of unorganized personal income figures for the United States with similar data for Great Britain. But if we secure a value for the average or most representative income for each country, together with a description of the distribution of personal incomes about that central value, we have a legitimate basis for comparative study. Finally, by the determination of these descriptive measures a foundation will have been laid for the processes of inference

— whether the purpose be to estimate population characteristics or to test hypotheses — that are usually the main concern of scientific inquiry.

The succeeding section is devoted to a discussion of one phase of this descriptive process, that involving the measurement of central tendencies. After the development of this subject of averages, problems relating to measures of variation and of skewness will be dealt with.

Measures of Central Tendency

We have seen that the representation of a frequency distribution by an average, a single typical figure, is justified because of the tendency of large masses of figures to cluster about a central value, from which the values of all observed cases depart with more or less regularity and smoothness. It is because of the concentration of cases about a central point on the scale that such representative figures have significance. The average represents the distribution as a whole because it is a typical value. If the individual items entering into a distribution vary widely in value and show no tendency toward concentration, no single value can represent them. Thus the arithmetic mean of the three numbers 3, 125, 1,000 is 376, but 376 is of limited usefulness as a substitute for the three values on which it is based. This fundamental requirement, that there be a tendency toward concentration about a central value, should be met if an average is to be representative.

If the general character of a frequency distribution be recalled, the logic of one sort of average will be clear at once. It was suggested above that that point on the x-scale at which the concentration is greatest, the value that occurs the greatest number of times, might be taken as typical of the entire distribution. This value is termed the *mode*, and the group in which it falls is called the *modal group*. If a frequency curve be drawn to represent a given distribution, the mode will be the *x-value corresponding to the maximum ordinate*.[6] The maximum ordinate itself measures the frequency of the modal group. Students frequently confuse these two values in determining the mode. It is not the distance along the y-scale but the distance along the x-scale that defines the value of the mode. Each ordinate merely measures the number of cases falling in a given class, not the value of the cases falling in that class.

[6] Strictly speaking, the mode is the x-value corresponding to the maximum ordinate of the ideal frequency curve that has been fitted to the given distribution.

As typical of a given distribution we might also select that point on the scale of x-values on each side of which one half the total number of cases falls. This value, which is called the *median*, is that which exceeds the values of one half the cases included, and is in turn exceeded by the values of one half the cases. Thus it has been estimated that in 1947 the median family income in the United States was $3,027; one half of the 37,000,000 families received less than this sum, while one half received more. When a distribution is represented by a frequency curve, the area under the curve is divided into two equal parts by an ordinate erected at that point on the x-axis corresponding to the median value. This follows, of course, from the definition of the median, and from the fact that the area under a frequency curve represents the total number of cases included in the distribution.

The *arithmetic mean* is a third type of average that may be used to represent a distribution. This is a *calculated* average, affected by the value of every item in the distribution. Herein, obviously, it differs from the mode and median, which depend primarily upon the relative position of the items in the frequency table and are not affected by the values of all individual items. The arithmetic mean is the center of gravity of a distribution; it would be the x-value of the point of balance of a frequency curve, if the curve could be blocked out and manipulated in solid form.

The *geometric mean* and the *harmonic mean* are two other averages; the characteristics of these will be discussed at a later point.

Notation. The computation or location of these various averages may involve somewhat lengthy processes if the number of cases included is great. If appropriate methods are employed, however, the labor of computation may be materially cut down. The use of the following symbols will simplify the explanation of these methods:

X: the value of an individual observation; a series of observations on a variable quantity is represented by X_1, X_2, $X_3 \cdots X_n$; x is also used as a general symbol for a variable

M, $\overline{X}$ or $\overline{x}$: the arithmetic mean of a sample [7]

---

[7] In later sections use will also be made of the symbol μ (the Greek letter *mu*) to represent the arithmetic mean. As has been noted, letters from the English alphabet are conventionally used to represent attributes of a sample, Greek letters for the corresponding attributes of the population that is being sampled. Thus M, the mean height of a sample of male college students, might be 5 feet 10 inches. This is taken to be an estimate of μ, the unknown mean height of the entire population of male college students.

d or x: the deviation of an individual observation from the mean; the deviation of a class midpoint from the mean

A or M': an arbitrary origin other than the mean

c: the deviation of the mean of a sample from the arbitrary origin

d' or x': the deviation of an individual observation or a class midpoint from an arbitrary origin

f: the number of items (observations) in a given class in a frequency distribution

N: the total number of items in a given series, or in a frequency distribution

Mo: the mode

Md: the median

M_g: the geometric mean

H: the harmonic mean

h: class-interval

Σ (Sigma): a symbol for the process of summation, meaning "the sum of"

The Arithmetic Mean. Using the above notation, the formula for the arithmetic mean is:

$$\overline{X} = \frac{\Sigma X}{N} \tag{4.1}$$

Thus the mean of the measures 2, 5, 6, 7, is equal to the sum of these measures divided by 4, which is $\frac{20}{4}$ or 5. The computation of the arithmetic mean when each measure is reported at its true value is thus a simple process of summation and division. The weekly earnings of 220 textile workers were listed in an earlier section. If these figures be added and the total divided by 220, the mean weekly wage is found to be $50.16841. In this case the task of adding 220 items is somewhat tedious; it is a task which would become almost impossible if one were dealing with the 37,000,000 family income figures, for example. For practical reasons, therefore, it is usually necessary to compute the required averages from the frequency distribution rather than from the original ungrouped data. To exemplify this process we may utilize data relating to the hourly earnings of workers in industrial chemical plants in 1946.

The importance of certain of the precautions mentioned in the section on classification, in connection with the choice of a class-interval, will be clear from this example. When the mean of a distribution is calculated from classified observations, we must assume an even distribution of cases within each class. The class-interval should be selected with this in mind, in order that errors introduced by the assumption may be minimized. If the items in each class are evenly distributed, the mid-value of each class may be taken as representative of all the observations included; when such a mid-value is multiplied by the number of items in the class, the product is approximately equal to the sum of all the individual items in the class. The formula for the mean thus becomes $\overline{X} = \frac{\Sigma(fX)}{N}$. Table 4–7 illustrates the procedure in detail.

TABLE 4–7

Calculation of the Arithmetic Mean of Straight-Time Average
Hourly Earnings of Workers in Industrial Chemical Plants
in the Southeastern States, January, 1946 *

Class-interval (cents per hour)	Midpoint X	Frequency f	fX
40– 49.9	45	2	90
50– 59.9	55	326	17,930
60– 69.9	65	500	32,500
70– 79.9	75	368	27,600
80– 89.9	85	202	17,170
90– 99.9	95	174	16,530
100–109.9	105	150	15,750
110–119.9	115	154	17,710
120–129.9	125	72	9,000
130–139.9	135	22	2,970
140–149.9	145	6	870
150–159.9	155	4	620
160–169.9	165	8	1,320
170–179.9	175	4	700
180–189.9	185	2	370
		1,994	161,130

$$\overline{X} = \frac{\Sigma(fX)}{N} \qquad (4.2)$$

$$= \frac{161,130}{1,994} = 80.8074 \text{ cents}$$

* These figures and similar data appearing in subsequent tables were compiled by the Wage Analysis Branch of the United States Bureau of Labor Statistics. See *Monthly Labor Review*, November, 1946. The detailed statistics were provided through the courtesy of Dr. Ewan Clague, Commissioner of Labor Statistics, and Mr. H. M. Douty, Chief of the Wage Analysis Branch, Bureau of Labor Statistics.

The value secured in this way is sometimes called a weighted arithmetic mean. What we do, in effect, is to secure the arithmetic mean of the 15 figures in the column headed X. We do not take a simple average of these figures, however, but *weight* each one in proportion to the number of cases falling in the class-interval of which it is the mid-value. It is precisely the procedure we should follow in calculating the mean of five men's incomes, two of whom, let us say, have incomes of $2,000 and three of whom have incomes of $3,000. Clearly it would not do to add the figures $2,000 and $3,000, dividing the sum by two. The figure $2,000 is given a weight of two, the figure $3,000 is given a weight of three, and the resultant sum, $13,000, is divided by five. Though the procedure in working from the frequency distribution is thus a form of weighting, the term "weighted average" has in general a more restricted meaning, to be explained at a later point, and should not be applied to an average computed from a frequency distribution.

Short method of computing the arithmetic mean. The calculation of the arithmetic mean from the frequency table is much easier, in general, than from the ungrouped data, but when the number of cases included is large even the computation from the frequency table by the method illustrated above may be laborious. The procedure may be greatly simplified.

From the method of computing the arithmetic mean it follows that the algebraic sum of the deviations of a series of individual magnitudes from their mean is zero. This may be readily demonstrated. We represent the series of magnitudes by X_1, X_2, X_3, ... X_n, their arithmetic means by $\overline{X}$, and the deviations of the various magnitudes from the mean by d_1, d_2, d_3, ... d_n. Then

$$\frac{X_1 + X_2 + X_3 + \cdots + X_n}{N} = \overline{X} \tag{4.3}$$

and

$$X_1 + X_2 + X_3 + \cdots + X_n = N\overline{X} \tag{4.4}$$

The number of terms, of course, is equal to N. Therefore, subtracting $\overline{X}$ N times from each side of the equation,

$$(X_1 - \overline{X}) + (X_2 - \overline{X}) + (X_3 - \overline{X}) + \cdots + (X_n - \overline{X}) = 0 \tag{4.5}$$

But $X_1 - \overline{X} = d_1$, $X_2 - \overline{X} = d_2$, etc., and formula (4.5) may be written

$$\Sigma d = 0 \tag{4.6}$$

Knowing this to be true we may measure the deviations of a series of magnitudes from any arbitrary origin, secure the algebraic sum of the deviations, and from this sum ascertain the difference between the arbitrary origin and the actual mean of the distribution. In effect, a constant has been added to (or subtracted from) each deviation, when the deviation is measured from the arbitrary origin instead of from the actual mean. This constant is the difference between the mean and the arbitrary origin. Since the constant is introduced N times, its value may be readily determined by dividing by N the sum of the deviations from the arbitrary origin.

If we let A represent the arbitrary origin, while $c = \overline{X} - A$, and $d_1', d_2', d_3', \ldots d_n'$ represent the deviations of the various magnitudes from A (i.e., $d_1' = X_1 - A$, $d_2' = X_2 - A$, etc.) then

$$d_1' = d_1 + c, \ d_2' = d_2 + c, \ d_3' = d_3 + c, \ldots d_n' = d_n + c$$

and

$$\Sigma d' = \Sigma d + Nc$$

But

$$\Sigma d = 0$$
$$\therefore \Sigma d' = Nc$$

and

$$c = \frac{\Sigma d'}{N}$$

From the known values of A and c the value of the actual mean may be obtained, for $\overline{X} = A + c$. The procedure is illustrated in the simple example given in Table 4–8.

TABLE 4–8

Computation of the Arithmetic Mean (Short Method)
(Ungrouped data)

X	f	d'	
5	1	-15	$A = 20$
15	1	-5	
25	1	$+5$	$c = \dfrac{\Sigma d'}{N} = \dfrac{+25}{5} = +5$
35	1	$+15$	
45	1	$+25$	$\overline{X} = A + c = 20 + 5 = 25$
	5	$+25$	

The work of computation may be still further abbreviated, for observations arranged in the form of a frequency distribution, by measuring the deviations in terms of the class-interval as a unit. Then, in finally applying the necessary correction, the difference between the true mean and the arbitrary origin may be again expressed in terms of the original units. The method may be illus-

trated in detail with reference to the wage data for which the mean
has already been calculated (see Table 4–9).

TABLE 4–9

Calculation of the Arithmetic Mean of Straight-Time Average
Hourly Earnings of Workers in Industrial Chemical Plants
in the Southeastern States, January, 1946 (Short method)

Class-interval (cents per hour)	Mid-point X	Frequency f	d' (in class-interval units)	fd' $-$	fd' $+$	Calculations
40– 49.9	45	2	− 4	8		Calculations
50– 59.9	55	326	− 3	978		$A = 85¢$
60– 69.9	65	500	− 2	1,000		
70– 79.9	75	368	− 1	368		1. Algebraic sum of devia-
80– 89.9	85	202	0			tions from A
90– 99.9	95	174	+ 1		174	− 2,354
100–109.9	105	150	+ 2		300	+ 1,518
110–119.9	115	154	+ 3		462	− 836
120–129.9	125	72	+ 4		288	
130–139.9	135	22	+ 5		110	2. Calculation of c (in
140–149.9	145	6	+ 6		36	class-interval units)
150–159.9	155	4	+ 7		28	
160–169.9	165	8	+ 8		64	$c = \dfrac{-836}{1,994} = -.41926$
170–179.9	175	4	+ 9		36	
180–189.9	185	2	+ 10		20	3. Reduction of c to origi-
Total		1,994		− 2,354	+ 1,518	nal units

Class-interval = 10¢
c (in original units)
$= -.41926 \times 10¢$
$= -4.1926¢$

4. Determination of $\overline{X}$
$\overline{X} = A + c$
$= 85 - 4.1926$
$= 80.8074¢$

The steps in this process of calculating the arithmetic mean by
the short method may be briefly summarized:

1. Organize the data in the form of a frequency distribution.
2. Adopt as the arbitrary origin the midpoint of a class near the center
of the distribution.
3. Arrange a column showing the deviation (d') of the items in each class
from the arbitrary origin, in terms of class-interval units. This deviation
will be zero for the items in the class containing the arbitrary origin,
− 1 for the items in the next lower class, + 1 for the items in the next
higher class, and so on.

4. Multiply the deviation of each class by the frequency of that class, taking account of signs. These products are entered in the column fd'.
5. Get the algebraic sum of the items entered in the column fd'.
6. Divide this sum by the total frequency (N). The quotient is the correction (c) in class-interval units.
7. Multiply the correction (c) by the class-interval. The product is the correction in terms of the original units.
8. Add this correction (algebraically) to the arbitrary origin (A); the sum is the mean ($\overline{X}$).

Location of the Median. The median is a value of a variable so selected that 50 percent of the total number of cases, when arranged in order of magnitude, lie below it and 50 percent above it. For many frequency distributions this is a useful and significant figure.

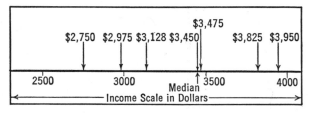

FIG. 4.10. Illustrating the Location of the Median with Ungrouped Data (personal incomes of seven individuals).

Ungrouped data. When an investigator is handling unclassified observations the location of the median is a simple matter. The data having been arranged in order of magnitude, it is necessary only to count from one end until that point on the scale of values is reached that divides the number of cases into two equal parts. As a simple example we may assume that the following seven figures represent the annual incomes of seven individuals:

    $2,750 $2,975 $3,128 $3,450 $3,475 $3,825 $3,950

The scale of values extends from $2,750 to $3,950, and seven items are arranged along this scale. The value $3,000 has two items on one side and five items on the other, so obviously does not conform to our definition of the median. The value $3,450, which coincides with the income of one of the seven individuals, is the median in this case. Three items lie on each side of this value; or, if we assume the central item to be cut in two, $3\frac{1}{2}$ items lie on each side of this point. This case is illustrated in Fig. 4.10. This diagram may help to bring out the fact that the median is a point on a scale so located that it cuts the frequencies in two.

The problem is slightly different when an even number of cases is included. This condition is exemplified in Table 4–10 which shows

TABLE 4–10

Average Hourly Earnings in Selected Industries,
January, 1947 *

Industries	Cents per hour
Hotels (year-round)	64.8
Fertilizers	81.0
Cotton manufactures, except smallwares	91.4
Sawmills and logging camps	93.6
Retail trade	95.1
Canning and preserving	97.5
Silk and rayon goods	97.5
Boots and shoes	99.8
Cigarettes	104.1
Furniture	104.5
Cement	107.9
Radios and phonographs	108.4
Flour	110.1
Clocks and watches	110.6
Paper and pulp	112.9
Telephone	113.3
Leather	117.4
Paints, varnishes, and colors	118.1
Wholesale trade	119.7
Slaughtering and meat packing	120.3
Aluminum manufactures	121.3
Textile machinery	122.7
Electrical equipment	123.2
Machinery and machine-shop products	126.2
Refrigerators and refrigeration equipment	126.7
Steel castings	129.8
Machine tools	132.6
Blast furnaces, steel works, and rolling mills	133.3
Aircraft engines	135.8
Engines and turbines	136.8
Automobiles	138.9
Locomotives	139.7
Shipbuilding and boatbuilding	142.1
Forgings, iron, and steel	143.0
Petroleum refining	146.3
Bituminous coal mining	149.0
Newspapers and periodicals	157.2
Anthracite coal mining	158.9

* From *Monthly Labor Review*, April, 1947.

the average earnings per manhour in each of 38 selected industries in January 1947.

In this case the median must be a value on each side of which 19 industries lie. Therefore any value exceeding 119.7 cents (average earnings in wholesale trade) and less than 120.3 cents (average earnings in slaughtering and meat packing) will satisfy the definition of a median. Under these conditions, where the median is really indeterminate, a value half-way between two limiting values is accepted, by convention. The median of the 38 figures would thus be 120.0 cents.

Grouped data. The task of locating the median is essentially the same when the data are in the form of a frequency distribution. The fact that the real values of the individual items are not known, because of the groupings by classes, complicates the problem slightly. We may illustrate the procedure with reference to data on the distribution of family income, as classified in Table 4–11.

TABLE 4–11

Distribution of Money Income among Families in 1947 *

Income class	Number of families (in thousands)	
Under $500	1,640	$\dfrac{N}{2} = \dfrac{37,279}{2} = 18,639.5$
$ 500 to $ 999	2,386	
1,000 to 1,499	2,908	
1,500 to 1,999	3,280	$Md = \$3,000 + \left(\dfrac{223.5}{4,213} \times \$500\right)$
2,000 to 2,499	4,213	
2,500 to 2,999	3,989	$= \$3,000 + \$27$
3,000 to 3,499	4,213	$= \$3,027$
3,500 to 3,999	3,131	
4,000 to 4,499	2,572	
4,500 to 4,999	1,752	
5,000 to 5,999	2,870	
6,000 to 9,999	3,318	
10,000 and over	1,007	
Total	37,279	

* U.S. Bureau of the Census. Current Population Reports: *Consumer Income*, Series P–60, No. 5, Feb 7, 1949. The present table is derived from the percentage distribution given in the Census publication.

This example is especially appropriate because the median may be accurately determined, whereas the mean could not be.

In the present case the location of the median involves the determination of that value on each side of which 18,639.5 items lie. We may assume that we start at the lower end of the scale and move through the successive classes. When we reach the upper limit of the first class (that including items having values from 0 to $500) we have left behind us 1,640 cases, while 35,639 lie in front of us. (The counting unit is 1,000 families). When the upper limit of the second class is attained, 4,026 items have been passed. The upper limit of the sixth class has below it, 18,416 items while below the upper limit of the seventh class are 22,629 items. Somewhere between the lower and upper limits of this seventh class lies the desired point, that which has 18,639.5 items on each side of it. How far must we move through this class, from $3,000 to $3,500 in order to reach this point?

It will be recalled that, for purposes of calculation, the assumption is made that there is a uniform distribution of the items lying within any given class. Since before we reach the seventh class 18,416 cases have been counted, only 223.5 of the 4,213 included in this class are needed to complete the desired number, 18,639.5. On the assumption of even distribution the required 223.5 cases will lie within a distance on the scale equal to $\frac{223.5}{4213}$ of the class-interval. The class-interval is $500; $\frac{223.5}{4213}$ of $500 is equal to $27. As we move up the scale, then, having reached $3,000, we proceed an additional distance equal to $27. At a point on the scale having a value of 3,027 is the dividing line on each side of which lie 18,639.5 cases. This is the value of the median.

The process of computation is shown at the right of the frequency table. The following is a summary of the steps involved in the location of the median:

1. Arrange the data in the form of a frequency distribution.
2. Divide the total number of measures by 2; this gives the number that must lie on each side of the point to be located.
3. Begin at the lower end of the scale and add together the frequencies in the successive classes until the lower limit of the class containing the median value is reached.
4. Determine the number of measures from this class which must be added to the frequencies already totaled to give a number equal to $N/2$.
5. Divide the additional number thus required by the total number of cases in the class containing the median. This indicates the fractional part of the class-interval within which the required cases lie.
6. Multiply the class-interval by the fraction thus set up.
7. To the lower limit of the interval containing the median add the result of the multiplication process indicated in (6). This gives the value of the median.

The last three steps constitute merely a simple form of interpolation.

The entire process may be reversed by beginning at the upper end of the scale and counting downwards. In this case the final operation is one of subtraction from the upper limit of the interval containing the median.

$N/2$ may be a fractional value, as in the example given, or a whole number. The operation is precisely the same in the two cases.

Location of the Mode. The mode is the value of the x-variable corresponding to the maximum ordinate of a given frequency curve. The concept of a modal value is a thoroughly easy one to grasp. It is the most common wage, the most common income, the most common height. It is the point where the concentration is greatest, a characteristic which is effectively brought out by Fechner's term for this average, *dichtester wert,* or *thickest value.* It is not so easy, however, to locate the true mode in a given case. In general statistical work an approximate value only is secured for the mode.

The method of determining this approximate modal value may be illustrated by reference to the distribution shown in Table 4–12.

TABLE 4–12

Frequency Distribution of 5-Percent Bonds
(This table is based upon quotations on the New York Stock Exchange on December 31, 1948, on domestic bonds with coupon rate of 5 percent) *

Quoted price Class-interval	Midpoint X	Frequency f
Less than 80		11
80– 89.9	85	7
90– 99.9	95	14
100–109.9	105	29
110–119.9	115	7
120–129.9	125	3
130 and more		2
		73

* Bonds of corporations in default or in bankruptcy or receivership are excluded.

There is wide dispersion of the 11 cases falling below 80; the existence of this "open-end" class and another at the top of the scale makes it impossible to compute the mean, as the table stands. The mode is therefore an appropriate average to employ.

The class having limits of 100–109.9 contains the greatest number of cases. This appears to be the modal group, and the midpoint of this class, 105, may be tentatively accepted as the value of the approximate mode. But with different classifications quite different values might be secured for the mode. When the original bond quotations are tabulated with varying class-intervals the results in Table 4–13 are secured. (Only the frequencies of the central classes

TABLE 4–13

Selected Class Frequencies
Distribution of 5-Percent Bonds

(a)		(b)		(c)		(d)	
Class-interval =	5	Class-interval =	5	Class-interval = 2.5		Class-interval = 1	
Class-interval	f	Class-interval	f	Class-interval	f	Class-interval	f
85– 89.9	4	82.5– 87.4	4	97.5– 99.9	5	100–100.9	3
90– 94.9	7	87.5– 92.4	3	100.0–102.4	9	101–101.9	5
95– 99.9	7	92.5– 97.4	7	102.5–104.9	8	102–102.9	2
100–104.9	17	97.5–102.4	14	105.0–107.4	8	103–103.9	5
105–109.9	12	102.5–107.4	16	107.5–109.9	4	104–104.9	2
110–114.9	3	107.5–112.4	7	110.0–112.4	3	105 105.9	3
						106–106.9	5
						107–107.9	4

are shown. It is not necessary, for this purpose, to present each of the tables as a whole.) With a class-interval of 5 a value of 102.5 is secured for the mode; a class-interval of 5, again, but with different class limits, yields a mode of 105. With a class-interval of 2.5 a value of 101.25 is obtained. Finally, a class-interval of 1 gives three modes: 101.5, 103.5, and 106.5. Further changes in classification would give still other values. The mode thus appears to be a curiously intangible and shifting average. Its value, for the same data, seems to vary with changes in the size of the class-interval and in the location of the class-limits.

These difficulties arise primarily from limitations to the size of the sample being studied. The true mode, that value which would occur the greatest number of times in an infinitely large sample, could be located exactly if we could increase indefinitely the number of cases included. For, given sufficient cases, the approximate mode approaches the true mode as the class-interval decreases. Grouping in large classes obscures details, and as these classes are reduced in size more of the details are seen and a truer picture of the actual distribution is secured. But since most practical work is necessarily based upon relatively small samples, the increase in the number of classes reveals gaps and irregularities, and causes such a loss of symmetry and order that doubt arises as to where the point of greatest concentration really lies. The different tabulations of bond prices furnish an excellent example of this.

By mathematical methods it is possible to estimate the value of the true mode without securing an infinite number of cases. The smoothing process has been briefly explained. One sort of smoothing involves the fitting of an appropriate type of ideal frequency curve to the data of a given frequency distribution. This gives, theoretically, the distribution which would be secured by the process first indicated, that of decreasing indefinitely the size of the class-interval and increasing indefinitely the number of cases. The value of the x-variable corresponding to the maximum ordinate of this ideal fitted curve is the estimated mode.[8]

For most practical purposes approximate values of the mode are adequate, and these may be secured by much simpler methods. A first and rough approximation may be obtained by taking the mid-value of the class of greatest frequency, a method suggested above. If the general rules for classification which were outlined in an earlier section have been followed, this procedure will not generally involve a gross error.

It is possible, given a fairly regular distribution, to secure, by a process of interpolation within the modal group, a closer approximation than is obtained by accepting the mid-value of this group as the mode. Referring again to the tabulation of bond prices in Table 4–12 it will be noted that the distribution on the two sides of the modal class is not symmetrical. The modal class is that with a mid-value of 105. The class next below, with a mid-value of 95, contains 14 cases, while that next above, with a mid-value of 115, contains but 7 cases. The disproportion is continued in the succeeding classes below and above, more cases being bulked below the modal class than above. For other purposes we have assumed an even distribution of cases between the upper and lower limits of each class, but it is probable that this is not true of the modal class in the present case. Judging from the distribution outside this class, it is likely that the concentration is greater in the lower half of the class-interval, that is, between 100 and 105. The mode, therefore, probably lies below the mid-value 105, rather than precisely at that point. We may attempt to locate it within the group by

[8] A method of approximating the true mode is discussed in Chapter 6.

weighting, assuming a pull toward the lower end of the scale equal to 14 (the number in the class next below) and a pull toward the upper end of the scale equal to 7 (the number in the class next above). This may be expressed by a formula, employing the following symbols:

l = lower limit of modal class
f_1 = frequency of class next below modal class in value
f_2 = frequency of class next above modal class in value
h = class-interval

The interpolation formula is

$$Mo = l + \left(\frac{f_2}{f_2 + f_1} \times h\right) \tag{4.7}$$

Applying this formula to the bond price data presented in Table 4–12, we have

$$Mo = 100 + \left(\frac{7}{21} \times 10\right) = 100 + 3.33 = 103.33$$

A closer approximation may sometimes be secured by basing the weights (represented by f_2 and f_1) upon the total frequencies of the two or three classes next above the modal class and the same number below. If two classes on each side are included in the present case, a value of 103.23 is secured for the mode of bond prices.

In some cases the problem of locating the mode is complicated by the existence of several points of concentration, rather than the single point which has been assumed in the preceding explanation. A distribution of this type is called bi-modal; when plotted, a frequency curve having two humps is obtained. If the data are homogeneous such a distribution is the result of paucity of data and of the method of classification employed. It may be due to the use of a class-interval too small, with respect to the number of cases included in the sample. An approximate mode may be determined in such cases by shifting the class-limits and increasing the class-interval, carrying on this process until one modal group is definitely established. This reverses the process by which the true mode may be located when the number of cases is infinitely large. With a limited number of cases the location of the point where the concentration is greatest necessitates increasing the size of the class-interval, in order to get away from the irregularities due to the smallness of the sample.

If the distribution remains bi-modal in spite of changes in the class-intervals and class-limits, it is probable that the data reflect the influence of quite different sets of forces. Thus if hourly wage data for a sample of anthracite coal miners and for a sample of hotel workers were combined in a single frequency distribution, two modal points would be expected (see averages in Table 4–10, p. 95). The significance of a frequency distribution is lost if it contains a mixture of observations relating to essentially different groups.

Determination of modal value from mean and median. Another method of securing an approximate value for the mode, a method based upon the relationship between the values of the mean, median, and mode, may be employed in certain cases. In a perfectly symmetrical distribution mean, median, and mode coincide. As the distribution departs from symmetry these three points on the scale are pulled apart. If the degree of asymmetry is only moderate the three points have a fairly constant relation. The mode and mean lie farthest apart, with the median one third of the distance from the mean towards the mode. (If the asymmetry is marked, no such relationship may prevail.) Having the values of any two of the averages in a moderately asymmetrical frequency distribution, therefore, the other may be approximated. In fact, however, the method should only be employed in determining the value of the mode, as the other two values may be computed more accurately by other methods. The value of the mode itself should only be determined in this way when more exact methods are not applicable or are not called for.

The following formula is based upon this relationship:

$$Mo = \text{Mean} - 3(\text{Mean} - Md) \qquad (4.8)$$

Applying this formula to the telephone pole data shown in Table 3–10, the following result is secured:

$$Mo = 9.33 - 3(9.33 - 9.015) = 8.385$$

This value is slightly below the mid-value of the modal class, 8.5, and is also less than the value 8.49 which is secured by weighting within the modal group (using four classes on each side).

For some purposes, particularly those that involve the averaging of *rates* or *ratios* rather than quantities, none of the averages that have been described is suitable. The geometric and the harmonic means are types of averages that should be familiar because they are particularly appropriate for such purposes.

The Geometric Mean. The geometric mean is the nth root of the product of n measures; its value thus is represented by:

$$M_g = \sqrt[n]{a_1 \cdot a_2 \cdot a_3 \cdots a_n} \qquad (4.9)$$

The geometric mean of the numbers 2, 4, 8, is

$$\begin{aligned} M_g &= \sqrt[3]{2 \times 4 \times 8} \\ &= \sqrt[3]{64} \\ &= 4 \end{aligned}$$

It is obvious from the method of computation that if any one of the measures in the series has a value of zero the geometric mean is zero.

The actual computation of the geometric mean is greatly facilitated by the use of logarithms. In this form

$$\text{Log } M_g = \frac{\log a_1 + \log a_2 + \log a_3 + \cdots + \log a_n}{N} \qquad (4.10)$$

The logarithm of the geometric mean is equal to the arithmetic mean of the logarithms of the individual measures.

When the measures, of which the geometric mean is desired, are to be weighted, the separate weights are introduced as exponents of the terms to which they apply. Thus if we represent the sum of the weights by N and the weights corresponding to the terms a_1, a_2, a_3, ... a_n, respectively, by w_1, w_2, w_3, ... w_n, the formula for the geometric mean is

$$M_g = \sqrt[n]{a_1^{w_1} \cdot a_2^{w_2} \cdot a_3^{w_3} \cdots a_n^{w_n}} \qquad (4.11)$$

This is equivalent to repeating each term a number of times, the number corresponding to the amount by which it is weighted. (This, of course, is precisely what is done in securing a weighted arithmetic mean.) When logarithms are employed the formula for the weighted geometric mean becomes

$$\text{Log } M_g = \frac{w_1 \log a_1 + w_2 \log a_2 + w_3 \log a_3 + \cdots + w_n \log a_n}{N} \qquad (4.12)$$

A method of computing the geometric mean may be illustrated with reference to Table 4–14, which shows the distribution of the

TABLE 4–14

Computation of the Geometric Mean of Preferred Stock Prices

Class-interval	X	f	$\log X$	$f \log X$
$ 20–$ 39.9	30	3	1.47712	4.43136
40– 59.9	50	5	1.69897	8 49485
60– 79.9	70	10	1.84510	18.45100
80– 99.9	90	18	1.95424	35.17632
100– 119.9	110	19	2.04139	38.78641
120– 139.9	130	3	2.11394	6.34182
		58		111.68176

$$\text{Log } M_g = \frac{111.68176}{58} = 1.92555$$
$$M_g = \$84.25$$

prices of 58 preferred stocks with a 5-percent dividend rate. The table is based upon closing prices on the New York Stock Exchange and the New York Curb Exchange on December 31, 1948.

Characteristics of the geometric mean. The nature of the geometric mean may be understood by considering its relation to the terms it represents, as an average.

If the arithmetic mean of a series of measures replace each item in the series, the *sum* of the measures will remain unchanged. Thus, the sum of the numbers 2, 4, 8 is 14. The arithmetic mean of these three numbers is $4\frac{2}{3}$; if this value be inserted in the place of each of the three measures the sum remains 14. It is characteristic of the geometric mean that the *product* of a series of measures will remain unchanged if the geometric mean of those measures replace each item in the series. Thus the product of 2, 4, 8 is 64. The geometric mean of the three numbers is 4; if this value replace each of the three measures the product remains 64.

Again, it is true of the arithmetic mean that the sum of the deviations of the items above the mean equals the sum of the deviations of the items below the mean (disregarding signs). The sums of the differences between the individual items and the mean are equal. In the case of the geometric mean the products of the corresponding ratios are equal. If the ratios of the geometric mean to the measures which it exceeds be multiplied together, the product will equal that secured by multiplying together the ratios to the geometric mean of the measures exceeding it in value. For example, the geometric mean of the numbers 3, 6, 8, 9 is 6. The following equation may be set up:

$$\frac{6}{3} \times \frac{6}{6} = \frac{8}{6} \times \frac{9}{6}$$

The last example brings out the most important characteristic of the geometric mean. It is a means of averaging ratios. Its chief use in the field of economic statistics has been in connection with index numbers of prices, where *rates* of change are of major concern, and where equal *relative* changes should usually be regarded as of equal importance. An example frequently cited is that of two cases of price change, one a ten-fold increase, from 100 to 1,000, the other a fall to one tenth of the old price, from 100 to 10. The arithmetic mean of 1,000 and 10 is 505, the geometric mean is $\sqrt{1,000 \times 10}$, or 100. When the average is of the latter type it is seen that the two equal ratios of change have balanced each other. The arithmetic mean, 505, is quite incorrect as a measure of average ratio of price change. This subject is discussed at greater length in the chapter on index numbers.

What has been said in an earlier section in regard to the advantages of logarithmic charting for certain purposes bears upon the use of the geometric mean. This average is sometimes called the logarithmic mean, as its logarithm is simply the arithmetic mean of the logarithms of the constituent measures. Wherever percentages of change are being averaged, where ratios rather than absolute differences are significant, the use of the geometric mean is advisable.

A problem involving the use of the geometric mean arises in computing the average rate of increase of any sum at compound interest. If p_o represent the principal at the beginning of the period, p_n the principal at the end of the period, r the rate of interest, and n the number of years in the period, the sum to which p_o will amount at the end of the n years, if interest is compounded annually, is represented by the equation:

$$p_n = p_o(1 + r)^n \tag{4.13}$$

It follows from this that:

$$r = \sqrt[n]{\frac{p_n}{p_o}} - 1 \tag{4.14}$$

Thus, if $1,000 at compound interest amounts to $1,600 at the end of 12 years, there has been an increase of 60 percent. The arithmetic mean is 5 percent, but this is not the rate at which the money increased. The true rate is:

$$r = \sqrt[12]{\frac{1,600}{1,000}} - 1$$
$$= \sqrt[12]{1.60} - 1$$
$$= 1.04 - 1$$
$$= .04, \text{ or } 4\%$$

Precisely the same problem arises whenever rates of increase or decrease are to be averaged. The use of the arithmetic mean gives an incorrect result.

The geometric mean as a measure of central tendency. A question arises as to the type of frequency distribution the central tendency of which would be best represented by the geometric mean. When the absolute measures, plotted on the arithmetic scale, give a fairly symmetrical distribution, the arithmetic mean is clearly preferable to the geometric mean. But when the absolute figures thus plotted give an asymmetrical frequency curve of such a type that the asymmetry would be removed and a symmetrical curve secured by plotting the logarithms of the measures, the geometric mean would appear to be preferable. Such a distribution would be one in which not the absolute deviations about the central tendency but the *relative* deviations, the deviations as ratios, were symmetrical. The arithmetic mean of the logarithms of the various measures (which value is, as has been shown, the logarithm of the geometric mean of the original measures) would be the best representative of the central tendency in such a distribution. The curve thus plotted would be symmetrical about the logarithm of the geometric mean. A frequency curve representing the logarithms of percentage changes in prices would tend to show this symmetry about the logarithm of the geometric mean of these changes. These percentage changes, as natural numbers, group themselves in an asymmetrical form, with the range of deviations above the arithmetic mean greatly exceeding the range below. This arises, of course, from the fact that prices of given commodities may increase 1,000 percent or more from a given base, but cannot fall more than 100 percent from any given base. The section on index numbers contains a fuller discussion of this particular phase of the subject.[9]

[9] Walsh, Ref. 187, lays down the following criteria for the use of averages:

(a) When there are no conceivable or assignable upper or lower limits to the values of the terms in a series, the arithmetic average should be employed.

The construction of a frequency distribution in which logarithms are tabulated would be laborious, if the logarithm of each item to be entered had to be determined, before tabulation. It is possible, however, with no great trouble to construct a true logarithmic distribution, with class-interval constant in terms of logarithms. The 58 quotations on preferred stocks tabulated in Table 4–14, range from $23.00 to $124.50. The logarithm of 23.00 is 1.36173; the logarithm of 124.50 is 2.09517. The range in logarithms is 0.73344. We may select 0.12 as a suitable logarithmic class-interval for the present purpose. For convenience in tabulating the data we set up two series of class limits, one in terms of logarithms, one in terms of the corresponding natural numbers. In constructing the distribution natural numbers may be tabulated, utilizing the class limits defined in natural terms. All subsequent calculations may be carried through in terms of logarithms. The distribution appears in Table 4–15.

If the geometric mean is considered appropriate for a given series, the type of distribution represented by Table 4–15 is more logical than that shown in Table 4–14, and the descriptive measurements secured from Table 4–15 have correspondingly greater va-

TABLE 4–15

Distribution of 5-Percent Preferred Stocks on the Basis of Market Price

Class-interval (natural numbers)	Class-interval (logarithms)	Midpoint (logarithms) X	Frequency f	fX
$ 22.39–$ 29.51	1.35–1.46999	1.41	1	1.41
29.52– 38.90	1.47–1.58999	1.53	1	1.53
38.91– 51.28	1.59–1.70999	1.65	3	4.95
51.29– 67.60	1.71–1.82999	1.77	10	17.70
67.61– 89.12	1.83–1.94999	1.89	12	22.68
89.13– 117.49	1.95–2.06999	2.01	27	54.27
117.50– 154.88	2.07–2.18999	2.13	4	8.52
			58	111.06

(b) When there is a definite lower limit at or above zero and no upper conceivable or assignable limit, the geometric average should be employed. Because this is true of price changes Walsh believes the geometric average to be the correct one to use in making index numbers of prices.

(c) When in practice, or in the nature of things, certain upper and lower limits are found to exist and the above criteria cannot be employed, a study of the actual dispersion of the data is necessary. In this case, if the mode is found nearer to the arithmetic average, that average should be employed; if the mode is found nearer to the geometric average, that average should be used.

lidity. We may derive the mean of the logarithms of the preferred stock prices by dividing ΣfX of Table 4–15 (111.06) by 58. The derived value is 1.91483. The antilog of this is $82.19, which is the geometric mean of the distribution. This differs somewhat from the value $84.25 secured from Table 4–14. The difference is due, in part, to the use of different class-intervals and class limits in the two cases. With a relatively small number of observations such differences would be expected to lead to different results. Differing assumptions concerning the internal distribution of items within the several classes would also contribute to a discrepancy between the two results. The value obtained from Table 4–15 is probably a closer approximation to the actual geometric mean than is that obtained from Table 4–14.

A frequency curve based upon the logarithms of the measures included, rather than upon the natural numbers, has been employed to advantage in plotting data relating to income distribution. When natural numbers are plotted, the range of income distribution is so large that it is physically impossible to prepare a chart that will reveal the characteristic features of all sections of the curve. The process of plotting on double logarithmic paper (which is, of course, equivalent to plotting the logarithms of both x's and y's) meets this difficulty, giving a true impression of the whole distribution and the relations between its parts, and, at the same time, brings out certain important features that are obscured in the natural scale chart. In particular, this device appears to smooth into a straight line that part of the curve lying above the mode, a fact which led Vilfredo Pareto to enunciate what has been known as Pareto's Law concerning income distribution. An intensive study of the distribution of income in the United States has led the staff of the National Bureau of Economic Research to call into question certain conclusions drawn from Pareto's generalizations, though the value of the double logarithmic scale for the presentation of income data has been recognized.

The Harmonic Mean. The harmonic mean is a type of average capable of application only within a restricted field, but which should be employed to avoid error in handling certain types of data. It must be used in the averaging of time rates and it has distinctive advantages in the manipulation of some types of price data. As will be seen in Chapter 13, on Index Numbers, the harmonic mean is subject to certain biases that correspond inversely to those to which the arithmetic mean is subject. A mutual offsetting of biases is thus possible. The following example will illustrate the method of employing the harmonic mean.

A given commodity is priced, in three different stores, at "four for a dollar," "five for a dollar," and "twenty for a dollar." The average price per unit is required. The arithmetic average of the figures given (4, 5, and 20) is $9\frac{2}{3}$. If we take this to be the average number sold per dollar, the average price would appear to be $1.00 ÷ $9\frac{2}{3}$, or $10\frac{10}{29}$ cents each. But the original quotations are equivalent to unit prices of 25 cents, 20 cents, and 5 cents; the arithmetic average of these prices is $16\frac{2}{3}$ cents apiece. The discrepancy between $10\frac{10}{29}$ cents and $16\frac{2}{3}$ cents is due to a faulty use of the arithmetic mean in averaging quotations in the "so many per dollar" form. Such a mean is, in effect, a weighted average, with greater weight being given to quotations involving a larger number of commodity units.

The correct result may be secured by taking the harmonic mean of the three original quotations. *The harmonic mean of a series of numbers is the reciprocal of the arithmetic mean of the reciprocals of the individual numbers.* Thus if we represent the numbers to be averaged by $r_1, r_2, \ldots r_n$, the formula for the harmonic mean, H, is

$$\frac{1}{H} = \frac{\frac{1}{r_1} + \frac{1}{r_2} + \frac{1}{r_3} + \cdots + \frac{1}{r_n}}{N} \tag{4.15}$$

Using the figures just quoted:

$$\frac{1}{H} = \frac{\frac{1}{4} + \frac{1}{5} + \frac{1}{20}}{3}$$

$$= \frac{10}{60} = \frac{1}{6}$$

$$H = 6$$

The harmonic mean of 4, 5, and 20 is 6, the average number of units sold per dollar. The average price per unit is $16\frac{2}{3}$ cents.

The computation of the harmonic mean of a series of magnitudes is greatly facilitated by the use of prepared tables of reciprocals.[10]

---

[10] *Barlow's Tables of Squares, Cubes, Square Roots, Cube Roots and Reciprocals*, New York, Spar and Chamberlain.

Relations among Different Averages

When different averages are located or computed for a given series of observations, certain relationships are found to prevail among them.

1. The arithmetic mean, the median, and the mode coincide in a symmetrical distribution.
2. In a moderately asymmetrical distribution the median lies between the mean and the mode, approximately one third of the distance along the scale from the former towards the latter. Hence, for this type of distribution there is an approximation to the following relationship:

$$Mo = M - 3(M - Md)$$

3. The arithmetic mean of any series of magnitudes is greater than their geometric mean.
4. The geometric mean of any series of magnitudes is greater than their harmonic mean. The only exception to the last two rules is found when all the measures in the series are equal, in which case arithmetic mean, geometric mean, and harmonic mean are equal.
5. The geometric mean of any two terms is equal to the geometric mean of the harmonic and arithmetic means of those terms. Thus if the terms be 2 and 8, the harmonic mean is $3\frac{1}{5}$, the geometric mean 4, and the arithmetic mean 5. But 4 is also the geometric mean of $3\frac{1}{5}$ and 5. This relationship does not hold when the series includes more than two terms, unless the terms constitute a geometric series.
6. If the dispersion of data tends towards symmetry when the data are plotted on an x-scale in natural numbers, the mode and median will generally be found closer to the arithmetic than to the geometric average. If the dispersion tends toward symmetry when data are plotted on a logarithmic (or ratio) x-scale, the mode and median will generally be found closer to the geometric than to the arithmetic average.

Characteristic Features of the Chief Averages

The arithmetic mean

1. The value of the arithmetic mean is affected by every measure in the series. For certain purposes it is too much affected by extreme deviations from the average.
2. The arithmetic mean is easily calculated, and is determinate in every case.
3. The arithmetic mean is a computed average, and hence is capable of algebraic manipulation.
4. The arithmetic mean is a stable statistic, in a sampling sense. (The meaning of this important statement will be developed more fully at a later point.)

The median

1. The value of the median is not affected by the magnitude of extreme deviations from the average.
2. The median may be located when the items in a series are not capable of quantitative measurement.
3. The median may be located when the data are incomplete, provided that the number and general location of all the cases be known, and that accurate information be available concerning the measures near the center of the distribution.

The mode

1. The value of the mode is not affected by the magnitude of extreme deviations from the average.
2. The approximate mode is easy to locate but the determination of the true mode requires extended calculation.
3. The mode has no significance unless the distribution includes a large number of measures and possesses a distinct central tendency.
4. The mode is the average most typical of the distribution, being located at the point of greatest concentration.

The geometric mean

1. The geometric mean gives less weight to extremely high values than does the arithmetic mean.
2. It is strictly determinate in averaging positive values.
3. The geometric mean is the form of average to be used when rates of change or ratios between measures are to be averaged, as equal weight is given to equal ratios of change. It is particularly well adapted to the averaging of ratios of price change.
4. The geometric mean is capable of algebraic manipulation.

The harmonic mean

1. The harmonic mean is adapted to the averaging of time rates and certain similar terms. It has been employed in the field of economic statistics in the measurement of price movements.
2. The harmonic mean is capable of algebraic manipulation.

This summary has been designed to show that each type of average has its own particular field of usefulness. Each one is best for certain purposes and under certain conditions. The characteristics and limitations of each one should be understood in order that it may be appropriately employed. A complete description of a frequency distribution often calls for the determination of two or three of the chief averages, as well as other statistical measurements. The arithmetic mean is perhaps the most useful single average. The simplicity of its computation, the possibility of employing it in algebraic calculations and the fact that its meaning is perfectly definite and familiar make it highly serviceable in statistical work. Its sphere of usefulness is not universal, however, and it should only be employed when the given conditions render it suitable. A fuller appreciation of the distinctive virtues of the geometric mean is leading to a wider employment of that measure in many types of statistical work.

REFERENCES

Croxton, F. E. and Cowden, D. J., *Applied General Statistics*, Chap. 9.

Dixon, W. J. and Massey, F. J. Jr., *Introduction to Statistical Analysis*, Chap. 3.

Freund, J. E., *Modern Elementary Statistics*, Chap. 4.

Lewis, E. E., *Methods of Statistical Analysis in Economics and Business*, Chap. 3.

Riggleman, J. R. and Frisbee, I. N., *Business Statistics*, 3rd ed., Chap. 8.

Rosander, A. C., *Elementary Principles of Statistics*, Chap. 4.

Simpson, G. and Kafka, F., *Basic Statistics*, Chaps. 10, 11, 12.

Spurr, W. A., Kellogg, L. S. and Smith, J. H., *Business and Economic Statistics*, Chap. 10.

Treloar, A. E., *Elements of Statistical Reasoning*, Chap. 3.

Waugh, A. E., *Elements of Statistical Method*, 3rd ed., Chaps. 4, 5.

Wilks, S. S., *Elementary Statistical Analysis*, Chap. 3.

Yule, G. U. and Kendall, M. G., *An Introduction to the Theory of Statistics*, 14th ed., Chap. 5.

The publishers and the dates of publication of the books named in chapter reference lists are given in the bibliography at the end of this volume.

CHAPTER **5**

.
.
.

Some Characteristics of Frequency Distributions: Measures of Variation and Skewness

In the preceding chapters we have been concerned, first, with methods of reducing a mass of quantitative data to a form in which the characteristics of the mass as a whole may be readily determined and, in the second place, with methods of describing the assembled data. The first object is accomplished with the formation of a frequency distribution. The second is partially accomplished when there has been obtained a single significant value in the form of an average which represents the central tendency of the distribution. But any average, by itself, fails to give a complete description of a frequency distribution. Other values are needed before the chief characteristics of a given distribution have been defined and effective comparison with other distributions made possible. The first of these is a measure of the degree to which the items included in the original distribution depart or *vary* from the central value, the degree of *"scatter," variation* or *dispersion.* The second is a measure of the degree of symmetry of the distribution, of the balance or lack of balance on the two sides of the central value. A third measure sometimes employed to define the pattern of variation takes account of the distribution of observations as between classes near the mean and classes at the tails of a distribution. This attribute, termed *kurtosis,* will be discussed at a later point. The present chapter deals with measures of variation and skewness.

Nature and Significance of Variation

The fact of variation in collections of quantitative data has been pointed out in earlier sections and the bearing of this fact upon the work of the statistician indicated. Practically every collection of quantitative data, consisting of measurements from the social, biological, or economic field, is characterized by variation, by quantitative differences among the individual units. And this fact of variation is as important as the fact of family resemblance. Biological variation has been a fundamental factor in the evolutionary process. No measurement of a physical characteristic of a racial group, such as height, is complete without an accompanying measure of the average variation in the group in this respect. The material well-being of the people of a country depends upon the degree of variation in income among income recipients, as well as upon the size of the average income. The price movements that are characteristic of economic changes are not uniform throughout the price system. They are unequal from sector to sector, and it is the inequalities that both reflect and necessitate economic adjustments.

The whole body of statistical methods may, indeed, be regarded as a set of techniques for the study of variation. It is variation that creates various types of frequency distributions. The powerful tools of correlation analysis have been constructed for studying relations among variations in different quantities. Comparisons of measures of variation provide means of testing hypotheses. When we generalize statistical measures we attempt to define the limits of accuracy of such generalizations, and for this purpose use still other measures of variation. When we deal with observations that are ordered in time, and for which the chronological sequence is significant, we face new aspects of variation. Changes from month to month and from year to year in national income, in the level of wholesale prices, in the physical volume of production, have profound economic significance. Products of a manufacturing process are marked by variation, no matter how fine the tolerance limits imposed. A new and important body of statistical techniques has been developed to distinguish between those variations in quality that are due to assignable causes (and are thus open to control) and those that are due to chance — "chance" meaning the mass of floating or random causes that cannot be separately defined.

Accurate and sensitive measures of variation are thus necessary at all levels and for all types of statistical work. For our immediate purposes, which have to do with the description of observations organized in frequency distributions, the need of such measures as supplements to measures of central tendency is to be emphasized. An average by itself has little significance unless the degree of variation in the given frequency distribution is known. If the variation is so great that there is no pronounced central tendency an average has limited significance. With a decrease in the degree of variation an average becomes increasingly meaningful.

Variation may be expressed in terms of the units of measurement employed for the original data, or may be expressed as an abstract figure, such as a percentage, which is independent of the original units. When the original units are employed *absolute variability* is measured; when an abstract figure is secured we have a measure of *relative variability*, more suitable for comparison than the former type. Measures of absolute variability are first considered.

Notation. A few symbols not hitherto employed will be used in this chapter. Explanations will come later, but it may be helpful to present the more important of these at this point:

s: the standard deviation of a sample

s^2: the variance of a sample

s_a^2: the mean-square deviation from an arbitrary origin

s': an estimate of the standard deviation of a population (this symbol used chiefly with small samples)

s'^2: an estimate of the variance of a population (this symbol used chiefly with small samples)

υ: the standard deviation of a population

σ^2: the variance of a population

$M.D.$: the mean deviation

Q_1: the first quartile

$Q.D.$: the quartile deviation

D_8: the eighth decile

V: the coefficient of variation

sk: the skewness of a distribution

Measures of Variation

The Range. A rough measure of variation is afforded by the *range*, which is the absolute difference between the value of the smallest item and the value of the greatest item included in the distribution. From the array in Chapter 3, showing the weekly earnings of textile workers, we may note that the smallest observation is

$38.80, the largest $67.60. The range, therefore, is $67.60 − $38.80, or $28.80. If the original data were not to be had the range could be approximated from the frequency table. It would be the difference between the lower limit of the lowest class and the upper limit of the highest class. Thus for bricks classified according to transverse strength (Table 3–13 in Chap. 3), the range is from 225 to 2025, or 1800 (pounds per square inch).

The magnitude of the range, it is obvious, depends upon the values of the two extreme cases only. A single abnormal item would change the range materially. It is, therefore, a somewhat erratic measurement, likely to be unrepresentative of the true distribution of items. For small samples, however, particularly when the sampling operation is repeated and an average of successive results utilized, the range has certain distinct advantages. These have led to its rather extensive employment in inspections designed to maintain the quality of industrial products.

The Standard Deviation and the Variance. The standard and most widely used measure of variation, the *standard deviation*, is the square root of the mean of the squared deviations of the individual observations from their mean. Such deviations are termed *residuals*. The deviations are always measured from the arithmetic mean, since the sum of their squares is a minimum under these conditions. We may note that in statistical work extensive use is made also of the square of the standard deviation (i.e., s^2 for a sample, σ^2 for the population). This quantity is termed the *variance*.

The standard deviation of a sample. The procedure employed in computing s^2 and s is illustrated by a simple example in Table 5–1.

TABLE 5–1

Computation of the Standard Deviation

X	d	d^2		
3	− 6	36	$\overline{X} = 9$	
6	− 3	9	$s^2 = \Sigma d^2/N$	(5.1)
9	0	0	$\quad = \frac{90}{5} = 18$	
12	+ 3	9	$s = \sqrt{\Sigma d^2/N}$	(5.2)
15	+ 6	36	$\quad = \sqrt{18} = 4.24$	
		90		

The sum of the squared deviations from the mean of the five observations here shown is 90. The mean of this quantity is 18, the variance. The square root of 18 is 4.24, the standard deviation.

The symbol s will be used throughout to represent the standard deviation of a sample, taken as the square root of $\Sigma d^2/N$. However, the student should at this stage be introduced to a slight modification of this procedure which yields a measure we may represent by s', derived from

$$s' = \sqrt{\frac{\Sigma d^2}{N-1}} \tag{5.3}$$

In the present case $s' = \sqrt{\dfrac{90}{4}} = 4.74$. This quantity is of importance in the theory of sampling, and becomes of practical concern when samples are small. It is to be preferred to s when the investigator is using sample results as bases for estimates concerning the population from which the sample was drawn. To make the distinction clear we may at this point briefly anticipate certain ideas which will be discussed more fully in later chapters.

Estimating the standard deviation of a population. In general, in deriving a statistical measurement from a sample, we do so as a step preliminary to an estimate of a population characteristic. The mean of a sample is of value to us as an approximation to the mean of a parent population; the standard deviation of a sample is an approximation to the population σ. Our problem, in the latter case, is that of estimating the variation prevailing in a population of which both the mean and the standard deviation are unknown to us. Regarding the problem in this light, let us consider the nature of the information provided by successive observations. A single observation provides the basis of an estimate of the mean of the parent population. It provides no basis for an estimate of the degree of variation in that population. For all that we know when we have but one observation, all the members of the parent population may have a single uniform value. When we have *two* observations, however, we have a basis for an estimate of the variation in the population; when we have three observations we have an added basis for such an estimate. In the language of Statistics, two observations provide us with one *degree of freedom* for estimating the variation in the parent population, three observations provide us with two degrees of freedom for such an estimate, etc. One degree of freedom is lost, for an estimate of variation, when we have only the information about the parent population that is provided by the observations in our sample. If, in some independent way, we knew the mean of the parent population, there would be no loss of degrees of freedom for such an estimate. A single observation, the deviation of which from the known mean of the parent population could be measured, would provide the basis for an estimate of variation. But we seldom have such independent information. In effect, in default of such information, we use up one degree of freedom in estimating the mean. This leaves $N - 1$ degrees of freedom for the estimate of the standard deviation. The sum of the squared deviations is divided, thus, not by N, but by the number of degrees of freedom available for the given purpose. (As we shall see, the problem of determining degrees of freedom enters in various forms into later procedures.) When this is done in deriving s'^2, we may, from $\sqrt{s'^2}$, obtain an *unbiased* estimate of σ.[1]

For practical purposes it is convenient and permissible to use N as the divisor, rather than $N - 1$, when N is large, say in excess of 100. The difference between N and $N - 1$ is then negligible; either s or s' provides a satisfactory estimate of σ. (In general, with large samples we shall make no distinction between s and s'.) Even with a small sample N may be used as the divisor of Σd^2 if the derived measure is to be thought of as simply *descriptive* of a given set of observations, rather than as an estimate of a population characteristic.

Computation of the standard deviation. In the example given in Table 5–1 the five observations were ungrouped. When data are grouped in a frequency distribution the task of computing the standard deviation takes a slightly different form. The measurement of deviations from an arbitrary origin is essential in this case, as it greatly simplifies the calculations. In this process, the sample being quite large, the formula for an estimate of the standard deviation may be written

$$s = \sqrt{\frac{\Sigma f d^2}{N}} \tag{5.4}$$

where f represents a class-frequency, d the deviation of the midpoint of that class from the arithmetic mean, and N the total number of cases included. For the square of the standard deviation we have, of course,

$$s^2 = \frac{\Sigma f d^2}{N}$$

[1] The problem of estimation is discussed more fully in Chapter 7.

If a deviation from an arbitrary origin be represented by d' and the mean-square deviation from this origin be represented by s_a^2, we have

$$s_a^2 = \frac{\Sigma f(d')^2}{N}$$

The mean-square deviation from the mean (s^2) is less than the mean-square deviation from any other point on the scale. Hence s_a^2 is greater than s^2. We may represent by c the difference between the true mean and the arbitrary origin. It may be readily established [2] that

$$s^2 = s_a^2 - c^2 \tag{5.5}$$

The value of the standard deviation may be most easily determined, therefore, by computing s_a^2 and c^2. The operations involved are illustrated in detail in Table 5–2, showing the distribution of 83,114 chemical workers, classified on the basis of average hourly earnings in January 1946.

The entire calculation, it will be noted, is carried through in terms of class-interval units, the result being reduced to the original units in the final operation. In computing c, the difference between the true mean and the arbitrary origin, the algebraic sum of the deviations is divided by the number of cases. The arithmetic mean could be determined by reducing c to original units and adding this value (algebraically) to the value of the arbitrary quantity selected as origin, but this is not an essential step. The actual value of the mean need not be known in the computation of the standard deviation.

The *variance* of the distribution in Table 5–2 is, of course,

$$s^2 = (23.5357)^2 = 553.93$$

This can be obtained directly from the figures given below Table 5–2, by multiplying s^2 in class-interval units (5.5393) by the square of the class-interval (100).

[2] For $s^2 = \dfrac{\Sigma d^2}{N}$ but $\Sigma d = 0$

$s_a^2 = \dfrac{\Sigma(d')^2}{N}$ $\therefore \Sigma(d')^2 = \Sigma d^2 + Nc^2$

$d' = d + c$ $\dfrac{\Sigma(d')^2}{N} = \dfrac{\Sigma d^2}{N} + c^2$

$(d')^2 = d^2 + 2cd + c^2$ $s_a^2 = s^2 + c^2$

$\Sigma(d')^2 = \Sigma d^2 + 2c\Sigma d + Nc^2$ $s^2 = s_a^2 - c^2$

TABLE 5–2

Computation of Standard Deviation
Straight-Time Average Hourly Earnings of Workers in Industrial Chemical Plants, United States, January, 1946

(1) Class-interval (cents per hour)	(2) Mid-point (cents) X_m	(3) Fre-quency f	(4) Deviation from arbitrary origin d'	(5) fd'	(6) $f(d')^2$	(7) $(d'+1)^2$	(8) $f(d'+1)^2$
30.0– 39.9	35	1	– 8	– 8	64	49	49
40.0– 49.9	45	5	– 7	– 35	245	36	180
50.0– 59.9	55	422	– 6	– 2,532	15,192	25	10,550
60.0– 69.9	65	1,600	– 5	– 8,000	40,000	16	25,600
70.0– 79.9	75	3,661	– 4	– 14,644	58,576	9	32,949
80.0– 89.9	85	6,004	– 3	– 18,012	54,036	4	24,016
90.0– 99.9	95	10,564	– 2	– 21,128	42,256	1	10,564
100.0–109.9	105	13,136	– 1	– 13,136	13,136	0	0
110.0–119.9	115	15,048	0	0	0	1	15,048
120.0–129.9	125	13,116	1	13,116	13,116	4	52,464
130.0–139.9	135	8,219	2	16,438	32,876	9	73,971
140.0–149.9	145	4,565	3	13,695	41,085	16	73,040
150.0–159.9	155	4,519	4	18,076	72,304	25	112,975
160.0–169.9	165	1,051	5	5,255	26,275	36	37,836
170.0–179.9	175	988	6	5,928	35,568	49	48,412
180.0–189.9	185	82	7	574	4,018	64	5,248
190.0–199.9	195	91	8	728	5,824	81	7,371
200.0–209.9	205	17	9	153	1,377	100	1,700
210.0–219.9	215	10	10	100	1,000	121	1,210
220.0–229.9	225	6	11	66	726	144	864
240.0–249.9	245	2	13	26	338	196	392
250.0–259.9	255	2	14	28	392	225	450
270.0–279.9	275	1	16	16	256	289	289
310.0–319.9	315	2	20	40	800	441	882
340.0–349.9	345	2	23	46	1,058	576	1,152
		83,114		– 3,210	460,518		537,212

$N = 83,114$

Class-interval = 10 cents

c (in class-interval units) $= \dfrac{-3210}{83114} = -.03862$

c^2 (in class-interval units) $= .00149$

s_a^2 (in class-interval units) $= \dfrac{460518}{83114} = 5.54080$

s^2 (in class-interval units) $= s_a^2 - c^2 = 5.54080 - .00149 = 5.53931$

s (in class-interval units) $= 2.35357$

s (in original units) $= 2.35359 \times 10$ cents $= 23.5357$ cents

Correction for errors of grouping. We have pointed out in an earlier section that in basing computations on a frequency table we usually assume that the observations in each class may be treated as though they were concentrated at the midpoint of that class or, which is equivalent to this, that the observations grouped in a given class are distributed evenly between the class limits. Of course, this assumption is not strictly true. If one considers the structure of Table 5–2 it will be clear that the density of the items increases as one moves from either tail toward the modal class. It is a fair inference that, if the data relate to a continuous variable, this increase in density will characterize the observations *within* any class, as well as the items grouped in different classes. In general, that half of each class-interval that lies toward the mode will contain more observations than the other half, lying away from the mode. Thus the actual mean of the observations in a given class will not usually coincide with the midpoint of that class, but will deviate from the midpoint in the direction of the mode.

If the distribution is reasonably symmetrical, this fact will not lead to a systematic bias in the calculation of the mean, for there will be a tendency for positive errors in deviations measured in one direction from the mean to be offset by negative errors in deviations on the other side. But when the deviations are squared, as they are in computing the standard deviation and the variance, the error is systematic. The square of the deviation (from the mean of the total distribution) of a class midpoint will in general be greater than the square of the deviation of the actual mean of the observations in the given class from the mean of the distribution. Under these conditions the sum of the squared deviations derived from the grouped items, as in Table 5–2, will be greater than the true sum of the squared deviations, as this sum might be derived from ungrouped data.

W. F. Sheppard (Ref. 139) has established that the error in the variance due to the use of grouped data in computations amounts to about one twelfth of the square of the class-interval. This will be the case when two conditions prevail:

1. When the data tabulated are observations on a continuous variable.
2. When the frequencies taper off gradually at the two extremes. This latter condition is often defined as one in which the frequency curve fitted to the given distribution is characterized by "high contact" at both tails.

The application of Sheppard's correction is a simple process. If s^2 is the uncorrected variance derived from deviations in class-interval units (the variance thus measured is 5.53931 for the data in Table 5–2), we may write

$$\text{Corrected variance} = s^2 - \frac{1}{12} \qquad (5.6)$$

When the deviations are in original units of measurement, and h is the class-interval in such units, we have

$$\text{Corrected variance} = s^2 - \frac{h^2}{12} \qquad (5.7)$$

Applying this correction to the measures given in Table 5–2 we obtain a corrected variance, in class-interval units, of 5.45598, a corrected standard deviation, in original units, of 23.3580 cents.

The point should be stressed that the application of Sheppard's correction when the basic conditions are not fulfilled (e.g., when a U-shaped distribution, a J-shaped distribution, or any very skew distribution is being studied) may lessen rather than increase the accuracy of the estimate of the variance or the standard deviation. Moreover, the correction should be avoided when the number of observations tabulated is small, say below 500, with customary grouping.

The Charlier check. A check upon the accuracy of the calculations in Table 5–2 (the *Charlier check*) is afforded by the figures in columns (7) and (8). If deviations be measured, not from the arbitrary origin employed in computing the standard deviation, but from an origin one class-interval below, we secure a set of values equal to $d' + 1$. The squares of these values are given in column (7). Multiplying by the corresponding frequencies we have the quantities recorded in column (8), the sum of which is 537,212. This total stands in a definite relationship to the values secured in computing the standard deviation. For

$$\Sigma f(d' + 1)^2 = \Sigma f[(d')^2 + 2d' + 1]$$
$$= \Sigma f(d')^2 + 2\Sigma fd' + \Sigma f$$
or $$\Sigma f(d' + 1)^2 = \Sigma f(d')^2 + 2\Sigma fd' + N \qquad (5.8)$$

Inserting in this last equation the values secured from the calculations shown in Table 5–2, we obtain this check:

$$537,212 = 460,518 - 6,420 + 83,114$$
$$= 537,212$$

The following is a summary of the steps in the process of computing the standard deviation of items grouped in a frequency distribution:

1. Select as arbitrary origin the midpoint of a class near the center of the distribution.
2. Measure the deviations from this point of the items in each class, in class-interval units. Multiply the deviations by the corresponding class frequencies.
3. Divide the algebraic sum of the deviations by N. This gives c, in class-interval units. Compute c^2.
4. Square the deviations and multiply by the corresponding class frequencies.
5. Divide the sum of the squared deviations by N. This gives s_a^2, in class-interval units.
6. From the formula, $s^2 = s_a^2 - c^2$, compute s^2. Extract the square root of this value, securing s in class-interval units.
7. Multiply s, as thus computed, by the class-interval. The result is s in the original units of measurement.

If the population variance is to be estimated, derive the estimate from the relation

$$s'^2 = \frac{\Sigma d^2}{N-1}$$

Alternatively the estimate may be made from

$$s'^2 = s^2 \frac{N}{N-1}$$

Certain of the characteristics of the standard deviation and its relation to other measures of dispersion are described in a later section.

The Mean Deviation. An alternative but less useful measure of the dispersion of items about the central value of a sample is

TABLE 5–3

Computation of Mean Deviation

X	f	d	
3	1	6	$M = 9$
6	1	3	
9	1	0	$M.D. = \dfrac{18}{5} = 3.6$
12	1	3	
15	1	6	
		18	

afforded by the device of measuring the deviation of each item from this central value, in absolute terms, and averaging these deviations. A simple example is given in Table 5–3. The average (the mean and median coincide in this case) is 9. The deviations are added, taking no account of algebraic signs, and the total divided by the number of items. This procedure is described by the expression

$$M.D. = \frac{\Sigma |d|}{N} \qquad (5.9)$$

where $|\ |$ indicates that no account is taken of signs.

In general terms, the *mean deviation* of a series of magnitudes is the arithmetic mean of their deviations from an average value, either mean or median. In the process of summation and averaging the algebraic signs of the deviations are disregarded. It is good practice to take the deviations from the median when the mean deviation is to be used as a measure of dispersion, for the mean deviation is a minimum when the median is the point of reference.

When the observations are many the task of computing the mean deviation is less simple. With the data grouped in a frequency distribution, deviations may be measured from the median (or mean) and multiplied by class frequencies. Alternatively, deviations may be measured from the midpoint of the class containing the median (or mean), a later correction being made to offset the error resulting from the use of the class midpoint as origin, rather than the median (or mean). The mean deviation is useful in dealing with small numbers of observations when no elaborate analysis is called for. For extensive use it has certain logical and mathematical limitations (e.g., the disregard of plus and minus signs in adding the deviations is algebraically illogical). It is seldom employed when data have been organized in a frequency distribution.

Quantiles. The character of the variation characteristic of a given distribution of the variable x may be effectively indicated by selected *quantiles*. This is a general term for quantities defining points on the x-scale which divide the total frequencies in specified proportions. The median is a central quantile which, as we have seen, divides the total frequencies into two equal groups. *Quartiles*, as the term implies, are values which divide the total number of observations in a distribution into four equal groups. Thus the first quartile is that point on the scale of x-values below which lie one quarter of the total number of cases and above which lie three quarters of the total. (The second quartile and the median are, obviously, identical). The *deciles* divide the total frequencies into 10 equal groups; the *percentiles* divide them into 100 equal groups. Quantiles are simple and easily understood measures which may be used effectively in defining the degree and character of dispersion. In studies of the distribution of price relatives and other variables Wesley C. Mitchell made extensive use of such measures (Refs. 105 and 106).

In locating quantiles the count begins in all cases at the lower end of the x-scale. The two following examples will illustrate the procedure:

Location of the First Quartile (Q_1), Family Incomes (See Table 4–11)

$$N/4 = 9,319.75$$
$$Q_1 = \$1,500 + (2,385.75/3,280) \times \$500$$
$$= \$1,863.68$$

Location of Eighth Decile (D_8), Family Incomes (See Table 4–11)

$$N/10 = 3,727.9 \qquad D_8 = \$4,500 + (1,491.2/1,752) \times \$500$$
$$8N/10 = 29,823.2 \qquad = \$4,925.57$$

As is true of the median, the other quantiles will be indeterminate when a quantile value falls between given (ungrouped) values of the variable. In such a case, a value half-way between the two limiting values is conventionally employed.

The Quartile Deviation. In studying dispersion by means of quantiles one does not have a single measure, such as the standard or mean deviation. Such a single measure of variation may be computed readily from the quartiles, however. Within the range between the two quartiles, of course, one half of all the measures are included. The greater the concentration the smaller this interval, hence a fairly accurate measure of dispersion may be obtained from the relationship between these two quartiles. The quartile deviation is the *semi-interquartile range,* half the distance along the scale between the first and third quartiles. Thus if $Q.D.$ represent the quartile deviation, Q_1 the first quartile and Q_3 the third quartile,

$$Q.D. = \frac{Q_3 - Q_1}{2} \tag{5.10}$$

If the value of a point on the scale half-way between the first and third quartiles is represented by K, one half of all the measures in a frequency distribution will fall within the range $K \pm Q.D.$ For the data in Table 5–2, relating to the hourly earnings of workers in industrial chemical plants in 1946, we have (in cents):

$$Q_1 = 98.60$$
$$Q_3 = 129.07$$
$$Q.D. = \frac{129.07 - 98.60}{2}$$
$$= 15.235$$
$$K = 98.60 + 15.235$$
$$= 113.835$$

Thus one half of all the measures lie within the range 113.835 ± 15.235. This statement, together with the arithmetic mean of the hourly earnings of chemical workers in the year in question, constitutes a useful description of the distribution. In a perfectly symmetrical distribution the value of K will coincide with the value of the median (that is, the median will lie half-way along the scale from Q_1 to Q_3). The distribution of wage rates is almost symmetrical, the value of the median being 113.89 cents, as compared with 113.835 cents for K.

The probable error. In studying the results of astronomical and other physical measurements it has been found that the values secured by different observers for the same constant quantity vary. In such cases there is an obvious need of a measure of variation which may be used as an index of the reliability of given results. The traditional measure employed in such cases is termed the *probable error*. The probable error (or $P.E.$) is that amount which, in a given case, is exceeded by the errors of one half the observations.

For the normal distribution, which is the ideal type to which many observed distributions of errors of measurement tend to conform, the probable error is equal to 0.6745σ. For the normal distribution, that is, a distance equal to the probable error laid off on each side of the arithmetic mean will define limits within which one half of the total number of cases will fall.

This measure of variation has been employed in fields other than that in which it was originally applied, fields in which the name *probable error* is somewhat misleading. In such cases it is better to think of it as the *probable deviation*, that distance from the mean which will be exceeded by one half of the total deviations.

The probable error is a measure of dispersion which is fully significant only when it applies to a distribution following the normal law of error. In such cases it has a definite and precise meaning.

This is not so when it is applied to skew distributions, and its use in such cases is not advisable.

Relations among Measures of Variation

An understanding of the significance of the various measures of dispersion described above may be facilitated by a general comparison and a summary statement of the relations among them.

1. The *range* is a distance along the scale within which all the observations lie.
2. The *quartile deviation* or *semi-interquartile range* is a distance along the scale which, when laid off on each side of the point midway between the two quartiles, includes one half the total number of observations.
3. The *mean deviation* from the mean, in a normal or slightly skew distribution, is equal to about $\frac{4}{5}$ of the standard deviation. A range of $7\frac{1}{2}$ times the mean deviation, centering at the mean, will include approximately 99 percent of all the cases.
4. When a distance equal to the *standard deviation* is laid off on each side of the mean, in a normal or only slightly skew distribution, about two thirds of all the cases will be included. (In the normal distribution 68.27 percent of the observations will be included.) When a distance equal to twice the standard deviation is laid off on each side of the mean approximately 95 percent of the cases will be included (95.45 percent in a normal distribution). When a distance equal to three times the standard deviation is laid off on each side of the mean about 99 percent of all the observations will be included (99.73 percent in a normal distribution). This general rule that a range of six times the standard deviation, centering at the mean, will include about 99 percent of all the measures furnishes a useful check upon calculations.

    A study of Fig. 6.5 may help to make clear the significance of the standard deviation in a normal distribution.
5. The *probable error*, in a normal distribution, is equal to 0.6745σ. A range of twice the probable error, centering at the mean, will include 50 percent of all the observations. A range of eight times the probable error, centering at the mean, will include approximately 99 percent of all the observations.

Characteristic Features of the Chief Measures of Variation

The range

1. The range is easily calculated and its significance is readily understood. As a rough measure of the degree of variation the range is useful.
2. The value of the range is determined by the values of the two extreme cases. It is thus a highly unstable measure, the value of which may be greatly changed by the addition or withdrawal of a single figure.
3. This measure gives no indication of the character of the distribution within the two extreme observations.

The quartile deviation

1. The quartile deviation is a measure of dispersion that is easily computed and readily understood. It is superior to the range as a rough measure of variation.
2. The quartile deviation is not a measure of the variation from any specific average.
3. This measure is not affected by the distribution of the items between the first and third quartiles, or by the distribution outside the quartiles. The values of the quartile deviation might be the same for two quite dissimilar distributions, provided the quartiles happened to coincide. Because it is not affected by the deviations of individual items it cannot be accepted as an accurate measure of variation.
4. The quartile deviation is not suited to algebraic treatment.

The mean deviation

1. The mean deviation is affected by the value of every observation. As the *average difference* between the individual items and the median (or mean) of the distribution it has a precise significance.
2. The mean deviation is less affected by extreme deviations than the standard deviation.
3. Mathematically, the mean deviation is not as logical or as convenient a measure of dispersion as the standard deviation.

The standard deviation

1. The standard deviation is affected by the value of every observation.
2. The process of squaring the deviations before adding avoids the algebraic fallacy of disregarding signs.
3. The standard deviation has a definite mathematical meaning and is perfectly adapted to algebraic treatment.
4. The standard deviation is, in general, less affected by fluctuations of sampling than the other measures of dispersion.
5. The standard deviation is the unit customarily used in defining areas under the normal curve of error. (See Chapter 6.) The standard deviation has, thus, great practical utility in sampling and statistical inference.

The probable error

1. The probable error has a definite meaning in the case of a distribution following the normal law. It has not this precise meaning for other distributions, and should not be employed in describing them.
2. The definite relationship between the probable error and the standard deviation, for a normal distribution, permits the value of the probable error to be readily determined.
3. Traditionally, the probable error has been used as an index of the magnitude of sampling errors. It has now been generally displaced by the standard error (which will be discussed in Chapters 7 and 8). Its use is not recommended.

All the measures of variation described above may be utilized for particular purposes. The standard deviation, however, is the best general measure and should be employed in all cases where a high degree of accuracy is required. The probable error is, in effect, merely a fractional part of the standard deviation, with a definite but restricted field of usefulness.

The Measurement of Relative Variation

We have been dealing in the preceding section with absolute variability. The various measures of dispersion secured by the methods outlined describe the variability of the data in terms of absolute units of measurement. The standard deviation of a distribution of workers classified according to hourly wage rates would be in cents; that of a distribution of steel plants according to the tonnage of steel produced would be in tons. If the object in a given case is the description of a single frequency distribution it is desirable that the original unit be employed throughout, but if measures of variation of two different distributions are to be compared, difficulties are encountered. This is clear if the units are unlike, but even if the units are identical the same difficulty arises. Thus measures of variation in the weights of dogs and in the weights of horses might both have been computed in pounds. Because the standard deviation of horse weights is greater than the standard deviation of dog weights, it does not follow that the degree of variability is greater in the former case. A measure of absolute variation is significant only in relation to the average from which the deviations are measured. For comparison, therefore, it must be reduced to a relative form, and the obvious procedure is to express a given measure of variation as a percentage of the average from which the deviations have been measured. The quantity thus becomes an abstract number, a measure of the relative variability of the given observations, and may be compared with similar terms computed from other distributions.

The Coefficient of Variation. The measure of relative variation most commonly employed is that developed by Pearson, termed the *coefficient of variation*, and represented by the letter V. It is simply the standard deviation as a percentage of the arithmetic mean. Thus

$$V = \frac{\sigma}{M} \times 100 \tag{5.11}$$

Applying this formula to the results secured from the analysis of the distribution of workers in industrial chemical plants in 1946, classified according to average hourly earnings (Table 5–2), we have

$$V = \frac{23.54}{114.61} \times 100$$
$$= 20.54 \text{ percent}$$

This measurement may be compared with a similar coefficient relating to the distribution of steel workers in open hearth furnaces in 1933, classified according to average hourly earnings. For steel workers the standard deviation of hourly earnings was 18.68 cents. This indicates smaller dispersion than that found among chemical workers in 1946. However, the average hourly earnings of steel workers in 1933 (a depression year) was 50.14 cents. For the co-efficient of variation we have

$$V = \frac{18.68}{50.14} \times 100$$
$$= 37.26 \text{ percent}$$

The relative variation of hourly earnings for steel workers in 1933 was substantially greater than that of hourly earnings for chemical workers in 1946, although the absolute variation was much smaller for the steel group.

The coefficient of variation is affected, of course, by the value of the mean, as well as by the size of the standard deviation. If the mean should coincide with the origin (i.e., if $M = 0$), V would be equal to infinity for all values of the standard deviation other than zero. For distributions with mean values close to zero (e.g. distributions of corporations, in a year of depression, classified on the basis of net operating revenue) V is thus a somewhat ambiguous statistic.

When the median is the average employed, a measure of relative variation analogous to V may be obtained from the relation $M.D./Md;$ similarly, when the quantity K is used to define central tendency, relative variation may be measured by $Q.D./K$. These measures may be put in percentage terms if desired.

Measures of Skewness

Methods have been developed in the preceding sections for describing the central tendency of a frequency distribution and for measuring the degree of concentration, or degree of dispersion, about that central tendency. One further measure is needed, and that is one which indicates the degree of skewness or asymmetry of a given distribution. For it is essential to know, in regard to a given distribution, whether the observations are arranged symmetrically about the central value, or are dispersed in an uneven, asymmetrical fashion about that value. Having such a figure it will be possible effectively to summarize the characteristics of a frequency distribution in three simple terms — an average, a measure of dispersion, and a measure of skewness. There are two measures of skewness in current use.

If a frequency curve is perfectly symmetrical, mean, median, and mode will coincide. As the distribution departs from symmetry these three values are pulled apart, the difference between the mean and the mode being greatest. This difference may be used, therefore, as a measure of skewness. It is desirable in this case, as in measuring relative variability, to secure an index in the form of an abstract number, which may be compared with similar figures derived from other distributions. To this end, Pearson has proposed dividing the absolute difference between mean and mode by the standard deviation of the given distribution. His formula for the measure of skewness is

$$sk = \frac{M - Mo}{s} \tag{5.12}$$

In a symmetrical distribution, where mean and mode coincide, the value of this measure will be zero. Under other conditions the value may be positive or negative, depending upon the relative positions of the two averages on the scale.[3]

For moderately skew distributions the degree of skewness may be estimated more readily from the formula

$$sk = \frac{3(M - Md)}{s} \tag{5.13}$$

This corresponds approximately to the other formula, because of the fact that in a moderately asymmetrical distribution the median lies between the mean and the mode, about one third of the distance from the former towards the latter.

Because it is difficult to locate the mode by simple methods, a

[3] A means of approximating sk from sample data is given in Chapter 6.

measure of skewness more easily computed than Pearson's is desirable in some cases. Bowley has proposed such a method, based upon the relationship between the first and third quartiles and the median. If the distribution is symmetrical these two quartiles will be equidistant from the median; with an asymmetrical distribution this is not so. Therefore, if we let q_2 represent the difference between the upper quartile and the median and q_1 represent the difference between the median and the lower quartile, we may use the formula

$$sk = \frac{q_2 - q_1}{q_2 + q_1} \tag{5.14}$$

as a means of securing a measure of skewness. This value will vary between 0 and $\pm$ 1. For with perfect symmetry $q_2 = q_1$, and the measure is 0; with asymmetry so pronounced that the median and one of the quartiles coincide, either q_2 or q_1 becomes equal to 0, and the formula gives a value of $+$ 1 or $-$ 1. Bowley suggests that a value of 0.1 indicates a moderate degree of skewness, while a value of 0.3 indicates marked skewness.

The values secured from this measure are not, of course, comparable with the values secured from the application of Pearson's formula for measuring skewness.

Peakedness, or "Excess." Reference has been made to a fourth measurable characteristic of grouped data. This characteristic has to do with the degree to which observations are concentrated in the neighborhood of the mean and at the tails of a given distribution. The measurement of peakedness, or kurtosis, is discussed in Chapter 6 (pp. 172–3).

REFERENCES

Croxton, F. E. and Cowden, D. J., *Applied General Statistics*, Chap. 10.
Dixon, W. J. and Massey, F. J. Jr., *Introduction to Statistical Analysis*, Chap. 3.
Freund, J. E., *Modern Elementary Statistics*, Chap. 5.
Kendall, M. G., *The Advanced Theory of Statistics*, 3rd ed., Vol. I, Chap. 3.
Lewis, E. E., *Methods of Statistical Analysis in Economics and Business*, Chap. 4.
Mills, F. C., *The Behavior of Prices*, Chap. 3, sec. 4.
Riggleman, J. R. and Frisbee, I. N., *Business Statistics*, 3rd ed., Chap. 9.
Rosander, A. C., *Elementary Principles of Statistics*, Chap. 4.
Spurr, W. A., Kellogg, L. S. and Smith, J. H., *Business and Economic Statistics*, Chap. 11.

Treloar, A. E., *Elements of Statistical Reasoning*, Chap. 4.
Waugh, A. E., *Elements of Statistical Method*, 3rd ed., Chap. 6.
Wilks, S. S., *Elementary Statistical Analysis*, Chap. 3.
Yule, G. U. and Kendall, M. G., *An Introduction to the Theory of Statistics*, 14th ed., Chap. 6.

The publishers and the dates of publication of the books named in chapter reference lists are given in the bibliography at the end of this volume.

CHAPTER 6

Introduction to Statistical Inference and Probability: Binomial and Normal Distributions

In the opening chapter of this book we emphasized the significant distinction between *sample* and *population,* and noted that the central concern of statistics, as a method of inquiry, is with inferences that go beyond the observations that make up a given sample. In dealing with the organization and description of frequency distributions in the three preceding chapters, only incidental mention has been made of populations and their characteristics. These chapters dealt, in the main, with the problems faced in reducing masses of quantitative data to orderly form and in defining the attributes of the resulting distributions. But the organization and description are but a beginning of the statistician's task. These steps merely pave the way for processes of generalization aimed at knowledge transcending the immediate observations. We turn now to this central problem.

Deduction and Induction

The logical process by which one arrives at generalizations from a study of particular cases is termed *induction,* as opposed to *deduction,* which involves the drawing of specialized conclusions from general propositions. The distinction is familiar, but its bearing on the logical issues we here face is so direct as to warrant a brief review of the subject.

The syllogism of *deductive* reasoning, running from major premise and minor premise to conclusion, takes such a form as the following (to cite an example that is sanctified by immemorial usage):
Major premise: All men are mortal
Minor premise: Socrates is a man
Conclusion: Socrates is mortal.
  Or the following
Major premise: All the beans in this (specified) bag are white
Minor premise: These beans (i.e., a specific handful) are from this bag
Conclusion: These beans (the specific handful) are white.
In noting the necessary formal validity of such syllogisms, three points may be made:

1. There is complete internal consistency
2. The conclusions flow from the premises; they are consequences of universal propositions
3. In employing such a syllogism we are working with a closed system. All the relevant circumstances are before us, or are implied in the premises.

Inductive arguments corresponding, in subject matter, to the above illustrations would take the following form:

Premise: Socrates, Xenophon, Democritus (*et al*)—are men
Premise: Socrates, Xenophon, Democritus (*et al*)— are mortal
Conclusion: All men are mortal.
  Or:
Premise: These beans (a specific handful) are from this (specified) bag
Premise: These beans (the specific handful) are white
Conclusion: All the beans in this (specified) bag are white.

One sharp contrast between the two modes of reasoning is to be emphasized. The conclusions of the deductive arguments are implied in the two statements that introduce each argument. If the premises are true, the conclusion may not be questioned. Nothing is added by the conclusion, although the chains of reasoning may be highly valuable in revealing truths that are only implicit in the premises. The conclusions of the inductive arguments, however, are broader than the premises. Something new has been added. If the conclusions are true, human knowledge has been extended. But there is a price to be paid for this potential extension of knowledge. Inductive reasoning may be fruitful, but it is dangerous. There can be no certainty that the conclusions of inductive reasoning are true. Invalid, indeed quite false, conclusions may be drawn by the inductive process.

Certain of the essential qualities of inductive reasoning are summarized by the following statements:

1. The conclusions of an inductive argument hold only in terms of probabilities, never with certainty. For such conclusions, by the very definition of induction, apply to cases not included in the observations. When all the cases to be covered by a conclusion are included in the observations, the conclusion ceases to be an induction. Accordingly, although induction is a highly fruitful means of adding to human knowledge, it is always hazardous. A leap in the dark is always involved when we apply conclusions to cases not yet observed.

2. There is a necessary reference to circumstances outside the facts inherent in the premises. We are not working with a closed system, but with an open system, only part of which has been directly observed. Many of the unobserved parts are relevant to our argument and conclusions. Facts not always set forth in the premises are relevant to our confidence in the conclusions, e.g., the method employed in making the observations that enter into the premises. (How were the beans making up the handful selected?) Since no comprehensive account of all the circumstances that bear upon an inductive argument is ever possible, one who accepts the conclusions of inductive reasoning places dependence on the personal discernment and integrity of the persons making the observations and completing the argument. One may with justice paraphrase the advertising slogan, and say, "The priceless ingredient of every induction is the honor and integrity of its maker." One might be tempted to go further and say that it is less dangerous to have a scoundrel among deductively reasoning mathematicians than to have a scoundrel among statisticians!

3. We must assume that there exists some uniformity in the system of facts to which the premises and the conclusion of inductive reasoning relate. Here is the rational justification for the leap in the dark that induction always entails. This assumption, which has been termed, variously, the uniformity of nature, the routine of experience, "a limitation to the amount of independent variety" found in nature, is always present as an unspoken premise in induction. If there were not some uniformity in natural processes, if nature were marked by utter chaos, no amount of piling-up of evidence could justify an induction. We could say nothing about conditions beyond the limits of observation. It is clear that we must go beyond the immediate evidence in accepting this assumption of uniformity. That compound of judgment and of accumulated but unspecified experience that we use in distinguishing the "rational" from the "irrational," and which may give us confidence in the assumption of uniformity in a given situation, contains a *priori* elements. It is here that deduction (which is never really divorced from induction) enters into our empirical reasoning.

4. The verification of induction calls for objective reference. The formal validity of deduction (e.g., of a chain of mathematical reasoning) rests purely on internal consistency. "Mathematical truth," it has been said, "is the absence of contradiction." But the conclusions of inductive reasoning must be tested finally against observation; if they stand, it must be on the basis of consistency with the facts of nature in the given sphere.

Statistical Inference

The statements just made relate to induction as a general logical process. Our concern here is with *statistical induction*, or *statistical inference*. Such inference, which involves the generalization of statistical results, is akin to the more general process, in all respects covered by the four summary statements. It has, in addition, distinctive characteristics of its own. The problems with which it deals take two forms—*estimation*, and the *testing of hypotheses*.

Estimation. The problem of estimation may be put in the following form: A statistical measurement—an arithmetic mean, a standard deviation, a coefficient of variation—has been derived from the study of sample data drawn from a given population. At an earlier point the reader was introduced to the concept of a "population," as the statistician employs that term. In general, let us recall, a sample is assumed to have been drawn not from a finite population—the population that might be covered by actual enumeration—but from the infinite population, or universe, that would be generated if the forces or system of causes that brought this sample into being were to operate without limit. A population may be an aggregate of persons, things, or measurements; R. A. Fisher speaks of a population of "possibilities," referring to the possible results of an experiment many times repeated. The measurement derived from the sample—such a measurement is termed a *statistic*—defines some characteristic of that sample. The task of inference, in such a case, is to provide us with an estimate of the measurement defining the corresponding characteristic of the population. The measurement relating to the population is termed a *parameter*. Such an estimate may specify a particular value of the parameter (this is *point-estimation*). Alternatively, this form of inference may take the form of a statement defining limits within which the parameter may be expected to lie, together with a measure, in probability terms, of the reliability of this conclusion (this is *interval-estimation*). A significant feature of interval-estimation is this: The uncertainty that attaches to the conclusions of all inductions holds for the conclusion of such an inference, but in basing estimates upon statistical data we are able to provide a measure of the degree of uncertainty attaching to the conclusion. How this is done will be our concern in the following chapter. At this point we reiterate: Our certain knowledge is limited to *statistics* —to measurements of the characteristics of samples. We use this knowledge to the best of our ability to provide us with approximations to the true *parameters* which we can never know.

The other general statements made about inductive reasoning apply, also, to statistical inference. The assumption of uniformity in nature, or of a limited amount of independent variety in nature, is usually spoken of in the statistical world as the stability of large numbers. Regularities in birth rates and death rates, in price movements, and in seasonal processes are familiar examples of such stability.

The uniformity that statistical stability indicates is, of course, of supreme practical importance. If we could not be assured of a certain degree of stability in the results obtained from successive samples it would be quite invalid to generalize from the examination of a limited number of cases. No weight would attach to any study except one covering the entire universe of things or measurements composing the given population. Yet such all-inclusive studies are practically impossible. Index numbers of prices, of wages, of living costs, and of production; monthly counts of the labor force; surveys of corporate profits and of consumer spending —all must of necessity be based on the study of samples, and all must postulate stability. Therefore, when we generalize such a measure as an index of wholesale prices we do so on some such assumption as this: It is reasonable to suppose that, in the larger population to which this result is to be applied, there exists uniformity with respect to the characteristic we have measured. As a result of this uniformity we should expect that inferences based upon successive samples of the same size drawn from this population would belong to a family with common, stable, and definable characteristics. On this assumption we are able to attach measures of reliability to statistical inferences.

It is evident that in making this assumption, in saying "It is reasonable to suppose . . . ," we are introducing a hypothesis that is incapable of complete verification by purely statistical methods. There is thus, as we have already pointed out, an *a priori* element in every statistical induction. The statistical conclusion can never stand completely on its own feet. It must be endorsed by reason and judgment if it is to carry conviction.

The problem of statistical inference, in the words of Oskar Anderson, is that of so utilizing samples as to arrive at the best possible approximation to the characteristics of universes. In the task of estimation that is here entailed we must assume that these universes are stable, and that all their attributes are stable. Of course, an attribute of such a stable universe may not be exactly determined from the attribute of a single sample. However, measures defining the attributes of numerous samples drawn from the same universe (i.e., the same parent population) will be distributed in a systematic fashion about the universe parameter of which they are estimates. The precise determination of the characteristics of such a distribution of estimates is essential to the determination of the reliability of estimates. The power of statistical techniques has grown as our detailed knowledge of such distributions has expanded.

Tests of hypotheses. In testing hypotheses, the other form of statistical inference, there is also reference to a "population," but here the task is that of determining whether a sample yielding a given *statistic* (e.g., a stated arithmetic mean) could have been drawn from a population for which the corresponding *parameter* is known, or is given by hypothesis. Is the difference between the actual statistic and this parameter one that the chance fluctuations of sampling might bring about, or is the difference too great to be attributed to sampling fluctuations? This is the form taken by most tests of hypotheses, or *tests of significance.* The question is one that is always answered in terms of probability. If the probability that chance factors could account for the observed difference is very slight, the hypothesis is rejected. The difference is significant. If the probability is great enough to justify an explanation in terms of chance, we say that the observations are not inconsistent with the hypothesis. The difference is not significant. The hypothesis is not rejected.

These rather abstract statements will become much more definite when we discuss concrete instances of statistical inference, in Chapters 7 and 8. At this stage we would emphasize the following in summary of part of the preceding argument:

The conclusions of all inductive reasoning hold in terms of probability. The logician Charles S. Peirce used the words "uncertain inference" to describe induction—a suggestive phrase that points to a key aspect of induction.

Statistical inference, which is concerned with the generalization of quantitative results, is distinctive in that it is possible in such inference to provide measures of the probabilities attaching to conclusions. This is true whether the conclusions are estimates of limits within which population parameters fall, or statements relating to tests of significance. The task of the statistician in this major field of statistical endeavor is to provide the tools for defining these probabilities, and to set up working rules for the use of these tools.[1]

It is clear that the concept of probability lies at the very heart of the theories and practices of modern statistics. We turn now to a discussion of some elementary principles of probability. A detailed treatment of the theory of probability would carry us beyond the limits of the present volume. The discussion that follows is presented only as an introduction to the subject, with emphasis on certain ideas and distributions having a special bearing on statistical procedures.

Notation. For convenience of reference we here list the symbols that will be introduced in this chapter. Explanations will be given in the text.

p: the probability of the successful outcome of an event

q: the probability of the unsuccessful outcome of an event

n: the number of ways in which an event can occur; the number of events in a trial

$n!$: factorial n; the product of the integers from 1 to n

μ (mu): the mean of a population

μ': the mean of a population of relative frequencies

σ' (sigma): the standard deviation of a population of relative frequencies

y: an ordinate of a frequency curve

y_0: the maximum ordinate of a frequency curve

[1] In the present discussion of statistical inference no attempt is made to develop the general theory of statistical decision functions. The foundations of this general theory, which comprehends the problem of estimation and the testing of hypotheses as special cases, were laid by the late Abraham Wald in a series of brilliant contributions made during the years immediately preceding his untimely death in 1950. (See Wald, Ref. 184).

m' (with subscripts 1, 2, 3, . . .): moments about an arbitrary origin

$\overline{m}$ (with subscripts 1, 2, 3, . . .): raw moments about an arithmetic mean; central moments

m (with subscripts 1, 2, 3, . . .): central moments, after the application of Sheppard's corrections

μ (mu) (with subscripts 1, 2, 3, . . .): central moments of a population

β_1 (beta): a criterion of curve type (Pearsonian)

β_2: a criterion of curve type (Pearsonian)

χ (chi): a measure of skewness

d: the modal divergence; $\chi \times \sigma$

γ_1 (gamma): a measure of skewness

γ_2 (gamma): a measure of peakedness

Elementary Theorems in Probability

If an event can occur in n mutually exclusive and equally likely ways, a of which are to be considered as successful and b as unsuccessful, the probability p of a successful outcome may be written

$$p = \frac{a}{n}$$

and the probability q of an unsuccessful outcome may be written

$$q = \frac{b}{n}$$

It will be understood that the words "successful" and "unsuccessful" are used in a neutral sense. (Alternatively we might say that we include in the a group only outcomes marked by the possession of a certain property, in the b group outcomes marked by the absence of this property. But it will be convenient to use the traditional terms.) Since the sum of the successful and unsuccessful outcomes is equal to the total number of events, we have

$$a + b = n$$

Dividing by n,

$$\frac{a}{n} + \frac{b}{n} = 1$$

so that

$$p + q = 1$$

A probability, therefore, may be written as a ratio. The numerator of the fraction corresponding to this ratio represents the number of successful (or unsuccessful) outcomes, while the denominator represents the total number of possible outcomes. If the outcome or outcomes represented by a should be, in fact, impossible, this ratio would be zero. On the other hand, if only the outcome or outcomes represented by a were possible, a would equal n, and the ratio would be unity. The scale of probability thus extends from zero, representing the impossible, to unity, representing certainty.

The idea that a "probability" corresponds to a *frequency ratio* is one that is generally accepted today. However, for purposes of mathematical reasoning it is desirable that the concept have a precision and a generality that would be denied it if it were tied to empirically observable ratios. These purposes are served if a probability number be regarded, in Cramér's words, as "the conceptual counterpart" of an empirical frequency ratio. A probability is, in the last analysis, an abstract conception. Perhaps no die could be so flawlessly constructed that the probability of getting a 6 spot on a given throw is exactly 1/6. But we may conceive of, and build theorems on, an abstract entity for which p is exactly 1/6. It is these abstract entities, and the abstract probabilities attaching to them, that provide the foundation of the theory of probability. This theory in turn provides the conceptual framework for the study of the results of random experiments which are the direct concern of modern statistics.

If we toss a coin there are two possible outcomes, the turning up of a tail and the turning up of a head. If we regard these two possibilities as equally likely (as they are if we think of the conceptual counterparts of the frequency ratios we should get from numerous tossings) we have, as the probability of a tail

$$p = \tfrac{1}{2}$$

and of a head

$$q = \tfrac{1}{2}$$

If we roll a die, regarding a 6 spot as a favorable outcome,

$$p = \tfrac{1}{6}$$

and

$$q = \tfrac{5}{6}$$

If a card be drawn from a pack of 52 the chance of drawing the ace of spades is $\tfrac{1}{52}$, of failing in that endeavor, $\tfrac{51}{52}$.

The addition of probabilities. What is the chance of securing *either* an ace of spades *or* a two of spades in a single draw from a pack of 52 cards? *In such a case, where any one of several mutually exclusive outcomes will be considered favorable, the probability of a success is the sum of the separate probabilities.* In this example

$$p = \tfrac{1}{52} + \tfrac{1}{52} = \tfrac{1}{26}$$

The chance of drawing either a heart or a spade from a pack of playing cards is given by

$$p = \tfrac{13}{52} + \tfrac{13}{52} = \tfrac{1}{2}$$

The multiplication of probabilities. Two events are said to be independent when the outcome of one does not affect the outcome of the other. Thus the result of one throw of a die does not, presumably, affect the result of the next toss. *The probability of a compound event (i.e., a combination of two events, independent of one another) is the product of the probabilities of the separate events.* Thus the chance of securing an ace, followed by a 2 spot, in two successive throws of a die, is given by

$$p = \tfrac{1}{6} \times \tfrac{1}{6} = \tfrac{1}{36}$$

In computing the probability of a given outcome it is frequently necessary both to multiply and to add probabilities. For example, we wish to determine the chance of securing the total 5 from two dice thrown simultaneously. We may label the dice a and b to distinguish them. This total may be secured from any one of the four following combinations:

Die a	Die b
1	4
2	3
3	2
4	1

The chance of securing an ace with die a is $\tfrac{1}{6}$, of securing a 4 with die b is $\tfrac{1}{6}$. The chance of the two in combination is $\tfrac{1}{36}$. Similarly, the probability of each of the other three combinations is $\tfrac{1}{36}$. But any one of these four results will give a total of 5, and will be considered successful. Hence

$$p = \tfrac{1}{36} + \tfrac{1}{36} + \tfrac{1}{36} + \tfrac{1}{36} = \tfrac{1}{9}$$

We have in this example answered the question: What is the probability of securing exactly 5 in the toss of two dice? We might put the question: What is the chance of securing *at least* 5 in the toss of two dice? In this case a total of 5 or more will be considered a favorable outcome. Just as in the preceding example, we may work out the probability of securing each of the results that will be accepted as successful. The following summary indicates the probability of each of these totals:

$$\text{Probability of throwing 12 with two dice} = \frac{1}{36}$$

$$\text{``} \quad \text{``} \quad \text{``} \quad 11 \quad \text{``} \quad \text{``} \quad \text{``} \quad = \frac{2}{36}$$

$$\text{``} \quad \text{``} \quad \text{``} \quad 10 \quad \text{``} \quad \text{``} \quad \text{``} \quad = \frac{3}{36}$$

$$\text{``} \quad \text{``} \quad \text{``} \quad 9 \quad \text{``} \quad \text{``} \quad \text{``} \quad = \frac{4}{36}$$

$$\text{``} \quad \text{``} \quad \text{``} \quad 8 \quad \text{``} \quad \text{``} \quad \text{``} \quad = \frac{5}{36}$$

$$\text{``} \quad \text{``} \quad \text{``} \quad 7 \quad \text{``} \quad \text{``} \quad \text{``} \quad = \frac{6}{36}$$

$$\text{``} \quad \text{``} \quad \text{``} \quad 6 \quad \text{``} \quad \text{``} \quad \text{``} \quad = \frac{5}{36}$$

$$\text{``} \quad \text{``} \quad \text{``} \quad 5 \quad \text{``} \quad \text{``} \quad \text{``} \quad = \frac{4}{36}$$

$$\text{Sum of above probabilities} = \frac{30}{36}$$

The chance of throwing at least 5 in the toss of two dice is, therefore, $\frac{30}{36}$ or $\frac{5}{6}$.

The Binomial Expansion and the Measurement of Probabilities. It is possible to express certain of these fundamental relations in a generalized form. A simple illustration may be employed to exemplify the derivation of the desired general expression.

If two coins are tossed simultaneously there are four possible outcomes

$$\begin{array}{cccc} a \ b & a \ b & a \ b & a \ b \\ T \ T & T \ H & H \ T & H \ H \end{array}$$

(The two coins are represented, respectively, by the letters a and b.) In the first of these possible outcomes we get two tails (TT). This, which we may here regard as two successes, represents the compound probability $p \cdot p = p^2$. In the present case, where $p = \frac{1}{2}$, the probability of this compound event is $\frac{1}{2} \cdot \frac{1}{2} = \frac{1}{4}$. The fourth of the four possible outcomes (HH) represents two failures (i.e., no tail with either coin). The probability of this result is also

$\frac{1}{4}$ ($= q \cdot q = \frac{1}{2} \cdot \frac{1}{2}$). Each of the two other outcomes (the second and third) represents a combination of one success (T) and one failure (H). The probability of the second of these combinations, TH, is $\frac{1}{4}$ ($= p \cdot q = \frac{1}{2} \cdot \frac{1}{2}$); the probability of the third outcome, HT, is $\frac{1}{4}$ ($= q \cdot p = \frac{1}{2} \cdot \frac{1}{2}$). For the probabi'ity of such mixed result, one success and one failure (the order being here of no concern), we must add the probabilities of the separate outcomes, getting, in the present case, $2pq$, or $\frac{1}{2}$.

The generalization of this process of estimating the probabilities of various combinations of independent events, when the probabilities of these events are known, rests upon the fact that the probabilities of the several combinations are given by the successive terms of a binomial expansion. Thus, for the simple case of two events, we have

$$(p + q)^2 = p^2 + 2pq + q^2$$

The student will note that p^2 is the probability of two successes as has been demonstrated above; $2pq$ is the probability of a combination of one success and one failure; q^2 is the probability of two failures. For the case in which p (e.g., the probability of throwing a tail) $= q = \frac{1}{2}$, the probabilities of the several different outcomes are given by

$$(\tfrac{1}{2} + \tfrac{1}{2})^2 = \tfrac{1}{4} + \tfrac{1}{2} + \tfrac{1}{4}$$

If three coins, represented by the letters a, b, and c, are tossed simultaneously, we have eight possible outcomes

abc	abc	abc	abc	abc	abc	abc	abc
TTT	TTH	THH	THT	HTT	HTH	HHT	HHH

A count of the possible outcomes will show that the chance of getting 3 tails in a single toss of 3 coins is 1/8. The chance of getting 2 tails (combined with 1 head) is 3/8; the chance of getting 1 tail (combined with 2 heads) is 3/8; the chance of getting no tails is 1/8. Here, since we have three independent events, the exponent of the binomial is 3. The probabilities of the several possible outcomes are given by the successive terms of

$$(p + q)^3 = p^3 + 3p^2q + 3pq^2 + q^3$$

With $p = q = \frac{1}{2}$, we have

$$(\tfrac{1}{2} + \tfrac{1}{2})^3 = \tfrac{1}{8} + \tfrac{3}{8} + \tfrac{3}{8} + \tfrac{1}{8}$$

These are the probabilities shown by direct count in the example cited above.

This procedure applies generally. It may be shown that if there are n independent chance events, the probability of a "successful" outcome of a given event being p and the probability of an "unsuccessful" outcome being, q the probabilities of n successes, of n-1 successes, of n-2 successes, etc. are given by successive terms in the binomial expansion $(p + q)^n$.

If we wish to know not the separate probabilities but the probable frequencies of the various outcomes in a given number of trials, these may be computed from the expression

$$N(p+ q)^n \qquad\qquad (6.1)$$

where N represents the number of trials and n the number of independent events in a trial. Thus if there are 200 trials and there are two independent events in each trial, the probable frequencies are given by

$$200(p + q)^2 = 200(p^2 + 2pq + q^2)$$

With $p = q = \frac{1}{2}$ this gives us

$$200\left(\frac{1}{4}\right) + 200\left(\frac{1}{2}\right) + 200\left(\frac{1}{4}\right) = 50 + 100 + 50$$

which indicates the probable frequencies of 2 successes, 1 success, and no successes.

If there are three independent events, the probable frequencies in N trials are determined from the binomial expansion of

$$N(p + q)^3$$

If N equals 200, we have

$$200(p^3 + 3p^2q + 3pq^2 + q^3)$$

If p equals $\frac{1}{2}$, we have

$$200\left(\frac{1}{8}\right) + 200\left(\frac{3}{8}\right) + 200\left(\frac{3}{8}\right) + 200\left(\frac{1}{8}\right) = 25 + 75 + 75 + 25$$

These terms indicate, in order, the probable frequencies of 3 successes, 2 successes, 1 success, and no successes. The total frequencies secured by carrying through the process of multiplication will be equal to the number of trials, for all possible outcomes are covered by the expansion.

Thus when we know in advance[2] the probabilities attaching to similar but independent events, we may determine the probable frequencies of any given number of successes or failures. This is true whether p and q be equal or unequal. It is necessary only that p and q remain constant. There is here a fact of great significance in the development of statistical theory.

The Binomial Distribution

Certain points of importance may be made clear by comparing some experimental results with the theoretical frequencies given by the binomial expansion. Twelve dice were thrown a number of times. Each 4, 5, or 6 spot appearing was considered to be a success, while a 1, 2, or 3 spot was a failure. (In a typical throw we might have the following spots up: 3, 1, 5, 1, 2, 4, 4, 6, 3, 2, 3, 5. In this lot there are five successes, and the result is so tallied.) In a classical example recorded by W. F. R. Weldon[3] twelve dice were thrown in this way 4,096 times, a success being defined as above. The results are recorded in Col. (2) of Table 6.1, and the distribution is shown in Fig. 6.1. By computation we find the arithmetic mean and the standard deviation of this distribution to be, respectively, 6.139 and 1.712.

Let us compare with these results those we might expect, from given conditions, with 12 flawless (i.e., evenly balanced) dice. Twelve dice were thrown each time, hence we are dealing with 12 independent events. There were 4,096 trials. Since either a 4, 5, or 6 is considered a success, $p = q = \frac{1}{2}$.

---

[2] A distinction is sometimes drawn between *a priori* probabilities of the type described above, which are assumed to be known apart from experience, and *empirical* probabilities, which are derived from observation. As an example of the latter type we have, as the probability that a man aged 35 will live 10 years, the ratio 74,173/81,822. This is based upon the American Experience Table of Mortality, which shows that of 81,822 men living at age 35, there are 74,173 living 10 years later. (This particular table, we should note, is now somewhat out-dated, as a result of recent improvements in mortality experience.) Since the idea of *a priori* probabilities is a somewhat nebulous one, it would be preferable to distinguish between *conceptual* probabilities and *empirical* probabilities, the former being the conceptual counterparts of the frequency ratios that provide measures of empirical probabilities. (Cf. Cramér, Refs. 22, 23 and Neyman, Refs. 118, 119).

[3] Cited by F. Y. Edgeworth, *Encycl. Brit.*, 11th ed., Vol. XXII, 394.

For the terms in the binomial expansion we have

$$(p + q)^n = p^n + np^{n-1}q + \frac{n(n - 1)}{1 \cdot 2}p^{n-2}q^2$$
$$+ \frac{n(n - 1)(n - 2)}{1 \cdot 2 \cdot 3} p^{n-3}q^3 + \ldots + q^n$$

In the present case we have

$$4,096\left(\frac{1}{2} + \frac{1}{2}\right)^{12}$$

Expanding

$$4,096 \left(\frac{1}{4,096} + \frac{12}{4,096} + \frac{66}{4,096} + \frac{220}{4,096} + \frac{495}{4,096} + \frac{792}{4,096} + \frac{924}{4,096}\right.$$
$$\left. + \frac{792}{4,096} + \frac{495}{4,096} + \frac{220}{4,096} + \frac{66}{4,096} + \frac{12}{4,096} + \frac{1}{4,096}\right)$$

Completing the indicated multiplication we have the theoretical frequencies of the various possible successes in 4,096 throws of 12 dice. These are shown in column (3) of Table 6.1.

The distribution of the theoretical frequencies is shown in Fig. 6.1, with that of the observed frequencies. The relationship

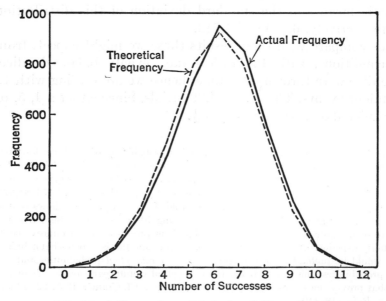

FIG. 6.1. A Comparison of Actual and Theoretical Frequencies in a Dice-Rolling Experiment.

of the two distributions appears to be close. (What is a "close" relationship will be considered at later points.)

TABLE 6–1

Comparison of Actual and Theoretical Frequencies in Dice-Rolling Experiment

(1) Number of successes	(2) Observed frequencies	(3) Theoretical frequencies
0	0	1
1	7	12
2	60	66
3	198	220
4	430	495
5	731	792
6	948	924
7	847	792
8	536	495
9	257	220
10	71	66
11	11	12
12	0	1
	4,096	4,096

The distribution defined by the entries in columns (1) and (3) of Table 6.1, and shown graphically by the broken line in Fig. 6.1, is a *binomial distribution*, one of central importance in statistical theory and in the applications of statistical methods. The general formula for the binomial distribution is

$$y = \frac{n!}{x!(n-x)!} p^x q^{n-x} \tag{6.2}$$

where n is the number of independent events in a trial, p is the probability of success in a single event, q is the probability of a failure, x is a stated number of successes, and y is the probability of obtaining the stated number of successes. The symbol $n!$ stands for "factorial n", which is the product of the integers from 1 to n; $x!$ is factorial x. To exemplify the use of this formula: we wish to determine the probability of obtaining just 3 heads in a single trial consisting of the toss of 4 coins. Substituting in the above equation the given values (i.e., for n substitute 4; for x, 3; for p, 1/2; for q, 1/2), we have

$$y = \frac{4 \cdot 3 \cdot 2 \cdot 1}{(3 \cdot 2 \cdot 1)(1)} \{(\tfrac{1}{2})^3 \cdot (\tfrac{1}{2})^1\} = \frac{24}{6} (\tfrac{1}{8} \cdot \tfrac{1}{2}) = 4/16$$

The probability of getting 3 heads in a toss of 4 coins is 4/16.

Certain of the characteristics of the binomial distribution may be briefly summarized:

It is a discrete distribution. Its graphic representation is marked by discontinuities of the type shown in Fig. 6.1.

Its form depends, in a particular case, on the parameters p and n (q, being equal to $1 - p$, is not counted as a separate parameter). The parameter n is always a positive integer.

The distribution will be symmetrical if p and q are equal, asymmetrical if p and q are unequal. However, as n increases, p and q (unequal) being unchanged, the degree of skewness decreases sharply. This approach to symmetry as n increases is graphically portrayed in Fig. 6.2. Here we have plotted the distributions derived by expanding $(0.8 + 0.2)$, i.e., $(q + p)$ with n equal, successively, to 6, 12, and 48. The frequencies shown on the y-axis are fractions of the total, for each distribution. With increasing values of n there is a notable increase in symmetry, even though p and q

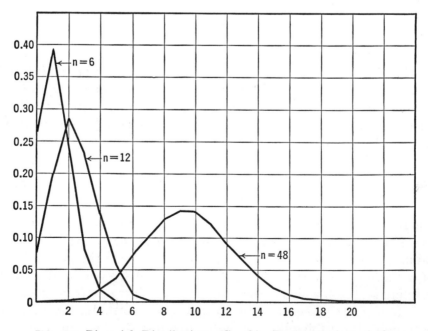

FIG. 6.2. Binomial Distributions. Graphic Representation of the Binomial $(0.8 + 0.2)^n$ for $n = 6$, $n = 12$, and $n = 48$.

are far from equal. There is also apparent a decline in the discontinuities that are so marked with low values of n. This point will call for further comment in the next section.

For the mean[4] of a binomial distribution we have

$$\mu = np \tag{6.3}$$

The variance[4] of a binomial distribution is given by

$$\sigma^2 = npq \tag{6.4}$$

and the standard deviation[4] by

$$\sigma = \sqrt{npq} \tag{6.5}$$

Substituting in the above equations the values of n, p, and q for the theoretical distribution represented in Table 6.1, we have

$$\mu = 12 \times 0.5 = 6$$

and

$$\sigma = \sqrt{12 \times 0.5 \times 0.5} = \sqrt{3} = 1.732$$

These may be compared with the mean of the observed frequencies, which is 6.139, and with the standard deviation of these frequencies, which is 1.712. The differences may reflect the influence of sampling fluctuations, or imperfections in the dice actually used by Weldon. At a later point we shall discuss methods by which these two effects may be distinguished.

Occasion often arises to deal with relative frequencies, or frequency ratios, when handling data entering into a binomial distribution. Thus the "successes" listed in column (1) of Table 6-1, might be measured as ratios to the total number of events in each throw of 12 dice, i.e., as 0/12, 1/12, 2/12, etc. The class frequencies would, of course, be the same. The mean (μ') of such frequency ratios binomially distributed, would be given by

$$\mu' = p$$

and the standard deviation (σ') by

$$\sigma' = \sqrt{\frac{pq}{n}} \tag{6.6}$$

For the theoretical relative frequencies represented in Table 6.1 we would have, therefore, a mean of 0.5, a standard deviation of 0.144.

The binomial distribution is one of a number of mathematical models that enter into statistical theory. Each of these models is an abstract generalization; its attributes and the axioms from which its qualities may be deduced may be defined with precision. These abstract conceptions may be built up without reference to

---

[4] Derivations of these formulas, which enter into subsequent discussion of sampling errors, are given in Appendix D.

events in the real world, and may have no bearing on such events. Of course, it may be found that natural events in some spheres correspond in some degree to a model thus built up. In the latter case, the model may contribute materially to an understanding of these events and to generalizations concerning such events. As the preceding example will have suggested, distributions of data in a number of fields correspond closely to the model provided by the binomial expansion. Such models, accordingly, provide working tools of high value in dealing with observational material.

The Normal Distribution

We may return to a consideration of the curve in Fig. 6.1 which represents the theoretical frequencies in the dice-throwing experiments. It is a perfectly symmetrical 12-sided polygon, the number of sides (excluding the base) corresponding to the number of independent events in the particular problem considered. With 6 events we should have a 6-sided figure, with 20 events a 20-sided figure, and so on. It is obvious that, as n increases, the number of sides to the polygon increasing correspondingly in number, the graph representing the expansion of the binomial $(p + q)^n$ approaches more and more closely a smooth curve.

This approach to continuity in binomial distributions as n increases will be found whether p and q be equal, as in the distributions represented in Fig. 6.1, or unequal, as in the distributions represented in Fig. 6.2. Moreover, if p and q be unequal, the skewness marking distributions corresponding to low values of n will decline as n increases. We have already noted (Fig. 6.2) the movement toward symmetry as n increased from 6, to 12, to 48, with p and q constant. As n approaches infinity, such a graph approaches a smooth, symmetrical curve. The limit which the binomial distribution thus approaches[5] is called the *normal distribution*. Its graphic representation, which is called the *normal curve of error*, is shown in Fig. 6.5, on page 158.

The normal distribution has long occupied a central place in the theory of statistics and in applications of this theory. It was first defined over 200 years ago by De Moivre, who recognized it as a

---

[5] In the exceptional case, when p approaches zero as n approaches infinity (the quantity np being constant), the limiting distribution is not the normal distribution but a discrete type called the Poisson distribution. This distribution has been found useful as a population model when the observed frequencies relate to the occurrence of very rare events, i.e., when p is very small.

continuous form marking the limit of the discrete binomial distribution. It was independently rediscovered by C. F. Gauss and P. S. Laplace in the early years of the nineteenth century. The rediscovery, which came from work on the distribution of errors of observation, led to great emphasis in the succeeding half century on the normal "law" as a model to which distributions of observations on all natural phenomena were supposed to conform. Correction of this excessive emphasis (a correction largely due to Karl Pearson and his co-workers in the Galton Laboratory of the University of London) served to place the normal distribution in proper perspective, as one among many distribution types occurring in nature. However, as Kendall remarks, "as the importance of the (normal) distribution declined in the observational sphere it grew in the theoretical, particularly in the theory of sampling." And as the theory of sampling has developed, to become the fundamental concern of statisticians, the normal distribution has retained its place as one of the pillars of modern statistics.

In writing the equation to this curve we express the frequency y as a function of the variable x. For convenience, the origin of the independent variable is taken at the mean; a given x stands, therefore, for a stated value of that variable expressed as a deviation from the mean x. This equation is written in several forms. The expression

$$y = \frac{1}{\sigma\sqrt{2\pi}}\, e^{-x^2/2\sigma^2} \tag{6.7}$$

is a basic form, relating to a curve having unit area. In this equation σ is the standard deviation of the given normal distribution, π is the constant 3.14159, and e is the constant 2.71828 (the base of the system of natural logarithms). When we say that the curve has unit area we mean that the total frequency, N, is equated to 1, for convenience in representation and calculation. To obtain ordinates for a particular distribution, the ordinates given by formula (6.7) are multiplied by N. The equation to a normal curve corresponding to a particular distribution is thus given by

$$y = \frac{N}{\sigma\sqrt{2\pi}}\, e^{-x^2/2\sigma^2} \tag{6.8}$$

We may note that the quantity $\dfrac{N}{\sigma\sqrt{2\pi}}$ in formula (6-8) is equal to the maximum ordinate (y_0) of the normal curve corresponding to a distribution of stated total frequency (N) and stated standard deviation (σ). Thus if N is 1000 and σ is 10, we should have

$$y_0 = \frac{1000}{10\sqrt{2\pi}}$$

Substituting 3.14159 for π we derive the value 39.894 for y_0. Having y_0 we may use the following form of the equation to the normal curve

$$y = y_0 e^{-x^2/2\sigma^2} \tag{6.9}$$

Thus the ordinate at any stated distance x from the maximum ordinate may be determined by multiplying the maximum ordinate by the quantity $e^{-x^2/2\sigma^2}$. (In a normal distribution mean, median and mode coincide. The maximum ordinate is, therefore, the ordinate at that point on the X-scale at which these three identical values fall). An ordinate 20 units above the mean, on the X-scale, would, for the above distribution, have the value

$$y = 39.894 \times 2.71828^{-400/200}$$

$$= 39.894 \times \frac{1}{2.71828^2}$$

$$= 5.399*$$

Finally, we may have an equation that refers to a curve of unit area, and with deviations from the mean of the X-variable expressed not in the original X-units, as in formulas (6.7), (6.8), and (6.9), but in units of the standard deviation of X. That is, the unit of measurement on the X-scale will be x/σ, where x is the deviation $(X - \mu)$. We obtain then an equation like (6.7) above, but with σ equal to 1. That is

$$y = \frac{1}{\sqrt{2\pi}} e^{-x^2/2} \tag{6.10}$$

This gives us an expression for the normal distribution in standard form, with zero mean, unit standard deviation, and unit area. Reversion to the original units of measurement for any variable, and to absolute frequencies, may be accomplished by simple adjustments, using given values of σ and N.

The curve plotted in Fig. 6.5 on p. 158, which shows frequencies rising to a maximum at the mean (which is also the mode and

---

* Tabled values greatly facilitate the calculation of ordinates. See Pearson and Hartley, Ref. 126; Fisher and Yates, Ref. 51.

median) and declining symmetrically for values of x above the
mean, is called the *normal frequency function*. The corresponding
cumulative distribution (cp. Fig. 3.13, p. 68), with frequencies
cumulated upward, is termed the *normal distribution function*.
This is shown graphically in Fig. 6.3. The cumulated frequency is,

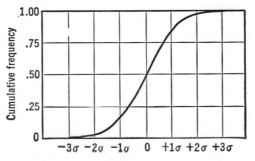

FIG. 6.3. The Cumulative Normal Curve:
The Normal Distribution Function.

of course, zero at the lower end of the range, N (or unity, for the
standardized normal form) at the upper end.

Properties of the Normal Distribution. Some of the major
properties of this distribution have already been noted. The
distribution is symmetrical (skewness = 0) and continuous. The
range extends theoretically from an x of $-\infty$ to an x of $+\infty$.
Actually, 0.997 of the area under the curve falls between ordinates
at $x = -3\sigma$ and $x = +3\sigma$. The general distribution is completely
defined by the parameters μ and σ. That is, when the location of
the mean has been established (as a base from which x is measured)
and the standard deviation has been specified, the distribution of
frequencies for a curve having unit area (i.e., with $N = 1$) may be
determined. (See formula 6.7 above.) To determine the absolute
frequencies corresponding to a specific set of observations the
quantity N must be known, in addition to μ and σ (see equation
6.8 above).

If the normal curve be regarded geometrically, we may note
that points of inflection occur at $\mu + \sigma$ and at $\mu - \sigma$.

The usual representation of the normal curve of error in its
standard form gives the impression that all normal frequency
curves are exactly alike (apart from variations in N). It is useful to
consider the effect on the curve of changes in the two parameters
μ and σ (N being constant). The effect of a change in μ is merely

to shift the curve along the x-scale, with no change in form. A change in σ affects the representation on both scales, and thus modifies the relative proportions of the plotted curve. The effect on the x-scale is obvious. But the y-scale is also affected, because the value of the maximum ordinate in a curve of unit area depends on the value of σ (for $y_0 = \dfrac{1}{\sigma\sqrt{2\pi}}$). The effect of varying σ from 6 to 10, and then to 20, with N constant at unity and with μ constant at 0, is shown by the curves plotted in Fig. 6.4.

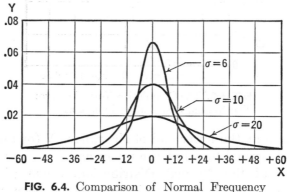

FIG. 6.4. Comparison of Normal Frequency Curves with Varying Standard Deviations.

The equation to the normal curve of error may be derived in several ways. It can be obtained as the equation to the limit curve of the binomial distribution.[6] Gauss's deduction of the error equation may be found in standard works on least squares. We have given the equation here without proof. At this stage the student will, perhaps, accept this model on an intuitive basis, as the limit of the binomial distribution. We may, however, throw light on reasons for the emergence of the normal distribution in varying observational fields by noting four basic conditions that must prevail among the factors affecting the individual events that make up a given population, if the distribution of observations is to be normal:

1. The causal forces must be numerous and of approximately equal weight.
2. These forces must be the same over the universe from which the observations are drawn (although their incidence will vary from event to event). This is the condition of homogeneity.

[6] Cf. Cramér (Ref. 23, 198-203) for a proof of the limit theorem for the binomial distribution, obtained by De Moivre in 1733.

3. The forces affecting individual events must be independent of one another.
4. The operation of the causal forces must be such that deviations above the population mean are balanced as to magnitude and number by deviations below the mean. This is the condition of symmetry.

Areas Under the Normal Curve. Practical applications of our knowledge of the normal distribution are greatly facilitated by prepared tables giving ordinates of the standardized normal curve for stated values of x/σ, and specifying fractional parts of the total area under the curve that lie between ordinates erected at stated distances from the mean. By simple computations these standard values of ordinates and areas may be modified for the N and the σ of any given distribution. Greater use is made of the tabulated areas than of the tabulated ordinates. Selected values from a table of areas are given in Table 6.2. The more detailed measurements needed for accurate computation are given in Appendix Table I. Areas as well as ordinates of the normal curve are given in Pearson and Hartley (Ref. 126) and Fisher and Yates (Ref. 51).

TABLE 6–2

Areas under the Normal Curve, in Terms of Abscissa
(Giving fractional parts of the total area between y_0 and ordinates
erected at varying distances from y_0)

x/σ	a	x/σ	a
0.0	.00000	2.0	.47725
0.1	.03983	2.1	.48214
0.2	.07926	2.2	.48610
0.3	.11791	2.3	.48928
0.4	.15542	2.4	.49180
0.5	.19146	2.5	.49379
		2.5758	.49500
0.6	.22575	2.6	.49534
0.7	.25804	2.7	.49653
0.8	.28814	2.8	.49744
0.9	.31594	2.9	.49813
1.0	.34134	3.0	.49865
1.1	.36433	3.1	.49903
1.2	.38493	3.2	.49931
1.3	.40320	3.3	.49952
1.4	.41924	3.4	.49966
1.5	.43319	3.5	.49977
1.6	.44520	3.6	.49984
1.7	.45543	3.7	.49989
1.8	.46407	3.8	.49993
1.9	.47128	3.9	.49995
1.96	.47500	4.0	.49997

Since the normal curve is symmetrical about the maximum ordinate, the values given in Table 6-2 apply to observations on either side of the mean. In using such a table, deviations from the mean are first expressed in units of the standard deviation. (The term *normal deviate* is applied to such a quantity, that is, to a deviation from the mean of a normal distribution expressed in units of the standard deviation of that distribution.) The proportion of the total area lying between any two ordinates may then be readily determined. For example: What proportion of the cases in a normal distribution lies between the maximum ordinate and an ordinate erected at a distance from the mean equal to $+ 1\sigma$? Reading down the x/σ column to 1.0, we find the value .34134 opposite it. This, in ratio form, is the proportion of cases falling within the limits indicated. Expressing this ratio as a percentage, we have 34.134 percent as the answer to our question.

Fig. 6.5 shows the relation of this area (the shaded area A) to

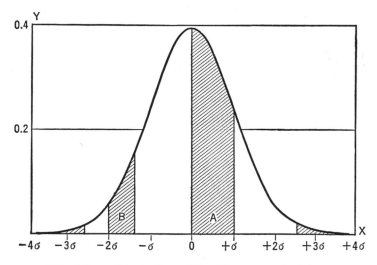

FIG. 6.5. An Illustration of the Measurement of Areas Under the Normal Curve.

the total area under the curve. (The ordinate values measured on the y-scale of Fig. 6.5 are those given by the standard formula (6.10), when $N = 1$ and $\sigma = 1$.)

What proportion of the total number of cases in a normal frequency distribution will fall between an ordinate erected at a distance from the mean equal to $- 1.4\sigma$ and one erected at $- 2\sigma$?

From the table we find that 41.924 percent of the total area will lie between y_0 and the ordinate at -1.4σ; 47.725 percent will lie between y_0 and the ordinate at -2σ. The difference, 5.801 percent, will fall between the ordinates at -1.4σ and at -2σ. This may be converted into actual frequencies by taking this proportion of the total number of cases in the given distribution. The shaded segment B in Fig. 6.5 represents the area thus marked off.

For certain purposes we wish to know the proportion of the total number of cases deviating by a stated amount or more *in either direction* from the mean of a normal distribution. If we wish to know the proportion of all cases deviating from the mean by 1.96σ or more, we must add to the area between $+1.96\sigma$ and the upper limit of the curve the area between -1.96σ and the lower limit of the curve. Each of these areas equals $0.50000 - 0.47500$, or 0.025. The percentage of cases deviating from the mean by $+1.96\sigma$ or more is 2.5; the percentage deviating by -1.96σ or more is 2.5. The percentage deviating above or below the mean by 1.96σ or more is 5.0. Similarly, it may be determined from the entries in Table 6-2 that just one percent of all the cases in a normal distribution will deviate from the mean, positively or negatively, by 2.5758σ, or more. This "one percent" area is represented by the sum of the shaded portions at the two tails of Fig. 6.5. The ordinates defining the inside limits of these segments are erected at $+2.5758\sigma$ and at -2.5758σ, while the outer limits are at infinity.

Special significance attaches to the two limits last mentioned, because of the uses made of them in interpreting errors of sampling. This topic is developed at a later point. Here we may note that the figures defining proportions of the total area under the normal curve falling in given areas may also be interpreted as probabilities. The probability that a given observation, made at random in a population distributed according to the normal law of error, will fall between the mean and a value one standard deviation above the mean is 0.34134; the probability that a given observation will deviate from the mean by 1.96σ or more is 0.05; the probability that a given observation will deviate from the mean by 2.5758σ or more is 0.01.

The method by which probabilities of occurrence may be determined from a table of areas under the normal curve, and by which the significance of a given normal deviate may be established, should be clearly understood. These methods enter in many ways into the work of a statistician.

A general theorem on dispersion. The statements made above, concerning the proportion of cases that will fall between ordinates erected at stated distances from the mean, or beyond ordinates erected at stated points, hold of course only for normally distributed observations. A useful general rule, relating to the proportion of cases falling beyond stated limits in a distribution of any type, is given by a theorem of Tchebycheff, known as *Tchebycheff's inequality*. We let k define a given distance from the mean of a frequency distribution, this distance being expressed in standard deviation units. Tchebycheff's theorem states that the proportion of the total area under the curve defining the distribution (i.e., the proportion of all cases) falling beyond ordinates erected a distance k from the mean will be equal to or less than $1/k^2$. Thus we should expect that for a given distribution the proportion of cases deviating from the mean (in either direction) by 4 standard deviations or more would be equal to or less than 1/16 of the total; the proportion deviating by 2 standard deviations or more would be equal to or less than 1/4. Concretely: In a population of income recipients with mean \$6,000 and standard deviation \$300, the proportion of persons with incomes that deviate from \$6,000 by \$600 or more will be equal to or less than one fourth of the total. Such a statement as this may be made without reference to the form of distribution. It is only necessary that the sample be large.

Tchebycheff's inequality provides a somewhat crude instrument. More precise statements may be made if the exact form of the distribution is known, or even if we know only that the distribution is unimodal and continuous. But the value of the Tchebycheff theorem lies in its complete generality. It may be used in a particular situation, where we have no knowledge of the form of distribution, to give an immediate and concrete indication of the degree of dispersion to be expected.[7]

The uses of the normal curve of error, and of the table of areas based thereon, are too varied to be enumerated at length here. A simple example may serve to introduce the subject.

Fitting a Normal Curve. The process of fitting a normal curve to a set of observations involves the computation of theoretical frequencies corresponding to the observed frequencies. This may be done from a table of areas under the normal curve (see Appendix Table I). Using such a table, in the manner indicated in the preceding section, the areas between the maximum ordinate and ordinates erected at the various class limits may be determined. By the simple process of subtraction the area within each class, and hence the theoretical frequencies, may then be computed.

[7] See Smith, Ref. 145, Cramér, Ref. 23, and Mood, Ref. 109, for discussions of the Tchebycheff theorem.

To illustrate the fitting procedure we make use of a frequency distribution based upon the annual number of telephone calls made by members of a sample of 995 residence telephone subscribers in Buffalo, New York.[8] It is a tenable preliminary assumption that the conditions giving rise to a normal distribution prevail among a population of residence telephone subscribers, although this assumption must be tested against the actual observations. Of course, the actual range of message use is not infinite; there is, indeed, a definite lower limit at zero on the scale of message use. But within the actual range of the observations the tailing off of frequencies is so pronounced that the existence of a boundary at zero does not, in fact, conflict with the theoretical conditions.

The actual distribution of telephone subscribers is given in Table 6-3. We shall require estimates of the mean and standard deviation of the assumed parent population; calculations of these two quantities are shown below the table.[9]

The computations shown in Table 6-3 yield 476.96 as the sample mean, 147.65 as the standard deviation of the sample. The sample mean may be used as an estimate of the population mean μ, but, as we have seen, the sample standard deviation s requires a modification if we are to have an unbiased estimate of the population σ (see p. 117 above). The correction is made in the variance. For an unbiased estimate of the population variance we have

$$s'^2 = \frac{N}{N-1} s^2$$

In the present case s^2, in class-interval units, is 8.7182. Thus

$$s'^2 = \frac{995}{994} \times 8.7182 = 8.7270$$

and $s' = 2.954$

To obtain s' in original units we multiply this value by the class-interval, 50. The unbiased estimate of the standard deviation of the population is then 147.70. (With a sample as large as the present one there is no difference, for practical purposes, between s and s'. With small samples s' is definitely superior to s.)

[8] The study from which this distribution was derived was made by the statistical division of the American Telephone and Telegraph Company. See "Introduction to Frequency Curves and Averages." *Statistical Bulletin, Statistical Methods Series, No. 1.* Issued by Chief Statistician, American Telephone and Telegraph Co.

[9] The entries in columns (7) and (8) are discussed at a later point in this chapter. They may be disregarded at this stage.

Our next task is to determine theoretical class frequencies, i.e., the frequencies to be expected for class-intervals of 0-50, 50-100,

TABLE 6–3

Annual Message Use of 995 Telephone Subscribers
(Illustrating the computation of the moments of a frequency distribution)

(1)	(2)	(3)	(4)	(5)	(6)	(7)	(8)
Interval of message use*	Mid-point	Fre-quency	Deviation of class midpoint from arbi-trary origin in class-in-terval units				
		f	x'	fx'	$f(x')^2$	$f(x')^3$	$f(x')^4$
0– 50	25	0	− 10	0	0	0	0
50– 100	75	1	− 9	− 9	81	− 729	6,561
100– 150	125	9	− 8	− 72	576	− 4,608	36,864
150– 200	175	19	− 7	− 133	931	− 6,517	45,619
200– 250	225	38	− 6	− 228	1,368	− 8,208	49,248
250– 300	275	50	− 5	− 250	1,250	− 6,250	31,250
300– 350	325	95	− 4	− 380	1,520	− 6,080	24,320
350– 400	375	85	− 3	− 255	765	− 2,295	6,885
400– 450	425	115	− 2	− 230	460	− 920	1,840
450– 500	475	132	− 1	− 132	132	− 132	132
500– 550	525	144	0	0	0	0	0
550– 600	575	116	1	116	116	116	116
600– 650	625	79	2	158	316	632	1,264
650– 700	675	54	3	162	486	1,458	4,374
700– 750	725	31	4	124	496	1,984	7,936
750– 800	775	11	5	55	275	1,375	6,875
800– 850	825	5	6	30	180	1,080	6,480
850– 900	875	6	7	42	294	2,058	14,406
900– 950	925	2	8	16	128	1,024	8,192
950–1,000	975	1	9	9	81	729	6,561
1,000–1,050	1,025	1	10	10	100	1,000	10,000
1,050–1,100	1,075	1	11	11	121	1,331	14,641
		995		− 956	9,676	− 22,952	283,564

CALCULATIONS

$$M' = 525$$
$$c = \frac{-956}{995}$$
$$= -0.9608$$

c (in original units)
$$= -0.9608 \times 50$$
$$= -48.04$$
$$M = M' + c$$
$$= 525 - 48.04$$
$$= 476.96$$

$$s^2 = \frac{9676}{995} - (-0.9608)^2$$
$$= 9.7246 - 0.9231$$
$$= 8.8015$$

Applying Sheppard's corrections†
$$s^2 = 8.8015 - 0.0833$$
$$= 8.7182$$
$$s = 2.953$$

s (in original units)
$$= 2.953 \times 50$$
$$= 147.65$$

* As here classified an item having a value of 50 was put in the class having 50 as an upper limit. Items falling on other class limits were similarly disposed of.
† At this point we use the same symbol s^2 for the uncorrected and corrected variances. In a later more general application of Sheppard's corrections different symbols will be employed.

etc., in a distribution of 995 observations drawn from a normal population having a mean of 476.96 and a standard deviation of 147.70. The computations shown in Table 6-4 are based upon a table of areas under the normal curve similar to that given in Appendix Table I. (Sheppard's table, which was used, gives

TABLE 6–4

Illustrating the Computation of Theoretical Frequencies from a Table of Areas

(1) Class limit	(2) Deviation from mean in units of σ $\dfrac{x}{\sigma}$	(3) Proportion of area between y_0 and ordinate at $\dfrac{x}{\sigma}$	(4) Number of cases between y_0 and ordinate at $\dfrac{x}{\sigma}$	(5) Theoretical frequencies, by classes		
0	− 3.23	.4993810	496.88			
50	− 2.89	.4980738	495.58	0–	50	1.92*
100	− 2.55	.4946139	492.14	50–	100	3.44
150	− 2.21	.4864474	484.02	100–	150	8.12
200	− 1.88	.4699460	467.60	150–	200	16.42
250	− 1.54	.4382198	436.03	200–	250	31.57
300	− 1.20	.3849303	383.01	250–	300	53.02
350	− .86	.3051055	303.58	300–	350	79.43
400	− .52	.1984682	197.48	350–	400	106.10
450	− .18	.0714237	71.07	400–	450	126.41
500	+ .16	.0635595	63.24	450–	500	134.31
550	+ .49	.1879331	186.99	500–	550	123.75
600	+ .83	.2967306	295.25	550–	600	108.26
650	+ 1.17	.3789995	377.10	600–	650	81.85
700	+ 1.51	.4344783	432.31	650–	700	55.21
750	+ 1.85	.4678432	465.50	700–	750	33.19
800	+ 2.19	.4857379	483.31	750–	800	17.81
850	+ 2.53	.4942969	491.83	800–	850	8.52
900	+ 2.87	.4979476	495.46	850–	900	3.63
950	+ 3.20	.4993129	496.82	900–	950	1.36
1,000	+ 3.54	.4997999	497.30	950–1,000		.18
1,050	+ 3.88	.4999478	497.45	1,000–1,050		.15
1,100	+ 4.22	.4999878	497.49	greater than 1,050		.05
						995.00

* The theoretical distribution shows .62 of a case below − 3.23σ. To preserve formal consistency this amount has here been added to the theoretical frequency between 0 and 50.

areas to two more decimal places than does Appendix Table I.) The procedure employed should be clear from the previous illustration. For the lower limit of the class falling between 50 and 100 on the x-scale, the deviation from the mean in standard deviation

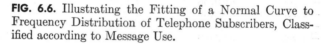

FIG. 6.6. Illustrating the Fitting of a Normal Curve to Frequency Distribution of Telephone Subscribers, Classified according to Message Use.

units is $\dfrac{50 - 476.96}{147.70}$, or -2.89. From the table of areas we find that the proportion of the total area falling between an ordinate at the mean and an ordinate 2.89 standard deviations below the mean is .4980738. Multiplying by 995, this proportion is expressed in terms of total frequencies for a sample of 995 cases drawn from the assumed normal population. This gives 495.58 cases as the number to be expected between the mean and an ordinate at 50 on the x-scale. A similar calculation gives us 492.14 as the number of cases to be expected between the mean and an ordinate at 100 on the x-scale. The difference between 495.58 and 492.14, or 3.44, is the theoretical frequency in the class whose limits are 50 and 100 on the x-scale. This process, repeated for each of the other classes, gives us the theoretical distribution by classes shown in column (5) of Table 6-4.

This theoretical distribution may be compared, class by class, with the distribution of actual frequencies as given in column (3) of Table 6-3. (For more convenient comparison, see columns (2) and (3) of Table 15-9.) Or the comparison of the actual distribution and fitted curve may be made graphically, as in Fig. 6.6. It is apparent by inspection that the normal curve gives a fairly good fit to the data, although there are several classes in which the differences are marked. A natural question arises as to the reason for the failure of the normal curve to fit at all points. There are two possible answers to such a question. The failure to fit may be due merely to chance fluctuations such as are found in any sample. We may have an underlying law of distribution of residence subscribers, classified by message use, which accords perfectly with the normal law of error, but the particular sample selected may be marked by certain irregularities which would be ironed out if a very large number of cases were included. On the other hand, the differences may be due to the fundamental failure of such a distribution to accord with the normal law of error. Such a law may not describe the distribution of telephone calls, in which case the normal curve should not be employed.

At this stage we may note, without discussion, that the differences between theoretical and observed frequencies in the present example are small enough to be attributed to chance fluctuations of sampling. The reasoning that supports this conclusion is presented in a later section (Chapter 15). The evidence is clear, however, that the discrepancies between the observed frequencies and those in the corresponding normal distribution are not excessively large. The observed facts are not inconsistent with the hypothesis that residential telephone subscribers, classified according to frequency of telephone use, are distributed in accordance with the normal law of error.

This conclusion gives generality to the results of our study. We know the attributes of distributions following the normal law of error, and once the identification of an actual distribution with this standard type has been effected we may draw upon this knowledge. In using the original frequency table we are limited to the classes there established. We may now go beyond this and determine how many cases may be expected within stated limits. We may compute the probability of a case falling between any two points on the x-scale, or above or below any given value. The observed results, standing alone, are restricted in their significance to the particular observations recorded, but the theoretical frequencies have no such limitations. They apply generally, to the entire population from which the sample was drawn. In so far as we are assured of the representative character of our sample we have a basis for inference that would be afforded by no amount of study of the particular distribution as a thing apart. This fact, that a knowledge of the theoretical frequencies permits *generalization* beyond the limits of direct observation, is perhaps the most important of the advantages derived from the identification of an actual distribution with an ideal type, such as the normal distribution.[10]

The Moments of a Frequency Distribution

It is appropriate at this point to introduce certain concepts and procedures that make possible a straightforward and systematic description of the characteristics of a frequency distribution, and that facilitate inferences concerning parent populations. The method to be discussed involves the computation of the "moments" of a frequency distribution.

"Moment" is a familiar mechanical term for the measure of a force with reference to its tendency to produce rotation. The strength of this tendency depends, obviously, upon the amount of the force and upon the distance from the origin of the point at which the force is exerted. The concept is illustrated in Fig. 6.7. Here we show a force of 8 pounds being exerted at

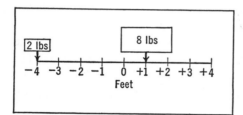

FIG. 6.7. Illustrating the Concept of Moments.

a distance 1 foot above the origin at zero. This is exactly balanced by a force of 2 pounds exerted 4 feet below the origin. The condition of equilibrium is defined by the equality of positive and negative products. If either force were exerted elsewhere on the scale, or if the origin were shifted, the sum of the pressures which are measured by the moments would not be zero.

The term "moment" is used in statistics in a quite analogous sense, the class frequencies being looked upon as the forces in question. The column diagram shown in the upper panel of Fig. 6.8 may be regarded as a solid figure, with each column exerting a pressure on the x-axis measured by the number of observations in the class in question. The "moment" contribution of each column is measured by the product of the class frequency and the corresponding deviation (x') from M' (M' being the origin—indicated by the arrow—which is 100 on the original x-scale). The sum of the fx' products, di-

---

[10] In this chapter we have discussed only two of a number of theoretical distributions that are used by statisticians. Other distributions of special importance in the theory of sampling will be discussed in subsequent chapters. Explanations of the Poisson distribution will be found in standard works. A comprehensive system of ideal frequency distributions, developed by Karl Pearson, is described by Elderton, Ref. 35. For a discussion of the Pearson and other distribution functions see also Kendall, Ref. 78, Vol. I, Chapters 5-6 and Mood, Ref. 109, Chapter 6.

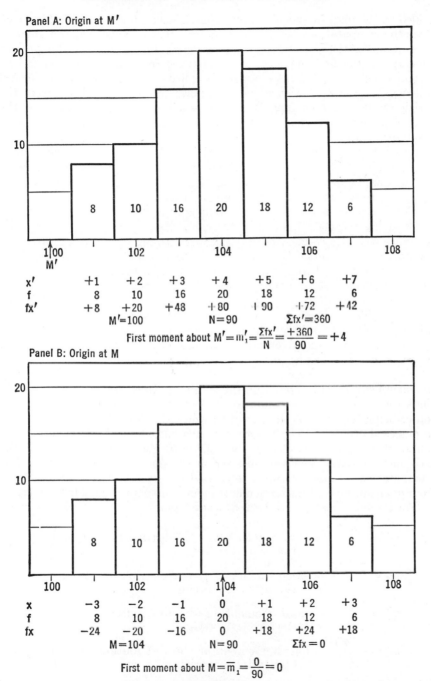

FIG. 6.8. Showing the Computation of the First Moment of a Frequency Distribution.

vided by the total frequencies, gives a net measure termed the *first moment*. (See the computations below the diagram.) It is obvious that the value of the moments depends upon the location of the origin. In the present illustration the first moment, with reference to an origin at 100 on the original scale, is +4. This quantity is called the *first* moment of the frequency distribution because the first powers of the deviations from the origin are used in its computation. The squares of the deviations yield the second moment, the cubes of the deviations the third moment, etc., as we shall see.

In the lower panel of Fig. 6.8 the origin is shifted to 104 on the original x-scale, which is the midpoint of the central class and, in the present case, the arithmetic mean, M. Here we use the symbol x for a deviation. With reference to this origin the first moment is zero.

The moments of a distribution about any origin may be computed by multiplying the class frequency, for each class, by a given power of its distance along the x-axis from the origin, summing the resulting products, and dividing by the number of cases. These moments constitute sensitive measures of the attributes of frequency distributions. In particular, the degree and character of variation are defined by these moments with great accuracy. Slight differences in patterns of variation are reflected in the moments. These moments yield, moreover, the basic descriptive measures already discussed, and other highly serviceable measures.

We now set forth a systematic procedure for computing the moments of a frequency distribution and for deriving from them various descriptive statistics. For the moments of a sample we shall use the symbol m, for the moments of a parent population the symbol μ. In each case subscripts will indicate the order of the moments defined by a particular measure (the order being the same as the power to which the deviations are raised). In a practical problem it is convenient to compute, first, the moments about an arbitrary origin, correcting these later to obtain moments about the arithmetic mean, which are most significant for statistical purposes. The computation of moments may be carried to any required order; the first four moments give all the refinements of measurement needed in most cases.

For the first calculations, therefore, we have

$$m_1' = \frac{\Sigma f(x')}{N} = \text{first moment of the distribution about the arbitrary origin.}$$

$$m_2' = \frac{\Sigma f(x')^2}{N} = \text{second moment of the distribution about the arbitrary origin}$$

$$m_3' = \frac{\Sigma f(x')^3}{N} = \text{third moment of the distribution about the arbitrary origin}$$

$$m_4' = \frac{\Sigma f(x')^4}{N} = \text{fourth moment of the distribution about the arbitrary origin}$$

$$\left.\right\} \quad (6.11)$$

The central moments, or moments about the mean as origin, may be represented by the same symbol, but with a bar. These central moments may be derived by simple algebraic processes from the moments about the arbitrary origin. Thus

$$\left.\begin{aligned}
\overline{m}_1 &= 0 \\
\overline{m}_2 &= m_2' - m_1'^2 \\
\overline{m}_3 &= m_3' - 3m_1'm_2' + 2m_1'^3 \\
\overline{m}_4 &= m_4' - 4m_1'm_3' + 6m_1'^2\,m_2' - 3m_1'^4
\end{aligned}\right\} \tag{6.12}$$

If these moments are calculated, as they usually are, from data organized in the form of a frequency distribution, the assumption is made that the items in each class can be treated as though they were concentrated at the midpoint of that class. We have called attention at an earlier point to the errors of grouping that may be involved in this procedure, and to Sheppard's corrections for such errors (see p. 121). We there noted, in particular, that the standard deviation computed from grouped data is subject to a systematic bias when the distribution relates to a continuous variable, and when the frequency curve of the distribution is characterized by "high contact"—that is, when the curve tapers off gradually in both directions. Under these conditions this bias will affect all even moments—the second, fourth, sixth, etc. Thus if we wish to avoid errors of grouping, and approximate the moments of the continuous distribution that corresponds to the broken distribution we actually have, all even moments must be adjusted. For present purposes we need concern ourselves only with corrections for the second and fourth moments.

We shall employ the symbol m, with suitable subscript, to represent a corrected moment about the sample mean. (The uncorrected moments, represented by m' and $\overline{m}$, are called "raw" moments.) The application of Sheppard's corrections gives us the following final formulation, which applies to central moments:

$$\left.\begin{aligned}
m_1 &= 0 \\
m_2 &= \overline{m}_2 - 1/12 \\
m_3 &= \overline{m}_3 \\
m_4 &= \overline{m}_4 - \overline{m}_2/2 + 7/240
\end{aligned}\right\} \tag{6.13}$$

In applying the corrections $1/12$ and $7/240$, the corresponding decimal values, 0.08333 and 0.02917, will generally be employed. It is assumed in making these corrections that the class-interval unit has been employed in measuring deviations from the mean. For moments in original units the corrections take the following form (h standing for the class-interval):

$$\left.\begin{aligned}
m_2 &= \overline{m}_2 - \tfrac{1}{12}h^2 \\
m_4 &= \overline{m}_4 - \tfrac{1}{2}\overline{m}_2 h^2 + \tfrac{7}{240}h^4
\end{aligned}\right\} \tag{6.14}$$

We may illustrate the computation of moments with reference to the distribution of telephone subscribers, classified by number of calls made per year, that was given in Table 6-3. We use the sums of columns (5), (6), (7), and (8) of that table for this purpose. Calculations are shown below. Sheppard's corrections are applied, since the curve is marked by reasonably high contact. It is a discontinuous distribution, but the unit (1) is so small in comparison with the range that it may be treated as continuous.

$$m_1' = -\frac{956}{995} = -0.960804$$

$$m_2' = \frac{9,676}{995} = 9.724623$$

$$m_3' = -\frac{22,952}{995} = -23.067337$$

$$m_4' = \frac{283,564}{995} = 284.988945$$

$$\overline{m}_1 = 0$$

$$\overline{m}_2 = m_2' - m_1'^2 = 9.724623 - 0.923144 = 8.801479$$

$$\overline{m}_3 = m_3' - 3m_1'm_2' + 2m_1'^3 = -23.067337 + 28.030370 - 1.773922$$
$$= 3.189111$$

$$\overline{m}_4 = m_4' - 4m_1'm_3' + 6m_1'^2\, m_2' - 3m_1'^4$$
$$= 284.988945 - 88.652760 + 53.863384 - 2.556586 = 247.642983$$

$$m_1 = 0$$

$$m_2 = \overline{m}_2 - 1/12 = 8.801479 - 0.083333 = 8.718146$$

$$m_3 = \overline{m}_3 = 3.189111$$

$$m_4 = \overline{m}_4 - \overline{m}_2/2 + 7/240 = 247.642983 - 4.400739 + 0.029167$$
$$= 243.271411$$

The Use of Moments in Defining the Characteristics of a Frequency Distribution

These final values, m_1, m_2, m_3, m_4, are the first four central moments of the sample distribution. They are approximations to μ_1, μ_2, μ_3, and μ_4, the central moments of the population from which the sample was drawn. From the sample moments we may derive the major measurements that describe the sample distribution and that indicate the distribution type to which it belongs.

Criteria of curve type. Two fundamental criteria, represented by the letter beta, with subscripts 1 and 2, are derivable from the second, third, and fourth moments about the mean. For the distribution of telephone subscribers we have

$$\beta_1 = \frac{m_3^2}{m_2^3} \tag{6.15}$$

$$= \frac{10.170429}{662.632015} = 0.015349$$

$$\beta_2 = \frac{m_4}{m_2^2} \tag{6.16}$$

$$= \frac{243.271411}{76.006070} = 3.200683$$

Each of these is an abstract measure, for the moments in numerator and denominator have been raised to the same order. (The order of m_b^a —where

b defines the moment and a defines the power to which m_b is raised—is given by $a \times b$.) Thus for β_1, the numerator is the third moment squared, the denominator is the second moment cubed. In deriving β_2 the fourth moment has been divided by the square of the second moment.

The criterion β_1 is, essentially, an index of the skewness of the distribution. Its square root, indeed, is a standard measure of skewness. This quantity is equal to zero for the normal distribution, and will be zero for any symmetrical distribution. (The student will note that the third moment, which in squared form is the numerator of the fraction giving β_1, is derived from the sum of the cubed deviations from the mean. This sum will be zero if plus and minus deviations are perfectly symmetrical.) β_1 will be plus (it is given the sign of mean minus median) if the distribution is asymmetrical with a tail extending to the right. It will be minus for an asymmetrical distribution with the longer tail to the left.

The formula for the criterion β_2 may also be written m_4/s^4 or, for population characteristics, μ_4/σ^4. For the normal distribution this ratio is equal to 3. Values in excess of 3 have been taken to indicate a relatively heavy concentration of frequencies near the central tendency, while values below 3 have been taken to indicate a relative deficiency of frequencies near the central tendency. (The comparison in each case is with a normal distribution having the same standard deviation.) However, as we shall note again below, this particular interpretation of β_2 is not altogether safe.

These criteria have their greatest usefulness in connection with Karl Pearson's system of ideal frequency curves. They enable the investigator to identify the ideal type, normal or otherwise, to which a given sample distribution appears to belong. This subject, which will not be explored here, is developed by Elderton (Ref. 35); basic tables and charts relevant to this family of curve types, and of wide general utility, will be found in Pearson's *Tables for Statisticians and Biometricians*.

Derivation of Descriptive Measures. We now briefly summarize the operations by which descriptive measures are derived from the sample moments. Illustrative data relate to the distribution of telephone subscribers (see Tables 6-3 and 6-4, and computations on pages 162 and 165). The symbols have been previously explained.

Central tendency.

$$M = M' + (m_1' \times h) \qquad (6.17)$$

$$= 525 + (-0.9608 \times 50)$$

$$= 476.96$$

Variation. The standard deviation is the square root of the second moment. Since the moments cited above are in class-interval units, appropriate modification is needed:

$$s = \sqrt{m_2} \times h \qquad (6.18)$$

$$= \sqrt{8.71815} \times 50$$

$$= 147.65$$

Skewness. The basic measure of skewness is $\dfrac{M - Mo}{\sigma}$. However, the modal value of a sample cannot be rigorously defined. Pearson derives the quantity χ (chi) from β_1 and β_2, in the following relation:

$$Skewness = \chi = \frac{\sqrt{\beta_1}\,(\beta_2 + 3)}{2(5\beta_2 - 6\beta_1 - 9)} \qquad (6.19)$$

We have noted that $\sqrt{\beta_1}$ is sometimes used as a measure of skewness. The fuller expression (formula 6.19) is more satisfactory in that, for the Pearson curves, it gives a quantity equal to, $\dfrac{M - Mo}{\sigma}$. Substituting the values of β_1, β_2, and σ for the telephone distribution, we have

$$\chi = -\,0.05558$$

(The sign of the skewness is given by the sign of mean minus median. The mean is 476.96, the median is 482.39, hence the skewness is negative.)

The measure of skewness given above is used in general in connection with the Pearson system of frequency curves. An alternative measure represented by the Greek gamma with subscript 1 has also been used as a coefficient of skewness. This is given by $\gamma_1 = m_3/s^3$; for population values $\gamma_1 = \mu_3/\sigma^3$.

The modal divergence. The distance d between the mean and the mode may be determined from

$$d = \chi \times \sigma$$
$$= -\,0.05558 \times 147.65 \qquad (6.20)$$
$$= -\,8.21$$

Location of the mode. We have noted above that the mode is an elusive value, impossible to define rigorously from sample data. Having the mean and the modal divergence, however, we may derive a value for the mode. (We should note that what we thus derive is the x-value of the maximum ordinate of the ideal frequency curve, of the Pearson family, that could be fitted to the sample distribution.) The mode as thus estimated is the mean less the modal divergence:

$$Mo = M - d \qquad (6.21)$$
$$= 476.96 - (-\,8.21)$$
$$= 485.17$$

This gives a truer approximation to the modal value than any of the methods discussed in Chapter 4.

Peakedness or "excess." The quantity $\beta_2 - 3$ is a traditional measure of an attribute of a frequency distribution, or frequency curve, which goes by various names—peakedness, kurtosis, excess, or concentration. Its value is zero for the normal curve. In general, positive values indicate relatively high concentration of frequencies near the central tendency—

high, that is, in comparison with the distribution of frequencies in a normal distribution with the same standard deviation. In general, negative values indicate a deficiency of cases near the central tendency, in comparison with a normal distribution of the same standard deviation. The measure of peakedness is represented by the Greek gamma with subscript 2. In the present case we have

$$\gamma_2 = \beta_2 - 3 \qquad (6.22)$$
$$= 3.201 - 3$$
$$= + 0.201$$

This would indicate a distribution slightly more peaked than the normal (Cp. Fig. 6.6). However, these relations are not invariable. Certain patterns of variation can show peakedness with the quantity $\beta_2 - 3$ negative, and conversely. Accordingly, $\beta_2 - 3$ is not to be taken as a clear-cut index of peakedness, or the reverse.

The methods of utilizing moments discussed in this section provide a straightforward procedure for defining the essential attributes of a frequency distribution. The mean and mode as measures of central tendency, the standard deviation as a measure of dispersion, χ as a measure of skewness, and $\beta_2 - 3$ as a measure of degree of concentration (the interpretation of this measure must be somewhat qualified) may be computed directly from the first four central moments of a frequency distribution. Because of their uses for these and other purposes, moments are tools of high value in statistical analysis.

REFERENCES

Anderson, R. L. and Bancroft, T. A., *Statistical Theory in Research*, Chaps. 2, 3.

Clark, C. E., *An Introduction to Statistics*, Chaps. 2, 3, 4.

Cramér, H., *The Elements of Probability Theory and Some of its Applications*, Part I.

Cramér, H., *Mathematical Methods of Statistics*, Chaps. 13, 15, 17.

David, F. N., *Probability Theory for Statistical Methods*, Chaps. 1-5.

Dixon, W. J. and Massey, F. J. Jr., *Introduction to Statistical Analysis*, Chaps. 4, 5.

Elderton, W. P., *Frequency Curves and Correlation*, 4th ed., Chap 3.

Feller, W., *An Introduction to Probability Theory and its Applications*, Vol. I, Chaps. 1-7.

Goulden, C. H., *Methods of Statistical Analysis*, 2nd ed., Chap. 3.

Hoel, P. G., *Introduction to Mathematical Statistics*, 2nd ed., Chaps. 2, 5.

Kelley, T. L., *Fundamentsls of Statistics*, Chap. 8.

Kendall, M. G., *The Advanced Theory of Statistics*, 3rd ed., Vol. I, pp. 116-120, 128-133, 164-183.

Marschak, J., "Probability in the Social Sciences," Chap. 4 of Lazarsfeld, P. F., ed., *Mathematical Thinking in the Social Sciences*.

Mather, K., *Statistical Analysis in Biology*, 2nd ed., Chaps. 2, 3.
Mood, A. M., *Introduction to the Theory of Statistics*, Chap. 2.
Neyman, J., *First Course in Probability and Statistics*, Chap. 2.
Rosander, A. C., *Elementary Principles of Statistics*, Chaps. 5, 7, 13, 25, 26.
Tintner, G., *Mathematics and Statistics for Economists*, Chaps. 20, 23.
Tippett, L. H. C., *The Methods of Statistics*, 4th ed., pp. 48-78.
Treloar, A. E., *Elements of Statistical Reasoning*, Chaps. 5, 6.
Walker, H. M. and Lev, J., *Statistical Inference*, Chap. 2.
Waugh, A. E., *Elements of Statistical Method*, 3rd ed., pp. 155-211.
Wilks, S. S., *Elementary Statistical Analysis*, Chaps. 4, 5, 6, 8.
Yule, G. U. and Kendall, M. G., *An Introduction to the Theory of Statistics*, 14th ed., Chaps. 7, 8.

The publishers and the dates of publication of the books named in chapter reference lists are given in the bibliography at the end of this volume.

CHAPTER **7**

. . .

Statistical Inference: Problems of Estimation

At various stages in the preceding discussion we have spoken of the problems involved in passing from the known facts provided by a sample to generalizations about the population from which the sample was drawn. In particular, our concern in such generalizations is with the unknown values of the *parameters* that define attributes of such a parent population. In estimating a parameter (a mean, a median, a standard deviation) we may wish to obtain a single figure which, in some sense, represents the best guess we can make as to the actual value of the parameter in question. Alternatively, our estimate may take the form of a statement specifying limits within which, with a given degree of confidence, we may expect the actual value of the parameter to fall. The estimate of a single figure is called a *point estimate*; the statement that presents limits, rather than a single figure, is called an *interval estimate*. In the present chapter we shall deal with certain criteria and methods that have to do with point estimation, and shall then proceed to a more extended discussion of interval estimates and of the probabilities that attach thereto. But first the basic idea of randomness calls for brief discussion. For the samples to which the theory of probability may be applied must be random samples.

Random Variables and Random Samples

We think of a variable as a quantity that may take any of a number of different values. The addition of the word *random* modifies the concept materially. A *random variable* may take any of a number of values; the individual values will be marked by irregularity in their occurrence, but when many individual values are brought together regularity of arrangement will appear. The regularity may be of many types, for different random variables, but for any one such variable there is orderliness in its mass behavior. Another way of putting this is to say that when many individual values of a random variable are organized (as in a frequency distribution) orderliness that takes the form of a definite distribution function will emerge. The separate values will be members of a "population" with definable attributes.

We should stress that randomness is the key to the orderliness that thus appears. The practical importance of this fact is very great. As Shewhart has said, "The ability to randomize a set of numbers or a set of objects by means of some distinguishable physical operation provides the scientist with a powerful technique for making valid predictions." For the prediction that is impossible with reference to individual members of a population of random variables is possible with reference to members of such a population in the mass. Some of the conditions under which random series appear have been suggested in discussing the normal distribution. Here the forces affecting individual events must be independent; each event must be affected by a multiplicity of forces; there must be equality of forces tending to generate values above and below the mean value. Such a distribution is, of course, just one of many possible random distributions. The conditions noted may be modified rather substantially, and randomness may remain. The regularities represented by distribution functions are of diverse types. In all cases individual events are unpredictable, but the stability of large numbers generates regularity, and makes possible prediction (in probability terms) concerning mass behavior.

As we shall see, deliberate achievement of the randomness that makes valid prediction possible calls for design and most careful planning (see Chapter 19). At this stage we may note that if we are to have a *random sample*, which is the necessary basis of a valid inference, we must have a sample the elements of which are independent events, that all these events must come from the same population, and that the method of drawing the sample must be such that the probability of being chosen is definable for each member of the population (by "element of a sample" we here mean a single observation). In the actual field work of sampling elaborate techniques are often necessary to ensure that these conditions are in fact met in a given case.

We may here note a special term used for distributions of random variables. When we have specified for any distribution the relative frequency with which values of a random variable fall within each of a number of defined classes, we have a *probability distribution*. (Relative frequencies, as we have seen, may be interpreted as probabilities.) The binomial and normal distributions are probability distributions; there are many others. Every random variable has its distinctive probability distribution. Such a distribution may be defined by a *frequency function* of the familiar type, with frequencies rising to a maximum and then declining, or by a *distribution function* showing cumulative frequencies or probabilities.

Notation. The symbols employed in this chapter accord in general with the system previously outlined. We may note the following:

s': an unbiased estimate of σ

m: the mean of a distribution of sample means

σ_m: the standard deviation of a distribution of sample means; the standard error of a mean; also written $\sigma_{\bar{x}}$

s_m: the estimated standard error of a sample mean; also written $s_{\bar{x}}$

θ (theta): a population parameter (a general symbol)

t_e: a statistic regarded as an estimate of θ

$\hat{\theta}$: the maximum likelihood estimate of θ

σ_s: the standard deviation of a distribution of sample s's; the standard error of the standard deviation

s_s: the estimated standard error of a sample s

σ_{md}: the standard error of the median

s_{md}: the estimated standard error of a sample median

σ_{q_1}: the standard error of the first quartile

σ_{d_1}: the standard error of the first decile

f_s: the number of successful outcomes out of n events

$n-f_s$: the number of unsuccessful outcomes out of n events

s_p: the estimated standard error of a proportion, or of a relative frequency

pe: a percentage

s_{pe}: the estimated standard error of a percentage

N_p: the total number of cases in a finite population

Sampling Distributions: Preliminary Discussion

When a sample has been drawn, by random processes, from a given population, we may from the sample (which is composed of X_1, X_2, X_3, . . . X_n) estimate any characteristic of the parent population. The mean of the sample is an estimate of the mean of the population; the standard deviation of the sample can be corrected to give an unbiased estimate of the standard deviation of the population; a measure of skewness of the sample provides an estimate of the skewness of the population. If we should draw many random samples from a given population, all samples being of the same size, the means of the various samples ($\overline{X}_1$, $\overline{X}_2$, $\overline{X}_3$, etc.) would give us a series of varying estimates of the population mean. These varying estimates would constitute a random variable. Every sample mean may be regarded as an observed value of this new random variable (new in that the unit of observation here is not one member of the original population of X's, but one member of a new population of $\overline{X}$'s). These means may be organized in a frequency distribution. Similarly, a series of standard deviations derived from successive samples may be put in the form of a frequency distribution. Such a distribution, composed of the means of successive samples, or of the standard deviations of successive samples, would have the general characteristics of the distributions discussed in earlier chapters. In each distribution observations would tend to concentrate about a central value; frequencies would tail off, symmetrically or asymmetrically, about this central value. As the number of observations was increased, discontinuities that might be present when the number of observations was small would be reduced; there would be a clear tendency toward a continuous frequency curve as the total frequencies increased. The smooth frequency curve which would thus be approached would be the graphic representation of what is called a *sampling distribution*.

The attributes of such sampling distributions are of supreme importance in the theory and practice of statistics. The power of statistical inference derives from the knowledge we now possess of the sampling distributions of standard deviations, coefficients of correlation, and other statistical measurements. For knowledge of such distributions—which are probability distributions—enables us to specify the probabilities that attach to the conclusions of statistical inferences. To understand how this is done we must know something about the sampling distributions of the chief statistical measurements. As a basis for the discussion that is to follow we first briefly note the characteristics of the sampling distribution of the arithmetic mean.

We have seen above that the means of successive random samples of size N, all drawn in the same way from the same parent population, constitute a random variable. Observations on this random variable (i.e., the various mean values) can be organized in a frequency distribution. This distribution—and this is a fact of central importance in theoretical and practical statistics—will be normal, or will tend toward the normal type, whether the population from which the samples have been drawn be normally distributed or not. If the parent population is normal, the distribution of sample means will be normal; if the parent population is not normal, the distribution of sample means will be asymptotically normal, that is, will approach the normal form as N increases.[1] Moreover, the mean and the standard deviation of the distribution of means will bear definite relations to the parameters of the parent population. The mean of the sampling distribution, which we may represent by the symbol m_m, will be equal to μ, the population mean. Or, more precisely, as the number of samples increases the mean of the distribution of means will approach μ or converge in probability [2] to μ. The standard deviation of the sampling distribution, which we may represent by s_m or, in the limit, σ_m, will in the same sense be equal to the population σ divided by the square root of the number of observations in each sample; that is $\sigma_m = \sigma/\sqrt{N}$. The mean and the standard deviation completely define a normal distribution; the sampling distribution

---

[1] This approach to normality of distributions of means has been established for samples drawn from infinite populations with finite standard deviations, regardless of distribution type; it holds also for samples drawn from finite populations under quite general conditions. For a discussion of the validity of the normal approximation see Cochran (Ref. 17, pp. 22-28) and the references there cited.

W. A. Shewhart gives a striking illustration of the emergence of the normal distribution among means of samples drawn from parent distributions of diverse types. Shewhart drew many samples, each containing four observations, from a normal parent population, from a rectangular parent population (i.e., one for which the frequency distribution was rectangular in shape), and from a right triangular parent population (i.e., one for which the frequency distribution took the form of a right triangle). In each of the three cases the distribution of sample means was acceptably normal. See Shewhart, Ref. 140, 179-184.

[2] For the mathematical meaning of convergence in probability see Cramér, Ref. 23, p. 252.

of means of samples drawn from a population of given mean and standard deviation is thus completely determined.

Since we are normally concerned about the degree of dispersion to be found among a series of means, standard deviations, or other statistics derived from successive samples from a given parent population, our chief interest, in respect of measures descriptive of sampling distributions, is usually in those that define the degree of variation in such distributions. For the sampling distribution of the mean this, as just noted, is σ_m. The knowledge that $\sigma_m = \sigma/\sqrt{N}$ suffers from one important practical limitation. We do not usually know σ, the standard deviation of the parent population. However, for large samples the standard deviation s of the sample may be accepted as a good estimate of σ, for s tends to approach σ (i.e., "converge in probability" to σ) for such samples. (For small samples it is well to use s', the unbiased estimate of σ, in preference to s. See p. 117.) If we use s or s' as an approximation to σ we employ the symbol s_m, instead of σ_m, for the standard deviation of the sampling distribution of the mean. (We may note that this measure, σ_m or s_m, is called the *standard error of the mean.*) Having s_m and knowing that it measures the dispersion of sample means in a distribution that is normal, or acceptably so, we may interpret it with confidence as a measure of sampling reliability. We shall see shortly how such measures are used in estimation.

Each sampling distribution may be thought of as a population of estimates. We are interested in such distributions because of their basic role in the process by which we estimate population parameters, or seek to define the limits within which such parameters may be expected to fall. It is the process of estimation which is our central concern.

Point Estimation

Criteria. Before further discussion of the characteristics of specific sampling distributions it will be well to note certain general criteria that may be applied in evaluating estimates, and to consider methods that may be open to us in the making of estimates. For we wish to employ methods that will give us good estimates. How may we distinguish good methods of estimation from poor ones? What standards of judgment are appropriate?

Statisticians have developed four major criteria that are applied in the appraisal of estimates, and thus in the evaluation of methods of estimation. They distinguish *unbiased* from biased estimating methods, *consistent* methods from those that are not consistent, *efficient* from inefficient methods, *sufficient* methods from methods that are not sufficient. We do not here attempt to present the mathematical reasoning behind these various criteria. Our purpose will be served by brief statements of the nature of these criteria and by a summary indication of the considerations that have led students of the logic of statistics to define these principles.[3]

A given statistic t_e is an *unbiased* estimate of the corresponding population θ if θ is the mathematical expectation of t_e. To say that θ is the mathematical expectation of t_e is to say that as the number of samples increases the arithmetic mean of the t_e values obtained from the samples approaches (or converges in probability to) θ. (It is here assumed that all the t_e's are derived from samples of fixed size N.) A sample mean $\overline{X}$ is an unbiased estimate of μ, the corresponding population parameter. A sample variance s^2, computed from $s^2 = \Sigma(X - \overline{X})^2/N$, is not an unbiased estimate of the population variance σ^2, for the mean of the sampling distribution of s^2 will be smaller than σ^2. (This fact has been noted in Chapter 5 in discussing the method of deriving from a sample an estimate of the population σ.) An unbiased estimate of σ^2 may be obtained by dividing $\Sigma(X - \overline{X})^2$ by $N - 1$ instead of by N.

A given statistic t_e is a *consistent* estimate of the parameter θ if, as the sample size N increases without limit, the values of t_e converge in probability to θ. This criterion differs from the preceding in that N was taken to be fixed in the preceding case, whereas N is thought of as tending to infinity in the present case.

A sample mean $\overline{X}$ is a consistent, as well as an unbiased, estimate of μ, the population mean. The sample statistic s^2, computed from $s^2 = \Sigma(X - \overline{X})^2/N$, is a consistent although not an unbiased estimate of the population variance σ^2. For as N gets larger and larger the difference between s^2 and σ^2 tends to get smaller and smaller; s^2 approaches σ^2. This is not incompatible with the fact that from samples of fixed size we would get a distribution of s^2

---

[3] Basic work in the development of systematic methods of estimation was done by R. A. Fisher in two path-breaking papers that appeared in the nineteen-twenties. (See Fisher, Ref. 47, papers 10, 11. The criteria employed in evaluating point estimates, and the method of maximum likelihood for obtaining point estimates, are due to Fisher.

values the mean of which would not be σ^2, but something less than σ^2.

In considering the idea of *efficiency* in estimates we may revert to the concept of sampling distributions. Estimates such as sample means, standard deviations, or measures of skewness, when derived from many samples of the same size drawn from the population whose parameters are to be estimated, form frequency distributions. In the limit, each of these constitutes a population of estimates. In the long run we may expect to get better estimates from statistics the distribution of which is concentrated about the parameter we are estimating, than from statistics having a distribution marked by extreme dispersion. For the reliability of the estimate (if it be an unbiased estimate) depends on the degree of concentration found in its sampling distribution. This concentration, as measured by the variance (σ^2) of the sampling distribution, a quantity which is termed the *sampling variance*, is the quality to which the term efficiency applies. Of two estimates, that with the smaller variance is the more efficient. An estimate marked by minimum variance is an *efficient* estimate.

When we consider the attributes of specific sampling distributions we shall be particularly interested in their variances, or their standard deviations. These indexes of efficiency and of reliability are of central importance in statistical inference.

The final criterion used in evaluating methods of estimation is the standard of *sufficiency*. If a statistic derived from a sample contains all the information that the sample contains, relevant to the parameter in question, that statistic provides a *sufficient* estimate. Sufficiency is a very desirable attribute of an estimate, but a somewhat exceptional one. The statistic $\overline{X}$ as an estimate of the mean of a normal population is sufficient, as well as efficient; the variance s^2 computed, for a sample, from $s^2 = \Sigma(X - \mu)^2/N$, where the population mean, μ, is known, is also both sufficient and efficient. But few statistics embody all the relevant information contained in a given sample.

Methods of Estimation. The problem of point estimation, we may recall, is that of determining single numbers which, for given reasons, may be regarded as acceptable estimates of the unknown values of specified parameters. The preceding statements indicate certain qualities that good estimates should have, and other qualities that may characterize poor estimates. Having decided on criteria, there remains the important question: What methods of estimation may be employed in estimating population parameters from the data of actual samples? How shall we proceed to estimate a population mean or standard deviation, or any other parameter, with confidence that the number obtained will meet some or all of our criteria? Three methods of estimation may be noted.

The nature of *the method of least squares* is suggested by its name. When we employ this method for estimating, say, a population mean, we find that value from which the sum of the squares of the deviations of the observed values (i.e., the squares of the residuals) is a minimum. The arithmetic mean of a series of observations meets this condition; the mean of a sample is a least squares estimate of the mean of the population from which the sample has been drawn. A least squares fit of a straight line to scattered points is that line for which the sum of the squares of the deviations is a minimum. The least squares principle is one with a long tradition, and one that has been extensively employed in practice. It has a practical advantage in that the procedures followed in applying it are relatively simple. As we shall see, this method is widely used in correlation studies, and in defining the trends of time series. However, except in the important special case of a normally distributed variate the justification for its use is largely one of convention and expediency. For normally distributed observations the results obtained when estimates are based on least squares procedures have logical validity.

When *the method of moments* is used in estimation, we assume that a certain number of the moments of the parent population (e.g., the first two, or the first four) are equal to the moments of the sample. The desired parameters are then estimated from the assumed population moments. This method, which is due to Karl Pearson, is generally used in fitting frequency curves of the Pearson family. The practical procedures involved have the advantage of simplicity, in most cases, but the method is not an efficient one except for distributions of the normal type.

The principle of least squares and the method of moments are, thus, of limited validity when generally applied. The method which is now standard has wider applicability and sounder logical foundations. This is *the method of maximum likelihood*, developed by R. A. Fisher.[4] For present purposes we shall indicate the basic

---

[4] Ref. 47, papers 10, 11, 24, 26. The procedure is explained, with applications, in standard works on mathematical statistics.

characteristics of this method, without attempting to set forth the details of its application in specific cases.

The essence of the method of maximum likelihood may be explained in the following terms: We are working with a sample of n observations, from a population of known form. The drawing of this sample is the observed event. On the basis of the information given us by this sample we are to estimate a certain population parameter, θ (it is assumed that only one parameter is here involved). From the many possible estimates of θ we choose that one $\hat{\theta}$, if it exists, that renders the probability of the occurrence of the observed event as great as possible. (Back of this procedure lies, of course, the basic assumption that the sample is representative of the population from which it has been drawn.) This principle lends itself to a straightforward mathematical procedure by which may be derived the maximum likelihood estimates of parameters of the standard distribution functions.

It will be of interest at this point to cite a few examples of estimates that meet the maximum likelihood condition. For a sample of observations drawn from a normal population, the mean $\overline{X}$, estimated from $\Sigma X/N$, is the maximum likelihood estimate of μ, the mean of the parent population. (In the case of a normally distributed variate the least squares method of estimating μ and the maximum likelihood method are equivalent.) The mean $\overline{X}$ of a sample from a Poisson distribution is, similarly, the maximum likelihood estimate of the population mean. The maximum likelihood estimate of the variance σ^2 of a normally distributed variate is given by

$$s^2 = \frac{\Sigma(X - \overline{X})^2}{N} \qquad (7.1)$$

However, this is not an unbiased estimate. The *best unbiased estimate*[5] of σ^2 is given by the quantity

$$s'^2 = \Sigma(X - \overline{X})^2/(N - 1) \qquad (7.2)$$

We may, obviously, derive the best unbiased estimate of the variance from the relation

$$s'^2 = \frac{N}{N - 1} s^2$$

[5] This term, which is employed by J. Neyman, defines that one among several possible unbiased estimates (if they exist) that has minimum variance.

The point should be stressed that there is no definitive argument in favor of any one method of estimation. The method of maximum likelihood has, however, strong practical claims in its support. The estimates it yields are consistent. If in a given case an efficient estimate exists, the method of maximum likelihood will give it. For large samples maximum likelihood estimates tend toward normality. Maximum likelihood estimates will be sufficient, if sufficient estimates exist for a given parameter. Estimates given by the method of maximum likelihood are not necessarily unbiased, as the above illustration has indicated. That is, the parameter we may be seeking to estimate in a given case is not necessarily equal to the arithmetic mean of the population of maximum likelihood estimates that make up the given sampling distribution. However, corrections to eliminate bias may be made (as was indicated in the case of the variance). In most cases in which estimates of population parameters are sought, the method of maximum likelihood provides the standard of reference (i.e., the standard against which results obtained by other methods are appraised), if not the standard procedure.[6]

For many problems maximum likelihood estimates are readily arrived at. When samples are drawn from normal populations maximum likelihood estimates are identical with least squares

---

[6] The nature of this procedure may be briefly noted, although applications of the method of maximum likelihood are not developed in this book. We are to derive from a sample of n observations $(X_1, X_2 \ldots X_n)$ an estimate of a population parameter θ. The method entails two steps:

1. Set down the likelihood function of the sample. This is the function that defines the probability of obtaining that particular sample (when the sample relates to a continuous variable this is spoken of as the probability density at the sample point). The observed sample values and the unknown parameter θ enter into the expression for the function. When there is but one parameter to be estimated we may write for the likelihood function

$$L = f(X_1, X_2, X_3, \ldots X_n; \theta)$$

Since the n sample values are known, the likelihood function L becomes a function of θ alone.

2. Determine that estimate of θ among the many possible estimates which will maximize L (i.e., which will make as great as possible the probability of obtaining the particular sample). This is done by a process of differentiation that locates the point at which the likelihood function has a maximum. The equation to be solved can be written in the form

$$\frac{\partial L}{\partial \theta} = 0$$

The solution gives $\hat{\theta}$, the maximum likelihood estimate of θ.

estimates for arithmetic means, standard deviations, and measures of correlation. For other problems the maximum likelihood technique may be more complex and more demanding of time and effort. In such cases the simpler least squares technique is customarily used, particularly if the populations being sampled are believed to depart only moderately from the normal form. Under these conditions least squares estimates provide good approximations to maximum likelihood estimates.

Interval Estimation: Confidence Limits

The object of point estimation is to pick out a single value which, in some specified sense, may be regarded as the "best" estimate of some unknown parameter. But an estimate of this sort, while pinpointed on a unique value, is quite unlikely to coincide with the true value of the parameter that concerns us. If we are dealing with a continuous variable there is an infinity of possible wrong estimates, and but one right estimate. Perhaps we have studied a sample of income recipients in the United States in a given year, and on the basis of the information provided by the sample reach the conclusion: The true mean income of income recipients in the United States in the year X was \$4,244. Although this may be the "best" estimate that we can make, it is almost certainly not the correct figure (which may fall at any point over a wide range). To the conclusion as it stands no probability statement may be attached. But for logical and practical reasons the information given by our sample will be of greatest use to us if a conclusion summarizing the relevant information given by the sample can be put in a form to which a probability statement may be attached. Since we shall be generalizing from a sample the conclusion will be an uncertain one, in any event, but we should like to be able to put some measure to the degree of uncertainty involved.

The theory of interval estimation leads to a conclusion of the following sort: The true mean income of income recipients in the United States in the year X lay between \$4,146 and \$4,342. This is a statement that may be true or false, for the true mean income of the population in question was either between the stated limits or it was not. Whether it is true or false we do not know. But the merit of the method of interval estimation is that it enables us to attach a specific probability to a family of statements of the type just cited, and thus to define the degree of confidence we may have in any single statement of this sort.

An Example: estimation of μ when σ is known. The method of interval estimation now generally employed may be explained, first, in terms of a hypothetic example. We shall assume that an investigator is seeking to estimate the mean μ of a normal population having a standard deviation σ equal to 40. That is, the investigator knows that the distribution is normal, and knows the standard deviation of the distribution, but does not know its mean. We assume now that the investigator has drawn 1,000 samples from this population, each including 400 observations. For each of these samples he has calculated $\bar{X}$. Let us say that the calculated values of $\bar{X}$ are 99.5, 102.1, 95.8, 98.7, 101.4 . . . , etc., to a total of 1,000 figures. We have seen above that the means of samples of fixed size N, drawn from a given population, will be distributed normally, with a standard deviation equal to $\sigma/\sqrt{N}$. Thus we know that the 1,000 means, of which 5 have been given above, will make up a normal distribution, with standard deviation $40/\sqrt{400}$, or 2. We know, therefore, that the investigator is drawing from a population that may be represented by the graph shown in Fig. 6.5. The mean of this population, μ, is unknown to the investigator, but he does know the limits within which stated proportions of the population of means will fall. Sixty-eight percent will fall within $\mu \pm 2$; 95.45 percent will fall within $\mu \pm 4$; 99.7 percent will fall within $\mu \pm 6$.

We must now permit the investigator to draw the inference that is possible on the basis of the information given him by each successive sample. We do so at this point without explanation, other than to note that 95 percent of the area under a normal curve falls within ordinates erected 1.96σ below the mean and 1.96σ above the mean. This is to say that in using the multiples of σ indicated below, the investigator is working with a 95 percent "confidence interval," a phrase that will be explained shortly.

After drawing the first sample, of which the mean is 99.5, our investigator makes the statement:

1. "The mean μ of the population from which I am drawing falls between 95.58 and 103.42."

After drawing each of the succeeding samples he makes a statement similar in form, but different in the limits it specifies. The four succeeding statements, corresponding to the second, third, fourth, and fifth sample means given above, are:

2. "The mean μ falls between 98.18 and 106.02."
3. "The mean μ falls between 91.88 and 99.72."
4. "The mean μ falls between 94.78 and 102.62."
5. "The mean μ falls between 97.48 and 105.32."

The reader will observe that the limits set in each statement are derived by subtracting 3.92, i.e., 1.96 × 2, (2 being the standard deviation of the distribution of means), from the given sample mean, and by adding 3.92 to the given sample mean. Thus 95.58 = 99.5 − 3.92; 103.42 = 99.5 + 3.92.

If, now, we may assume that we (the author and the reader) have a piece of information not available to the investigator, we may check the accuracy of his several statements. This added information is that the true mean of the population from which the samples have been drawn is exactly 100. We note that four of the five statements are true, and that one (the third) is false. The mean μ does not fall between 91.88 and 99.72. The relation of each statement to the facts may be more clearly apparent in Fig. 7.1.

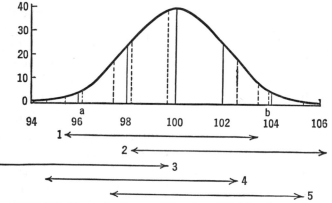

FIG. 7.1. Normal Curve Showing Distribution of Sample Means, with 0.95 Confidence Intervals Based on Five Samples.*

* Parameters of population from which samples were drawn: Mean = 100 (not known to investigator). Standard deviation = 40 (known to investigator). Each sample N = 400.

The statements, in order, are represented by the numbered lines drawn below the graph of the normal curve representing the distribution of means. Each of these lines indicates the location of ordinates at the limits of the specified interval. Four of these intervals include the true mean, μ; one does not.

The ordinates a and b are erected at points on the x-scale falling 1.96σ below and 1.96σ above the mean μ. The area between them is 95 percent of the area under the curve. It will be noticed that if a point corresponding to a sample mean falls anywhere within the area between ordinates a and b, the interval $\overline{X} \pm 1.96\sigma$ will include the mean μ. In all such cases statements of the type given on page 187 will be true. If a sample point falls outside ordinate a or ordinate b, the interval $\overline{X} \pm 1.96\sigma$ will not include the mean μ. In all such cases, statements of the type cited in the examples above will be false. But since $\overline{X}$'s of the type here considered will be normally distributed, 95 percent of them, in the long run, will fall within the limits $\mu \pm 1.96\sigma$. Thus for 95 percent of all cases, statements of the type here discussed will be true, while 5 percent will be false. If our investigator were to base upon each of his 1,000 $\overline{X}$'s statements similar to the 5 cited above, we should expect that about 950 of them would be true, while about 50 would be false. (We say "about," because 1,000, although a large number, is finite, and the chances of sampling could easily lead to some departure from these figures.) In an actual inquiry the investigator would probably draw but one sample. Thus the only generalization he would make would be, say, "The mean μ falls between 95.58 and 103.42." This is true or false. The investigator does not know which. He does not say that the probability is 0.95 that it is true. The actual probability that it is true is either 1 (i.e., the statement is in fact true) or 0 (i.e., the statement is in fact false). But he does know that of many statements of this type, based upon operations of the same kind, 95 out of 100 would be true. In other words, this particular statement belongs to a family of statements of which 95 out of 100 would be true. His confidence in the statement is measured by a "probability coefficient" of 0.95. Hence the term *confidence interval*, used to describe the interval between 95.58 and 103.42.

This mode of phrasing a statistical inference departs from the method that was prevalent several decades ago. In particular, the reader will note, the parameter μ, which is to be estimated, is regarded as a *constant*, not as a variable quantity. In most practical problems we are trying to estimate a value that is clearly a constant, although an unknown one. Thus we may not use language (such as, "The probability is 0.50 that the true mean falls between such and such limits") that implies that a parameter is variable.

Since the parameter is a constant, statements specifying limits within which it is said to lie are either true or false. *Probabilities attach to the family of statements*, all made in the same way, but specifying varying intervals. What is variable in such a family of statements is the *location of the interval*, not the parameter that is being estimated.

We must note, finally, that the example cited above illustrates a special situation—that in which the σ of the parent population is known. Because σ is known, the intervals specified in the various statements are all of the same width. Where σ is not known the procedure and the interpretation of the conclusions are similar, but the ranges set forth in different statements will be unequal. This case calls for brief attention.

An example : estimation of μ when σ is not known. We shall now assume that an investigator has drawn ten samples, with $n = 101$ in each case, from a given population, which may or may not be normal. The population mean and standard deviation, which are not known to the investigator, are, in fact, 80 and 20, respectively. From the observations in each sample the investigator computes the mean, $\overline{X}$, and the standard deviation, s' $\{s'$ being regarded as an estimate of σ, is derived from $s' = \sqrt{\Sigma x^2/(N - 1)}\ \}$. The several values of $\overline{X}$ and of s' are given in Table 7-1. The standard error of

TABLE 7–1

Illustrating the Estimation of a Population Mean
Means and Standard Deviations derived from Ten Samples from a given
Population, with 0.95 Confidence Intervals Based Thereon

(1) Sample number	(2) Mean	(3) Standard deviation	(4) Estimated standard error of $\overline{X}$	(5) Confidence interval for $P = 0.95$
	X	s'	$s_{\overline{x}}$	$\overline{X} \pm 1.96\ s_{\overline{x}}$
1	81.2	19.8	1.98	77.32 to 85.08
2	79.6	21.4	2.14	75.41 to 83.79
3	84.0	19.2	1.92	80.24 to 87.76
4	82.1	22.6	2.26	77.67 to 86.53
5	80.6	20.2	2.02	76.64 to 84.56
6	78.2	17.3	1.73	74.81 to 81.59
7	78.8	20.9	2.09	74.70 to 82.90
8	81.4	18.5	1.85	77.77 to 85.03
9	79.1	19.5	1.95	75.28 to 82.92
10	80.3	21.1	2.11	76.16 to 84.44

(Population parameters: $\mu = 80$, $\sigma = 20$. Each sample $N = 101$)

the mean of each of the ten samples is now estimated (from $s_{\bar{x}} = s'/\sqrt{N}$). On the basis of the information given by each sample the investigator now estimates an interval within which the mean may be expected to fall. Since he has decided to work with a confidence coefficient of 0.95 the confidence limits are derived, in each case, by subtracting from and by adding to the sample mean the quantity $1.96s_{\bar{x}}$. Thus from the data of sample No. 1 the conclusion reached is:

"The mean μ falls between 77.32 and 85.08."

(The lower limit, 77.32 is, of course, $81.2 - (1.96 \times 1.98)$ while the upper limit, 85.08, is $81.2 + (1.96 \times 1.98)$. These limits appear as the entries in column (5) of Table 7-1. This statement may be true or it may be false. On the theory of interval estimation the investigator believes that of 100 statements, each based on an operation similar to that which yields the first statement, 95 will be true and 5 false. The "confidence intervals" specified in 10 such statements, each based on the information given by a sample of 101 observations drawn from the same parent population, are shown in column (5) of Table 7-1. They are shown graphically in Fig. 7.2.[7]

The ten confidence intervals thus set forth differ in location. The central point of each is the mean of one of the ten samples. In this respect they are like the confidence intervals cited in the preceding example (p. 188). But they differ from those previously cited in that their ranges differ. Thus the range of the first confidence interval in Table 7-1 is 7.76, that of the second is 8.38. The smallest interval is 6.78, given by sample No. 6; the greatest is 8.86, given by sample No. 4. The ranges differ, of course, because the investigator has to use the standard deviations of the several samples as estimates of the population σ, which he does not know. Some of these sample standard deviations are below the true σ (in sample No. 6, s' is but 17.3, as compared with the σ value 20); some are above. There are two factors, therefore, in the variations among the confidence intervals estimated from the several samples —varying central points and varying ranges. But the notable fact is that in spite of the two varying factors, 95 percent of the ranges

---

[7] This graph is of a type first suggested by Walter Shewhart. See Fig. 8.4 which gives a reproduction of an illuminating chart from Shewhart's *Statistical Method from the Viewpoint of Quality Control.*

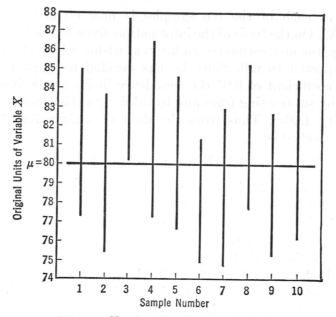

FIG. 7.2. Showing the Range of Each of Ten Interval Estimates of a Population Mean, with Confidence Coefficient of 0.95 (Population parameters, $\mu = 80$, $\sigma = 20$, not known to investigator. Each sample $N = 101$).

thus specified will in the long run include the true mean.[8] In the illustration here given, in Table 7-1 and Fig. 7.2, nine of the ten confidence intervals cited do in fact include the mean, 80. Only for sample No. 3, which gave a mean value well in excess of the population μ, does the confidence interval fail to include μ. It will be understood, of course, that in both this example and the one preceding, the investigator who is estimating the location of the population mean is without the information we possess, in studying Fig. 7.1 and Fig. 7.2. He does not know where any interval falls, with respect to the true mean μ. To make clear what is actually happening, the reader has here been given information not available to the investigator. The latter possesses only the information needed for defining each of the confidence intervals and the corresponding probability coefficient, together with the knowledge that each statement asserting that μ falls within a given confidence

[8] No formal proof of this statement is here given. The memoirs by J. Neyman (Refs. 117 and 121) and other references given at the end of this chapter should be consulted by the interested student.

interval belongs to a family of statements of which, in the long run, 95 percent will be true. In a particular case this is not exact information, it is true, but it is information of high practical importance, and information on the basis of which decisions may be made and action taken.

We should note that the choice of the confidence coefficient 0.95 is in some respects arbitrary. If the investigator chooses to make statements that he would expect to be true, in the long run, only 1 time out of 2, he would choose a confidence coefficient of 0.50. The multiplier of the standard error of the mean (see heading to column (5), Table 7-1) would then be 0.6745 instead of 1.96. If he chose to make statements that he would expect to be true, in the long run, 99 times out of 100, he would choose a confidence coefficient of 0.99, and use a multiplier of 2.576. Thus, with the coefficient 0.99, the conclusion reached on the basis of the first sample drawn, for which the mean is 81.2 and the standard deviation 19.8, would be:

"The mean μ falls between 76.1 and 86.3."

Raising the confidence coefficient in this way, from a level of 0.95 to 0.99, increases the range of the confidence interval, of course, thus making the conclusion less precise. But it raises one's confidence in the truth of the statement, elevating it into a family of statements which may be expected to be correct 99 times out of 100. In defining confidence limits we may choose to have greater precision with less confidence, or less precision with greater confidence. The choice of confidence coefficients in given cases will depend on the nature of the problem faced, and to some extent on the temperament of the investigator. Coefficients of 0.95 and 0.99 are most commonly used.

In practical employment of the method of interval estimation the essential element is knowledge of the sampling distribution of the particular statistic—mean, standard deviation, coefficient of correlation—that is to be generalized. Is the sampling distribution normal for such a measure (e.g., a mean) computed from samples drawn from a normal parent population? for a measure computed from samples drawn from non-normal populations? Most important in such knowledge of sampling distributions is knowledge of the *character* of dispersion to be expected and of means of estimating the *degree* of dispersion. If we know that a given distribution is normal, or not too far removed from the normal type, and if we may make a reasonable estimate of the standard deviation of such a distribution, the specific information to be had from a single sample will give us the basis for setting the limits of a confidence interval and for asserting with a specified degree of confidence that the population parameter falls within this interval. If the sampling distribution departs significantly from the normal type the procedure is somewhat less simple, but inference is still possible. Important non-normal sampling distributions have been defined in detail, often in tabular form. Such tables, to which we shall have later reference, make it possible to estimate parameters and to test hypotheses with definable degrees of precision.

Some Standard Errors and Their Uses in Estimation

In the present section we shall give examples of procedures employed in defining confidence intervals, setting forth at the same time characteristics of the sampling distributions of various statistical measures.

The Arithmetic Mean. Table 5-2 in Chapter 5 shows the distribution of 83,114 workers in industrial chemical plants, classified according to their average hourly earnings in January, 1946. The arithmetic mean of this distribution is 114.61 cents; the standard deviation s is 23.54 cents. Accepting this standard deviation as an approximation to the standard deviation of the population from which this sample was drawn,[9] we have

$$s_m = \frac{s}{\sqrt{N-1}} = \frac{23.54}{\sqrt{83,113}} = 0.082$$

The true mean of the hourly earnings of wage workers in industrial chemical plants in January, 1946, is not known. The figure 114.61 cents is our best approximation to it. If we should

---

[9] We have derived s from the formula $s = \sqrt{\dfrac{\Sigma d^2}{N}}$. Accordingly, in estimating the standard error of M it is logical to use the formula $s_m = s/\sqrt{N-1}$. That is, N should be reduced by 1 either in the estimation of σ or in the derivation of s_m. (For samples as large as the one here considered the reduction of N by 1 is purely formal. It does not affect the result significantly.) If s_m is derived from the d's of the original data, the single operation is summed up in Bessel's formula

$$s_m = \sqrt{\frac{\Sigma d^2}{N(N-1)}}$$

draw many samples, each the size of the one we have here, we should have many mean values normally distributed and centering, we may assume, at the true value. The standard deviation of this normal distribution we estimate as 0.082 cents. If we wish to work with a probability coefficient of 0.95 we have as the lower limit of the desired confidence interval 114.61 − (1.96 × 0.082), or 114.45. As the upper limit we have 114.61 + (1.96 × 0.082), or 114.77. Our statistical inference, therefore, takes the following form: "The mean hourly earnings of the universe of industrial chemical workers in January, 1946, lay between 114.45 cents and 114.77 cents." This particular statement may be true or false. Of an infinitely large number of such statements, based upon similar operations, 95 percent will be true, 5 percent false.

If we should choose to work with a probability coefficient of 0.99 we should set the lower limits of the confidence interval at a point 2.576 s_m below the sample mean, the upper limit at a point 2.576 s_m above the sample mean. In this case our conclusion would be: "The mean hourly earnings of the universe of industrial chemical workers in January, 1946, lay between 114.40 cents and 114.82 cents."

The confidence intervals are narrow, of course, with samples as large as the one here considered. Means of samples of this size would be very closely concentrated—a fact that permits very accurate estimation.

When a measure derived from a sample is presented as an estimate of a population parameter it is customary to give the statistic in question with its standard error, rather than to write out the formal conclusion. Thus we would write, for the estimated mean of hourly earnings of industrial chemical workers, $M =$ 114.61 cents ± 0.08. The user of the statistic may then set up his own confidence interval, choosing the probability coefficient that he deems appropriate. It was the practice in earlier years to present the probable error of a statistic (i.e., 0.6745 the standard error) in this fashion, but the standard error is now generally employed. To avoid confusion, however, it is well to indicate that it is the standard error which is given.

In setting up confidence intervals for population means on the basis of information derived from samples, we have made use of three important facts—that the sampling distribution of $\bar{X}$'s is normal, or asymptotically normal, that the standard deviation of the sampling distribution of means may be defined in terms of the standard deviation of the parent population and of the sample N, and that when a sample is large the standard deviation of the parent population may be estimated with confidence from the standard deviation of the sample. By procedures somewhat similar to those that lead to the standard error of the mean, the standard errors of a number of other statistical measurements have been derived. It is true, under very general conditions, that the distributions of sample characteristics computed from sample moments tend toward normality as n approaches infinity.[10] The standard deviations of such sampling distributions are usually definable, as was true in the case of the mean, in terms of the parameters of the parent population and of sample N's. The standard errors of these measurements are generally approximated by substituting the known sample characteristic (e.g., the standard deviation of the sample, as in the preceding example) for the corresponding unknown population parameter. Thus it is true, remarkably, that by virtue of behavior characteristics of large numbers we are able to utilize information given by samples themselves in generalizing the results obtained from samples.[11]

Sampling a finite population. The procedures discussed above all relate to samples drawn from infinite populations. This is the assumption usually made in statistical inference. Even when the population sampled is in fact limited in size, we usually take our results to apply to the infinite population that would be generated if the forces that gave rise to the population actually in existence were to operate indefinitely without change in character. But the investigator sometimes wishes to work in terms of a population of limited and known size. The standard error of the mean of a sample

---

[10] The *central limit theorem* by which this fact is demonstrated is one of the notable mathematical discoveries and one of the most fundamental propositions in theoretical statistics. This theorem states that under quite general conditions the sum of any number of independent random variables tends toward normality in its distribution as n tends to infinity. The striking general feature of this theorem is that the separate components of the sum need not be normally distributed themselves. The fundamental role of the normal distribution in statistical theory derives in good part from the remarkable fact stated in this theorem. For proof of this theorem and discussion of its implications for statistics, see Cramer, Ref. 23, pp. 198-203, 213-220, and Kendall, Ref. 78, Vol. I, pp. 180-183.

[11] The procedures here discussed are applicable to large samples. For most purposes a sample of 100 may be considered "large." Samples for which N is less than 30 are always considered "small." (Special procedures appropriate to small samples are discussed below.)

drawn from such a population may be estimated from a modification of the customary formula. Using N as the number of cases in
the sample and N_p for the total number in the population, we
may write

$$s_m = \frac{s'}{\sqrt{N}} \sqrt{\frac{N_p - N}{N_p}} \qquad (7.3)$$

The effect of the modification is to reduce the sampling error of
the mean. If N_p is very much greater than N the reduction is very
slight; in effect the drawing in such a case has been made from an
infinite population. If the sample has covered every case in the
population, N_p and N will be equal and the standard error of the
mean will be zero.

The Standard Deviation. The standard deviation s, treated as a
random variable as was X above, has an asymptotically normal
distribution. (For small samples, as we shall see, the departure
from normality is great enough to call for distinctive treatment.)
For large samples, say with N in excess of 100, we may treat it as
a normally distributed variate. If the parent population is normal,
the standard deviation of a distribution of s's will be given by

$$\sigma_s = \sigma/\sqrt{2N} \qquad (7.4)$$

Not knowing the standard deviation of the population we substitute for σ (in the right-hand term above) the sample s. (No distinction is drawn between s and s', for we are dealing with large
samples.) Thus we have

$$s_s = s/\sqrt{2N} \qquad (7.5)$$

As an illustration of the process of estimating the standard
deviation of a normal population we may use the data on residence
telephone subscribers (see Table 6-3). As an estimate of σ we have
$s = 147.7$; $N = 995$. We have, therefore,

$$s_s = \frac{147.7}{\sqrt{1,990}} = 3.31$$

If we wish to work with a confidence interval of 0.99, we set
confidence limits below and above 147.7 by 2.576×3.31, or 8.5.
Thus our conclusion is: "The standard deviation of the population
of residence telephone subscribers lies between 139.2 and 156.2."

Our confidence that the statement is true is measured by a co-efficient of 0.99.

For samples drawn from a non-normal universe the standard deviation of the distribution of s's is given by

$$\sigma_s = \sqrt{\frac{\mu_4 - \mu_2^2}{4\mu_2 \cdot N}} \qquad (7.6)$$

where the μ's represent the moments of the parent population. If we let the symbol m_2 represent the second moment of the sample, and m_4 represent the fourth moment of the sample, we have as our estimate of the standard deviation of s, for a sample from a non-normal universe

$$s_s = \sqrt{\frac{m_4 - m_2^2}{4m_2 \cdot N}} \qquad (7.7)$$

This formula is to be applied and the results interpreted in the usual fashion. For large samples it may be taken as an estimate of the standard deviation of a normal distribution, since the distribution of the s's tends toward normality as n tends toward infinity.

We may note that the general formula for σ_s reduces to the simpler formula $\sigma/\sqrt{2N}$ for samples drawn from a normal parent population. For in the case of a normal distribution $\mu_4 = 3\mu_2^2$.

The Quantiles. We have used quantile as a generic term for measures such as the median, the quartiles, or the deciles, that divide the total frequencies in a distribution into specified proportions. Since every sample quantile may be regarded as an estimate of a corresponding population quantile, the usual problems of inference arise in the use of such measures in research. The sampling distributions of all quantiles tend toward normality as the sample size N increases. Thus for large samples we regard such sampling distributions as effectively normal, with means equal to the population quantiles that correspond to given sample quantiles. The standard deviations of the sampling distributions of the various quantiles (i.e., the standard errors of the quantiles) vary, as is to be expected. The following summary gives the standard errors of various quantiles, derived from samples drawn from normal parent populations. If the samples are large, the stated measures give good approximations to the standard errors of quantiles for samples from non-normal parent populations, provided that the parent distributions are not extremely skew.

Quantile	Standard error
Median	$\sigma_{md} = 1.2533\sigma/\sqrt{N}$
First quartile	$\sigma_{q_1} = 1.3626\sigma/\sqrt{N}$ (σ_{q_3} identical)
First decile	$\sigma_{d_1} = 1.7094\sigma/\sqrt{N}$ (σ_{d_9} identical)
Second decile	$\sigma_{d_2} = 1.4288\sigma/\sqrt{N}$ (σ_{d_8} identical)
Third decile	$\sigma_{d_3} = 1.3180\sigma/\sqrt{N}$ (σ_{d_7} identical)
Fourth decile	$\sigma_{d_4} = 1.2680\sigma/\sqrt{N}$ (σ_{d_6} identical)

The σ of each formula stands, of course, for the standard deviation of the parent population. If this is not known the sample s (or s') will be substituted for it, with a corresponding change in the symbol for the standard error.

It will be noticed that the sampling error of the median is some 25 percent greater than the sampling error of the mean of a sample of similar size. The mean is, ordinarily, a more stable statistic than the median. (For a distribution with heavy concentration of observations near the modal value, i.e., a very peaked distribution, the stability of the median would be greater.) Quantiles near the center of the scale of x-values are marked by sampling errors smaller than those characteristic of quantiles near the limits of the range.

The Standard Error of a Proportion. In discussing the binomial distribution (Chapter 6) we noted that the standard deviation of a distribution of relative frequencies is given by $\sqrt{\dfrac{pq}{n}}$. This fact is very useful in generalizing results that take the form of frequency ratios, or relative frequencies, whether these are cited as proportions (e.g., 8/12) or as percentages. If we let f_s represent the number of "successful" outcomes out of n events, the relative frequency or proportion of successes will be f_s/n; the proportion of nonsuccesses will be $\dfrac{n-f_s}{n}$. Since f_s/n corresponds to p, of the

general formula given above, and $\dfrac{n-f_s}{n}$ corresponds to q, the for-

mula for the standard error of the proportion f_s/n may be written

$$s_p = \sqrt{\dfrac{\dfrac{f_s}{n}\cdot\dfrac{n-f_s}{n}}{n}} \qquad (7.8)$$

which reduces to

$$s_p = \sqrt{\dfrac{f_s(n-f_s)}{n^3}} \qquad (7.9)$$

Thus we may regard f_s/n as a random variable, normally distributed with standard deviation given by formula (7.9) above. For
accurate approximation by these processes n should not be small,
and neither p nor q should be very small.

To illustrate this procedure we shall assume that a sample poll
has been taken of election preferences in a given community. Of
400 voters interviewed 320 ($= f_s$) favor candidate A, while 80
($= n - f_s$) favor candidate B. We are required to estimate the
proportion of all the voters favoring A. The sample proportion, p,
of successes is $320/400$ or 0.80. The standard error of this proportion is

$$s_p = \sqrt{\dfrac{320(400-320)}{400^3}}$$

$$= \dfrac{16}{800} = 0.02$$

The proportion and its standard error may be presented thus:

$$f_s/n = 0.80 \pm 0.02$$

If we wish to generalize, using 0.95 as the probability coefficient,
the limits of the desired confidence interval will lie $1.96\,s_p$ below
and above the given proportion, 0.80. The product $1.96\,s_p$ is equal
to 0.0392, which we round off to 0.04. We may then say "The
proportion of all voters favoring candidate A falls between 0.76
and 0.84." We make this assertion with confidence measured by
the indicated probability coefficient.

For proportions, as for arithmetic means, standard errors vary
inversely with the square root of n. Thus if we had covered only

100 cases in the above poll, the proportions being as they were in the larger sample, we should have

$$s_p = \sqrt{\frac{80(100 - 80)}{100^3}}$$

$$= 0.04$$

In the first example cited n was four times as great as in the second; the standard error in the first case was one half as large as in the second case.

It is frequently convenient to work with percentages, rather than with frequency ratios or proportions. When this is done, the standard error of the percentage is derived from a slight modification of equation (7.8). If we let $P_e = 100(f_s/n)$ and $100 - P_e = 100(n - f_s)/n$, equation (7.8) becomes

$$s_{pe} = \sqrt{\frac{P_e(100 - P_e)}{n}} \tag{7.10}$$

For the first example cited we should have $P_e = 100 \times \frac{320}{400} = 80$. For the standard error of P_e we should have

$$s_{pe} = \sqrt{\frac{80 \times (100 - 80)}{100}} = 2$$

The result would be given as

$$P_e = 80 \pm 2$$

Sampling errors and significant figures. In deciding upon the number of figures to be recorded as significant, measures of sampling errors are, of course, pertinent. A useful general rule laid down by Truman L. Kelley follows: *In a final published constant, retain no figures beyond the position of the first significant figure in one third of the standard error; keep two more places in all computations.* Its application may be illustrated with reference to the figures on hourly earnings of 83,114 chemical workers (Table 5-2). The mean, to four places, is 114.6138 cents. The standard error of the mean is .082 cents. One third of this is .0273. The first significant figure is in the column of hundredths. By the rule, therefore, the arithmetic mean should be given as 114.61 cents. Two more places, or four decimal places in all, should be retained in calculations.

Some Limitations to Measures of Sampling Errors. The importance of such measures of reliability as have been discussed above is, of course, great. With their aid we may give precision to our judgments concerning the margins of error involved in extending statistical results beyond the limits of actual observation. Yet limitations attach to them, and these must not be forgotten in a purely mechanical application of statistical tests.

Reference has been made to limitations arising out of the size of samples. We have noted the striking fact that many of the sampling distributions that concern statisticians are only "asymptotically normal," tending toward normality as n increases. When this is the case procedures that may be justified in handling large samples may be invalid for small samples. ". . . asymptotic expressions," as Cramér says, "are sometimes grossly inadequate when we are dealing with small samples."[12] Here we should like to have knowledge of the exact form of sampling distributions. However, knowledge of *exact* sampling distributions is limited. The exact distribution of the mean, $\overline{X}$, has been established for very general conditions. Distributions of other statistical measures defining attributes of samples from normal universes have been systematically studied, and some generally applicable findings obtained. For measures other than the mean, derived from samples drawn from non-normal universes, knowledge of exact distributions is limited. Fortunately, however, the tendency toward normality as n increases enables us to generalize with a fairly high degree of confidence when we are dealing with many of the statistics that are currently employed in handling mass data, *provided* that our samples be large. When this is so, the methods discussed in the present chapter may be used in drawing warranted conclusions. Moreover, exact distributions have been defined for certain small sample characteristics, and techniques have been developed for the practical application of this information. These will be discussed in the following chapter.

In deriving and using the measures of sampling error discussed in this chapter we make certain assumptions about the character of the samples employed and about the nature of the sampling process that has generated these samples. A basic assumption is

---

[12] Cramér, Ref. 23. See pp. 378-9 for a general statement on the limitations of our knowledge in this field.

In general, as we have noted, we should regard a sample as small when N is less than 30; we regard a sample as large when N is greater than 100. Under certain circumstances, however, (see Chapter 9 on correlation for examples) a sample of 100 may not be considered large.

that our samples are *random*. Only when we generalize from random samples may we speak in terms of probabilities. (Means of assuring randomness have been mentioned in Chapter 1; they are more fully discussed in Chapter 19.) A sample is drawn under *random* conditions if the separate events (the selections, or drawings of sample elements) are independent, and the probability of inclusion in the sample is known, or definable, for all members of the population. We have conditions of *simple random sampling* if the events (the selections) are independent and if the probability of inclusion in the sample is the same for all members of the population. (The condition of independence, strictly interpreted, would mean that in sampling from a finite population a given drawing would have to be replaced before the next drawing were made. If the finite number is reasonably large such replacement may be neglected.) The various measures of sampling error described in this and the following chapter are applicable when the conditions of simple random sampling have been realized.[13]

The degree to which the stated conditions of random sampling are fulfilled, in a given case, is in part subject to conscious control. Elaborate techniques have been developed to improve the approximations to these conditions that are achieved in actual field investigations. In particular, much may be done to ensure randomness in the sample, and something can be done to ensure the independence of individual events. Perfect fulfillment of all the conditions is, however, difficult to realize in the handling of social and economic data. The standard errors we have discussed in this chapter, we must emphasize, can give no indication of the possibility of fluctuations in successive samples arising from errors unrelated to random sampling. Fluctuations due to bias and faults arising from lack of representativeness of the sample quite elude this method of measuring the reliability of statistical inferences. The reduction of such biases and the avoidance of such faults must be the constant concern of the statistical investigator.

The element of time adds one serious difficulty to the problem of statistical induction in the realm of economics, and in the social sciences generally. A universe that extends over time is subject to

---

[13] In Chapter 19 we develop an additional, though related, condition, bearing on sample design in simple random sampling. If a sample of n elements is to be regarded as a simple random sample, the conditions of selection must be such that every possible set of n elements in the population has the same chance of being chosen.

elements of change that are not present among data relating to a cross-section of time. Conditions of pig iron production, of banking, of foreign trade, of income distribution change from year to year, even from month to month. We may hardly assume that data relating to different time periods reflect the play of identical forces. When we deal with data from different periods we are, as Oskar Anderson has pointed out, drawing from different universes. The structural changes that occur in economic organization are manifestations of this state of never-ending transition. Accordingly the homogeneity of all populations extending over time is suspect. In particular are hazards faced when an induction extends to a time period not covered by the data of observation.

In the application of statistical methods proper choice of objectives, wise planning, and effective field work are of at least equal importance with skill in the use of statistical techniques. This is especially true as regards problems of sampling. Here chief emphasis falls on soundness and accuracy in the field work. The problems of field work are specialized and particular, arising out of specific problems and conditions. Appropriate special knowledge is needed for the selection and validation of the sample.

Much may be done to strengthen a statistical induction by making actual statistical tests of the homogeneity of the population and of the stability of sampling results. By the study of successive samples the representativeness of statistical measures may be determined; and by testing the subordinate elements of a given sample, when broken up into significant subgroups, the inherent stability of a sample may be checked. The uniformity of nature in a given field is assumed in every induction. The induction is strengthened by every piece of evidence that supports the assumption.

REFERENCES

Anderson, R. L. and Bancroft, T. A., *Statistical Theory in Research*, Chaps. 9, 10.

Clark, C. E., *An Introduction to Statistics*, Chap. 5.

Cramér, H., *Mathematical Methods of Statistics*, Chaps. 32, 34.

Fisher, Sir Ronald (R. A.)., *Contributions to Mathematical Statistics*, Papers 10, 11, 25, 26, 27.

Johnson, P. O., *Statistical Methods in Research*, Chap. 6.

Mood, A. M., *Introduction to the Theory of Statistics*, Chap. 11.

Neyman, J., "Outline of a Theory of Statistical Estimation based on the Classical Theory of Probability," *Philosophical Transactions of the Royal Society*, 1937.

Neyman, J., *Lectures and Conferences on Mathematical Statistics and Probability*, 2nd ed., Chap. 4.

Rosander, A. C., *Elementary Principles of Statistics*, Chaps. 15, 16, 17.

Shewhart, W. A., *Economic Control of Quality of Manufactured Product*, Chap. 13.

Shewhart, W. A., *Statistical Method from the Viewpoint of Quality Control*, pp. 92-110.

Waugh, A. E., *Elements of Statistical Method*, 3rd ed., Chap. 9.

Wilks, S. S., *Elementary Statistical Analysis*, Chaps. 9, 10.

Wilks, S. S., *Mathematical Statistics*, Chap. 6.

Yule, G. U. and Kendall, M. G., *An Introduction to the Theory of Statistics*, 14th ed., Chaps. 17, 18.

The publishers and the dates of publication of the books named in chapter reference lists are given in the bibliography at the end of this volume.

CHAPTER

Statistical Inference: Tests of Hypotheses

In introducing the subject of statistical inference we drew a distinction between estimation, the object of which is to locate a population parameter at a point or within stated limits, and the testing of hypotheses. We concern ourselves now with the theory of such tests and with their application.

The testing of hypotheses that refer to the actual world involves, in one form or another, the setting of hypotheses against data of observation. If observed facts are clearly inconsistent with a given hypothesis, it must be rejected. If the facts are not inconsistent with the hypothesis, the hypothesis is tenable. These simple statements require elaboration, of course, but they contain essential truths about the process by which scientific theories are tested, prior to acceptance or rejection. So far as the immediate evidence is concerned acceptance is always qualified; rejection often is. In the tests here in question decisions are made in terms of probabilities.

The procedures here to be discussed relate to statistical hypotheses. A *statistical hypothesis* is one that specifies properties of a distribution of a random variable. These properties (or parameters) are the hypothetical values with which we compare measures derived from an actual sample. The difference between an observed statistic and the corresponding hypothetical parameter is the central quantity with which the test deals. If this difference is small (what constitutes a "small" difference will be considered below) we may say that the facts are not inconsistent with the hypothesis; if the difference is great, we conclude that the facts are not consistent with the hypothesis.

The techniques and theory of statistical tests have been developed over the last half century, the greatest progress having been made in the last thirty years. Karl Pearson, "Student," R. A. Fisher, Jerzy Neyman and E. S. Pearson have made major contributions. The argument that is here briefly sketched deals with the theories of Neyman and E. S. Pearson.[1]

Notation. Certain symbols not hitherto used will be introduced in this discussion. The more important of these are given below:

H, H_0, H_1: hypotheses

T: a deviation from the mean of a normal distribution expressed in units of the standard deviation; a normal deviate

D: the difference between two arithmetic means

s_n: the standard error of the difference between means; written also as $s_{\bar{x}_1 - \bar{x}_2}$

$s_{s_1 - s_2}$: the standard error of the difference between two standard deviations

$s_{p_1 - p_2}$: the standard error of the difference between two proportions

t: the ratio of a normally distributed variable with zero mean to the square root of an independently distributed estimate of the variance of that variable

On the Theory of Statistical Tests

The theory of statistical tests may be introduced by citing two general principles:

1. In testing a particular statistical hypothesis H_0 we imply that it may be wrong. That is, we admit that there are hypotheses alternative to the one being tested. These alternative hypotheses should be considered explicitly in choosing an appropriate test.

2. When we test a hypothesis we should like to avoid errors. In the choice of a test we therefore try to minimize the frequency of errors that may be committed in applying it.

The Neyman-Pearson theory thus recognizes the hypothesis H_0,

[1] See Neyman and Pearson, Refs. 122, 123; Neyman, Refs. 116, 121.

the one explicitly defined as the subject of the test, and a family of alternative hypotheses, a member of which may be represented by H_1. When a test has been chosen (on principles to be referred to below) and applied, the investigator faces the possibility of two kinds of errors:

1. *An error of the first kind* (Type I) is committed when two conditions prevail:
   (a) The hypothesis H_0, which is being tested, is in fact true;
   (b) The result of the test leads to the rejection of the hypothesis H_0.

2. *An error of the second kind* (Type II) is committed when two conditions prevail:
   (a) The hypothesis H_0, which is being tested, is in fact false (some alternative hypothesis H_1 is true);
   (b) The result of the test leads to the acceptance of the hypothesis H_0.

The existence of two kinds of possible errors is distinctive of the problems faced in testing hypotheses. In *interval estimation*, one of the forms of statistical inference discussed in the preceding chapter, the investigator makes the flat statement that a given parameter falls within stated limits. The statement is false if the parameter in question does not fall within those limits. The investigator faces the possibility of but one type of error. A new theoretical problem is faced, thus, when we pass from interval estimation to the testing of hypotheses. The solution of this problem gave new power to statistical tools. In the present discussion we deal briefly with the general nature of the solution, before passing to applications.

In general terms, it is obviously desirable that tests should be employed that make the chances of both kinds of errors as small as possible. Since it is generally considered more important to avoid an error of the first kind than it is to avoid an error of the second kind, the test employed should be one that leads very infrequently to the rejection of a true hypothesis. This leads to the following working principle, in selecting among possible tests: An attempt is made, first, to control errors of Type I. That is, the probability of a Type I error is fixed arbitrarily at a level of significance, say α (alpha), which would ordinarily be one of the conventional limits 0.05 or 0.01. In comparing two tests for both of which the probability of a Type I error is α, we would choose that one for which the probability of a Type II error is the smaller.

Any test of this sort is in effect a rule that specifies "properties" the observations should possess if the hypothesis to be tested is to be accepted. If they do not possess these properties, the hypothesis is rejected. The crucial properties are usually defined in terms of *regions* (in n-dimensional space—the number of dimensions depending on the number of coordinates of the sample point E). If the point E, which is defined by the observations included in the sample, falls within the *acceptance region*, the hypothesis is judged to be tenable; i.e., it is accepted. If the point E falls within the *critical region*, which is also termed the *rejection region*, the hypothesis is rejected. Using the symbol W to denote the whole sample space (i.e., the region within which points derived from all possible samples will fall), we may represent by w the region of rejection, by W-w the region of acceptance. The two regions are complementary. As we have noted, the probability that E will fall within w, the region of rejection, when the hypothesis is in fact true is called the *significance level* of the test. Where the significance level is to be set in a given case must be determined by the investigator, with reference to the possible consequences of errors of each of the two types.[2]

An example. We may illustrate the procedure by reference to a simple example (after Mood), involving a choice between two alternative hypotheses. The test will be based upon a single observation. Let us assume that a given population of x's is described by either the probability function A or the function B, which are shown in Fig. 8.1. We are to test H_0, which is the hypothesis that the population in question has the distribution A. We set the significance level at 0.05. The single alternative hypothesis is H_1, which specifies that the population has the distribution B. One or the other is true.

The single observation x_1 on which the test is to be based will give us a point on the x-axis. Our problem is to define on this axis *intervals of acceptance* and of *rejection* (these correspond, of course,

[2] A logical burglar, pondering possible professional operations on a certain bank, might set up the hypothesis:

The bank is equipped with a burglar alarm.

He commits an error of Type I if, the hypothesis being in fact true, he rejects it and tries to rob the bank. The consequence is his arrest. If the hypothesis is, in fact, false, and he accepts it, abstaining from the attempt, he commits an error of Type II. In consequence he foregoes a possibly fruitful operation. An error of Type I might well seem to him to be more serious in its adverse consequences.

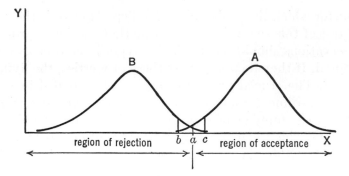

FIG. 8.1. An Illustration of Tests of Hypotheses Location of Regions of Acceptance and Rejection in a Simple Test.

to the *regions* set up for tests involving more dimensions). Having the information here assumed, i.e., information concerning the two distributions A and B, the problem is solved by locating on the x-axis the point a at which an ordinate of distribution A will divide the area under curve A into two segments including, respectively, 0.05 and 0.95 of the total (see Fig. 8.1). The region of acceptance will be the interval on the x-scale lying to the right of the point a; the region of rejection will be the interval to the left of a. H_0 will be accepted if the observation x_1 falls in the interval of acceptance, rejected if it falls in the interval of rejection.

It is clear that if H_0 is in fact true, the probability of x_1 falling to the right of point a is 0.95, of falling to the left, 0.05. Hence the possibility of an error of Type I (i.e., of rejecting H_0 when it is true) is 0.05. The location at point a of the division between the intervals of acceptance and rejection leaves open the possibility of an error of Type II (i.e., the acceptance of a false hypothesis). For if H_0 is in fact false (H_1 being true), there is a probability, though a small one, that an observation which is really drawn from distribution B will fall in the interval of acceptance for H_0. This probability is measured by the proportion of the total area of distribution B that falls in the interval of acceptance shown in Fig. 8.1.

The probability of an error of Type I, in respect of hypothesis H_0, may be modified at will. Thus if we wish to reduce the probability of such an error to, let us say, 0.0001, we could do so by setting at point b on the x-scale the dividing line between the intervals of acceptance and rejection for H_0. Point b has been so located as to divide the area under curve A into segments including, respectively 0.9999 and 0.0001 of the area under the curve. In so doing, of course, we increase the probability of a Type II error, for we increase the portion of the area under curve B that lies in the interval of acceptance for H_0. Conversely, we could move the point of division to c (see Fig. 8.1), which would, under the conditions here pictured, reduce to a negligible figure the probability of an error of Type II, but would increase materially the probability of an error of Type I.

A major criterion for choosing among possible tests has to do with their relative effectiveness in avoiding errors of Type II. It is, of course, desirable that when a given hypothesis H_0 is in fact false, the sample point E should fall in the critical region w, which is the region of rejection. When this occurs, the test is successful in detecting a false hypothesis. The probability that the test will do this is the measure of its *power*. Of two tests that are alike in respect of the probability of a Type I error, that one is the more powerful which is the more effective in detecting false hypotheses.

Neyman and Pearson have stressed one other criterion for use in evaluation of tests of hypotheses—that of bias. A stated hypothesis H_0, being tested, is either true or false. We should not like to reject it if it is true; we should like to reject it if it is false. If a given test is less likely to reject H_0 when it is true than when it is not true, the test is said to be *unbiased*. This is to say, for an unbiased test the probability that a stated hypothesis will be rejected is always a minimum when the hypothesis tested is true.

The object sought in the application of these various criteria is, of course, to minimize the chance of making a mistake, whether of Type I or of Type II. To this end, we wish to employ a technique that has high powers of discrimination—that will enable us to identify and thus to accept true hypotheses, and to identify and thus to reject false hypotheses.

The problem is not a simple one, nor have definitive solutions been reached for all problems of this sort. One important complexity arises out of the fact that in a particular case there may be many alternative false hypotheses, not merely one that may be set against a single true hypothesis. Thus we face a series of comparisons: H_0 the true hypothesis versus H_1' a given false hypothesis; H_0 against H_1'', another false hypothesis; H_0 against H_1''', a third false hypothesis, etc. For a fixed probability of a

Type I error, critical regions may vary from comparison to comparison.

Consider, as an example of this situation, the problem that is faced when one wishes to test the hypothesis that a sample yielding a given mean, say $\overline{X} = 38$, has been drawn from a parent population with mean $\mu = 40$. That is, the hypothesis H_0, which is true, is that $\mu = 40$. Actually there are a great many possible alternative hypotheses—that $\mu = 25$, that $\mu = 39$, that $\mu = 52$, etc. If, in fact, the hypothesis H_0 is true, a Type II error would be committed if the false hypothesis H_1' that $\mu = 25$ were accepted. But the Type II risk is very slight in this case, the difference between the true hypothesis and the false one being great. But for the alternative hypotheses $H_0 = 40$ and $H_1'' = 39$, the situation is different. The difference between the true and the false hypotheses is very small. The danger of a Type II error (which would be committed if the false hypothesis H_1'' were accepted) is very much greater than in the first example. Similarly, for other possible false hypotheses probabilities of a Type II error will vary. Which is to say, the critical region w' for one test will not be the same as the critical region w'' for another test.

It will be true, under rare circumstances, that there is one critical region that provides the best test for all admissible alternatives. That is, for a given Type I risk the test corresponding to this particular critical region reduces to a minimum the probability of a Type II error regardless of which alternative hypothesis is considered. Such a test is called a *uniformly most powerful test*. It is the most powerful in detecting all false hypotheses. This, of course, is a happy situation for the investigator. It is rarely encountered, however, unless the family of alternative hypotheses is deliberately restricted. Usually the statistician must content himself with tests that fall short of being "best," in this sense. This being so, the choice of tests calls for discrimination, and for the utilization of all information relevant to a given situation.

The examples that follow illustrate procedures that are employed in testing various statistical hypotheses. (Applications of other tests will be given in later chapters.) These specific examples will give a measure of concreteness to the general statements about the theory of tests of significance. The examples to be cited are simple, intended only to indicate the nature of such tests and to suggest their fruitfulness.

Some Tests of Significance

Significance of a Mean. Weldon's data (see Table 6-1), relating to results obtained from tossing dice, present a typical problem. It will be recalled that since the appearance of a 4, 5, or 6 spot was counted as a success, $p = 0.5$, and $q = 0.5$; 12 dice were tossed on each throw, hence $n = 12$; the number of throws, 4096, gives us the value of N. The theoretical value of the mean result is 6 $(= np)$; the theoretical value of the standard deviation is 1.732 $(= \sqrt{npq})$. The actual mean $\overline{X}$ was 6.139. Could this mean value have been obtained if the dice were actually true? Could our sample of 4096 tosses come from a population for which $\mu = 6$ and for which $\sigma = 1.732$?

At an earlier point we have discussed the sampling distribution of the arithmetic mean. We know that many means, derived from samples of size N drawn from a given parent population, will constitute a distribution having a mean (μ) equal to the mean of the parent population, and with standard deviation (σ_m) equal to $\sigma/\sqrt{N}$ (where σ is the standard deviation of the parent population and N is the sample size). With reference to our present problem, we know that the means of many samples drawn from a parent population with $\mu = 6.00$ and $\sigma = 1.732$ would be distributed normally with mean $= 6.00$ and $\sigma_m = 1.732/\sqrt{4096} = 0.027$. May we regard the mean we have actually obtained, 6.139, as a random member of such a distribution of arithmetic means?

The central measure in such a test is $\overline{X} - \mu$, the difference between sample mean and the mean of the assumed parent population. We set up the *null hypothesis* that the true difference is zero (the observed difference representing merely a random fluctuation). Are the observed facts consistent with this hypothesis?

In the application of the test we express the deviation of sample mean from hypothetical mean in units of the standard deviation of the distribution of the means. Thus we have

$$T = \frac{\overline{X} - \mu}{\sigma_m} \tag{8.1}$$

$$= \frac{6.139 - 6.00}{0.027} = 5.1$$

Since the distribution of sample means to which σ_m relates is normal (see p. 179), the quantity T, which measures a deviation from the mean of a normal distribution in units of the standard deviation of that distribution, is to be interpreted as a normal deviate. In the present case we have a deviation (from the mean of a normal distribution) equal to 5.1 standard deviations. Is such a deviation a likely occurrence? The answer, of course, is No. If our sample mean 6.139 is to be regarded as actually a member of a population of means having an average value of 6.00 and a standard deviation of 0.027, it represents an event that is to be expected less than 1 time in 1,000,000. Such an event is so improbable that we must dismiss it as a possibility. Chance could not have accounted for such a large deviation. We conclude: The observed facts are not consistent with the null hypothesis, which must therefore be rejected. This leaves us with the positive conclusion that the mean of the parent population from which the sample was drawn was not 6.00; the dice were not balanced and true. The rejection, it is to be noted, must be in terms of probability. It is not impossible that true dice would, in a very rare combination, yield results of the kind we have observed. But when the probability of such results is so small (if the hypothesis in question were in fact true) that only a miracle, in effect, would account for them, we may with high confidence reject the hypothesis.

A question of central importance must be faced here: How small should be the probability (corresponding to a particular deviate T) to warrant rejection of a stated hypothesis? Where should we set the significance level? We must answer, first, that the setting of such a boundary must be in part arbitrary. What one investigator would regard as highly improbable might be regarded by a temperamentally more optimistic man as not unlikely. However, as we have noted on earlier pages, there is a general consensus that sets the limit of customary rejection at either $P = 0.05$ or $P = 0.01$. In using the lower of the two as the limit, we would say: The event that can happen only 1 time out of 100, or less frequently, does not happen in ordinary experience. Therefore, if T is equal to or greater than 2.576 the hypothesis is to be rejected. The same type of reasoning would be used for a limit set at $P = 0.05$ (for which the normal deviate T would equal 1.96), except that an event happening only 1 time in 20, or less frequently, would be regarded as too unlikely to warrant acceptance of the hypothesis.

When we say that a T of 2.576 represents a deviation that will be reached or exceeded only 1 time in 100, we are taking account of deviations *above and below* the hypothetical true mean. In the particular case we are dealing with, the sample mean 6.139 *exceeds* the hypothetical mean 6.00, but in testing the significance of such a difference it is usually proper to ask whether such an *absolute* difference, regardless of sign, may be attributed to chance. We have no reason in this case to expect bias in one direction, rather than the other, or to formulate a hypothesis involving deviations in one direction only. In other words, the appropriate test in this instance is a two-tailed test, meaning that in interpreting T we take account of areas in both tails of the normal distribution. The region of rejection includes both extremes of that distribution. There are cases in which deviations in one direction only are of concern; in these cases a one-tailed test is appropriate.

We have suggested above that it is well to consider the possible consequences of errors of Type I and Type II, in choosing boundaries of the region of rejection. If one believes that an error of the first kind (i.e., the rejection of a true hypothesis) is particularly undesirable, the significance level of the test may be pushed out. Thus one might decide to reject a stated hypothesis only in case of a divergence between observed and hypothetical values so great that it would occur only 1 time out of 1,000, or less frequently. That is, the value of T in such a test as that cited above would have to be 3.291, or greater, to warrant the conclusion that the observations were inconsistent with the hypothesis. On the other hand, if the danger of accepting a false hypothesis were particularly to be avoided, one might work with a significance level of 0.10 (corresponding to a T of 1.645). By this means we would reduce the likelihood of accepting a false hypothesis, although we should thereby increase the probability of rejecting a true hypothesis. Thus the selection of the significance level is a problem that is in some ways peculiar to each test, to be solved by the individual investigator. The Weldon problem that has served as our illustration above involves no special considerations one way or the other, since its interest is historical. But to one making professional use of dice the matter would be of particular concern. For the acceptance of dice as accurate when they are not (a Type II error) would affect the hazards of play to the presumed disadvantage of one party.

A somewhat different example is provided by data relating to the financial experience of buyers and sellers of securities. Table

8-1, which is taken from the report of an exhaustive study by Paul F. Wendt, shows the distribution of customers of a New York Stock Exchange firm, classified by amounts of realized profits, or losses. The sample here represented was chosen by random processes from among all customers whose invested capital amounted to less than $5,000. The trading experience recorded fell between 1933 and 1938. The mean of the distribution shown in Table 8-1 is + $135.44. The estimated standard deviation of the population, s', is $1,214.90.

The universe of which this is a random sample is the total of all small investors (a group defined as those whose capital investment did not exceed $5,000) purchasing securities through member firms of the New York Stock Exchange during the period 1933-38. It is of some interest to know whether such investors gained or lost, on the whole, in this period. We may set up the null hypothesis that the true mean of realized profits and losses of this group was zero. Are the sample results consistent with this hypothesis? It seems appropriate to use a probability level of 0.01 in this test.

The test to be made is similar in form to that applied in the preceding case, except that we now have no information about the degree of dispersion in the parent population except that which is afforded by the sample. Accordingly, in estimating the standard error of the mean, we must use s' as an estimate of the population σ. Thus

$$s_m = \frac{s'}{\sqrt{N}} = \frac{1214.90}{\sqrt{395}} = 61.13$$

For the measure T, which expresses the difference between sample mean and hypothetical mean in units of the standard error of the mean, we have,

$$T = \frac{\overline{X} - \mu}{s_m} = \frac{135.44 - 0}{61.13} = 2.22$$

This is to be interpreted as a normal deviate; a distribution of arithmetic means of samples of the size here considered would be normal. Moreover, we should use a two-tailed test, since in testing the hypothesis we should take account of the possibility of deviations on the loss side as well as on the profit side. A deviation

TABLE 8–1

Frequency Distribution Showing the Investment Experience of 395 Customers
of a New York Stock Exchange Firm, 1933-1938*
(Realized profits and losses in a random sample of accounts having
invested capital of less than $5,000)

Class-interval† (dollars)	Midpoint (dollars)	Frequency
− 9,000 to − 8,000	− 8,500	1
− 4,000 to − 3,000	− 3,500	2
− 3,000 to − 2,000	− 2,500	7
− 2,000 to − 1,000	− 1,500	15
− 1,000 to 0	− 500	147
0 to + 1,000	+ 500	187
+ 1,000 to + 2,000	+ 1,500	23
+ 2,000 to + 3,000	+ 2,500	5
+ 3,000 to + 4,000	+ 3,500	2
+ 4,000 to + 5,000	+ 4,500	3
+ 5,000 to + 6,000	+ 5,500	1
+ 6,000 to + 7,000	+ 6,500	1
+ 9,000 to + 10,000	+ 9,500	1
		395

* Wendt, Ref. 189, p. 31.
† An entry exactly at the upper limit of any class, say with profits of $2,000, was put in the class next above.

of the magnitude here observed would occur, in a normal distribution, about 2.6 times in 100 trials. At the significance level we have set up, a difference as great as the one here recorded between the sample mean and the hypothetical value zero could occur as the result of random sampling fluctuations. We must conclude that the observations are not inconsistent with the hypothesis that small investors, on the whole, neither gained nor lost in the period 1933-38; we therefore accept the hypothesis.

Significance of a Difference between Two Means. A problem that arises frequently in statistical investigations is that of determining whether two samples could have been drawn from the same parent population, or from parent populations which are alike in respect of some stated parameter. There would, of course, solely as a result of sampling fluctuations, be some difference between corresponding measurements derived from two samples drawn by random methods from the same universe. Arithmetic means would differ; measures of dispersion or of skewness would differ. This problem may be approached by comparing any two statistics (e.g., standard deviations of two samples), or by comparing the frequency distributions of the two samples, in full. Usually interest attaches to particular statistics. Do the mean incomes of doctors and lawyers differ significantly? Is the standard deviation of hourly earnings greater among textile workers than among steel workers? At this point we consider the procedure employed in testing the significance of the difference between two arithmetic means.

The office of the Surgeon General of the United States Army has recorded the heights of a sample of army inductees in 1943 and of a similar sample in 1917.[3] Summary measures follow:

	1943 sample	1917 sample
N	67,995	868,445
Mean height	68.11 inches	67.49 inches
Standard deviation	2.59 inches	2.71 inches

Are these results consistent with the hypothesis that the 1943 and the 1917 samples came from parent populations with equal arithmetic means? The null hypothesis is a statement, in effect, that no change occurred between 1917 and 1943 in the average height of American males of service age.

The measure that concerns us is D, the difference between the two arithmetic means. In the present case $D = 68.11 - 67.49$, or $+ 0.62$. The null hypothesis specifies that the true difference between the means is zero. If we were in fact drawing successive pairs of samples from parent populations with the same mean we should obtain a series of values of D, some plus, and some minus. The sampling distribution of D's thus derived has been established. The D's would be distributed in accordance with the normal law about a mean value zero. The parameter of this sampling distribution of immediate concern to us is its standard deviation. How great would the dispersion of these sample D's be? It has been determined that under these conditions the dispersion of D's would be measured by

$$\sigma_D = \sqrt{\frac{\sigma_1^2}{N_1} + \frac{\sigma_2^2}{N_2}} \tag{8.2}$$

where σ_1 is the standard deviation of the population from which the first sample comes, σ_2 is the standard deviation of the popula-

---

[3] "Height and Weight Data for Men Inducted into the Army and for Rejected Men." *Report No. 1-BM*, Army Service Forces, Office of the Surgeon General, Medical Statistics Division.

tion from which the second sample comes, and the two N's define the numbers of observations in the two samples. In fact we do not know the two σ's. We substitute for them the s's of the corresponding samples. We have, therefore, as our estimate of σ_D

$$s_D = \sqrt{\frac{s_1^2}{N_1} + \frac{s_2^2}{N_2}} \qquad (8.3)$$

(In view of the size of the samples we may neglect the loss of one degree of freedom in estimating s.) Formula (8.3) may be put in the form

$$s_D = \sqrt{s_{m_1}^2 + s_{m_2}^2} \qquad (8.4)$$

where each s_m is the standard error of the mean of a given sample.

In testing the null hypothesis in this case we shall use a confidence level of 0.01. The measurement needed for this test, derived from formula (8.3), is

$$s_D = \sqrt{\frac{2.59^2}{67,995} + \frac{2.71^2}{868,445}}$$
$$= \sqrt{0.000106}$$
$$= 0.01$$

The test is made in terms of T, the discrepancy between the observed D and the hypothetical value zero, expressed in units of the standard error of D. Thus we have

$$T = \frac{D - 0}{s_D} \qquad (8.5)$$
$$= \frac{0.62 - 0}{0.01}$$
$$= 62.0$$

This value of T, regarded as a normal deviate, represents an infinitely small probability. The observed difference between the sample means of 1943 inductees and 1917 recruits is far too great to be attributed to the play of chance. We may reject the null hypothesis with a very high degree of confidence. The two samples did not come from populations with equal arithmetic means.[4]

[4] If we had been testing the hypothesis that the two samples came from the same parent population, we should have regarded the two sample variances s_1^2 and s_2^2 as estimates of the same population variance. It would be appropriate in this case to use deviations from the two sample means as bases for a single pooled estimate of the population variance, using this single variance as the numerator of each of the terms under the radical sign in formula (8.3). See formulas (8.16) and (8.17) for a similar procedure with small samples.

In the example just cited the test relates to the standard error of the difference between independent random variables. As in earlier illustrations, we treat the mean of the 1943 sample as one value of a random variable. Other values of the variable would be the means of similar samples drawn from the same parent population. Similarly, the mean of the 1917 sample is regarded as an observed value of a random variable. The following general rule holds: *The standard error of the difference between two independent random variables is equal to the square root of the sum of their variances.* This is precisely what we have in formula (8.4). (The standard error of the *sum* of two independent random variables is also equal to the square root of the sum of their variances.) Emphasis should be placed on the word *independent*. If the random variables compared (in this case the means) are not independent, the standard error of their difference will be reduced by an amount depending on the degree of correlation between the two variables, while the standard error of their sum will be correspondingly increased.[5] In the present instance the variables are completely independent. As an example of related variables we may cite the discount rates of commercial banks and of Federal Reserve banks, discussed in the following chapter. These rates are not independent random variables, for commercial bank rates in a given district are immediately affected by changes in Federal Reserve rates in that district. The standard error of the difference between the means of these two sets of rates would not be given by formula (8.2).

For tests of this sort, when samples are large, it is not necessary that the parent populations from which the samples come be normal in their distribution. For samples of the size here considered the distributions of means would be normal, and the distribution of D's would be normal, whether parent populations were normal or not. For the full accuracy of such tests, equality of the variances of the parent populations from which the samples come is a necessary condition when samples are small and unequal in size. (Other considerations enter also when samples are small, as we shall see.) For large samples, however, a difference between population variances will not invalidate the test.

---

[5] The general concept of correlation will be introduced in Chapter 9. In the meantime the student unfamiliar with the concept may simply take the term to be synonymous with nonindependent.

Significance of a Difference between Two Standard Deviations. In Table 8-2 we have distributions of workers in industrial chemical plants in New England and in southeastern states, the workers being classified on the basis of straight-time hourly earnings in 1946. The average hourly wages in the two districts differ substantially; for New England plants the average rate was 104.50

TABLE 8–2

Distributions of Workers in Industrial Chemical Plants by Straight-Time Average Earnings, January, 1946, New England and the Southeast*

(1)	(2)	(3)
Average hourly earnings† (cents)	Number of workers	
	New England	Southeast
30.0— 39.9	1	0
40.0— 49.9	0	2
50.0— 59.9	23	326
60.0— 69.9	74	500
70.0— 79.9	184	368
80.0— 89.9	174	202
90.0— 99.9	119	174
100.0—109.9	312	150
110.0—119.9	428	154
120.0—129.9	145	72
130.0—139.9	117	22
140.0—149.9	22	6
150.0—159.9	9	4
160.0—169.9	0	8
170.0—179.9	5	4
180.0—189.9	2	2
190.0—199.9	2	
200.0 209.9	5	
210.0 219.9	2	
220.0 229.9	1	
Total	1,625	1,994

* Source: Wage Analysis Branch, U. S. Bureau of Labor Statistics.
† Excludes premium pay for overtime and night work.

cents per hour, while in the Southeast it was 80.81 cents. Are the standard deviations of the distributions of wages in the two districts significantly different?

We have cited above the general rule that the standard error of the difference between two independent random variables is equal to the square root of the sum of their variances. The random variables we here deal with are standard deviations; the standard deviation of each of the two distributions is regarded as a member of a population of such measures, a population that could be derived from successive samples from the same parent population. The variance of each of the standard deviations is, of course, the square of its standard error. This rule is applicable to the present problem.

Using the symbol $s_{s_1-s_2}$ for the standard error of the difference between two standard deviations, and $s_{s_1}^2$ and $s_{s_2}^2$ for the respective variances of these standard deviations, we have

$$s_{s_1-s_2} = \sqrt{s_{s_1}^2 + s_{s_2}^2} \tag{8.6}$$

When the parent populations are normal the variance of each standard deviation may be estimated from the relation $s_s^2 = \dfrac{s^2}{2N}$, where the s of the right-hand member is the standard deviation of the sample, used as an estimate of the population standard deviation. Since we may not assume that the two distributions given in Table 8-2 are normal, we shall derive estimates of the variances of the two standard deviations from the more general relation previously cited

$$s_s^2 = \frac{m_4 - m_2^2}{4m_2 \cdot N}$$

The m's in this equation are moments about the mean.

Following are the relevant measures for wage earners in the two groups of industrial chemical plants:

New England	Southeast
$s = 23.16$	$s = 22.72$
$s_s^2 = 0.336$	$s_s^2 = 0.193$

The difference between the standard deviations is 0.44. For the standard error of this difference we have

$$s_{s_1-s_2} = \sqrt{0.336 + 0.193} = 0.727$$

Expressing the difference in units of its standard error,

$$T = \frac{0.44}{0.727} = 0.605$$

The difference between the two standard deviations is clearly nonsignificant.[6]

---

[6] In Chapter 16 we shall deal with a broad range of problems involving the comparisons of standard deviations and variances, and shall develop other methods of analysis.

Significance of a Difference between Proportions. Another test of great practical utility involves the comparison of proportions, or percentages. We may have for samples for each of two industries the percentage of workers unemployed at a given time. Is an observed difference attributable to chance, or does it provide evidence of a real difference between the industries in the incidence of unemployment? The percentage of short business cycles recorded for the United States is smaller than the percentage of short cycles in the experience of Great Britain. Is the observed difference in relative frequencies indicative of a real difference between the forces determining cycle durations in the two countries?

For the standard error of a proportion, such as f_s/n (f_s being the frequency of successes and n the total number of independent events), we have
$$\sigma_p = \sqrt{pq/n} \tag{8.7}$$
where p is the proportion in question and q is $1 - p$.

In a problem of the type here in question, the critical figure is the difference between relative frequencies, or proportions. If two measures of relative frequency are independent of one another we may apply the general rule cited above for the standard error of the difference between two independent random variables (p. 220). Each of the two proportions is here regarded as a member of a series of random variables. In testing the relevant null hypothesis, the variance of the first random variable is $\bar{p}\bar{q}/n_1$; the variance of the second is $\bar{p}\bar{q}/n_2$. (Here p, the weighted mean proportion $(n_1p_1 + n_2p_2)/(n_1 + n_2)$, is our best estimate of the population p.) The two variances differ only in respect of n, for by hypothesis the samples come from the same universe. Thus we have
$$s_{p_1 - p_2} = \sqrt{\frac{\bar{p}\bar{q}}{n_1} + \frac{\bar{p}\bar{q}}{n_2}} \tag{8.8}$$
where $s_{p_1 - p_2}$ is the estimated standard error of the difference between two proportions.

To illustrate the use of this test we may use data cited by Wendt in his study of the financial experience of customers of a Stock Exchange firm for the period 1933-38. Wendt divided the members of a sample of 285 customers into an "investment" group, whose dealings were largely in bonds and in dividend-paying common and preferred stocks, and a "speculative" group, whose dealings were largely in low-priced, speculative shares.[7] Of 98 customers in the

---

[7] Wendt, Ref. 189, pp. 149-158. What I have here termed the "speculative" group is Wendt's "full-lot speculative."

investment group 68 showed profits while 30 showed losses. (These are *realized* profits and losses. The record was less favorable after adjustment for book profits and losses.) Thus we have $p_1 = 68/98$, or 0.694; $q_1 = 1 - 0.694 = 0.306$. In the speculative group 105 customers out of 187 showed profits, while 82 showed losses. Therefore $p_2 = 105/187 = 0.561$; $q_2 = 0.439$. The investment group, as here sampled, fared better in respect of realized gains than did the speculative group. For the difference between p_1 and p_2 we have $0.694 - 0.561$, or 0.133. Is this difference indicative of a real difference between the "populations" from which the investment and speculative samples come? In this test we shall use an 0.01 level of significance.

On the assumption that the conditions of simple sampling (see p. 203) prevailed in Wendt's operations, we may estimate the standard error of the difference between the two proportions from the relation shown in formula (8.8) on page 223. The weighted mean proportions are $\bar{p} = 0.607$, $\bar{q} = 0.393$. Thus we have

$$s_{p_1-p_2} = \sqrt{\frac{0.2386}{98} + \frac{0.2386}{187}}$$

$$= 0.061$$

The observed difference between the two proportions is 0.133. We set up the null hypothesis, that the true difference between the two relative frequencies in the populations from which they come is zero. In applying the test for significance we are asking, therefore, whether the quantity 0.133 may be regarded as a single observation on a normally distributed variate with a mean of zero and a standard deviation of 0.061. (The distribution of the quantity $p_1 - p_2$ will approach normality for large samples. We may therefore assume normality in the present instance, although with small samples this assumption would not be warranted.) Expressing the deviation of the observed difference from the hypothetical difference in units of the standard error of the difference, we have

$$T = \frac{0.133 - 0}{0.061} = 2.18$$

A deviation as great as this, or greater, might be encountered about 2.9 times in 100 trials as a result of chance fluctuations. Since we are working with an 0.01 criterion in this case, we are not justified in rejecting the hypothesis. The difference is large enough, it is true, to suggest that the parent population of which the investment group was a sample fared somewhat better in realized gains than did the "speculative" population. But the difference is not clearly significant.

In the following example we have "population" values for the p's and q's, together with values from a sample drawn from the parent population. The *World Almanac* has reported that 8.28 percent of all males in the United States are named John; 0.43 percent are named Clarence. Of a sample of 400,000 males having common surnames (such as Smith, Brown, or Jones) 5.48 percent were named John, 1.04 named Clarence. These proportions suggest that parents whose surnames are common are less likely than are parents with uncommon surnames to select a common given name for their sons, and more likely to select a relatively uncommon given name. In this case, since we have a population value, we may estimate the standard error of a proportion from the general expression for the standard deviation of a distribution of relative frequencies, $\sqrt{pq/n}$. We may ask: Does the proportion of males in the sample who are named John, 0.0548, differ materially from the universe proportion, 0.0828? For a sample of this size

$$s_p = \sqrt{\frac{0.0828 \times 0.9172}{400,000}} = 0.000436$$

We here use the universe values of p and of q, and the N of the sample for the n (the number of independent events) of the formula. The test then takes the form

$$T = \frac{p_0 - p_a}{s_p} \qquad (8.9)$$

where p_0 is the observed proportion of males named John in the sample of 400,000, p_a is the anticipated proportion, on the hypothesis that the probability of a male having the given name of John is the same in the sample of 400,000 as in the general population, and s_p is the standard error of the proportion in question for samples of 400,000. In this case

$$T = \frac{0.0548 - 0.0828}{0.000436} = -64.2$$

This value of T, interpreted as a normal deviate, represents, of course, a deviation so extreme as to be impossible. The probability of being named John is significantly smaller for the members of the group with common surnames than it is for members of the population of males at large. A similar test applied to the sample proportion named Clarence also indicates a clearly significant difference, the sample proportion this time being in excess of the universe proportion.

Generalizing from Small Samples; the *t*-Distribution

In applying the tests discussed in preceding pages we have made use of the fortunate fact that the sampling distributions of many statistics tend toward normality as n increases. This condition of asymptotic normality makes it possible to test for significance many measurements derived from large samples without special attention to the exact form of the sampling distributions in question, or to the form of the parent populations from which the samples were drawn. But when samples are small, procedures valid for large samples may be very crude and inaccurate. If one must make a decision on a sample including only 6 or 8 observations it is of little help to know that a statistic derived from a sample of 1,000 observations would be a normally distributed variable. If rational action is to be taken in such a case we need more exact knowledge of distributions of sample characteristics, for samples drawn from specified parent populations. Pioneer work in this field has been done by "Student" (W. S. Gosset), R. A. Fisher, and others, but our knowledge of exact sampling distributions is still limited in scope. Within certain not unimportant areas, however, we can generalize from small samples with a fair measure of confidence. At this point we shall discuss one such sampling distribution, the first to be accurately defined, and shall exemplify some of its uses.

We have made use in earlier pages of the fundamental fact that the deviation of a sample mean from the mean of a parent population, when this deviation is expressed in units of the standard error of the sample mean, gives a quantity T which may be interpreted as a normal deviate.[8] That is

$$T = \frac{\overline{X} - \mu}{\sigma_m} \tag{8.10}$$

T may be taken to be a normal deviate for large samples even when we have to approximate σ_m with s_m, the latter being an

---

[8] I should emphasize that the symbol T, as here used, is not to be confused with Hotelling's T, the generalized Student ratio.

estimate of the standard error of the mean based on the information provided by the sample alone. The formula for T, thus derived, is

$$T = \frac{\overline{X} - \mu}{s/\sqrt{N - 1}} \tag{8.11}$$

where s is the standard deviation of the sample. T may be regarded as a ratio—the ratio of a normally distributed variate, $\overline{X} - \mu$, to its estimated standard error, $s/\sqrt{N - 1}$. If in place of s we should use $s'\,(= \sqrt{\Sigma d^2/N - 1})$, we should have

$$T = \frac{\overline{X} - \mu}{s'/\sqrt{N}}$$

When N is as large as 30 the error involved in interpreting T as a normal deviate is not appreciable, except for extreme deviations; if N is as large as 100 the error is very small indeed. But when N is small the expression given above for T does not yield a normal deviate. A consistent bias is introduced, one that leads to a persistent and, for very small samples, a very considerable departure from normality. For such small samples a method appropriate to large samples breaks down badly. Asymptotic normality then becomes a very weak reed on which to lean.

The Work of "Student." In the first decade of this century W. S. Gosset, who wrote under the pseudonym "Student," became aware of the deficiencies of the conventional ratio (which we have termed T above), when it was applied to small sample results. His studies indicated that the difficulty lay in unsuspected aberrations of s, the standard deviation derived from the sample.[9] The distribution of s for small samples, he discovered, departs systematically from the normal form. This leads to inaccuracy in the estimation of σ, and hence to faulty estimates of the standard error of the mean when the procedure appropriate to large samples is applied to small samples. Student was able to define the sampling distribution of s^2. He then investigated the distribution of the ratio $(\overline{X} - \mu)/s$, a quantity which has been termed z; in establishing its exact distribution Student made one of the great forward steps in sampling theory. (See Student, Ref. 153, 1908). Seventeen years later R. A. Fisher provided a more rigorous theoretical foundation

---

[9] F. R. Helmert had established the sampling distribution of s^2 some thirty years earlier, but this fact was not known to Gosset. See Deming and Birge, Ref. 31.

for Student's ratio, and at the same time put the ratio in the form in which it is now generally employed. This is

$$t = \frac{\overline{X} - \mu}{s/\sqrt{N-1}} \tag{8.12}$$

where $\overline{X}$ is the mean of a sample, μ is the mean of the parent population from which the sample has been drawn, s is the standard deviation of the sample (derived[10] from $\sqrt{\Sigma d^2/N}$) and N is the number of observations in the sample. (The distinctive feature of the formula for t, as will be brought out later, is that the s in the denominator is the sample s, used as such and not as an estimate of the population σ. The standard deviation of the population does not enter into the determination of t.) The quantity t, it is obvious, equals $z\sqrt{N-1}$, where z is Student's original ratio $(\overline{X} - \mu)/s$. The sampling distribution of t (which is sometimes spoken of as Student's t, sometimes as Fisher's t) is one of the fundamental instruments of sampling today. In considering this distribution and its uses we may first give attention to the nature of the bias that is present in s when samples are small.

The essential feature of the sampling distribution of s is effectively revealed by the results of an interesting experiment conducted by W. A. Shewhart.[11] Shewhart drew 1,000 samples, each consisting of four observations, from a normally distributed parent population with a known standard deviation, equal to unity. The standard deviation, s, of each sample was computed, with 4 as the divisor of Σd^2. The distribution of these 1,000 values of s is represented by the dots in Fig. 8.2.[12] (The line running through the dots defines the theoretical distribution of the s's to be expected, with samples of 4, on the basis of Student's theory. There is a notably close agreement between the theoretical and observed distributions.) Traditional sampling concepts would lead us to expect a normal distribution of s's, centered at 1, the value of σ in the parent population. Instead, the distribution is definitely skew, with the measurements clustering about a central tendency well below

---

[10] If instead of s we have s', derived from $\sqrt{\Sigma d^2/N-1}$, t would be given by $\dfrac{\overline{X} - \mu}{s'/\sqrt{N}}$.

[11] W. A. Shewhart, Ref. 140, 163-173, 185-6.

[12] The figure is here reproduced with the permission of Dr. Shewhart and his publishers.

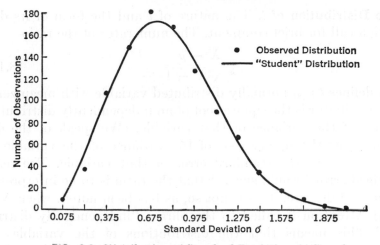

FIG. 8.2. Distribution of Standard Deviations in Samples of Four Drawn from a Normal Universe.

unity. The mode of the 1,000 values of s here represented is, in fact, 0.717 and the arithmetic mean is 0.801. There is a clear tendency for these s's, based on samples of 4, to understate the true value. As estimates of σ they are clearly biased.[13]

---

[13] The degree of error involved in using s as an approximation to σ, for small samples, is indicated by the following figures, taken from W. A. Shewhart (*loc. cit.*, 185). They define the relation between the modal s, for samples of size N drawn from a population of which the standard deviation is known, and the true σ of that population.

Size of sample N	Modal s as a decimal fraction of true σ
3	.577
4	.707
5	.775
6	.817
7	.845
8	.866
9	.882
10	.894
15	.931
20	.949
25	.959
30	.966
50	.980
100	.990

The fractions given above define relations that are to be expected on the basis of error theory, as modified by Student to take account of conditions affecting small samples. The modal value of the 1,000 standard deviations obtained by Shewhart in his empirical test of this theory was, as we have seen, .717 of the standard deviation of the universe. This result is very close indeed to the expected value of .707, for samples in which $N = 4$.

The Distribution of t**.** The nature of t and the form of its distribution call for brief comment. The numerator of the ratio

$$\frac{\overline{X} - \mu}{s/\sqrt{N-1}} \tag{8.13}$$

which defines t is a normally distributed variable with mean zero; the denominator is the square root of an independently distributed estimate of the variance of that variable. (We speak of the denominator as the square root of the variance of the variable in question, not as the standard error of that variable. The term "standard error" would suggest that the ratio is to be interpreted as a normal deviate. This is not so, as has been noted, when N is small.) Attention is called to the phrase "independently distributed." This means that the distributions of the variables in numerator and denominator of expression (8.13) are independent of one another. This is an essential condition. Only when $\overline{X}$ and s^2 are independent variables is the ratio given by formula (8.13) distributed in the form defined by Student and Fisher. *This condition holds only for samples drawn from a normal parent population.* In a single sample thus drawn, $\overline{X}$ may be small (i.e., well below μ in value) and s^2 large (i.e., well above σ^2 in value); in another sample $\overline{X}$ may be large and s^2 small; in a third sample both may be small, or both large. The sampling distribution of t is restricted, in its fully accurate applications, to samples from normal parent distributions.

We have noted above that no population parameter is involved in the derivation of the t ratio. In the computation of T, for testing the deviation of a sample mean from an assumed population mean (formula 8.10), we use σ; when we do not know σ we use s', a quantity derived from the sample but used as an approximation to σ. But in the computation of t, only the sample mean and the standard deviation of the sample (and, of course, N) are employed. Herein lies its great value. *The theoretical distribution of t relates to a quantity derivable from observations.*

The distribution of t may be defined by the equation

$$y = \frac{y_0}{\left(1 + \dfrac{t^2}{n}\right)^{\left(\frac{n+1}{2}\right)}} \tag{8.14}$$

In this expression y is an ordinate at a stated distance t from an origin at zero on the t-scale; y_0 is the maximum ordinate at $t = 0$;

n is the number of degrees of freedom of t. This will be $N - 1$ in a problem of the type here discussed; in other cases more than one degree of freedom may be lost. It will be clear that from the maximum ordinate at zero on the t-scale the t-curve falls away symmetrically for plus and minus values of t. For very small values of n the curve is flat-topped, with a larger proportion of the area in the tails than is found in a corresponding normal distribution. Since areas under the curve are to be interpreted as relative frequencies, or probabilities, this fact means that large deviations from the mean are more probable for the t-distribution than for the normal distribution. As n gets larger the t-distribution approaches the normal form. With n as large as 30, as we have noted, the difference is small. Relations between t-distributions and the normal form are shown in Fig. 8.3, in which are plotted t-curves for $n = 2$ and $n = 25$, together with a normal frequency curve.

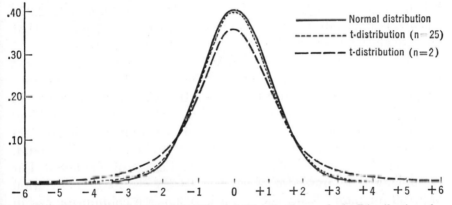

FIG. 8.3. Frequency Curves of the Normal Distribution and of t-Distributions for $n = 2$ and $n = 25$.

Tabulations of the t-distribution greatly facilitate the use of this measure in practice. Extracts from two such tabulations are given in Table 8-3. The entries in Part A of that table define the percentile values of t for varying values of n. As has been indicated above, the form of the distribution varies as n changes. There is a specific distribution of t for every value of n.

We may briefly explain the entries in Part A of Table 8-3. If we had a graph of the t-distribution for $n = 10$, an ordinate erected on the horizontal scale (the t-scale) at a point 2.764 units to the left of the mean would cut off a tail that included 0.01 of the total area under the curve. As for the normal distribution, such a proportion is to be read as a probability. There is only 1 chance out of 100 that a random drawing from such a distribution would give a measure falling in this tail of the distribution. The figure cited, 2.764, which is the first percentile value of t for a distribution with 10 degrees of freedom, is found in the column headed $t_{.01}$ (the subscript to t defines the percentile) in the line for which $n = 10$. Since the distribution is symmetrical, the 99th percentile value of t ($t_{.99}$) is also 2.764, but this represents a point to the right of the mean. (Deviations to the left of the mean, corresponding to percentiles below 0.50, are, of course, negative; those corresponding to percentiles above 0.50 are positive. These signs are not given in the table, but will be understood.)[14]

Since the form of the t-distribution varies with n, the percentile values of t in a given column of Part A of Table 8-3 change from line to line. Thus, at the 99th percentile, t is 31.821 when n is 1; it is 6.965 when n is 2, drops to 2.457 when n is 30, and to 2.326 when n is infinitely large. These reductions mean, of course, that large deviations become less and less likely, as n increases.

The entries in Part B of Table 8-3 are those given in most presentations of the t-distribution. These are the measures that would be used in a two-tailed test, the kind usually made in employing the t-distribution. In making such a test we are asking: What is the probability of a given deviation (or one that is greater) *above or below* the mean of the t-distribution? This question could, if desired, be answered with reference to Part A of Table 8-3. For example, with a sample for which $n = 10$, the chance of a deviation of 3.169 (or more) *below* the mean is 0.005 (see column for $t_{.005}$ in Part A); the chance of a deviation of 3.169 (or more) *above* the mean is 0.005 (see column headed $t_{.995}$ of Part A.) The sum of these probabilities, or 0.01, measures the probability of a deviation of 3.169, or more, in either direction. But we may obtain this combined probability more directly from the entries in Part B of Table 8-3. In the column headed 0.01 in the line for $n = 10$, we

---

[14] In using subscripts for percentiles, with the meaning indicated in the text, I am employing a notational scheme introduced by Dixon and Massey (Ref. 32) and followed by Walker and Lev (Ref. 186). This scheme differs from current practice (which is exemplified in Part B of Table 8-3) but is to be preferred as a simpler and more straightforward representation of the t-distribution. Strictly speaking, only the columns in Table 8-3 that give .01, .05, .95, and .99 values of t define percentiles; however, the fractional percentile values given, for $t_{.005}$ etc., are of special interest, as will appear.

TABLE 8–3

Part A: Distribution of *t*: Percentile Values

n	$t_{.005}$	$t_{.01}$	$t_{.025}$	$t_{.05}$	$t_{.95}$	$t_{.975}$	$t_{.99}$	$t_{.995}$
1	63.657	31.821	12.706	6.314	6.314	12.706	31.821	63.657
2	9.925	6.965	4.303	2.920	2.920	4.303	6.965	9.925
3	5.841	4.541	3.182	2.353	2.353	3.182	4.541	5.841
4	4.604	3.747	2.776	2.132	2.132	2.776	3.747	4.604
5	4.032	3.365	2.571	2.015	2.015	2.571	3.365	4.032
6	3.707	3.143	2.447	1.943	1.943	2.447	3.143	3.707
7	3.499	2.998	2.365	1.895	1.895	2.365	2.998	3.499
8	3.355	2.896	2.306	1.860	1.860	2.306	2.896	3.355
9	3.250	2.821	2.262	1.833	1.833	2.262	2.821	3.250
10	3.169	2.764	2.228	1.812	1.812	2.228	2.764	3.169
20	2.845	2.528	2.086	1.725	1.725	2.086	2.528	2.845
30	2.750	2.457	2.042	1.697	1.697	2.042	2.457	2.750
∞	2.576	2.326	1.960	1.645	1.645	1.960	2.326	2.576

Part B: Values of *t* Corresponding to Stated Probabilities in Two-Tailed Test

				Probability				
n	0.80	0.50	0.40	0.20	0.10	0.05	0.02	0.01
1	.325	1.000	1.376	3.078	6.314	12.706	31.821	63.657
2	.289	.816	1.061	1.886	2.920	4.303	6.965	9.925
3	.277	.765	.978	1.638	2.353	3.182	4.541	5.841
4	.271	.741	.941	1.533	2.132	2.776	3.747	4.604
5	.267	.727	.920	1.476	2.015	2.571	3.365	4.032
6	.265	.718	.906	1.440	1.943	2.447	3.143	3.707
7	.263	.711	.896	1.415	1.895	2.365	2.998	3.499
8	.262	.706	.889	1.397	1.860	2.306	2.896	3.355
9	.261	.703	.883	1.383	1.833	2.262	2.821	3.250
10	.260	.700	.879	1.372	1.812	2.228	2.764	3.169
20	.257	.687	.860	1.325	1.725	2.086	2.528	2.845
30	.256	.683	.854	1.310	1.697	2.042	2.457	2.750
∞	.253	.674	.842	1.282	1.645	1.960	2.326	2.576

The entries in Part B are extracts from a more detailed table (Table IV) in R. A. Fisher's *Statistical Methods for Research Workers*, Edinburgh, Oliver and Boyd. The table is printed here through the courtesy of Dr. Fisher and his publishers. (See also Fisher and Yates, *Statistical Tables*, Ref. 51.

find 3.169, the deviation that will be reached or exceeded 1 time in 100. The entries in Part B all refer to absolute deviations, i.e., without regard to sign. They are thus directly adapted for use in applying a two-tailed test, whereas the entries in Part A are adapted to a one-tailed test.

It will be noted that the several entries in Part B of Table 8-3 in the column for which the probability is 0.01 are the same as the corresponding entries in Part A in the columns headed $t_{.005}$ and $t_{.995}$; that the entries in Part B in the column for which the probability is 0.05 are the same as the corresponding entries in Part A in the columns headed $t_{.025}$ and $t_{.975}$. The reason for the identities has been indicated: the probability of a stated absolute deviation, as given in Part B, is the sum of the probabilities corresponding to the same deviation, plus and minus, as given in Part A.

The table of areas under the normal curve is usually given in a form comparable to that used in Part B of Table 8-3. In the last line (for which the entry in the n column is ∞) we have the familiar values of T (a normal deviate) corresponding to probabilities of 0.01, 0.05, etc. Thus for a probability of 0.01 the corresponding normal deviate is 2.57582. These entries in the last line of Part B of Table 8-3 are the limiting values of t, the values which t approaches, for stated probabilities, as n increases. For an n infinitely large, t and T coincide. Even for n as large as 30 the approach to the normal values is fairly close. Which means, of course, that we need resort to the t-distribution only when dealing with small samples.

Some Uses of the *t*-Distribution

Significance of a Mean: Small Samples. In determining whether the mean of a sample drawn from a normal population deviates significantly from a stated value (the hypothetical value of the population mean), we compute t from the ratio previously given:

$$t = \frac{\overline{X} - \mu}{s/\sqrt{N-1}}$$

In interpreting t when the arithmetic mean of a sample is being tested for significance, $n = N - 1$.

A study of interest rates paid on business loans by various classes of borrowers[15] revealed that large borrowers (i.e., those

---

[15] The study, made by the Board of Governors of the Federal Reserve System, related to loans outstanding in November, 1946. See Youngdahl, Ref. 198. The rates given for individual groups in this example are weighted averages of the rates paid by individual borrowers, weights being the dollar volume of loans outstanding at each rate. In combining rates for retail trade groups in the present example, to get an average for all retail trade, no weights were used.

with assets of \$5,000,000 or more) in five retail trade groups paid the following average rates:

Retail trade	Average interest rate on business loans Percent
Food, liquor, tobacco, and drugs	1.8
Apparel, dry goods, and dept. stores	1.9
Home furnishings, metal products, and building materials	2.0
Automobiles, parts, and filling stations	1.7
All other	2.2

The arithmetic average of these five group rates is 1.92 percent; the standard deviation s (derived with N as the divisor of the sum of squared deviations) is 0.172. Our problem is to determine whether the mean rate paid by these groups of large retail merchants differs significantly from the mean rate paid by all business borrowers in the United States. We shall here use 2.9 percent, the weighted mean of the average rates paid by 100 groups of business borrowers, as the population mean. It is appropriate to use a significance level of 0.01 in testing the null hypothesis in this case. For t we have

$$t = \frac{\overline{X} - \mu}{s/\sqrt{N-1}} = \frac{1.92 - 2.9}{0.172/\sqrt{5-1}} = \frac{-0.98}{0.086}$$

$$= -11.4$$

This test of significance should be a two-tailed test, since we are concerned with the probability of a deviation as great as 0.98 above or below the population mean. From Part B of Table 8-3 (or from Appendix Table III), we find that for $n = 4$, the value of t corresponding to a probability of 0.01 is 4.604. The observed value of t is far greater than this. On the level of significance here employed, we should reject the null hypothesis. The interest rates paid by large retail borrowers are significantly lower than those paid by business borrowers as a whole.

Setting Confidence Limits: Small Samples. The examples just cited have involved tests of hypotheses using small sample results. We revert briefly to *estimation*, with reference to the special problems that are faced when estimates of population parameters are based on small samples. The procedure employed is similar to that outlined in Chapter 7, for large samples, but use is made of the t-distribution rather than the normal distribution in setting limits corresponding to a chosen confidence level.

We have the following observations on the yield of alfalfa, in tons per acre, on four plots each of which received 18 inches of irrigation water during the growing season.[16]

5.69; 6.46; 7.02; 8.02

We are required to set confidence limits for the mean of the population from which this sample comes. For the sample we have

$$\overline{X} = 6.7975$$

$$s = \sqrt{\frac{\Sigma d^2}{N}} = 0.849$$

Consider the relation

$$t = \frac{\overline{X} - \mu}{s/\sqrt{N - 1}}$$

We have the values of s and N, hence the degrees of freedom $n \, (=N - 1)$. Let us say that the confidence level for the estimate is to be 0.95. Knowing P and n we may readily determine from the t-table the appropriate value of t. For a P of 0.05 and an n of 3, $t = 3.182$. The unknown quantity in the above equation is the numerator of the right-hand term, the range $\overline{X} - \mu$. We wish to set limits on either side of $\overline{X}$ within which we may, with the stated degrees of confidence, expect μ to fall. The desired range may be written (from the equation nine lines above)

$$\overline{X} - \mu = t \times s/\sqrt{N - 1} \tag{8.15}$$

$$= 3.182 \times (0.849/\sqrt{3})$$

$$= 1.5592$$

The desired limits of the confidence interval are thus 6.7975 ± 1.5592. Rounding off the fractions we may write this: 6.80 ± 1.56. We may say, with confidence measured by a probability of 0.95, that the mean of the population from which the sample comes falls between 5.24 tons and 8.36 tons.

We may take opportunity at this point to give an example of estimation from small samples that will serve, at once, to demonstrate modern procedures in interval-estimation and to illustrate the use of the t-distribution in such estimation. The data employed are from W. A. Shewhart (Ref. 140) and the graphic illustration

[16] Beckett and Robertson, Ref. 10.

given is taken, with permission, from the same author (Ref. 141, p. 59). Shewhart set up a normal universe with mean zero. From this universe he drew 100 samples, with four observations in each sample; for each sample he computed $\overline{X}$ and s (the latter derived with 4 as the divisor of Σd^2). On these two statistics for each sample he then based a statement setting confidence limits corresponding to a confidence level of 0.50. That is, each statement belonged to a family of statements of which, in the long run, one half would be expected to be true and one half false. The 100 samples thus provided bases for 100 estimates of confidence intervals.

The two following hypothetical sets of drawings will illustrate the procedure:

| Sample A | + 0.5, − 0.3, − 0.6, + 0.8 |
| Sample B | − 2.1, + 0.5, − 2.6, − 0.2 |

In the first sample the mean $\overline{X} = + 0.10$, $s = 0.570$. For a P of 0.50 and an n of 3, $t = 0.765$. Following the method employed in the preceding example, we compute

$$t \times s/\sqrt{N - 1} = 0.765 \times 0.570/1.732 = 0.25$$

Limits of the 0.50 confidence interval for an estimate of the population mean, based on this sample, are − 0.15 and + 0.35. (These, of course, are derived from + 0.10 − 0.25 and + 0.10 + 0.25). The second sample, of which the mean is − 1.0 and s is 1.366, provides the basis of a similar estimate. By an identical procedure we set 0.50 confidence limits at − 1.60 and − 0.40.

The evidence of the first sample warrants the statement, "The mean of the parent population lies between − 0.15 and + 0.35." The evidence of the second sample warrants the statement, "The mean of the parent population lies between − 1.60 and − 0.40." Since Shewhart's illustration was experimental, we know the parent mean. It is zero. Thus the first statement is true, the second is false. Shewhart's data provided him with bases for 100 such statements. The range and location of each of the 100 confidence intervals thus set up are shown in the left-hand panel of Fig. 8.4, which is reproduced from Shewhart's *Statistical Method from the Viewpoint of Quality Control.*

This figure is an illuminating representation of statistical inference. The heavy horizontal bar is drawn at zero on the vertical scale, that is, at the value of the population mean. Each

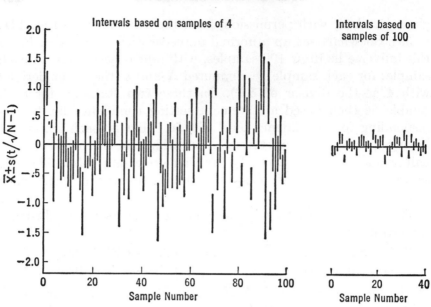

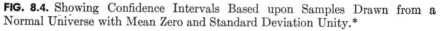

FIG. 8.4. Showing Confidence Intervals Based upon Samples Drawn from a Normal Universe with Mean Zero and Standard Deviation Unity.*

* Reproduced with permission from W. A. Shewhart, *Statistical Method from the Viewpoint of Quality Control*, Washington, D. C., The Graduate School, U. S. Department of Agriculture, 1939.

vertical line depicts a confidence interval based on one of the 100 samples. The center of each vertical line is located at the value of a sample mean. The range of the corresponding confidence interval above and below that sample mean is determined by an operation similar to that represented by formula (8.15) above.[17] The vertical lines differ greatly, it is clear, in the location of their midpoints, and in their range. If a sample mean fell close to the true mean of the population the center of the corresponding bar would be close to the heavy central bar; if not, the center of the line would be far from the central bar. If the sample s were small the range of the corresponding vertical line would be narrow; if the sample s were large, the length of the corresponding vertical line would be great. In the diverse locations and varied lengths

[17] For the entries in this panel the range of each confidence interval is given by $\overline{X} \pm 0.4417s$, where s is the sample standard deviation. The coefficient 0.4417 is derived from $t/\sqrt{N-1}$ (i.e., from 0.765/1.732.) For present purposes it is convenient to divide by 1.732, the first term of the right-hand member of formula (8.15) instead of the first factor in the second term. That is, we divide t, instead of s, by $\sqrt{N-1}$, since s varies from sample to sample, while the other quantities do not. We may note that $t/\sqrt{N-1}$ is Student's original z (see p. 228).

of these vertical lines we have a vivid picture of the play of chance in shaping the results of sampling operations.

Yet, despite the diversity of sample results, a soundly based procedure makes rational estimation possible. According to sample theory approximately half of the confidence intervals set up by Shewhart should include the population mean (his confidence level was 0.50). If a given vertical line in Fig. 8.4 cuts across the heavy central line this means, of course, that the confidence interval in question does in fact include the population mean. It is of interest to note that 51 of the 100 confidence intervals represented on the diagram do in fact include the parent mean; 49 do not. The agreement with expected results is very close indeed.

The fact that small sample theory makes rational estimation possible when we have but a few observations does not, of course, remove the uncertainties from sampling procedures. Nor does it mean that small samples are as good as large ones. Apart from the consideration that the use of the *t*-distribution is fully accurate only with samples drawn from normal universes, the investigator who works with very small samples must know that his estimates will vary widely from sample to sample. Moreover, he must content himself with relatively wide confidence intervals. Precision of statement is less, of course, the wider the intervals employed. Large samples are more stable than small ones (in the sense that the means of large samples will be clustered much more closely about the population mean), and they permit more precision in inferences based on them.

These attributes of large samples, and their great superiority to small samples, are well illustrated by the right-hand panel of Fig. 8.4. This presents confidence intervals relating to the same parent population as does the left-hand panel. Here, however, each vertical line defines the limit of a confidence interval (at confidence level 0.50) designed to include the population mean, but based upon a sample of 100 observations.[18] The vertical scale is the same as for the left-hand panel, so the results may be compared. The centers of the vertical lines in the right-hand panel (these centers are located, as we have noted, at the sample means) are much more closely concentrated about the population mean. More striking, however, is the fact that the ranges of the confidence

---

[18] The range of each confidence interval in this case is given by $\overline{X} \pm 0.0769s$ (the value 0.0769 being derived from $t/\sqrt{N-1}$, or $0.765/\sqrt{99}$).

intervals based on samples of 100 are much smaller. Each inference drawn from large sample results is far more precise, in the limits it sets up, than is an inference based on a much smaller sample. (Of the 40 confidence intervals based on large samples, we may note, 45 percent include the population mean, while 55 percent do not. These percentages stand reasonably close to the long-run expectation of 50 percent right and 50 percent wrong.) The meaning of this is obvious, of course. Inferences based on small samples are inherently less reliable than inferences based on large samples. However, when we must infer from small samples, under the conditions set forth, we can have a trustworthy procedure.

Significance of a Difference between Two Means: Small Samples. The method we have employed above for testing the significance of the mean of a sample from a normal universe may be applied in determining whether the means of two samples differ significantly. This very important extension of Student's procedure, which is due to R. A. Fisher, is applicable in testing the hypothesis that the two samples whose means are compared are from the same normal parent population. Here, as in the previous example, Student's distribution gives us an unbiased test.

In form, this test follows that discussed above in dealing with the same problem for large samples. On the assumption that the samples are from the same population it is appropriate to pool the sums of the squared deviations from the respective means of the two samples in deriving a single s', which is our best estimate of the standard deviation of the population. Thus we have

$$s' = \sqrt{\frac{\Sigma d_1^2 + \Sigma d_2^2}{N_1 + N_2 - 2}} \qquad (8.16)$$

Having this estimate s', we compute the standard error of the difference between means from the customary formula

$$s_{\bar{x}_1 - \bar{x}_2} = \sqrt{\frac{s'^2}{N_1} + \frac{s'^2}{N_2}} \qquad (8.17)$$

$$= s'\sqrt{\frac{N_1 + N_2}{N_1 N_2}} \qquad (8.18)$$

The ratio of $\bar{X}_1 - \bar{X}_2$ to $s'\sqrt{(N_1 + N_2)/N_1 N_2}$ is distributed in the t-distribution. That is

$$t = \frac{\bar{X}_1 - \bar{X}_2}{s'\sqrt{\frac{N_1 + N_2}{N_1 N_2}}} = \frac{\bar{X}_1 - \bar{X}_2}{s'}\sqrt{\frac{N_1 N_2}{N_1 + N_2}} \qquad (8.19)$$

The quantity t, in this case, is to be interpreted with n, the degrees of freedom, equal to $N_1 + N_2 - 2$. (We may think of one degree of freedom being lost in the calculation of each of the two components of s', in formula (8.16) above.)

We may illustrate the application of a test of this sort by comparing a sample of six small cities with a sample of five large cities, in respect of average family expenditures on current consumption (Table 8-4). The unit observation for present purposes is

TABLE 8-4

Average Family Expenditures on Current Consumption in Samples of Small and Large Cities*

Small Cities	Average family expenditures on consumption	Large Cities	Average family expenditures on consumption
Grand Junction, Colo.	$3,538	Providence, R. I.	$3,916
Madill, Okla.	3,190	Milwaukee, Wis.	4,331
Camden, Ark.	3,094	Youngstown, Ohio	4,106
Garrett, Ind.	3,699	Kansas City, Mo.	3,989
Pulaski, Va.	3,326	Cincinnati, Ohio	4,186
Dalhart, Texas	3,548		
Average	3,399.17		4,117.60

* The data are from U. S. Bureau of Labor Statistics Bulletin 1097 (revised June, 1953), *Family Income, Expenditures and Savings in 1950.* In the present illustration cities with population of 2,500 to 30,500 are classed as small; those with population of 240,000 to 1,000,000 as large. Cities and metropolitan areas with populations of 1,000,000 and over are not included.

a city average of consumption expenditures by a sample of individual families resident in that city. (The number of families in such a sample ranged from 65 in small cities to 250 in the group of large cities.)

The figures cited in Table 8-4 indicate that family expenditures on current consumption are less in small cities than they are in large cities, but an objective test is needed. Again we shall use a significance level of 0.01. For the computation of s' (using the relations shown in formula 8.16) we have

$$s' = \sqrt{\frac{273,557 + 109,741}{11 - 2}} = 206.4$$

For t (from formula 8.19)

$$t = \frac{4{,}117.60 - 3{,}399.17}{206.4} \sqrt{\frac{30}{11}}$$

$$= 5.75$$

Consulting the t-table (Part B of Table 8-3, or Appendix Table III) we find that for $n = 9$ the value of t corresponding to a probability of 0.01 is 3.250. The present value is clearly significant. The two samples of cities could not have come from one homogeneous parent population. Average family expenditures for purposes of current consumption appear to be clearly higher in large cities than in small cities.

The hypothesis here tested is that two samples, the means of which are compared, come from the same normal universe. The direct test is applied to the difference between means, but since the sample s's enter into the calculations their values obviously affect the outcome. It is possible that a significant value of t might appear in a test of this sort because samples were drawn from populations with different standard deviations, rather than different means. This would lead, properly, to the rejection of the hypothesis, although the factor responsible for the rejection would not be a difference in means. But this possibility, as Fisher suggests, is not great. If there is reason to believe that the sample standard deviations differ significantly, their difference may be tested.

Some General Considerations Bearing on Tests of Hypotheses

Our chief concern in this chapter has been with the testing of statistical hypotheses (in dealing with small samples we reverted briefly to an aspect of the subject of estimation). This discussion has touched upon some of the more general aspects of the theory of inquiry, but it has dealt, in the main, with methodology. In concluding the discussion it is proper to stress certain logical considerations that were not fully developed in the preceding pages. Three points of central importance are to be made.

1. A generalization (a hypothesis) suggested by the observations in a given sample cannot be tested against that sample. There

must be *predesignation* of the hypothesis, or of the population parameter, that is to be tested.[19] If a given sample of business cycles should suggest that the mean duration of business cycles in the United States is 40 months, we could hardly use the mean of that sample in testing the hypothetical mean of 40 months. The fallacy of such a test is obvious, yet this type of circularity is not uncommon. A technique for forecasting the level of wholesale prices, the prices of securities, or the state of business is often tested against the historical record that suggested the technique. Of course, this is not to say that an investigator should not be open-minded to theories that may be suggested by observations. But when a theory is thus suggested, it must be tested against a new set of observations. (We have already referred to the rule that an investigator should, *before* he applies a test of significance, designate the confidence level according to which he will accept or reject the hypothesis in question. The principle here is the same.)

2. Statistical evidence never provides positive proof of the truth of a hypothesis. The essence of statistical testing is that the facts are given a chance to disprove hypotheses; the facts do not prove hypotheses. The reader will have noticed the form of the conclusion reached after a test is applied. One may say, "The observations are not inconsistent with the hypothesis," or, "The observations are not consistent with the hypothesis." The second statement, it is clear, is more decisive than the first. When we reject a hypothesis we may be able to do so with a high degree of confidence. If the difference between an observed statistic and a hypothetical parameter is so great that chance might be expected to lead to such a divergence only 1 time in 10,000,000 trials, the investigator may be reasonably sure that there is a true difference, and so reject the hypothesis. (But

---

[19] A player might draw (with replacement) from a pack of cards a four of diamonds, a king of spades, a five of clubs, and a nine of clubs, and then exclaim at the remarkable fact that just these four cards should have turned up—a combination to be expected only 24 times in 7,311,616 trials (the order of draw is not assumed to matter). This is not remarkable after the event. It would only have been remarkable had the player predesignated the result by announcing before his draw that these four particular cards would appear. Without this predesignation the player is, in effect, setting up the hypothesis that he will draw a four of diamonds, a king of spades, a five and a nine of clubs *after* he has drawn those precise cards.

In an incident famous in baseball history Babe Ruth, being heckled by the opposing team, pointed to a spot in the right-field bleachers and then proceeded, on the next pitch, to hit a home run to that precise spot. This was predesignation.

there will always remain a slight probability that the rejection was unjustified.) However, acceptance of a hypothesis can never carry the degree of confidence that would attach to a rejection based on a 1/10,000,000 probability. Indeed, these facts are more likely to be consistent with a false hypothesis (of which there will be legion) than with the true hypothesis. Choice among hypotheses with which the facts are consistent must be based on rational grounds, not on empirical evidence. This last statement carries us to the third of our three points.

3. If we are to have confidence in a hypothesis it must have support beyond the statistical evidence. It must have a rational basis. This phrase suggests two conditions: The hypothesis must be "reasonable," in the sense of concordance with *a priori* expectations. Secondly, the hypothesis must fit logically into the relevant body of established knowledge. Reference to statistical evidence is essential and important in determining the degree of confidence we may have in a hypothesis, but the support we get from this side is of a negative sort. We say of it that it does not disprove the hypothesis. Positive elements of support come from the side of reason.[20]

REFERENCES

Anderson, R. L. and Bancroft, T. A., *Statistical Theory in Research,* Chap. 11.
Churchman, C. W., *Theory of Experimental Inference.*
Clark, C. E., *An Introduction to Statistics,* Chap. 6.
Cramér, H., *Mathematical Methods of Statistics,* Chaps. 30, 31, 35.
Deming, W. E., *Some Theory of Sampling,* pp. 537-554.
Dixon, W. J. and Massey, F. J. Jr., *Introduction to Statistical Analysis,* Chap. 7.
Fisher, Sir Ronald (R. A.), *Contributions to Mathematical Statistics,* Papers 7, 13.

---

[20] The condition that a hypothesis must have a rational basis is, of course, necessary. Yet the investigator should heed a warning voiced by Lord Russell against excessive emphasis on conformity to expectations and to existing knowledge, in appraising ideas about nature. If hypotheses that do not conform to existing knowledge were to be *ipso facto* rejected, the advance of knowledge would be seriously retarded. Since there is a danger of self-delusion in research, danger of finding only that for which one is looking, the completely unexpected may sometimes have a sounder claim than does that which appears to be perfectly rational because it conforms so nicely to existing patterns of thought. Thus, says Russell, the quantum theory, which broke sharply with the body of traditional thought about the physical world, has for that very reason strong claim to acceptance.

Fisher, Sir Ronald (R. A.), *The Design of Experiments*, 4th ed.,

Fisher, Sir Ronald (R. A.), *Statistical Methods for Research Workers*, 11th ed., Chap. 5.

Freeman, H. A., *Industrial Statistics*, Chap. 1.

Goulden, C. H., *Methods of Statistical Analysis*, 2nd ed., Chap. 4.

Hoel, P. G., *Introduction to Mathematical Statistics*, 2nd ed., Chap. 10.

Kendall, M. G., *The Advanced Theory of Statistics*, 3rd ed., Vol. II, pp. 96-106, 269-306.

Mather, K., *Statistical Analysis in Biology*, 2nd ed., Chaps. 4, 5.

Mood, A. M., *Introduction to the Theory of Statistics*, pp. 245-270.

Neyman, J., "Basic Ideas and Some Recent Results of the Theory of Testing Statistical Hypotheses," *Journal of the Royal Statistical Society*, Vol. 105, 1942.

Neyman, J., *Lectures and Conferences on Mathematical Statistics and Probability*, 2nd ed., Chap. 1, part 3.

Neyman, J., and Pearson, E. S., "Contributions to the Theory of Testing Statistical Hypotheses," *Statistical Research Memoirs*, Vol. 1, 1936; Vol. 2, 1938.

Neyman, J. and Pearson, E. S., "On the Problem of the Most Efficient Tests of Statistical Hypotheses," *Philosophical Transactions of the Royal Society*, Vol. 231, 1933.

Rosander, A. C., *Elementary Principles of Statistics*, Chaps. 24, 27.

Shewhart, W. A., *Economic Control of Quality of Manufactured Product*, Chap. 14.

Shewhart, W. A., *Statistical Method from the Viewpoint of Quality Control*, pp. 56-63.

"Student," "The Probable Error of a Mean," *Biometrika*, Vol. 6, 1908.

Tintner, G., *Mathematics and Statistics for Economists*, Chap. 25.

Tippett, L. H. C., *The Methods of Statistics*, 4th ed., pp. 80-103, 141-149.

Tippett, L. H. C., *Technological Applications of Statistics*, Chaps. 8, 9.

Wald, A., *Statistical Decision Functions*.

Walker, H. M. and Lev, J., *Statistical Inference*, Chaps. 3, 7.

Wilks, S. S., *Elementary Statistical Analysis*, Chap. 11.

Wilks, S. S., *Mathematical Statistics*, Chap. 7.

Yule, G. U. and Kendall, M. G., *An Introduction to the Theory of Statistics*, 14th ed., Chap. 21.

The publishers and the dates of publication of the books named in chapter reference lists are given in the bibliography at the end of this volume.

CHAPTER 9

The Measurement of Relationship: Linear Correlation

Introduction

The problems we have discussed in the preceding chapters have dealt primarily with the behavior of a single variable. The arrangement of the values of a single variable along a scale may be described by measures of central tendency, or of location, and by accompanying measures that define the pattern of variation about a central value. The examples of statistical inference so far considered have dealt with the estimation of parameter values for a single variable, or to tests involving hypothetical values of such a variable. In dealing with theoretical distributions in Chapter 6 we introduced the concept of frequency, measured along the vertical or y-axis of a coordinate system, as a function of a variable x, usually measured as a deviation along the horizontal axis. That is, the frequency of occurrence of a single value is presented as *dependent* upon the magnitude of the deviation of that value from a specified origin. The mathematical expression for such a theoretical distribution is a statement of a *functional relation* between a dependent and an independent variable. Such relations of a simple type were briefly considered in Chapter 2. We now open a more systematic discussion of methods employed in the measurement of relations among variable quantities. Our concern here will be with the manner in which two (or more) variables fluctuate with reference to one another. A suggestive general term for such joint behavior is *covariation*; the term commonly employed in statistical literature is correlation. In the present chapter we deal with the simplest form of covariation, linear correlation between two variables.

As a familiar example of simple correlation we may refer again to the relation between the number of rings in the trunk of a tree (Y) and the age of the tree (X). For an X-value of 3, Y will be equal to 3; for an X-value of 5, Y will be equal to 5. This relation is shown in Fig. 2.3, on p. 11. Here we have a perfect relationship; X determines Y completely. All the plotted points lie on a straight line that can be drawn through them. Fig. 9.1 (based on Table 9-1)

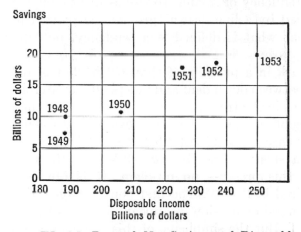

FIG. 9.1. Personal Net Savings and Disposable Personal Income in the United States, 1948-1953.

TABLE 9–1

Personal Net Savings and Disposable Personal Income in the United States, 1948-1953 (in billions of dollars)

	Personal net savings	Disposable personal income
1948	10.0	188
1949	7.6	188
1950	12.1	206
1951	17.7	226
1952	18.4	237
1953	20.0	250

shows a different situation. Here are plotted aggregate personal net savings, in billions of dollars, as estimated for the United States for the years 1948-53, and corresponding figures for aggregate disposable personal income (i.e., personal income less personal taxes). It is to be expected that personal savings will be affected by the magnitude of personal income. It is also to be expected that the relationship will be imperfect, since factors other than size of income affect consumers' decisions on the division of income between consumption and saving. These expectations are borne out by Fig. 9.1. (The period covered is, of course, too short to provide evidence of anything like a consistent relationship; these fragmentary data are here used merely for illustrative purposes.) The general tendency of savings to rise as disposable income rises may be defined by a line drawn through the plotted points, but it is clear that what is defined is a tendency, not an invariant relationship.

The first task in a problem of this sort is that of defining the relationship between dependent and independent variables, whether it be perfect, as in the tree example, or merely a tendency to which there are exceptions, as in the other example. In general terms, for the linear case, we must establish the values of a and b in the equation to a straight line, $Y = a + bX$. For the first example given above this presents no problem. It is obvious that the equation desired is $Y = X$. The first constant on the right hand side of the general expression disappears, i.e., $a = 0$; the constant b is equal to 1. But the simplicity of this problem is quite exceptional. The situation represented in Fig. 9.1 is the usual one. Any two of the six points here plotted would define a straight line; fifteen different lines might be obtained. But no one of these lines would be accepted as satisfactorily defining the relationship that concerns us. What we want is the single straight line that best describes the *average relationship* between Y and X, that best defines the tendency for Y and X to vary together. We wish to determine values of a and b in the general equation to a straight line that may be regarded as *best* in the light of the evidence we have.

A simple illustration will serve to demonstrate an approximative method and the preferred method of doing this. Nine points (1,3; 2,4; 3,6; 4,5; 5,10; 6,9; 7,10; 8,12; 9,11—the X-value being given first in each pair of coordinates) are plotted in Fig. 9.2. Our problem is the fitting of a straight line to these points. By inspection, rough values of a and b may be determined. A transparent

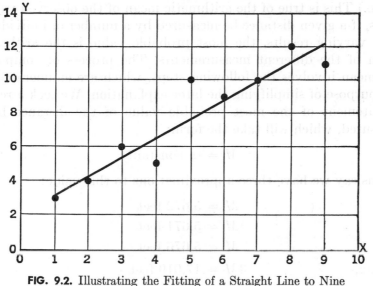

FIG. 9.2. Illustrating the Fitting of a Straight Line to Nine
Points.

ruler may be used in approximating the desired function. The
slope of the line thus laid out may be measured, the y-intercept
determined, and the desired equation thus approximated. Obviously this is a loose and uncertain method; the results obtained by
different individuals may be expected to differ widely. We need a
more objective procedure for selecting a line that may be considered
"best." One such procedure for determining the constants a and b
for such a line of best fit is the method of least squares. Reference
has been made to this method in preceding chapters, in connection
with the problem of estimation. Some of its limitations were there
noted. We here deal with it in simple terms as a generally useful
procedure for estimating the values of constants when observations
conflict.[1]

The Method of Least Squares. Assume that we have a number
of observed values of a certain quantity, and that these observed
values differ. We wish to obtain the most probable value of the
quantity being measured. It is capable of demonstration that the
most probable value of the quantity is that value for which the
sum of the squares of the residuals is a minimum. (A "residual" is
of course a difference between an estimated value and an observed

---

[1] See Appendix C for a more detailed discussion of least squares procedure, together
with a description of certain checks upon the calculations.

value.) This is true of the arithmetic mean of the observed values. Thus, if a given distance be measured by a number of individuals, with varying results, the most probable value is the arithmetic mean of the different measurements. The process of computing the mean involves the following steps, which are enumerated for the purpose of simplifying the later explanation. We seek a result, a statement of the most probable value of the distance being measured, which will take the form:

$$M = \text{(a constant)}$$

Let us say we have three approximations to this value:

$$M = 5,672 \text{ feet}$$
$$M = 5,671 \text{ feet}$$
$$M = 5,676 \text{ feet}$$

adding, $$3M = 17,019 \text{ feet}$$

Since there is but one unknown, M, it may be derived directly from this equation, and we have

$$M = 5,673 \text{ feet}$$

This is the value for which the sum of the squares of the deviations is a minimum.

A similar problem arises when the relation between two variables is being measured. Our goal in this case is an equation describing this relationship. However, we have secured varying results that do not agree precisely as to the constants in the equation of relationship.

In other words, our plotted points do not all lie on the same line. What are the most probable values of the constants in the required equation? The answer is analogous to that given when a single quantity was being measured. We seek the constants which, when the resulting equation is plotted, will give a line from which the deviations of the separate points, when squared and totaled, will be a minimum. Assuming that each pair of measurements gives an approximation to the true relationship between the variables, we wish to find the most probable relationship, and this is given by the line for which the sum of the squared deviations is a minimum.

We have, in the present example, nine pairs of values for X and Y. Substituting these values in the generalized form of the linear equation, $Y = a + bX$, we secure the following observation equations:

$$3 = a + 1b$$
$$4 = a + 2b$$
$$6 = a + 3b$$
$$5 = a + 4b$$
$$10 = a + 5b$$
$$9 = a + 6b$$
$$10 = a + 7b$$
$$12 = a + 8b$$
$$11 = a + 9b$$

Any two of these equations could be solved as simultaneous equations, and values of a and b secured. But these values would not satisfy the remaining equations. Our problem is to combine the nine observation equations so as to secure two *normal equations*, which, when solved simultaneously, will give the most probable values of a and b. The first of these normal equations is secured by multiplying each of the observation equations by the coefficient of a, the first unknown in that equation, and adding the equations obtained in this way. Since the coefficient of a in the present case is 1 throughout, the nine observation equations are unchanged by the process of multiplication. The second of the normal equations is secured by multiplying each of the observation equations by the coefficient of b, the second unknown in that equation, and adding the equations obtained. Thus the first equation is multiplied throughout by 1, the second by 2, and so on. The process of securing the two normal equations is illustrated in Table 9-2.

TABLE 9–2

Derivation of Normal Equations from Observation Equations

$3 = a + 1b$	$3 = 1a + 1b$
$4 = a + 2b$	$8 = 2a + 4b$
$6 = a + 3b$	$18 = 3a + 9b$
$5 = a + 4b$	$20 = 4a + 16b$
$10 = a + 5b$	$50 = 5a + 25b$
$9 = a + 6b$	$54 = 6a + 36b$
$10 = a + 7b$	$70 = 7a + 49b$
$12 = a + 8b$	$96 = 8a + 64b$
$11 = a + 9b$	$99 = 9a + 81b$
$70 = 9a + 45b$	$418 = 45a + 285b$

The two normal equations are

$$70 = 9a + 45b$$
$$418 = 45a + 285b$$

It remains to solve these equations for a and b. By multiplying the first equation by 5 and subtracting it from the second, a may be eliminated; a value of $\frac{68}{60}$, or 1.133, is found for b. Substituting this value in either of the equations, a value of 2.111 is secured for a. The equation to the best fitting straight line is, therefore,

$$Y = 2.111 + 1.133X$$

In the actual application of the method it is not necessary to write out and total the equations, as is done above. We need only insert the proper values in the two equations,[2]

$$\Sigma(Y) = Na + b\Sigma(X) \tag{9.1}$$

$$\Sigma(XY) = a\Sigma(X) + b\Sigma(X^2) \tag{9.2}$$

where Σ indicates a summation process.

The work of computation is facilitated by a tabular arrangement similar to that shown in Table 9-3. The normal equations for a

TABLE 9–3

Computation of Values Required in Fitting a Straight Line

X	Y	XY	X^2	
1	3	3	1	$N = 9$
2	4	8	4	$\Sigma(X) = 45$
3	6	18	9	$\Sigma(Y) = 70$
4	5	20	16	$\Sigma(X^2) = 285$
5	10	50	25	$\Sigma(XY) = 418$
6	9	54	36	
7	10	70	49	
8	12	96	64	
9	11	99	81	
—	—	—	—	
45	70	418	285	

specific problem are secured by substituting in the standard equations (9.1) and (9.2) above the values given at the right of that table. The results are of course identical with those obtained from the observation equations.

[2] General rules for the formation of normal equations are given in Appendix C.

When the equation to the best fitting straight line has been obtained the values of Y corresponding to given values of X may be computed and compared with the observed values. Table 9-4 presents the results secured.

TABLE 9–4

Comparison of Observed and Computed Values of a Variable Quantity*

X	Y_0 (observed)	Y_c (computed)	v $(Y_0 - Y_c)$	v^2	Xv
1	3	$3.2\frac{4}{9}$	$-.2\frac{4}{9}$	.0597	$-.2\frac{4}{9}$
2	4	$4.3\frac{7}{9}$	$-.3\frac{7}{9}$	.1427	$-.7\frac{5}{9}$
3	6	$5.5\frac{1}{9}$	$+.4\frac{8}{9}$	.2390	$+1.4\frac{6}{9}$
4	5	$6.6\frac{4}{9}$	$-1.6\frac{4}{9}$	2.7041	$-6.5\frac{7}{9}$
5	10	$7.7\frac{7}{9}$	$+2.2\frac{2}{9}$	4.9381	$+11.1\frac{1}{9}$
6	9	$8.9\frac{1}{9}$	$+.0\frac{8}{9}$	.0079	$+.5\frac{3}{9}$
7	10	$10.0\frac{4}{9}$	$-.0\frac{4}{9}$	.0020	$-.3\frac{1}{9}$
8	12	$11.1\frac{7}{9}$	$+.8\frac{2}{9}$	.6760	$+6.5\frac{7}{9}$
9	11	$12.3\frac{1}{9}$	$-1.3\frac{1}{9}$	1.7190	-11.8
			0.0	10.4885	0.0

* The common fractions are retained in certain columns in order that the sum of the deviations may be exactly zero.

The sum of the deviations of the plotted points from the line is zero. The sum of the deviations when each is multiplied by the corresponding value of X is also zero. The accuracy of the actual calculations involved in fitting may be tested in this way. The sum of the squares of the deviations, 10.4885, is a minimum. Any change in the value of a or b would give a line for which the sum of the squared deviations would exceed 10.4885.

We have discussed the technique of least squares because of its bearing on the problem of defining relations between variables. This problem is faced in all fields of inquiry. In some cases in the realm of the physical sciences the relations that prevail are invariant. Thus the speed of a body falling in a vacuum is a direct function of the time it has fallen. In a perfect vacuum the relationship is perfect; there are no departures from the relation specified by the equation $y = gt$ (where y is the speed, t the time of fall, and g the gravitational constant). But in the social and biological sciences perfect mechanical relationships are not found. We find tendencies, relationships that hold on the average. Observations do not accord without exception to a mathematically definable "law." Causal forces are complex, not single, and isolation of one or two factors is usually impossible. Thus the height and weight of individuals are related, but not in a mechanical way; the price of cotton is related to the supply of cotton, but other factors also influence the price; earnings are influenced by the productivity of labor, but are not determined by this factor alone. In all such cases as these the determination of an equation of relationship calls for an averaging process by which "most probable" values of the constants in the equation may be estimated from varying observations. The method of least squares is an instrument appropriate to this problem. This method, we should note, is fully justified as a means of estimating "most probable" values of desired constants only when the distribution of deviations is normal. Practically, the method is used as a convenient and simple procedure for approximating the desired values even when more complex procedures (maximum likelihood for non-normal cases) would give more defensible results.

Notation. In general the system of notation employed in this chapter on correlation follows the practice of earlier chapters. Certain new symbols are introduced.

$s_{y.x}$: the standard error of estimate of Y, as estimated from X

$s_{x.y}$: the standard error of estimate of X, as estimated from Y

r: the coefficient of correlation; often with subscripts, as r_{yx}, the first subscript indicating the dependent variable, the second the independent variable

ρ (rho): a population value of a coefficient of correlation

b_{yx}: a coefficient of regression, subscripts indicating dependent and independent variables

β_{yx}: (beta with subscript yx) the population value of b_{yx}

Y_c or y_c: a value of Y or of y computed from a regression equation

d_{yc}: the deviation of a value of Y_c from the mean Y

v: a residual; the deviation of Y from Y_c

s_{yc}: the standard deviation of a series of Y_c values

p or p_{xy}: the mean product of the paired values of two variables, the origin being at the point of averages; this quantity is sometimes called the *covariance*

s_{xy}: the covariance of a sample; p_{xy}

σ_{xy}: the population covariance; the population equivalent of p_{xy}

p': the mean product of the paired values of two variables, the origin being elsewhere than at the point of averages

d_{yx}: a coefficient of determination, subscripts indicating dependent and independent variables; a quantity equal to r_{yx}^2

z': a logarithmic transformation of r

ζ (zeta): the population value of z'

s_r: an estimate of the standard error of r; when written σ_r, the population value of s_r

$s_{z'}$: the estimated standard error of z'

s_b: an estimate of the standard error of the coefficient of regression; when written σ_b, the population equivalent

r_r: a value of Spearman's coefficient of rank correlation obtained from a sample

ρ_r: a population value of Spearman's coefficient

s_{rr}: the estimated standard error of r_r

τ (tau): Kendall's coefficient of rank correlation (the symbol τ is used for a sample measure, the practice thus departing from the general rule that Greek letters stand for population parameters)

S: the total score, indicative of the degree of concordance of two rankings (Kendall)

P: the positive component of S

Q: the negative component of S

s_{sc}: the estimated standard error of the score S

As in earlier chapters, capital letters (X, Y) are used to represent original values of the variables, as measured from the zero points on the scale of actual values. Small letters (x, y) are used for values of variables expressed as deviations from their respective arithmetic means. Small letters with prime marks (x', y') are used for deviations from arbitrary origins.

The Relation between Family Expenditures for Current Consumption and Family Income after Taxes: Averages by Cities

As a typical example, illustrating the derivation of descriptive measures, we consider the relation between expenditures for purposes of current consumption and current family income after taxes. The data, which relate to income and expenditures in 1950, are averages for 33 small cities which constitute a representative sample of United States cities with populations from 2,500 to 30,500.[2] These averages are given in columns (2) and (3) of Table 9-5. (In interpreting conclusions the reader will bear in mind that the city, not the individual family, is the unit of observation.)

These data are plotted in Fig. 9.3, each dot defining the position

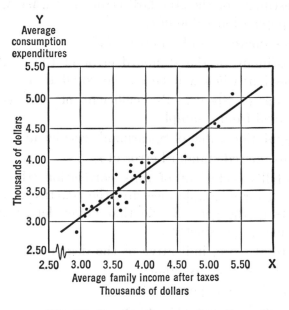

FIG. 9.3. Family Consumption Expenditures and Family Income: Averages by Cities,* 1950, with Line of Average Relation.

* A sample of 33 cities with populations of 2,500 to 30,500.

[2] The materials are from the Survey of Consumer Expenditures in 1950, conducted by the U. S. Bureau of Labor Statistics. Definitions, details of the sampling procedure, and some preliminary results are given in "Family Income, Expenditures, and Savings in 1950," *Bulletin No. 1097* (Revised) of the Bureau of Labor Statistics, June, 1953.

TABLE 9–5

Average Current Family Income after Taxes and Average Family
Expenditures for Current Consumption in Cities with Populations of
2,500 to 30,500 United States, 1950*
(Both variables in thousands of dollars)

(1)	(2)	(3)	(4)	(5)	(6)
	Average Current Family Income	Average Family Expenditures for Current Consumption			
City	X	Y	XY	X^2	Y^2
Anna, Ill.	3.60	3.40	12.2400	12.9600	11.5600
Antioch, Calif.	5.10	4.52	23.0520	26.0100	20.4304
Barre, Vt.	3.78	3.90	14.7420	14.2884	15.2100
Camden, Ark.	3.04	3.09	9.3936	9.2416	9.5481
Cheyenne, Wyo.	5.04	4.58	23.0832	25.4016	20.9764
Columbia, Tenn.	3.15	3.22	10.1430	9.9225	10.3684
Cooperstown, N. Y.	3.55	3.47	12.3185	12.6025	12.0409
Dalhart, Tex.	4.00	3.55	14.2000	16.0000	12.6025
Demopolis, Ala.	2.93	2.85	8.3505	8.5849	8.1225
Elko, Nev.	5.33	5.05	26.9165	28.4089	25.5025
Fayetteville, N. C.	3.47	3.40	11.7980	12.0409	11.5600
Garrett, Ind.	4.03	3.70	14.9110	16.2409	13.6900
Glendale, Ariz.	3.40	3.69	12.5460	11.5600	13.6161
Grand Forks, N. Dak.	4.02	3.95	15.8790	16.1604	15.6025
Grand Island, Nebr.	3.97	3.96	15.7212	15.7609	15.6816
Grand Junction, Colo.	3.58	3.54	12.6732	12.8164	12.5316
Grinnell, Iowa	3.59	3.28	11.7752	12.8881	10.7584
Laconia, N. H.	3.55	3.78	13.4190	12.6025	14.2884
Lodi, Calif.	4.07	4.10	16.6870	16.5649	16.8100
Madill, Okla.	3.18	3.19	10.1442	10.1124	10.1761
Middlesboro, Ky.	3.02	3.26	9.8452	9.1204	10.6276
Nanty-Glo, Pa.	3.78	3.78	14.2884	14.2884	14.2884
Pecos, Tex.	3.82	3.73	14.2486	14.5924	13.9129
Pulaski, Va.	3.45	3.33	11.4885	11.9025	11.0889
Ravenna, Ohio	3.88	3.72	14.4336	15.0544	13.8384
Rawlins, Wyo.	4.71	4.26	20.0646	22.1841	18.1476
Roseburg, Ore.	4.58	4.04	18.5032	20.9764	16.3216
Salina, Kan.	3.60	3.40	12.2400	12.9600	11.5600
Sandpoint, Idaho	3.28	3.32	10.8896	10.7584	11.0224
Santa Cruz, Calif.	3.69	3.34	12.3246	13.6161	11.1556
Shawnee, Okla.	3.08	3.19	9.8252	9.4864	10.1761
Shenandoah, Iowa	3.97	3.67	14.5699	15.7609	13.4689
Washington, N. J.	4.06	4.15	16.8490	16.4836	17.2225
Total	125.30	121.41	469.5635	487.3518	453.9073

* Readers should note the following comment by the Bureau of Labor Statistics: "Experience suggests that average family income is usually understated. . . . It is therefore quite incorrect to interpret the entire difference between reported income and expenditure as saving or dis-saving."

of a single city in respect of average family expenditure for consumption and average current income. Such a figure is termed a "scatter diagram." It is clear from this diagram that there is a relationship between the two variables. In general, the cities with high average family incomes are also those with high average family expenditures for consumption. The relationship, however, is not perfect. Two cities with almost the same average family income may differ materially in average expenditures for consumption. Thus for Dalhart, Texas, with average family income of $4,000, average consumption expenditures were $3,550, while for Washington, New Jersey, where average family income was $4,060, average expenditures for consumption were $4,150. Were the relation between the two variables perfect, cities having the same average family income would have the same average expenditures for consumption.

The Equation of Average Relationship. Our first problem is the derivation of an equation to describe this relationship which, while not perfect, is clearly existent. We shall assume that the relationship is linear, and shall employ the method of least squares in estimating the best values of the constants a and b in an appropriate equation. This calls for the solution of the normal equations

$$\Sigma(Y) = Na + b\Sigma(X)$$
$$\Sigma(XY) = a\Sigma(X) + b\Sigma(X^2)$$

The values required for the solution of these equations may be derived from the data as arranged in Table 9-5. Substituting, we have

$$121.4 = 33a + 125.30b$$
$$469.5635 = 125.30a + 487.3518b$$

Solving,

$$a = 0.8707$$
$$b = 0.7396$$

The required equation is

$$Y = 0.8707 + 0.7396X$$

This line is plotted in Fig. 9.3.

A mathematical expression has now been secured for the relation between the two variables being studied, average family expenditures for consumption and average family income after taxes. The former is the dependent or Y-variable in the equation, the latter the independent or X-variable. This equation constitutes a measure of the functional relationship between these two variables, but it is only an expression of *average* relationship. How significant is the equation? If the relationship were perfect, and the plotted points all lay on the line describing this relationship, the equation could be used with confidence as an accurate instrument for determining the value of one variable from a value of the other. But a line with a definite equation may be fitted to points that depart very widely from it, that are widely dispersed. In such a case the equation may have the appearance of describing a precise relationship but the variation is so great that it cannot be used with confidence. It is the same problem as that which arises when an average is employed. We must know how significant the average is, how great the concentration about it, before we may use it intelligently. So the equation of relationship between variables means little unless we know to what extent it holds in practical experience. We must have a measure of the dispersion about the line we have fitted.

In describing the frequency distribution, the standard deviation is used as the best general measure of variation. It is, obviously, the measure we need in determining the reliability of the equation of average relationship. The standard deviation about this line will not only serve as a general index of the significance of this equation but will enable us to measure the degree of accuracy of estimates based upon the equation.

Computation of the Standard Error of Estimate. The standard deviation about a line of average relationship, being a measure of the accuracy of estimates, may be termed the *standard error of estimate*. (The term *standard deviation* is generally confined to the root-mean-square deviation about the arithmetic mean.) The standard error of estimate is represented by the symbol $s_{y \cdot x}$, usually written with subscripts to indicate dependent (first subscript) and independent variables.

In the computation of $s_{y \cdot x}$ we must know the computed value of Y that corresponds to each given value of X. By substituting the given values of X in the equation

$$Y = 0.8707 + 0.7396X$$

normal Y values may be computed. The deviations of the actual

Y values from the computed may be determined. The root-mean-square of these deviations, or residuals, which are represented by the symbol v, is the required measure. A method of computation is illustrated in Table 9-6. From this table we have

$$s_{y \cdot x} = \sqrt{\frac{\Sigma v^2}{N}} = \sqrt{\frac{0.8868}{33}}$$

$$= 0.164 \text{ (in thousands of dollars)}$$

The measure $s_{y \cdot x}$ is to be interpreted in precisely the same way as the standard deviation about an arithmetic mean. Given a normal distribution of items about the line of relationship, 68 percent of all the cases will lie within a range of $\pm s$ (in this case 0.164), 95 percent will fall within $\pm 2s$ (in this case 0.328) and 99.7 percent will fall within $\pm 3s$ (here, 0.492). If there were no scatter about the line fitted to the points representing the corresponding values of X and Y, $s_{y \cdot x}$ would have a value of zero, and the value of Y could be estimated from the value of X with perfect accuracy. The less the dispersion about the line, the smaller the value of $s_{y \cdot x}$. The value of $s_{y \cdot x}$ serves, therefore, as an indicator of the significance and usefulness of the line that describes the relation between the two variables. The standard error of estimate, it should be noted, is expressed in the same units as the original Y-values.[3]

The making of estimates. We may, for the moment, consider the significance of these results. Let us assume that, not knowing the average family expenditures for current consumption in a given city, we are under the necessity of estimating it. Two methods are open to us. We may, in the first place, base the estimate upon our knowledge of the Y-variable alone. The arithmetic average of the 33 city entries for Y_0, given in Table 9-6, is 3.679 (the unit, it will be remembered, is \$1,000). With no specific information as to average expenditures for consumption in a particular city, the

---

[3] For descriptive purposes, and for consistency in the various calculations illustrated in this part of Chapter 9, we derive the standard error of estimate from $\sqrt{\Sigma v^2/N}$. However, if we are thinking of $s_{y \cdot x}$ as an estimate of a population value, $\sigma_{y \cdot x}$, the divisor in the expression under the radical sign should be $N - 2$, not N. The reasoning that justifies this is similar to that which leads to the use of $N - 1$ rather than N in estimating a population σ. In deriving an estimate of the standard error of estimate from observations we use up two degrees of freedom, in effect, when we use these observations in the fitting of the straight line. Hence there are only $N - 2$ degrees of freedom for the observations to deviate from the line. It will be desirable to use $N - 2$ as the divisor in dealing with certain problems of inference in later sections of this chapter.

TABLE 9–6

Illustrating the Computation of Residuals and their Squares

(1) City	(2) Actual Y_0	(3) Computed Y_c	(4) (2)–(3) v	(5) v^2

Columns (2) and (3): Average Expenditures for Current Consumption (in thousands of dollars)

(1) City	(2) Y_0	(3) Y_c	(4) v	(5) v^2
Anna, Ill.	3.40	3.53	− 0.13	0.0169
Antioch, Calif.	4.52	4.64	− 0.12	0.0144
Barre, Vt.	3.90	3.67	+ 0.23	0.0529
Camden, Ark.	3.09	3.12	− 0.03	0.0009
Cheyenne, Wyo.	4.58	4.60	− 0.02	0.0004
Columbia, Tenn.	3.22	3.20	+ 0.02	0.0004
Cooperstown, N. Y.	3.47	3.50	− 0.03	0.0009
Dalhart, Tex.	3.55	3.83	− 0.28	0.0784
Demopolis, Ala.	2.85	3.04	− 0.19	0.0361
Elko, Nev.	5.05	4.81	+ 0.24	0.0576
Fayetteville, N. C.	3.40	3.44	− 0.04	0.0016
Garrett, Ind.	3.70	3.85	− 0.15	0.0225
Glendale, Ariz.	3.69	3.39	+ 0.30	0.0900
Grand Forks, N. Dak.	3.95	3.84	+ 0.11	0.0121
Grand Island, Nebr.	3.96	3.81	+ 0.15	0.0225
Grand Junction, Colo.	3.54	3.52	+ 0.02	0.0004
Grinnell, Iowa	3.28	3.53	− 0.25	0.0625
Laconia, N. H.	3.78	3.50	+ 0.28	0.0784
Lodi, Calif.	4.10	3.88	+ 0.22	0.0484
Madill, Okla.	3.19	3.22	− 0.03	0.0009
Middlesboro, Ky.	3.26	3.10	+ 0.16	0.0256
Nanty-Glo, Pa.	3.78	3.67	+ 0.11	0.0121
Pecos, Tex.	3.73	3.70	+ 0.03	0.0009
Pulaski, Va.	3.33	3.42	− 0.09	0.0081
Ravenna, Ohio	3.72	3.74	− 0.02	0.0004
Rawlins, Wyo.	4.26	4.35	− 0.09	0.0081
Roseburg, Ore.	4.04	4.26	− 0.22	0.0484
Salina, Kan.	3.40	3.53	− 0.13	0.0169
Sandpoint, Idaho	3.32	3.29	+ 0.03	0.0009
Santa Cruz, Calif.	3.34	3.60	− 0.26	0.0676
Shawnee, Okla.	3.19	3.15	+ 0.04	0.0016
Shenandoah, Iowa	3.67	3.81	− 0.14	0.0196
Washington, N. J	4.15	3.87	+ 0.28	0.0784
Total				0.8868

arithmetic mean of all the city figures would be taken as the most probable value for the city in question. (The most probable value of a series of observations is the mean of the series.) The accuracy of this estimate depends on the degree of dispersion about the mean, which may be defined by the standard deviation. In the present case the standard deviation has a value of 0.468. Here is a measure of the reliability of estimates based on the mean of all the Y's.

Another method of estimating current family expenditures for consumption in a given city is open to us if we have information concerning average family income in that city. For as a result of the study described in the preceding pages we know that the average relationship between consumption expenditures and family income (as averaged by cities) is defined by the equation

$$Y = 0.8707 + 0.7396X$$

If in a given city average current family income, after taxes, is 4.000 (in thousands of dollars), it may be estimated from this equation that current consumption will be 3.8291, or 3,829 to the nearest dollar. This is the most probable value of Y as determined from the equation of average relationship. Is this estimate any better than the previous one, which took the mean Y as the most probable value? Does our knowledge of the average relationship between X and Y aid us in estimating the value of Y from a known value of X?

The answers to these questions are given by the *standard error of estimate*, and by the relation between the standard error of estimate and the standard deviation of Y. The standard error of estimate is 0.164. The standard deviation of Y is 0.468. Clearly the estimate made from the equation is more accurate than the estimate based upon the value of the mean Y. From our knowledge of the relationship between the two variables, even though that relationship is by no means constant or perfect, we are able to reduce materially the errors of estimate. (The reader will be aware that, in working with data obtained from samples, estimates of the mean Y and of the constants a and b in the equation of regression are themselves subject to errors. These errors do not enter into the comparison of the standard deviation of Y and the standard error of estimate.)

The Coefficient of Correlation. We have now secured two measures that aid us in describing the relationship between variable quantities. The first is the fundamental equation of relationship, the expression of the degree of change in one variable associated, on the average, with a given change in the other. The second is the *standard error of estimate*, the measure of the degree of "scatter" about the line of average relationship. The standard error resembles the standard deviation in that it is a measure expressed in absolute terms, in the units employed in measuring the original Y-values. This measure enables us to determine the probability that an observed value will fall within specified limits of an estimate based upon the equation of relationship.

In measuring variation it has been found that an abstract measure of variability is needed, one which is divorced from the absolute terms of the given problem. Such a measure is particularly needed, it was noted, when different distributions are to be compared. So, for measuring the *degree of variability*, a coefficient of variation is employed. There is need of a somewhat similar measure in connection with our present problem. We need a measure of the *degree of relationship* between two variables, an abstract coefficient that is divorced from the particular units employed in a given case. Such a measure is termed a coefficient of correlation.

This measure may be explained in terms of the preceding discussion. It was found that the usefulness of estimates based upon the equation of relationship could be determined by comparing the standard error of estimate of Y (the measure of scatter about the line of relationship) with the standard deviation of Y. If the standard error of estimate be as great as the standard deviation the equation of relationship is of no use to us, but if the standard error be less than the standard deviation the accuracy of estimates may be improved by using this equation. The significance of the equation is thus indicated by the relation between the standard error of estimate and the standard deviation. But these are both in absolute terms, so that by dividing one by the other an abstract measure may be secured. Thus we might write

$$\text{Measure of correlation} = \frac{s_{y \cdot x}}{s_y}$$

A somewhat more useful measure is secured by putting the ratio in this form:

$$\text{Measure of correlation} = r = \sqrt{1 - \frac{s_{y \cdot x}^2}{s_y^2}} \tag{9.3}$$

This measure, when used in connection with a linear equation, is called the *coefficient of correlation* and, as is indicated in formula (9.3), is represented by the symbol r.

A brief consideration of this formula[4] will help to make clear the

---

[4] In deriving the mean squares $s_{y \cdot x}^2$ and s_y^2 that enter into the formula (9.3), the same N must be used as the divisor of the two relevant sums of squares. That is, there is no reduction of N to take account of degrees of freedom lost. See footnote p. 260.

significance of r. If there is no dispersion about the line of relationship, $s_{y \cdot x}$ will have a value of zero; the equation describes a perfect relationship between the two variables. In this case, as is clear from the formula, r must have a value of 1.

The maximum value of $s_{y \cdot x}$ is one that is equal to s_y. Under these conditions, when the equation of relationship is of no aid in improving our estimates, the formula will give zero as the value of r. Such a value indicates that there is no relationship between the two variables; in other words, that the straight line of best fit is horizontal, passing through the mean of the Y's. It shows that there is no tendency for the high values of Y to be associated with high values of X or for high values of Y to be associated with low values of X. The two variables fluctuate in absolute independence. In such a case the deviation of each point from the fitted line is equal to its deviation from the mean, and the two root-mean-square deviations are equal, as stated.

Zero and unity are thus the limits to the value of r. The values found in practical work fall somewhere between these limits, approaching unity in cases where the degree of relationship is high. The greater the value of r, the greater the confidence that may be placed in the equation as an expression of a relation which is approximated in a high percentage of cases. In the example presented above, dealing with average family expenditures for consumption and average family income after taxes, we have

$$r = \sqrt{1 - \frac{(0.164)^2}{(0.468)^2}}$$

$$= 0.937$$

This coefficient indicates a definite and fairly close connection between these two variables for the cities included in the sample.

The coefficient of correlation may be made more meaningful by giving it the sign of the constant b in the equation of relationship. This sign indicates whether the slope of the line is positive or negative and, when attached to r, enables us to tell whether the relationship is direct or inverse. Thus in the present case high values of one variable are paired with high values of the other. The correlation is positive and the coefficient should be written

+ 0.937. As an example of negative correlation we may cite cotton production and cotton prices. Here the relation is inverse: high values of one variable are generally associated with low values of the other.

The Coefficient of Determination. In the preceding pages we sought to measure the relation between two variable quantities by deriving a linear *equation of average relationship*, supplementing this equation by a *standard error of estimate* and a *coefficient of correlation*. The standard error of estimate defines the degree of variation, in absolute terms, about the line of relationship; the coefficient of correlation provides an abstract measure of the degree of relationship between two variables, when this relationship is defined by a straight line. It will be helpful now, in introducing a final relevant measure, to view the problem of correlation in a somewhat different light.

An investigator uses the methods of correlation analysis because he is concerned about the fact of variation in some quantity that interests him. Thus in seeking to understand crop-yield variations from year to year one may study the effect of variations in rainfall on yields. In the example cited on earlier pages, the concern of the investigator is to explain, in some sense, the rather wide variations among the city averages defining family expenditures for current consumption. From this point of view the problem is set by the fact of variation in the dependent variable; the magnitude of the problem, we may say, is indicated by the variance, or the standard deviation, of the dependent variable.

The variance, among small cities, of average family expenditures for consumption is given by $s_y^2 = 0.21907$ (standard deviation $s_y = 0.468$). This is a measure of the dispersion among the observed values of Y, as given in column (2) of Table 9-6 (p. 261) and as plotted in Fig. 9.3 (p. 256). This dispersion among the observed values of Y is what we are seeking to explain. We may compute a similar measure among the computed values of Y, as these are derived from the linear equation of average relationship. These Y_c's are given in column (3) of Table 9-6. The variance of these computed values, which we may represent by $s_{y_c}^2$, is 0.1922. As a final measure, derived from the difference between the members of each pair of observed and computed values (see columns (4) and (5) of Table 9-6), we have $s_{y \cdot x}^2 = 0.0269$. This is the variance of the residuals, the square of the standard error of estimate

$(s_{y \cdot x} = 0.164)$ to which we have already been introduced. These three variances stand in an interesting relation:

$$s_y^2 = s_{y \cdot x}^2 + s_{y_c}^2 \tag{9.4}$$

$$0.2191 = 0.0269 + 0.1922$$

That is, the original variance of Y is equal to the sum of the variance of the computed values of Y and the variance of the residuals, which measure the difference between observed and computed values.[5] The original variance has been broken into two components. One of these components, $s_{y \cdot x}^2$, may be taken to reflect the influence, on average family expenditures for consumption, of factors other than variations in average family income.

---

[5] Following is a proof of this relation:

A least squares fit to the observed values, Y_0, gives us the equation

$$Y_c = a + bX \tag{1}$$

The series Y_0 and Y_c (Y_c being a computed value) have the same mean, $\overline{Y}$.

Let
$$d = Y_0 - \overline{Y}$$
$$d_c = Y_c - \overline{Y}$$
$$v = Y_0 - Y_c$$

It follows from the least squares fitting process (see Appendix C) that

$$\Sigma v = 0 \tag{2}$$
$$\Sigma vX = 0 \tag{3}$$

Since $\qquad\qquad d_c = Y_c - \overline{Y}$

then, from (1)

$$d_c = a + bX - \overline{Y}$$
$$= a - \overline{Y} + bX \tag{4}$$

If we multiply each residual v by the constant $a - \overline{Y}$, and add, we have, from (2)

$$\Sigma(a - \overline{Y})v = 0 \tag{5}$$

If we multiply each vX by the constant b and add, we have from (3)

$$\Sigma(bX)v = 0 \tag{6}$$

Adding (5) and (6),

$$\Sigma(a - \overline{Y} + bX)v = 0 \tag{7}$$

But from equation (4) the quantity in parentheses is equal to d_c.
Hence
$$\Sigma v d_c = 0 \tag{8}$$

From the initial expressions for d, v, and Y_c it follows that

$$d = v + d_c \tag{9}$$

Hence $\qquad\qquad d^2 = v^2 + 2vd_c + d_c^2 \tag{10}$

and $\qquad\qquad \Sigma d^2 = \Sigma v^2 + 2\Sigma vd_c + \Sigma d_c^2 \tag{11}$

But from (8) $\qquad \Sigma vd_c = 0$

Hence $\qquad\qquad \Sigma d^2 = \Sigma v^2 + \Sigma d_c^2 \tag{12}$

$$\Sigma d^2/N = \Sigma v^2/N + \Sigma d_c/N \tag{13}$$

and
$$s_y^2 = s_{y \cdot x}^2 + s_{y_c}^2 \tag{14}$$

These are the factors responsible for "scatter" about the line of average relationship. If we may speak in terms of "explanation," $s_{y \cdot x}^2$ measures the "unexplained variation" in Y. The other component, s_{yc}^2, may be thought of as a measure of the "explained variation" in Y. For, on the assumption that we are dealing here with a truly causal relationship, we may say that these computed values vary among themselves because they are associated with varying average family incomes—i.e., with varying values of X. If consumption expenditures were a rigid function of family income, with no other factors affecting such expenditures, Y and Y_c would be equal for each value of X; $s_{y \cdot x}^2$ would be zero, and s_{yc}^2 would equal s_y^2. In the present case the component representing "explained variation" is much larger than the component representing "unexplained variation." On the assumption that the two variables are causally related we may say that variation from city to city in average family income accounts for the major part of the variation from city to city in average family expenditures for consumption.

Since the variances cited stand in an additive relationship, we may express the "explained variation," as defined by s_{yc}^2, as a fractional part of the original variation of the Y's, as defined by s_y^2. Thus if we use the symbol d_{yx} to represent the proportion of the variation in Y attributable to, or determined by, variations in X, we may write

$$d_{yx} = \frac{s_{yc}^2}{s_y^2} \tag{9.5}$$

$$= \frac{0.1922}{0.2191} = 0.877$$

This is the *coefficient of determination.*

The coefficient of determination stands in a simple relation to the coefficient of correlation. As a general expression for the square of this coefficient we have

$$r_{yx}^2 = 1 - \frac{s_{y \cdot x}^2}{s_y^2} \tag{9.6}$$

This equation may be put in the form

$$r_{yx}^2 = \frac{s_y^2 - s_{y \cdot x}^2}{s_y^2} \tag{9.7}$$

But from equation (9.4) on p. 266 above we have

$$s_y^2 - s_{y \cdot x}^2 = s_{yc}^2 \tag{9.8}$$

The left hand member of equation (9.8) is the numerator of equation (9.7). Substituting in (9.8) the equivalent value, s_{yc}^2, we have

$$r_{yx}^2 = \frac{s_{yc}^2}{s_y^2} = d_{yx} \tag{9.9}$$

The coefficient of determination is equal to the square of the coefficient of correlation. This last equation, (9.9), provides an illuminating way of regarding the coefficient of correlation. The coefficient of correlation, squared, is equal to the variance of the computed values of Y (the "explained" variance) divided by the variance of the observed values of Y. With reservations to be noted shortly, r^2 may be said to measure the proportion of the variability of the dependent variable that is attributable to the independent variable.

The coefficient of determination is a highly useful measure, but one that is obviously open to misinterpretation. In the first place, the term itself may be misleading, in that it implies that the variable X stands in a determining or causal relationship to the variable Y. The statistical evidence itself never establishes the existence of such causality. All the statistical evidence can do is to define *covariation*, that term being used in a perfectly neutral sense. Whether causality is present or not, and which way it runs if it is present, must be determined on the basis of evidence other than the quantitative observations. (What constitutes causality in an ultimate sense may, indeed, be beyond the power of an investigator to establish.) Because this is so, the words "explained" and "unexplained" have been set within quotation marks in the preceding discussion.[6] In the present case there is a rational basis for assuming that expenditures for consumption are in part determined, in a meaningful sense, by the size of family income; there is some justification for the use of the term in this instance.

The second qualification has to do with the measure of variation employed. The additive relationship that permits the breaking of total variation into "explained" and "unexplained" components holds only for the variances. It does not hold for the standard

---

[6] Here, as in systematic semantics, quotation marks around a word may be taken to mean "Beware, it's loaded."

deviations. The fact that variation is measured by the square of the standard deviation must be borne in mind when a coefficient of determination is cited.

A third general point applies to all the measures of correlation discussed in the preceding pages. We have dealt only with the linear case—the case in which the function defining average relationship is a straight line. Measures similar to d_{yx} may be computed when other functions are used, but the function employed in a given instance must be specified if the measure is to be unambiguous.

With these reservations in mind, we may say that the evidence of our present sample of 33 small cities indicates that 87.7 percent of the variation from city to city in average family expenditures for consumption is due to variation in average family income, after taxes. Such a statement, properly qualified, is informative and useful.

Details of calculation. In the preceding section an attempt has been made to explain the various measures necessary in studying the relationship between variable quantities without introducing a detailed explanation of procedure. We may now return to a consideration of the details of calculation, including certain methods by which this calculation may be reduced to a minimum.

The procedure followed in the preceding illustration is a logical one to employ in deriving the three required values. This method is capable of general application, but the labor involved may be materially reduced by taking advantage of a short-cut method of deriving $s_{y.x}$. This method may be first explained with reference to data of the type dealt with above. And, for the present, the discussion will be confined to cases in which the relationship between variables may be described by a straight line.

The first problem is the derivation of the equation of relationship. A line of the type

$$Y = a + bX$$

is fitted by the method of least squares.

The next step is the computation of $s_{y.x}^2$, the square of the standard error of estimate. This was done in the above illustration by measuring the deviation of each individual observation from the fitted line, and getting the mean-square of these deviations.

It may be shown[7] that this value can be derived from the following equation:

$$s_{y \cdot x}^2 = \frac{\Sigma(Y^2) - a\Sigma(Y) - b\Sigma(XY)}{N}$$

The quantities a and b are the constants in the equation to the fitted straight line. The other values relate to the original observations. Substituting in this equation a and b and the other necessary values, taken from Table 9-5, we have[8]

$$s_{y \cdot x}^2 = \frac{453.9073 - (0.870745 \times 121.41) - (0.739628 \times 469.5635)}{33}$$

$$= 0.0269$$

$$s_{y \cdot x} = 0.164$$

From this point the procedure may follow that already described, r being computed from the formula

$$r = \sqrt{1 - \frac{s_{y \cdot x}^2}{s_y^2}}$$

The coefficient r may be secured, however, without computing $s_{y \cdot x}$

---

[7] The general formula for the standard error of estimate is

$$s_{y \cdot x}^2 = \Sigma v^2 / N \qquad (1)$$

where each
$$v = Y_0 - Y_c$$
$$= Y_0 - a - bX \qquad (2)$$

There will be as many equations of this type as there are points. Multiplying each equation by v, and adding, we have

$$\Sigma v^2 = \Sigma v Y_0 - a\Sigma v - b\Sigma vX \qquad (3)$$

But
$$\Sigma v = 0$$
and
$$\Sigma vX = 0$$
and therefore

$$\Sigma v^2 = \Sigma v Y_0 \qquad (4)$$

Returning to equation (2), we multiply throughout by Y_0 and add, securing

$$\Sigma v Y_0 = \Sigma Y_0^2 - a\Sigma Y_0 - b\Sigma(XY_0) \qquad (5)$$

Substituting the equivalent of $\Sigma v Y_0$ in equation (4), we have

$$\Sigma v^2 = \Sigma Y_0^2 - a\Sigma Y_0 - b\Sigma(XY_0) \qquad (6)$$

from which the given formula for $s_{y \cdot x}^2$ is derived. (The symbol Y of the text formula represents, of course, observed values of Y, for which the symbol Y_0 has been used in this note.)

[8] For the sake of formal consistency the values of a and b are here given to a greater number of decimal places than in the equation as first presented.

as an intermediate value. The above formula for r may be reduced to

$$r^2 = \frac{a\Sigma(Y) + b\Sigma(XY) - Nc_y^2}{\Sigma(Y^2) - Nc_y^2} \qquad (9.10)$$

where c_y is the difference between the mean Y and the origin employed in the calculations.[9] If the origin is zero on the original Y scale, c_y will be equal to the arithmetic mean of the Y's.

In the present case, using the data of Table 9-5, we have

$$c_y = \frac{121.41}{33} = 3.67909$$

The other values are the same as those employed above in computing $s_{y\cdot x}^2$. Substituting in formula (9.10), we have

$$r^2 = \frac{6.341362}{7.2292}$$

$$= 0.8772$$

$$r = + 0.937$$

In effect, then, the labor of fitting a straight line by the method of least squares gives us most of the quantities needed in securing s and r, the two other measures necessary for a complete description

---

[9] The formula

$$r^2 = 1 - \frac{s_{y\cdot x}^2}{s_y^2}$$

may be written

$$r^2 = 1 - \frac{\Sigma(v^2)}{\Sigma(y^2)}$$

in which y refers to deviations from the arithmetic mean of the Y's. But

$$\frac{\Sigma(y^2)}{N} = \frac{(\Sigma Y^2)}{N} - c_y^2$$

where Y represents a deviation from an arbitrary origin (in this case zero on the original scale) and c_y represents the difference between this origin and the mean of the Y's.

Therefore

$$r^2 = 1 - \frac{\Sigma(v^2)}{\Sigma(Y^2) - Nc_y^2}$$

Substituting in this equation the equivalent of $\Sigma(v^2)$, as given in footnote 7,

$$r^2 = 1 - \frac{\Sigma(Y^2) - a\Sigma(Y) - b\Sigma(XY)}{\Sigma(Y^2) - Nc_y^2}$$

Simplifying,

$$r^2 = \frac{a\Sigma(Y) + b\Sigma(XY) - Nc_y^2}{\Sigma(Y^2) - Nc_y^2}$$

of the relation between two variable quantities. The only additional quantities required are $\Sigma(Y^2)$ and c_y.

There is a logical validity in the sequence of operations described in the preceding pages, a sequence that yields, first, a least squares equation of average relationship, secondly, a measure of errors involved in basing estimates on such an equation and, thirdly, an abstract measure of degree of correlation. It will be convenient to call this method the "least squares" procedure. An alternative procedure yields the coefficient of correlation as the first measure obtained, with the constants in the equation and the standard error of estimate as supplementary measures. We shall call this latter method the "product-moment" method. (The methods are mathematically equivalent; different terms are employed for convenience of reference.) The arithmetic of the product-moment method is simpler when the number of observations is large and the data are organized in a double frequency table.

The Product-Moment Formula for the Coefficient of Correlation: Ungrouped Data

In the preceding examples the coefficient of correlation has been computed from the formula

$$r^2 = \frac{a\Sigma(Y) + b\Sigma(XY) - Nc_y^2}{\Sigma(Y^2) - Nc_y^2}$$

which is based upon relations involved in fitting a straight line by least squares. We shall show that this reduces to a simpler form often more appropriate in practice.

When a straight line is fitted to data, the origin being at the point of averages, the two normal equations

$$\Sigma(Y) = Na + b\Sigma(X)$$
$$\Sigma(XY) = a\Sigma(X) + b\Sigma(X^2)$$

become

$$\Sigma(y) = Na + b\Sigma(x)$$
$$\Sigma(xy) = a\Sigma(x) + b\Sigma(x^2)$$

where y and x measure deviations from the point of averages. The first of these equations disappears and the second reduces to

$$\Sigma(xy) = b\Sigma(x^2)$$

for

$$\Sigma(x) = 0 \text{ and } \Sigma(y) = 0$$

The slope, b, is the only constant required, and this may be computed from the relationship

$$b = \frac{\Sigma(xy)}{\Sigma(x^2)}$$

Under the same conditions the formula

$$r^2 = \frac{a\Sigma(Y) + b\Sigma(XY) - Nc_y^2}{\Sigma(Y^2) - Nc_y^2}$$

reduces to

$$r^2 = \frac{b\Sigma(xy)}{\Sigma(y^2)}$$

for $c_y = 0$ when the deviations are measured from the mean of the Y's. Substituting for b its equivalent, as just determined, we have

$$r^2 = \frac{\Sigma(xy) \cdot \Sigma(xy)}{\Sigma(y^2) \cdot \Sigma(x^2)}$$

But $\Sigma(y^2) = Ns_y^2$ and $\Sigma(x^2) = Ns_x^2$

Therefore

$$r^2 = \frac{\Sigma(xy) \cdot \Sigma(xy)}{N^2 s_y^2 s_x^2}$$

and

$$r = \frac{\Sigma(xy)}{Ns_x s_y} \tag{9.11}$$

in which x and y refer to deviations from an origin at the point of averages.

This formula may be given as

$$r = \frac{p}{s_x s_y} \tag{9.12}$$

in which

$$p = \frac{\Sigma(xy)}{N}$$

The quantity p is the *mean product* of the paired values of x and y, these variables being measured as deviations about their respective means. The mean product, which is sometimes represented by the symbol s_{xy}, is also termed the *covariance*, or the first *product-moment*. Since the first product-moment is one of the quantities entering into the formula given in (9.11) and (9.12) above, this is called the *product-moment formula* for r.

This formula has been given here in terms of statistics derived from samples. With reference to population characteristics we should use symbols for population parameters. Thus we should have

$$\rho = \frac{\Sigma(xy)}{N\sigma_x\sigma_y} \tag{9.13}$$

or

$$\rho = \frac{\sigma_{xy}}{\sigma_x\sigma_y} \tag{9.14}$$

In this last formula the symbol σ_{xy} stands for the population covariance, that is, for the mean product of paired X and Y values making up the parent population. It is the population equivalent of p. (The symbols s_{xy} and σ_{xy} are not to be confused with $s_{x \cdot y}$ and with $\sigma_{x \cdot y}$, the standard error of estimate when X is estimated from Y.

The computation of the coefficient of correlation from this formula proceeds along lines somewhat different from those outlined in the preceding section. As we have seen, both the arithmetic mean and the standard deviation may be readily computed by the selection of an arbitrary origin from which all deviations are measured, a later correction being made to offset the error involved in using this arbitrary origin. Similarly, the mean product p may be computed by a short method, requiring the use of assumed means and the application of a correction at the end of the process.

If x' and y' represent deviations from points arbitrarily selected as assumed means, while p' represents the mean product of such deviations, then

$$p' = \frac{\Sigma(x'y')}{N}$$

The computation of p' is not difficult, for deviations may be measured from central points, and may be expressed in class-interval units. Having p' we may secure the true mean product from the formula

$$p = p' - c_x c_y$$

in which c_x and c_y represent the differences between the true and assumed means of the x's and y's, respectively.[10]

An example. This method may be illustrated with reference, first, to ungrouped data, using the figures for family income (X) and family expenditures for consumption (Y), by cities. The values required for this computation, as given in Table 9-5, are

$$N = 33$$
$$\Sigma(X) = 125.30$$
$$\Sigma(Y) = 121.41$$
$$\Sigma(X^2) = 487.3518$$
$$\Sigma(Y^2) = 453.9073$$
$$\Sigma(XY) = 469.5635$$

The mean product may be computed from the formula

$$p = \frac{\Sigma(xy)}{N} = \frac{\Sigma(x'y')}{N} - c_x c_y$$

We may select as arbitrary origin the actual origin on the two original scales. Hence we have

$$p = \frac{\Sigma(XY)}{N} - c_x c_y \qquad (9.15)$$

(When the arbitrary origin is at zero on the original scales, the

[10] The following is a proof of this relationship:
$$x' = \text{deviation of any point from assumed mean of } x\text{'s}$$
$$x = \text{deviation of same point from true mean of } x\text{'s}$$
$$c_x = \text{difference between true and assumed means of } x\text{'s}$$
$$y' = \text{deviation of same point from assumed mean of } y\text{'s}$$
$$y = \text{deviation of same point from true mean of } y\text{'s}$$
$$c_y = \text{difference between true and assumed means of } y\text{'s}$$
$$x' = x + c_x$$
$$y' = y + c_y$$
$$x'y' = (x + c_x)(y + c_y) = xy + c_x y + c_y x + c_x c_y$$
For the sum of all such products for N points, we have
$$\Sigma(x'y') = \Sigma(xy) + c_x\Sigma(y) + c_y\Sigma(x) + Nc_x c_y$$
But
$$\Sigma(y) = 0 \text{ and } \Sigma(x) = 0.$$
Therefore
$$\Sigma(x'y') = \Sigma(xy) + Nc_x c_y$$
$$\frac{\Sigma(x'y')}{N} = \frac{\Sigma(xy)}{N} + c_x c_y$$
$$\frac{\Sigma(xy)}{N} = \frac{\Sigma(x'y')}{N} - c_x c_y$$
$$\text{or } p = p' - c_x c_y$$

symbol X corresponds to x' and Y corresponds to y', as used in the formulas.)

For the two standard deviations

$$s_x = \sqrt{\frac{\Sigma(X^2)}{N} - c_x^2}$$

$$s_y = \sqrt{\frac{\Sigma(Y^2)}{N} - c_y^2}$$

These measures may be computed readily from the values secured from Table 9-5:

$c_x = 125.30/33 = 3.79697$ $c_y = 121.41/33 = 3.67909$
$c_x^2 = 14.41698$ $c_y^2 = 13.53570$

$$p = \frac{469.5635}{33} - (3.79697 \times 3.67909)$$

$$= + 0.25981$$

$$s_x = \sqrt{\frac{487.3518}{33} - 14.41698} \qquad s_y = \sqrt{\frac{453.9073}{33} - 13.53570}$$

$$= 0.5927 \qquad\qquad\qquad\qquad = 0.4680$$

Solving for the coefficient of correlation

$$r = \frac{p}{s_x s_y} = \frac{+ 0.25981}{0.5927 \times 0.4680}$$

$$= + 0.93666$$

The equation to the straight line that describes the average relationship between X and Y may be derived from the values required for the preceding calculations. When the origin is at the point of averages this equation may be written

$$y = \rho \frac{\sigma_y}{\sigma_x} x \qquad (9.16)$$

or, in terms of sample measures

$$y = r \frac{s_y}{s_x} x \qquad (9.17)$$

Substituting the proper values,[11] we have

$$y = + 0.93666 \frac{0.4680}{0.5927} x$$

$$= 0.7396x$$

[11] For purposes of numerical consistency r is carried to five places in this calculation.

This is the equation secured by the method of least squares. The constant term representing the y-intercept disappears, since the origin is at the point of averages, through which the least squares line must pass.[12]

When the product-moment method is employed in computing the coefficient of correlation and in determining the equation of regression, the standard error, $s_{y \cdot x}$, may be derived by a simple change in the formula first presented for r. From the expression

$$r^2 = 1 - \frac{s_{y \cdot x}^2}{s_y^2}$$

we may secure the formula

$$s_{y \cdot x} = s_y \sqrt{1 - r^2} \qquad (9.18)$$

which enables us to compute $s_{y \cdot x}$, if we have s_y and r. In the present case,

$$s_{y \cdot x} = 0.4680 \sqrt{1 - 0.877332}$$
$$= 0.164$$

The Product-Moment Method: Classified Data

In the examples presented above we have had only 33 observations. With a larger number it becomes difficult to retain the individual values in the study of relationships. These individual items must be grouped in significant classes, and all computations

---

[12] That the formula $y = \rho \frac{\sigma_y}{\sigma_x} x$ is equivalent to the formula based upon the method of least squares may be readily demonstrated. When the line passes through the point of averages, the equation, $Y = a + bX$, becomes $y = bx$.

But $b = \frac{\Sigma(xy)}{\Sigma(x^2)}$. We may write, accordingly, $y_c = \frac{\Sigma(xy)}{\Sigma(x^2)} x$.

This is equivalent to $\qquad y_c = \rho \frac{\sigma_y}{\sigma_x} x$

for the latter may be written

(1) $y_c = \dfrac{\Sigma(xy)}{N\sigma_y\sigma_x} \cdot \dfrac{\sigma_y}{\sigma_x} x$ \qquad (3) $y_c = \dfrac{\Sigma(xy)}{N\sqrt{\dfrac{\Sigma(x^2)}{N}} \cdot \sqrt{\dfrac{\Sigma(x^2)}{N}}} x$

(2) $y_c = \dfrac{\Sigma(xy)}{N\sigma_x \cdot \sigma_x} x$ \qquad (4) $y_c = \dfrac{\Sigma(xy)}{\Sigma(x^2)} x$

(The symbol y_c is employed for the computed value of y, in these equations, to avoid confusion with the actual y's which appear in the right-hand members of the equations.)

X—Federal Reserve Bank Discount Rate

Discount Rate	1.25 to 1.74%	1.75 to 2.24%	2.25 to 2.74%	2.75 to 3.24%	3.25 to 3.74%	3.75 to 4.24%	4.25 to 4.74%	4.75 to 5.24%	5.25 to 5.74%	5.75 to 6.24%	6.25 to 6.74%	6.75 to 7.24%
7.75 to 8.24%										1	1	2
7.25 to 7.74%										11 (|||| |||| ||)	11 (|||| |||| |)	5
6.75 to 7.24%								4	5	27 (|||| |||| |||| |||| |||| ||)	11 (|||| |||| |)	16 (|||| |||| |||| |)
6.25 to 6.74%						13	13	12	7	12 (|||| |||| ||)	1	3
5.75 to 6.24%				13	14		45 (|||| |||| |||| |||| |||| |||| |||| |||| |||| |||||)		6	12 (|||| |||| ||)		

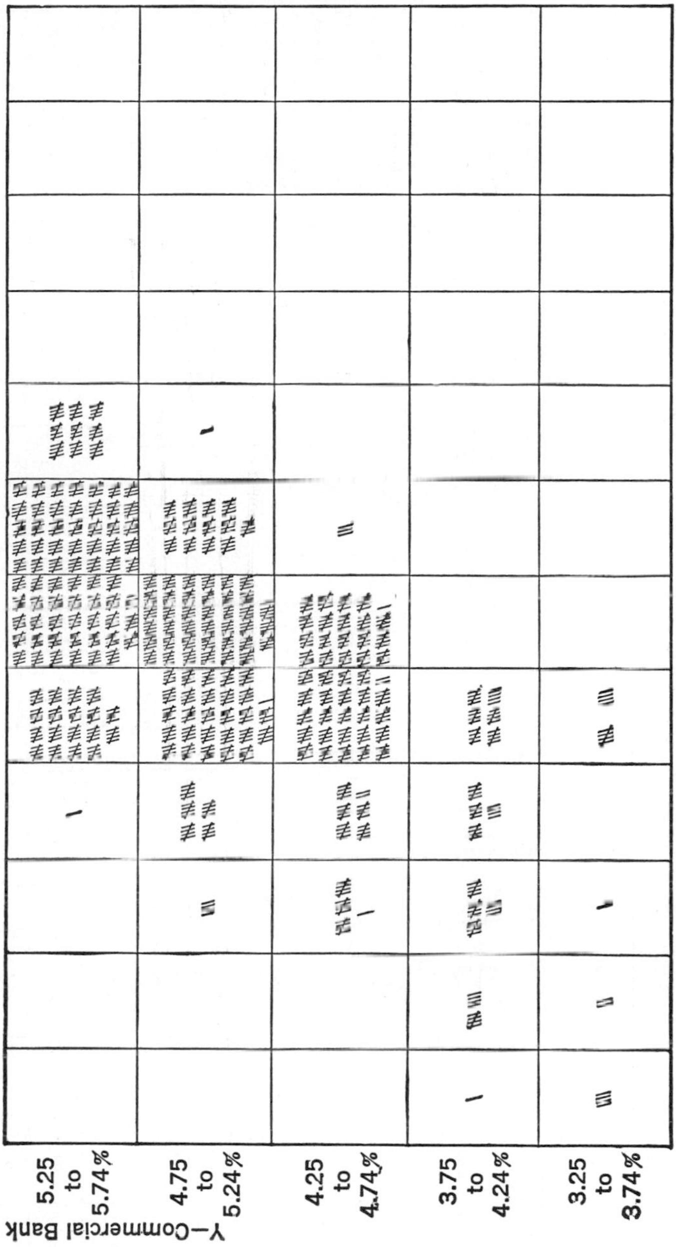

FIG. 9.4. Tabulation of Items in a Correlation Table.

LINEAR CORRELATION

TABLE 9–7

Correlation Table Showing the Relation between Federal Reserve Bank Discount Rates and the Discount Rates of Commercial Banks, and Illustrating the Computation of Quantities Needed in the Measurement of Correlation

Each cell in the grid below is shown as: (product per pair $x'y'$) / (cell frequency f) / (cell total). The X columns are headed by class interval with midpoint in parentheses.

Y — Discount rates of commercial banks (percent) (row labels) vs **X — Discount rates of federal reserve banks (percent)** (column headers)

Class interval	Mid-point	f	d'	fd'	fd'²	1.25–1.74 (1.50)	1.75–2.24 (2.00)	2.25–2.74 (2.50)	2.75–3.24 (3.00)	3.25–3.74 (3.50)	3.75–4.24 (4.00)	4.25–4.74 (4.50)	4.75–5.24 (5.00)	5.25–5.74 (5.50)	5.75–6.24 (6.00)	6.25–6.74 (6.50)	6.75–7.24 (7.00)	Total	Σ(x'y')
7.75–8.24	8.00	4	+5	20	100										+15 / 1 / (+15)	+20 / 1 / (+20)	+25 / 2 / (+50)		85
7.25–7.74	7.50	17	+4	68	272										+12 / 7 / (+84)	+16 / 9 / (+144)	+20 / 1 / (+20)		248
6.75–7.24	7.00	117	+3	351	1,053								+3 / 5 / (+15)	+6 / 4 / (+24)	+9 / 63 / (+567)	+12 / 9 / (+108)	+15 / 36 / (+540)		1,254
6.25–6.74	6.50	62	+2	124	248							0 / 4 / (0)	+2 / 22 / (+44)	+4 / 10 / (+40)	+6 / 22 / (+132)	+8 / 1 / (+8)	+10 / 3 / (+30)		254
5.75–6.24	6.00	366	+1	366	366					−2 / 9 / (−18)	−1 / 21 / (−21)	0 / 146 / (0)	+1 / 150 / (+150)	+2 / 8 / (+16)	+3 / 32 / (+96)				223
5.25–5.74	5.50	475	0	0	0				0 / 1 / (0)	0 / 90 / (0)	0 / 164 / (0)	0 / 175 / (0)	0 / 45 / (0)						
4.75–5.24	5.00	402	−1	−402	402			+4 / 4 / (+16)	+3 / 25 / (+75)	+2 / 111 / (+222)	+1 / 196 / (+196)	0 / 65 / (0)	−1 / 1 / (−1)						508
4.25–4.74	4.50	264	−2	−528	1,056			+8 / 16 / (+128)	+6 / 27 / (+162)	+4 / 122 / (+488)	+2 / 96 / (+192)	0 / 3 / (0)							970
3.75–4.24	4.00	77	−3	−231	693	+18 / 1 / (+18)	+15 / 9 / (+135)	+12 / 19 / (+228)	+9 / 19 / (+171)	+6 / 29 / (+174)									726
3.25–3.74	3.50	16	−4	−64	256	+24 / 4 / (+96)	+20 / 2 / (+40)	+16 / 1 / (+16)		+8 / 9 / (+72)									224
Total		1,800		−296	4,446														4,492
f						5	11	40	72	370	477	393	223	22	125	20	42	1,800	
d'						−6	−5	−4	−3	−2	−1	0	+1	+2	+3	+4	+5		
fd'						−30	−55	−160	−216	−740	−477	0	223	44	375	80	210	−746	
fd'²						180	275	640	648	1,480	477	0	223	88	1,125	320	1,050	6,506	

must be based upon these grouped data. This means, merely, that we must handle data organized in frequency distributions. Since we are dealing with two variables, however, the simple frequency table must be modified to meet the needs of the present problem. Such a modified frequency table, arranged to facilitate the computation of the values needed in studying relationship, is termed a *correlation table* or a *bivariate frequency table*. When the investigator is working with such a table, the product-moment method usually offers the simplest and easiest procedure.

Construction of a Correlation Table. As a typical problem involving the construction of a correlation table we may consider the relation between discount rates of commercial banks and the corresponding discount rates of Federal Reserve banks. Since the paper discounted by commercial banks may be rediscounted by Federal Reserve Banks for member banks, some degree of relationship between the rates may be expected. Our present object is the measurement of that relationship.

The first step is the tabulation of the original observations. Monthly values of each variable were secured for each of the twelve Federal Reserve cities over a period of 150 months.[13] In the process of tabulation the items must be combined so that a Federal Reserve bank discount rate is paired with the corresponding rate charged by the commercial banks of the same city. Fig. 9.4 illustrates the method of tabulation.

Tabulation having been completed, a correlation table designed to facilitate later computations may be constructed. Table 9-7 illustrates a suitable form. In this table, it will be noted, an arbitrary origin (M') is employed for each variable. M' is 4.50 for the X's, 5.50 for the Y's. Deviations represented by x' and y' are measured in class-interval units from this origin. In each compartment of the correlation table there are three figures, involved in the computation of $\Sigma(x'y')$. The figure in the center indicates the number of items falling in that compartment. Thus there are seven pairs having X values between 5.75 and 6.25 (midpoint 6.0) and Y values between 7.25 and 7.75 (midpoint 7.5). For each of these pairs x' (the deviation from the assumed mean of the X's)

---

[13] The period covered extended from July, 1920, to December, 1932. For the first part of this period discount rates of the Federal Reserve banks relate to trade acceptances; for later years they are "rates for member banks on eligible paper." The commercial bank rates are those charged on customers' prime commercial paper. The customary rate over a given 30-day period was taken as of the middle of that period.

is $+3$, in class-interval units, and y' (the deviation from the assumed mean of the Y's) is $+4$, in class-interval units. For each pair, therefore, $x'y' = +12$. This figure appears at the top of the compartment. But there are seven pairs in this compartment, so the sum of $x'y'$ for this group is $+84$. This figure appears in parentheses at the bottom of the compartment. To secure $\Sigma(x'y')$ for the entire table it is necessary to add algebraically the values secured in this way for all compartments. The addition is first carried out for the different rows, the subtotals being given in the column at the right of the table. It is found that $\Sigma(x'y') = +4{,}492$, in class-interval units.

TABLE 9–8

Calculation of the Coefficient of Correlation between the Discount Rates of Commercial Banks and of Federal Reserve Banks*
(Calculations based on the entries in Table 9.7)

$M'_x = 4.50$	$M'_y = 5.50$	$p = \dfrac{\Sigma(x'y')}{N} - c_x c_y$
$c_x = \dfrac{-746}{1{,}800} = -.414$	$c_y = \dfrac{-296}{1{,}800} = -.164$	$= \dfrac{+4{,}492}{1{,}800} - [(-.414)(-.164)]$
$c_x^2 = (-.414)^2 = .171$	$c_y^2 = (-.164)^2 = .027$	$= +2.4956 - .0679$
$s_{x'}^2 = \dfrac{6{,}506}{1{,}800} = 3.614$	$s_{y'}^2 = \dfrac{4{,}446}{1{,}800} = 2.470$	$= +2.4277$
$s_x^2 = s_{x'}^2 - c_x^2$	$s_y^2 = s_{y'}^2 - c_y^2$	$r = \dfrac{p}{s_x s_y}$
$= 3.614 - .171$	$= 2.470 - .027$	$= \dfrac{+2.4277}{(1.855)(1.563)}$
$= 3.443$	$= 2.443$	
$s_x = 1.855$	$s_y = 1.563$	$= \dfrac{+2.4277}{2.8994}$
$M_x = 4.50 - .5(.414)$	$M_y = 5.50 - .5(.164)$	
$= 4.293$	$= 5.418$	$r = +.837$

Note: The class-interval unit has been employed in all the computations shown in this table.

* We here use $s_{x'}^2$ to represent the mean square deviation of the x's about the arbitrary origin M'_x, and $s_{y'}^2$ to represent the mean square deviation about M'_y. These symbols correspond to s_a^2 in Chapter 5.

The Computation of r and the Derivation of the Equation of Relationship. Details of the computation of the coefficient of correlation are given in Table 9-8. The standard deviations and the mean product p, all in class-interval units, are obtained by familiar methods. The coefficient r is then determined from the relation

$$r = \frac{p}{s_x s_y} = \frac{+\,2.4277}{1.855 \times 1.563}$$

$$= +\,0.837$$

It is convenient in such an operation to keep all the quantities entering into the final calculation in class-interval units, as is here done. Sheppard's corrections may be used, when appropriate, in estimating the two standard deviations that enter into the calculation of r. They have not been employed in the present example because the discount rates of Federal Reserve banks are not a continuous variable.

In deriving the equation to the straight line that describes the average relationship between x and y from the general equation

$$y = \rho \frac{\sigma_y}{\sigma_x} x \qquad (9.19)$$

we substitute the sample values s_y and s_x for the population measures σ_y and σ_x. In this use s_y and s_x should be expressed in units of the original scales.[14] This is done by multiplying the present values by the class-intervals.

$$s_x \text{ (in original units)} = 1.855 \times .50 = .9275$$
$$s_y \text{ (in original units)} - 1.563 \times .50 - .7815$$

Substituting the given values in the formula, we have

$$y = .837 \frac{.7815}{.9275} x$$

$$= .705x$$

The Lines of Regression. In the above discussion certain terms ordinarily employed in the treatment of correlation have been purposely omitted. Several of these should be explained.

The equation to the line of best fit in the preceding illustration was found to be

$$y = .705x$$

when the origin was taken at the point of averages. In this equation y is expressed as a function of x; that is, x is taken to be the

---

[14] When the class-intervals happen to be the same, as in the present case, the change is not necessary, as the relation between numerator and denominator is not altered. In practice it is advisable always to express the two standard deviations in original units at this stage of the calculations.

independent variable and y the dependent variable. The equation expresses the average variation in y (discount rates of commercial banks) corresponding to a change of one unit in x (discount rates of Federal Reserve banks). This line of relationship corresponds precisely to a line of trend, which describes the average change in a given series accompanying a unit change in time. A line which thus describes the average relationship between two variables is termed a *line of regression*. Its equation is termed a *regression equation*, and the quantity $\rho \frac{\sigma_y}{\sigma_x}$ (or in sample values $r \frac{s_y}{s_x}$) which gives the slope of such a line is called a *coefficient of regression*. The use of these terms dates back to early studies by Galton, dealing with the relation between the heights of fathers and the heights of sons. Sons, Galton found, deviated less on the average from the mean height of the race than their fathers. Whether the fathers were above or below the average, the sons tended to go back or *regress* towards the mean. He therefore termed the line which graphically described the average relationship between these two variables the *line of regression*. The term is now used generally, as indicated above, though the original meaning has no significance in most of its applications.

In any given case equations to two lines of regression may be computed. One is an expression of the average relationship between a dependent Y-variable and an independent X-variable; the other describes the relationship between a dependent X-variable and an independent Y-variable. The significance of the two may be indicated graphically.

Figure 9.5 is derived directly from the correlation table shown in Fig. 9.4. The circle in each column represents the mean Y-value of all the items falling in that column. Thus in the third column there are 40 cases, including all those with X-values falling between 2.25 percent and 2.75 percent. The Y-values vary, however, being distributed as shown in Table 9-9. Similar mean values are obtained for the other columns. These are plotted in Fig. 9.5, together with the line of regression of Y on X.

In Fig. 9.5 the X-variable (Federal Reserve bank discount rates) is independent. As it increases from 4.0 percent to 4.5, 5.0, 5.5 percent, and so on, the average of commercial bank rates increases also. An average commercial bank rate of 4.29 percent was associated with an average Federal Reserve bank rate of 2.5 percent;

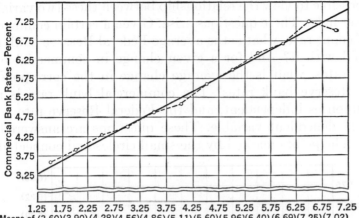

FIG. 9.5. Showing the Relation between Discount Rates of Commercial Banks and Federal Reserve Bank Discount Rates. (The broken line connects the means of the columns and the straight line shows the average change in commercial bank rates corresponding to a unit change in Federal Reserve bank rates; i.e., it represents the regression of Y on X.)

TABLE 9–9

Computation of the Arithmetic Mean of an Array

Class-interval	Midpoint m	Frequency f	fm
1.75 — 5.24	5.0	4	20.0
4.25 — 4.74	4.5	16	72.0
3.75 — 4.24	4.0	19	76.0
3.25 — 3.74	3.5	1	3.5
		40	171.5

$$M = \frac{171.5}{40} = 4.2875$$

an average commercial bank rate of 4.56 percent was associated with an average Federal Reserve bank rate of 3.0 percent, and so on. (The commercial bank rates cited are the means of the entries in the columns referred to.) The slope of the straight line, which is the line of regression or the line of average relationship, measures the average increase in commercial bank rates corresponding to a unit increase in Federal Reserve bank rates.

It is possible to view the relationship between these two variables in another light. These questions arise: Given a certain commercial bank discount rate, what is the average Federal Reserve bank rate associated with it? And for a given change in commercial bank discount rates, what is the average change in the corresponding Federal Reserve bank rates? The commercial bank rate is now looked upon as independent, and the Federal Reserve rate as an associated dependent variable. These questions are answered by Fig. 9.6. The points marked by the small circles and connected by

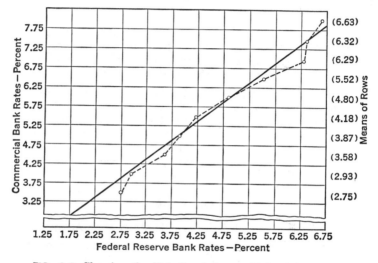

FIG. 9.6. Showing the Relation between Federal Reserve Bank Discount Rates and the Discount Rates of Commercial Banks. (The broken line connects the means of the rows and the straight line shows the average change in Federal Reserve bank rates corresponding to a unit change in commercial bank rates; i.e., it represents the regression of X on Y.)

the broken line show the locations of the arithmetic means of the items falling in the various rows. Thus the 16 X-items in the bottom row have an average value of 2.75 percent. This is the average Federal Reserve bank discount rate associated with a commercial bank rate of 3.5 percent. The average Federal Reserve bank rate associated with a commercial bank rate of 4.0 percent is 2.93 percent, and so on. The straight line fitted to these points indicates the relationship between the two, its slope measuring the average increase (or decrease) in Federal Reserve bank rates associated with a unit change in commercial bank rates.

This is the line of regression of X on Y. The general formula for the equation to this line is:

$$x = \rho \frac{\sigma_x}{\sigma_y} y \qquad (9.20)$$

Substituting the present values, we have

$$x = .837 \frac{.9275}{.7815} y$$

or

$$x = .993y$$

The factors in this equation, it will be seen, are the same as those entering into the formula for the line of regression of y on x.[15] If r is equal to 1 the two lines coincide, and if, in addition, the two standard deviations are equal, the line of regression will bisect the angle formed by the axes. If the points be plotted on a chart scaled in units of the standard deviations, we have $y = rx$; the slope of the line of regression is then equal to the value of r.

The coefficient of regression is represented by the symbol b. In a simple correlation problem there are two such coefficients, representing the slopes of the two lines of regression. These are

$$b_{yx} = r \frac{s_y}{s_x} \qquad (9.21)$$

$$b_{xy} = r \frac{s_x}{s_y} \qquad (9.22)$$

(The subscripts indicate the relation between the two variables. The first subscript refers to the dependent variable in each case.)

[15] The formula

$$x = r \frac{s_x}{s_y} y$$

may be reduced to

$$x = \frac{\Sigma(xy)}{\Sigma(y^2)} y$$

This is the equation to a line fitted to the points plotted in Fig. 9.6 in such a way that the sum of the squares of the *horizontal deviations* is a minimum.
The formula

$$y = \frac{\Sigma(xy)}{\Sigma(x^2)} x$$

is the equation to the line for which the sum of the squares of the *vertical deviations* is a minimum. An understanding of this point may make clear the difference between the two lines of regression.

The coefficient r appears in both formulas. This being so, it is clear that r may be computed from the regression coefficients. For

$$\sqrt{b_{yx} \cdot b_{xy}} = \sqrt{r\frac{s_y}{s_x} \cdot r\frac{s_x}{s_y}} = \sqrt{r^2} = r$$

Thus if we know the slopes of the two lines of regression r may be determined. In the present example

$$r = \sqrt{.705 \times .993} = .837$$

Use of the Equations of Regression. The two equations of regression given above

$$y = .705x$$

and

$$x = .993y$$

describe relations between deviations from the respective arithmetic means. That is, the origin is at the point of averages, and to use the equations we cannot use the original values of X and Y but must express them as deviations from their means. For example, we wish to determine the normal commercial bank rate associated with a Federal Reserve bank rate of 6 percent. The mean value of the X-variable (Federal Reserve bank rates) is 4.293 percent. A rate of 6 percent represents a deviation from the mean of $+ 1.707$. Substituting this value in the first of the above equations, we have

$$y = .705 (+ 1.707)$$
$$= + 1.203$$

This is the average y-deviation associated with an x-deviation of $+ 1.707$. To get the normal commercial bank rate associated with a Federal Reserve rate of 6 percent the quantity $+ 1.203$ percent must be added to the mean commercial bank rate, 5.418 percent. The value we wish is thus 6.621 percent.

This calculation has been rather round-about because of the form of the equation of relationship. This equation can be put in more appropriate form for such computations.

Let

$$\overline{X} = \text{arithmetic mean of the } X\text{'s}$$
$$\overline{Y} = \text{arithmetic mean of the } Y\text{'s}$$

Then

$$y = r \frac{s_y}{s_x} x$$

may be written

$$Y - \overline{Y} = r \frac{s_y}{s_x} (X - \overline{X}) \qquad (9.23)$$

In this last equation X and Y represent the values of the variables on the original scales, and not as deviations from their respective means. In terms of the coordinate chart, it means shifting the origin from the point of averages to a point corresponding to zero on each of the original scales.

To illustrate the greater utility of the equation in this form, the equation

$$y = .705x$$

may be changed in the manner indicated. It becomes

$$Y - 5.418 = .705(X - 4.293)$$
$$= .705X - 3.027$$
$$Y = 2.391 + .705X$$

This is the equation with the origin so shifted that the original values may be employed directly. To determine the commercial bank rate normally associated with a Federal Reserve rate of 6 percent we may substitute the latter value in the equation just secured.

$$Y = 2.391 + (.705 \times 6.0)$$
$$= 6.621$$

Precisely the same results are secured as with the equation in the other form, but for many purposes it is preferable to have an equation in which the actual values may be inserted.

The equation

$$x = r \frac{s_x}{s_y} y$$

may be similarly changed to

$$X - \overline{X} = r \frac{s_x}{s_y} (Y - \overline{Y})$$

Zones of estimate. The significance of the standard error of estimate as a measure supplementary to an equation of regression is brought out graphically in Fig. 9.7. Here we have plotted the line of regression of Y on X (i.e., $Y = 2.391 + 0.705X$). "Zones of estimate," whose limits above and below the line of regression are

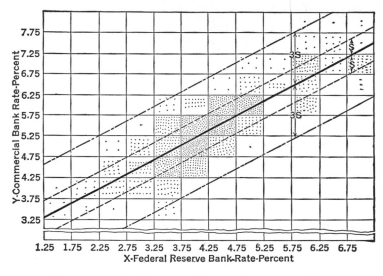

FIG. 9.7. Scatter Diagram of Federal Reserve and Commercial Bank Rates, with Line of Average Relationship and Zones of Estimate.

set by $s_{y \cdot x}$ or multiples of $s_{y \cdot x}$, are defined by broken lines. Within the zone having a width equal to $2S$, centering at the fitted straight line, 68 percent of all the points should fall, on the assumption that the distribution of y-deviations is normal over the entire range of x-values, and that the dispersion of y-deviations is constant over this range.[16] Within the zone having a width equal to $6S$, centering at the fitted straight line, 99.7 percent of all the points should fall, on the same assumption. The smaller the value of S the narrower these zones, and hence the more accurate the estimates that are based upon the equation of average relationship.

---

[16] The assumptions of normality and of constancy of dispersion restrict the practical use of the concept of zones of estimate. Logarithmic and harmonic transformations of the dependent variable may extend the range of use by yielding normal distributions of deviations, where deviations on the arithmetic scale are non-normal (See Mills (Ref. 102). Mood (Ref. 109, pp. 297-9) outlines a more precise procedure for defining prediction intervals (which are analogous to confidence intervals), but the procedure is restricted to normally distributed variates.)

Summary of Correlation Procedure

In the foregoing pages there have been presented two quite different methods of securing the values required in measuring the relationship between two variables. The steps in the two methods may be briefly summarized. The method of least squares is basic in both cases, but that term may appropriately be employed to describe the first method outlined, for the process of fitting the line is the first and fundamental step in that procedure.

The Least Squares Method.

1. Fit a straight line to the data by the method of least squares. A simple arrangement of the data in columns will permit the ready computation of the required values, $\Sigma(X)$, $\Sigma(Y)$, $\Sigma(X^2)$, $\Sigma(Y^2)$, $\Sigma(XY)$. The equation thus obtained describes the average relationship between the two variables.

2. Compute the standard error of estimate, $s_{y \cdot x}$, from the formula

$$s_{y \cdot x}^2 = \frac{\Sigma(Y^2) - a\Sigma(Y) - b\Sigma(XY)}{N}$$

The quantity $s_{y \cdot x}$ is a measure of the reliability of estimates based upon the equation of relationship, and is to be interpreted in the same way as is the standard deviation about an arithmetic mean.

3. Compute the coefficient of correlation, r, from the formula

$$r^2 = 1 - \frac{s_{y \cdot x}^2}{s_y^2}$$

or from

$$r^2 = \frac{a\Sigma(Y) + b\Sigma(XY) - Nc_y^2}{\Sigma(Y^2) - Nc_y^2}$$

Give r the sign of the constant b in the equation of regression. This coefficient is an abstract measure of the degree of relationship between the two variables, in so far as this relationship may be described by a straight line.

4. If an equation describing the regression of X on Y (X being dependent) is desired, the proper values may be substituted in the two normal equations

$$\Sigma(X) = Na + b\Sigma(Y)$$
$$\Sigma(XY) = a\Sigma(Y) + b\Sigma(Y^2)$$

The equation secured will be of the type

$$X = a + bY$$

The standard error of estimate, $s_{x \cdot y}$, may be computed by making the appropriate changes in the formula as given for $s_{y \cdot x}$. The value of r will be the same as in the preceding case, in which Y is dependent.

The Product Moment Method.

A.   Data to be handled as individual items.

1. Arrange the paired observations in parallel columns and compute the quantities $\Sigma(X)$, $\Sigma(Y)$, $\Sigma(X^2)$, $\Sigma(Y^2)$, $\Sigma(XY)$.

2. Divide these quantities throughout by N. For the first two of these quotients we may use the symbols c_x and c_y (i.e.,

$$\frac{\Sigma(X)}{N} = c_x$$

and

$$\frac{\Sigma(Y)}{N} = c_y)$$

3. Compute the mean product from the formula

$$p = \frac{\Sigma(XY)}{N} - c_x c_y$$

4. Compute the two standard deviations from the formulas

$$s_x = \sqrt{\frac{\Sigma(X^2)}{N} - c_x{}^2}$$

$$s_y = \sqrt{\frac{\Sigma(Y^2)}{N} - c_y{}^2}$$

5. Compute the coefficient of correlation from the formula

$$r = \frac{p}{s_x s_y}$$

6. Determine the equations of regression by substituting the proper values in the formulas

$$y = r \frac{s_y}{s_x} x$$

$$x = r \frac{s_x}{s_y} y$$

(Note: For each of these equations the origin is at the point of averages.)

7. If desired, transfer the origin to zero on the two original scales by substituting the arithmetic means in the equations

$$Y - \bar{Y} = r \frac{s_y}{s_x} (X - \bar{X})$$

$$X - \bar{X} = r \frac{s_x}{s_y} (Y - \bar{Y})$$

8. Compute the two standard errors of estimate from the formulas

$$s_{y \cdot x} = s_y \sqrt{1 - r^2}$$
$$s_{x \cdot y} = s_x \sqrt{1 - r^2}$$

B. Data to be classified.
 1. Construct a correlation table.
 2. Select an assumed mean for each variable. Measure the deviations of the various items from the assumed means in class-interval units.
 3. Compute c_x and c_y in class-interval units.
 4. Compute s_x and s_y in class-interval units.
 5. Compute $\Sigma(x'y')$ in class-interval units for each compartment of the correlation table. Total these figures to get $\Sigma(x'y')$ for the whole table.
 6. Determine the value of the mean product in class-interval units from the formula

$$p = \frac{\Sigma(x'y')}{N} - c_x c_y$$

 7. Compute r from the formula

$$r = \frac{p}{s_x s_y}$$

 8. Reduce s_x and s_y to original units.
 9. Determine the equations of regression by substituting the proper values in the formulas

$$y = r \frac{s_y}{s_x} x$$

and

$$x - r \frac{s_x}{s_y} y$$

10. If desired, transfer the origin to zero on the two original scales from the formulas

$$Y - \overline{Y} = r \frac{s_y}{s_x} (X - \overline{X})$$

$$X - \overline{X} = r \frac{s_x}{s_y} (Y - \overline{Y})$$

11. Compute the two standard errors of estimate from the formulas

$$s_{y \cdot x} = s_y \sqrt{1 - r^2}$$

$$s_{x \cdot y} = s_x \sqrt{1 - r^2}$$

It is advisable, in all cases, to construct scatter diagrams and to plot the lines of regression thereon. It is generally possible to derive from such diagrams a truer idea of the relations involved, and of the adequacy of the methods employed, than may be obtained from a study of the figures alone.

A limitation. A question naturally arises as to the degree of generality attaching to the measures of relationship described in the preceding pages. Are they limited to certain types of distributions, or may they be employed as absolutely general and universally valid measures?

As we have seen, the standard deviation has a precise and definite meaning with respect to distributions following the normal law. Having values of the mean and of the standard deviation, we know, in such instances, the exact percentage of cases in the population that will fall within any stated limits. If the distribution departs from the normal type the standard deviation is still a useful measure, but it cannot be interpreted in the same exact sense. Bearing this in mind, the formula

$$r^2 = 1 - \frac{s_{y \cdot x}^2}{s_y^2}$$

may be considered.

When the distribution of the original values of the dependent variable about their mean is normal and the distribution about the least squares line is normal, both $s_{y \cdot x}$ and s_y have specific and exact meanings, and it is perfectly legitimate to compute such a measure as r, based upon the relation of one to the other. Departures from normality in either case reduce the significance of this comparison. But just as the standard deviation remains a useful measure, even for distributions that depart from normality, so do the standard error of estimate and the coefficient of correlation. Care must be taken in their interpretation in such cases, however. It must be recognized that these measures have their full significance only in cases where the distributions of the two variables and the distributions of deviations from regression lines are normal, or approximately so.

A simple example may make clear the effect upon the value of the coefficient of correlation of an extreme departure from a normal distribution. In this example we shall use figures showing the population of each of ten cities and the number of television sets in each of these cities, in 1953 (see Table 9-10). When the first nine of these cities, omitting New York, are treated as a group, the following values are secured:

TABLE 9–10

Television Sets and Population in Ten U. S. Cities, 1953*
(both variables in tens of thousands)

City	Population X	Number of television sets installed Y
Denver	45	12
San Antonio	46	12
Kansas City	47	29
Seattle	48	25
Cincinnati	51	38
Buffalo	58	35
New Orleans	59	16
Milwaukee	65	43
Houston	67	22
New York City	802	345

* The data tabulated are estimates from the Bureau of the Census, *Sales Management*, and the National Broadcasting Company, as cited in *The Economic Almanac*, 1953-4, National Industrial Conference Board. Estimates of television sets are as of April 1, 1953.

$$s_y = 10.68$$

$$s_{y \cdot x} = 9.78$$

$$r = + 0.4027$$

The nine points and the line of regression are plotted in Panel A of Fig. 9.8.

When we include New York City in the group, the values secured for the sample of ten cities are

$$s_y = 96.30$$

$$s_{y \cdot x} = 9.23$$

$$r = + 0.9954$$

The ten points and the line of regression are plotted in Panel B of Fig. 9.8.

The reason for the markedly different results is obvious. The inclusion of the one very large city with the nine smaller cities greatly increases the standard deviations of both variables. That of the Y-variable (number of television sets) is raised from 10.68 to 96.30. But $s_{y \cdot x}$, the measure of the scatter about the fitted line, undergoes no such pronounced change in value. For the nine cities

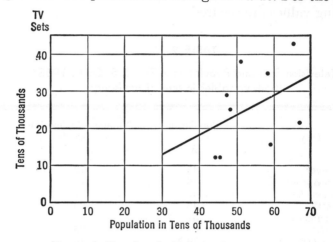

PANEL A. Showing the Relation between Number of Television Sets Installed and Population, in Nine United States Cities, 1953.

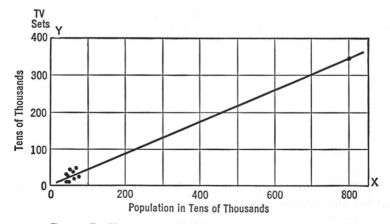

PANEL B. Showing the Relation between Number of Television Sets Installed and Population, in Ten United States Cities, 1953.

FIG. 9.8

it is 9.78; for the ten cities it is 9.23. This is due to the fact that the one exceptional case is given such great weight, in fitting by the method of least squares, that the fitted line must pass through or very near the point representing this observation. Accordingly, $s_{y \cdot x}$ is always affected less than s_y by a single very exceptional case. Since the value of r depends upon the relationship

$$r = \sqrt{1 - \frac{s_{y \cdot x}^2}{s_y^2}}$$

the presence of such a case always tends to increase the value of the measure of correlation. The introduction of the one exceptional case in the above example changes a low and nonsignificant correlation coefficient to one of virtual unity. The result, of course, is meaningless.

While this example represents an extreme instance, the same distortion will be present, in greater or less degree, whenever there is a departure from normality. In practice, use of the various measures of relationship is not restricted to perfectly normal distributions, but the measures we have discussed above lose some degree of significance when derived from non-normal distributions.

The measures of correlation and regression discussed in this chapter have so far been dealt with on the descriptive level only. But such measures, describing relations found in particular samples, are of interest to us primarily as bases for estimates of population parameters, and for tests of hypotheses. We now turn to these problems of inference.

Problems of Inference Involving Measures of Correlation and Regression

Sampling Distribution of the Coefficient of Correlation. The sampling distribution of r varies with the population value of the coefficient of correlation, ρ (rho), and with N, the size of the sample. For samples drawn from normal parent populations the distribution of r tends toward the normal type as N increases; this tendency is much more pronounced for values of ρ close to zero than for values of ρ that depart widely from zero. For ρ close to -1 and $+1$ the value of N must be very large if the distribution of r is to be symmetrical and approximately normal.

The reason for this is clear. If ρ, the population value, is close to unity, say $+ 0.98$, the sample r's have a possible range of only 0.02 in one direction, a possible range of 1.98 in the other direction. But if ρ is equal, say to $+ 0.04$ the range of possible deviation in one direction is very close to the range of possible deviation in the other direction. Under these conditions a distribution of r approaching symmetry is to be expected. This difference is shown graphically in Fig. 9.9. Here we have the sampling distribution of r for $\rho = + 0.10$ and $N = 8$, and the sampling distribution of r for $\rho = + 0.80$ and $N = 8$.

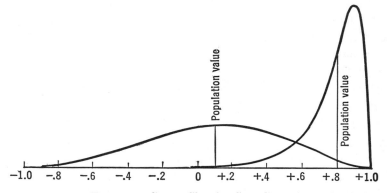

FIG. 9.9. Frequency Curves Showing Sampling Distributions of the Coefficient of Correlation. For Samples with $N = 8$, Drawn from Populations for which $\rho = + 0.10$ and $+ 0.80$.

Using the symbol σ_r for the standard error of r we have, as a general expression holding for samples drawn from normal parent populations,[17]

$$\sigma_r = \frac{1 - \rho^2}{\sqrt{N - 1}} \qquad (9.24)$$

There are two important restrictions on the use of formula (9.24). In the first place, it calls for ρ, the population value of r, and this is not usually known. Investigators frequently use r as derived from a given sample as an approximation to ρ, but the approximation may be a very poor one, especially if N is small. For the special case in which we are testing the hypothesis that a given sample is

---

[17] Since two variables are always involved in samplings of this sort, the term "bivariate normal parent" is often used for such a universe.

drawn from a population for which ρ is zero, formula (9.24) reduces to

$$\sigma_r = \frac{1}{\sqrt{N-1}} \qquad (9.25)$$

For such a test the uncertainty about ρ is, of course, removed.

The second restriction attaches to the interpretation of σ_r as the standard deviation of a normal distribution of sample r's. For samples of small and moderate size the sampling distribution of r may depart widely from the normal type, especially for high values of population ρ. If ρ were at all close to unity, N would have to be quite large if formula (9.24) were to be used with confidence for purposes of statistical inference.

Difficulties arising out of variations in the distribution of r as ρ and N change have been largely overcome. The distribution of r was exactly defined by R. A. Fisher in 1915 (Ref. 49). Tables prepared by F. N. David (Ref. 26) give detailed characteristics of distributions of r for varying values of ρ (0, .1, .2, .3, .4, .5, .6, .7, .8, .9), for N from 3 to 25, and for N of 50, 100, 200, and 400. For the N's and ρ's indicated, these provide more accurate bases for inference than do formulas (9.24) and (9.25).

The Transformation of r. Finally, escape from the limitations that grow out of the non-normality of distributions of r, under many conditions, is provided by an ingenious transformation due to R. A. Fisher (Ref. 50). Fisher has shown that a logarithmic function of r, for which the symbol z' may be used, is distributed in a form acceptably close to the normal for samples of quite moderate size. This function tends to normality rapidly as N increases. This is true regardless of the population value of the coefficient of correlation. For the transformation we have

$$z' = \tfrac{1}{2}\left\{\log_e(1+r) - \log_e(1-r)\right\} \qquad (9.26)$$

The scales of possible values of r and z' are, of course, quite different. For $r = 0$, $z' = 0$; for $r = 1$, $z' = \infty$. Negative values of r give negative values of z'.

Some of the differences between the distributions of r and of z' are brought out by a comparison of the distributions in Fig. 9.10. The pronounced skewness of the distribution of r's for samples of 12 drawn from a population for which $\rho = -0.80$ stands in sharp contrast to the nearly normal distribution of corresponding z''s.

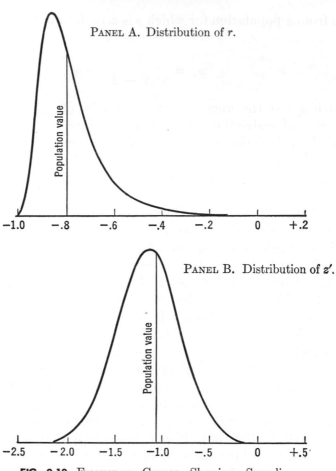

FIG. 9.10. Frequency Curves Showing Sampling Distributions of r and z'. Samples with $N = 12$, Drawn from Populations for which $\rho = -0.80$.

The sample values of z' may be thought of as estimates of a population value ζ (zeta). Close approximations to the mean and the standard deviation of a distribution of z''s are given by

$$\bar{z}' = \zeta + \frac{\rho}{2(N-1)} \qquad (9.27)$$

$$s_{z'} = \frac{1}{\sqrt{N-3}} \qquad (9.28)$$

It is apparent from formula (9.27) that z' has a slight upward bias, that is, that the mean of many sample values of z' would be slightly greater numerically than the population value ζ. This bias is measured by the term $\rho/2(N - 1)$. Correction for the bias may be made if necessary, using r as an estimate of ρ. More important is formula (9.28), giving the standard error of z'. This may be taken to be the standard deviation of a normally distributed variate. Its magnitude depends solely on the size of N, not at all on the population ρ. That is, the form of the distribution of z' is virtually independent of the degree of correlation. It does not vary, as does the distribution of r, with variations in the population ρ. As a result, the sampling errors to which z' is exposed may be estimated with considerable accuracy. (For very small samples David's tables are to be preferred to the z' transformation.)

Transformations of r to z', and from z' to r, are effected most readily by prepared tables (see Appendix Table V.) Examples of the use of such tabled values will be given shortly.

Among the advantages of the z'-transformation is that it replaces r by a function with a distribution of values corresponding more closely to the true significance of observed correlations than do those of r. Thus a change in the value of r from .88 to .98 is equivalent, on the r scale, to a change from .20 to .30. But the first of these differences represents, on the z' scale, a change from 1.38 to 2.30 (a range of .92) while the second represents a change in z' from .20 to .31 (a range of .11). The difference in the first case, on the z' scale, is more than eight times that indicated in the second case. In this the z' scale gives a far more accurate representation of the true significance of observed correlations than does the r scale. A difference of a stated number of points on the r scale is more significant for high values of r than for low values.

In dealing with correlation measures derived from samples from non-normal parent populations, the investigator is on less certain ground than when he works with samples from normal universes. For the distributions of such measures have not been defined with accuracy. It is customary in practice to use the measures of sampling error discussed above, without rigorous requirement of parent normality. Investigations of E. S. Pearson, indicating that sampling distributions of r are not greatly affected by departures from normality in the sampled populations, give some justification for this general practice. But in the present state of our knowledge material departure from parent normality must cloud inferences based on coefficients of correlation.

Examples of Inference in Linear Correlation. In illustrating the estimation of the sampling error of a given value of r, we may use the results cited on earlier pages, defining the relation between discount rates of commercial banks and corresponding discount rates of Federal Reserve banks. The value of r is $+ 0.837$, while N is 1,800. The sample is large, and we may use the relation

$$s_r = \frac{1 - \rho^2}{\sqrt{N - 1}}$$

Substituting r as an approximation to ρ, and using the given value of N we have

$$s_r = \frac{1 - 0.837^2}{\sqrt{1800 - 1}} = \frac{0.299431}{42.41} = 0.007$$

With confidence represented by a probability of 0.99 we may state that the population value of the coefficient of correlation in this case falls between 0.819 and 0.855. The lower of these limits is given, of course, by $+ 0.837 - (2.58 \times 0.007)$, the higher by $+ 0.837 + (2.58 \times 0.007)$.

The first question usually asked when a correlation study has been completed is: Is the value of r significant? More specifically: Is it consistent with the hypothesis that in the population from which the sample has been drawn there is no relation between the two variables here studied? This is, of course, another form of the null hypothesis. In the present case we wish to know whether the facts can disprove this null hypothesis.

In a study of the movements of commodity prices, 1,202 measurements were secured on the timing of advances in the prices of individual commodities during periods of general business revival. Paired with each measurement was a similar observation on the timing of the decline in the price of the given commodity during the succeeding period of general business recession.[18] We desire to know whether there is any relation between the sequence of price revival and the sequence of price recession. Is there a pattern in price movements during business cycles? Evidence of the existence of such a persistent pattern would lend support to the view that cycles represent true regularities in economic life.

These 1,202 pairs of observations yield a correlation coefficient of $+ 0.27$. This does not show a pronounced degree of relationship.

[18] See Mills, Ref. 100, p. 131.

Our chief concern, however, is not with the magnitude of r. We wish to know whether the result is consistent with the hypothesis that the true correlation is zero. For the standard error of r we have

$$s_r = \frac{1}{\sqrt{1,202 - 1}} = 0.029$$

By hypothesis, the population value of r is zero, so the numerator of the fraction is 1.

If the true value of r were zero, and the standard error of r were 0.029, what would the probability be that, as a result of chance, we should secure a coefficient of $+ 0.27$ from a given sample? Since this value represents a departure of more than 9 standard deviations from the hypothetical value of zero, the probability that the difference is due to chance is infinitely small. We conclude that the results are not consistent with the hypothesis that the sequence of price change during revival is unrelated to the sequence of decline in a succeeding recession. The null hypothesis is disproved.

Had the value of T $\left(\text{in this case } T = \frac{r - 0}{s_r}\right)$ been less than 2.58 the conclusion would of course have been different. In such a case the discrepancy between the sample r and the hypothetical value of zero could be attributed to sampling fluctuations. The result would not be inconsistent with the null hypothesis.

Having established that the results are not consistent with the hypothesis that the true value of r is zero, we may compute the standard error of r as actually derived, and estimate confidence limits for the population value. Using the sample r as an approximation to ρ we have

$$s_r = \frac{1 - 0.27^2}{\sqrt{1,202 - 1}} = 0.027$$

Limits derived from the sample r minus and plus 2.58 times s_r are equal, respectively, to $+ 0.20$ and $+ 0.34$. These are the 0.99 confidence limits for ρ.

In the preceding test of significance N was quite large, and it was safe to use formula (9.25), which assumes normality. For small samples other procedures should be employed. R. A. Fisher has shown that in testing the null hypothesis when N is small, a quantity following the familiar t-distribution may be derived from the relation

$$t = \frac{r\sqrt{N-2}}{\sqrt{1-r^2}} \tag{9.29}$$

This is equivalent, of course, to dividing the quantity $r - 0$ (i.e., the deviation of the given r from the hypothetical value of zero) by $\sqrt{1-r^2}/\sqrt{N-2}$. In consulting the t-table for the interpretation of the values thus obtained, n, the number of degrees of freedom, is taken as equal to $N - 2$. (The value of r which is tested here should be obtained without the use of Sheppard's correction.)

As an illustration, we may test the results obtained from a study of the relation between the production and the price of cotton in the United States, covering 35 observations. The value of r is $- 0.65$. We have

$$t = \frac{-0.65\sqrt{35-2}}{\sqrt{1-(-0.65)^2}} = -4.91$$

In consulting the t-table we find that for $n = 33$ the value of t corresponding to a probability of 1 percent is approximately 2.73. If the true value of t were zero, a value as great as 2.73 or greater would occur only 1 time out of 100, as a result of chance fluctuations of sampling. The present value of t is substantially greater than 2.73. It is highly improbable that it reflects a chance drawing from a population in which the true value of r is zero. There appears to be a significant negative correlation between the production and the price of cotton.

Tests of the null hypothesis, for r, may be most readily made by means of a table prepared by R. A. Fisher, showing the values of correlation coefficients at stated levels of significance. Selected values from this table are given in Table 9-11 and in Appendix Table IV. In simple correlation problems, this is to be read with n equal to $N - 2$.

The use of the table requires little explanation. If a sample is based on 12 pairs of observations, with n equal to 10, we would require a coefficient at least as high as 0.7079 before we accept it as significant, if our standard of significance is $P = .01$. For only 1 time out of 100 trials would a sample of 12 drawn from an uncorrelated population yield a value of r as great as 0.7079. If our standard of significance is $P = .05$ we would accept as significant

TABLE 9–11

Values of the Correlation Coefficient for Different Levels of Significance*

n	$P = .05$	$P = .02$	$P = .01$
1	.996917	.9995066	.9998766
2	.95000	.98000	.990000
3	.8783	.93433	.95873
4	.8114	.8822	.91720
5	.7545	.8329	.8745
6	.7067	.7887	.8343
7	.6664	.7498	.7977
8	.6319	.7155	.7646
9	.6021	.6851	.7348
10	.5760	.6581	.7079
11	.5529	.6339	.6835
12	.5324	.6120	.6614
13	.5139	.5923	.6411
14	.4973	.5742	.0220
15	.4821	.5577	.6055
16	.4683	.5425	.5897
17	.4555	.5285	.5751
18	.4438	.5155	.5614
19	.4329	.5034	.5487
20	.4227	.4921	.5368
25	.3809	.4451	.4869
30	.3494	.4093	.4487
35	.3246	.3810	.4182
40	.3044	.3578	.3932
45	.2875	.3384	.3721
50	.2732	.3218	.3541
60	.2500	.2948	.3248
70	.2319	.2737	.3017
80	.2172	.2565	.2830
90	.2050	.2422	.2673
100	.1946	.2301	.2540

* This table is printed here through the courtesy of R. A. Fisher and his publishers, Oliver and Boyd, of Edinburgh. The original appears as Table V.A of *Statistical Methods for Research Workers*.

of a real relationship an r of 0.5760, or greater, obtained from a sample of 12.

We have noted the great value of Fisher's z'-transformation in increasing the effectiveness of inference involving the coefficient of correlation. This transformation is particularly appropriate in estimating ρ for the population of cities which was sampled in deriving data on average family income and average family expenditures on consumption. Calculations cited on preceding pages give us an r of $+ 0.937$, measuring the relation between these two variables for a sample of 33 cities with populations from 2,500 to 30,500. Here we are dealing with a relatively small sample, drawn from a population for which ρ is, apparently, fairly close to unity. Under such conditions the distribution of r will depart materially from normality. Accordingly we shall transform r to z' in setting confidence limits for our estimate of the population ρ.

From Appendix Table V we determine that the value of z' corresponding to an r of $+ 0.937$ is $+ 1.71$. The sample size is 33. We have

$$s_{z'} = \frac{1}{\sqrt{N - 3}} = \frac{1}{\sqrt{33 - 3}} = \frac{1}{5.477} = 0.1826$$

This may be interpreted as the standard deviation of a normal distribution of z''s. We wish to set for z' population limits corresponding to a probability of 0.99. The lower limit will be $+ 1.71 - (2.58 \times 0.1826)$, or 1.24. The upper limit will be $+ 1.71 + (2.58 \times 0.1826)$, or 2.18. Thus we may make the statement, with a confidence of 0.99, that the population z' falls between 1.24 and 2.18. Transforming these limits back to the r scale (using Appendix Table V) we may, with a confidence of 0.99, set our population ρ between $+ 0.8455$ and $+ 0.9748$.

The null hypothesis, for r, may be tested with accuracy by means of the z'-transformation, for large samples for which prepared tables (such as Table 9-11 above) are not suitable.

The transformation to z' makes possible, also, an accurate test of the significance of the difference between two observed correlations. The standard error of the difference between two values of z is given by

$$s_{D_{z'}} = \sqrt{\frac{1}{N_1 - 3} + \frac{1}{N_2 - 3}} \tag{9.30}$$

where N_1 is the number of pairs of observations in the first sample, N_2 the number in the second.

This test may be illustrated with reference to observations on the timing of price changes during business cycles. For 111 commodities we have observations on the timing of price declines in two successive periods of business recession occurring in the late 90's and early 1900's. The degree of relation between the time sequences of commodity price changes in these two recessions is indicated by a coefficient of correlation of $+ 0.22$. For two similar (successive) periods in the 1920's the measure of correlation, based on the prices of 121 commodities, has a value of $+0.36$. There appears to have been a closer approach to a common pattern in the later period than in the earlier. In testing the significance of the difference between the two results we set up the hypothesis that the two samples were drawn from the same parent population, and that therefore the true value of the difference between the two coefficients is zero.

For the two samples we have

$$r_1 = +0.22; \ z_1' = +0.223; \ \frac{1}{N_1 - 3} = \frac{1}{108} = 0.0093$$

$$r_2 = +0.36; \ z_2' = +0.377; \ \frac{1}{N_2 - 3} = \frac{1}{118} = 0.0085$$

The difference to be tested is

$$D_{z'} = 0.377 - 0.223 = 0.154$$

The standard error of this difference is

$$s_{D_{z'}} = \sqrt{0.0093 + 0.0085} - 0.133$$

We wish to know whether $D_{z'}$ is significantly different from zero. We compute, therefore,

$$T' = \frac{D_{z'} - 0}{s_{D_{z'}}} = \frac{0.154 - 0}{0.133} - 1.16$$

Interpreting 1.16 as a normal deviate, we conclude that the difference is not significant. $D_{z'}$ differs from the hypothetical value of zero by only slightly more than one standard deviation. The results are not inconsistent with the hypothesis that the two samples are drawings from the same parent population. There is here no clear evidence that the degree of relationship between price movements in successive cycles was closer in the 1920's than in the earlier period.[19]

---

[19] The time factor enters to cloud statistical inductions relating to samples drawn from different periods. Such an induction should be supported by evidence indicating that fundamental conditions in the field in question have not been altered over the time interval involved. This caution does not, of course, affect the procedure illustrated above.

There is economic significance in another comparison, for which the same test may be used. We have referred above to observations dealing with the relation between the discount rates of commercial banks and of Federal Reserve banks. The sample used in the illustration includes 1,800 observations, covering the period 1920-1932. For this sample $r = +0.837$. Data from another sample, which includes 735 observations, cover the years 1922-1949. For this sample $r = +0.936$. There is overlapping in part, but the second sample is drawn in the main from a later period. A comparison of the results indicates that for recent years changes in commercial bank rates have been tied more directly to Federal Reserve bank rates than was true in the earlier period. (The comparison is not perfect, partly because of the overlapping, which would tend to make the sample results agree, and partly because of some technical differences in the data used. These differences do not preclude comparison, but they call for caution in the interpretation of conclusions.) Transforming the r's to z''s, and measuring the difference, we have $D_{z'} = 0.49$. The standard error of $D_{z'}$, derived from formula (9.30), is 0.044. Thus for the normal deviate, defining the difference in units of the standard deviation, we have

$$T = \frac{0.49 - 0}{0.044} = 11.1$$

In spite of the overlapping, the difference is clearly significant. There is here a strong indication that variations in the two discount rates have been more closely related in recent years than they were in the earlier period. The conclusion calls for moderate qualification because of data differences, but the fundamental indication is probably accurate.

Finally, making use of the z'-transformation, we may combine results secured from the measurement of correlation in different samples. If we have two values of r, obtained from samples drawn from the same population, a weighted average of the two will provide a better estimate of the true correlation than will either of the r's, taken separately. For the averaging process we transform the r's to z''s, weight each z' by the corresponding N, less 3, and average them. For example, we may combine the two coefficients defining relations between the time sequences of price changes in business cycles, since the test has indicated that they do not differ significantly. Here we have

$$\text{Average } z' = \frac{z_1'(N_1 - 3) + z_2'(N_2 - 3)}{(N_1 - 3) + (N_2 - 3)} \tag{9.31}$$

$$= \frac{(+0.223 \times 108) + (+0.377 \times 118)}{226}$$

$$= +0.303$$

The standard error of this weighted average z', we may note, is given by

$$s_{z'} = \frac{1}{\sqrt{N_1 - 3) + (N_2 - 3)}} \tag{9.32}$$

We may wish to transform this weighted z' back to the corresponding r. From Appendix Table V we obtain the value $r = +0.29$. This we may accept as the best estimate we have of the correlation between price declines in successive periods of business recession.

Sampling Errors of the Coefficient of Regression. In certain problems coefficients of regression are more meaningful than coefficients of correlation. For samples drawn from normal universes the standard error of the coefficient of regression b_{yx} may be estimated from

$$s_{b_{yx}} = \frac{s_{y \cdot x}}{s_x \sqrt{N - 1}} \tag{9.33}$$

where $s_{y \cdot x}$ is the standard error of estimate of y.[20] This measure may be used in the usual fashion in problems of estimation and in tests of significance, when the statistics have been derived from large samples. For small samples Fisher has established that "Student's" distribution can be used in testing the significance of the deviation of any sample b from a hypothetical value β (beta). For $(b - \beta)/s_b$, which is the ratio of the difference between observed and hypothetical values of b to the estimated standard error of b, is dis-

[20]
$$s_{y \cdot x} = \sqrt{\frac{\Sigma(y - y_c)^2}{N - 2}}$$

where y denotes a given value of the dependent variable and y_c denotes the corresponding value derived from the equation of regression. In the computation of $s_{y \cdot x}$ for this purpose N is reduced by the number of constants in the equation of regression. Two degrees of freedom have been used up, in effect, in computing y_c.

tributed in the t-distribution. Changing the form for convenience, we have

$$t = \frac{b_{yx} - \beta_{yx}}{s_{b_{yx}}} = \frac{b_{yx} - \beta_{yx}}{s_{y \cdot x}/(s_x\sqrt{N-1})} = \frac{(b_{yx} - \beta_{yx})(s_x\sqrt{N-1})}{s_{y \cdot x}}$$

$$t = \frac{(b_{yx} - \beta_{yx})\sqrt{\Sigma x^2}}{s_{y \cdot x}} \tag{9.34}$$

No population parameter (except that provided by the hypothesis to be tested) enters into the computation of t. Sample values alone are used, otherwise.[21]

As an example of the procedure employed in testing b for significance, in large samples, we may cite the equation to the trend line for New York City temperature, given in Chapter 10 and plotted in Fig. 10.3. Such a trend line is, in effect, a regression function, temperature being the dependent variable and time the independent variable. For the period 1871-1949 the equation of regression is $Y = 52.482 + 0.0346X$, where X is measured in years from an origin at 1910 and Y is measured in degrees Fahrenheit. The coefficient of regression defines an average annual increase in temperature of 0.0346 degrees. Does this coefficient reflect the play of chance, or is it significant of a real secular increase in the temperature of New York City? From formula (9.33) above we obtain $s_b = 0.006$. The null hypothesis to be tested is that $\beta = 0$. Deriving T, the normal deviate, in the customary fashion we have

$$T = \frac{b - \beta}{s_b} = \frac{0.0346 - 0}{0.006} = 5.77$$

The null hypothesis must be rejected. The evidence indicates that there has been a significant increase in mean annual temperatures in New York City over this period of 78 years. (We should note that a test of this sort would usually be of questionable validity, when applied to a series of observations ordered in time, because of the lack of independence of successive observations. With meteorological data, however, it is not unreasonable to assume

---

[21] In the expression under the radical sign in equation (9.34) x represents a deviation from the mean of the x's. For the transition from the previous equation, note that since

$$s_x = \sqrt{\frac{\Sigma x^2}{N-1}}, \quad s_x\sqrt{N-1} \text{ is equal to } \sqrt{\Sigma x^2}. \text{ The quantity } s_{y \cdot x} \text{ in the above equa-}$$

tions is derived as indicated in the preceding footnote.

that there is independence, apart from the slowly acting secular factor with which the test deals.)

Coefficients of Rank Correlation

Limitations arising from non-normality of the populations from which samples are drawn may be avoided, in dealing with certain problems, by the use of what are called *nonparametric* methods. It is the essence of these methods that they involve no assumptions about the parameters of the populations sampled. In certain cases freedom from such assumptions makes possible greater accuracy in the making of inferences—the major objective of most statistical work. In the study of correlation we may escape from parametric assumptions by ordering observations by size, and basing calculations upon the *ranks* thus established. Furthermore, the use of ordered arrangements makes it possible to deal, quantitatively, with individuals or other entities that may be ranked on the basis of qualities not open to exact measurement. Two coefficients of rank correlation will be briefly discussed.

Spearman's Coefficient. Data to be used in an example of the descriptive application of rank correlation methods are shown in Table 9-12. Here, for ten United States cities with populations of 1,000,000 or over, are given average family income after taxes and average family expenditures for consumption in 1950. These cities are ranked in order of average family income, from the highest to the lowest. In columns (4) and (5) of Table 9-12 the money values of income and consumption expenditures for these cities are replaced by measures of rank.

The degree of correlation is indicated by the degree of concordance between the two rankings. A precise measure of correlation is provided by Spearman's coefficient

$$r_r = 1 - \frac{6\Sigma d^2}{N^3 - N} \tag{9.35}$$

where d is the difference between the ranking of a given city in columns (4) and (5), and N is the number of cities included.[22]

[22] This formula may be derived from the usual product-moment formula, with x and y relating to ranks, not to measurements. In this derivation use is made of the fact that the sums of the squares of the deviations of the first N natural numbers from their mean is equal to $\frac{N^3 - N}{12}$.

TABLE 9–12

Illustrating the Computation
of the Spearman Coefficient of Rank Correlation
Family Income after Taxes and
Family Expenditures on Current Consumption, 1950
Averages for Ten Cities with Populations of 1,000,000 and Over*

(1)	(2)	(3)	(4)	(5)	(6)	(7)
	Average	Average	Rank on basis of		Differ-	
	money	expenditures	average	average	ence	
City	income	on	family	consumption	(4)−(5)	
	after taxes	consumption	income	expenditure	d	d^2
Chicago, Ill.	$5,080	$4,905	1	2	− 1	1
Cleveland, Ohio	4,876	4,671	2	3	− 1	1
New York, N. Y.	4,852	4,932	3	1	+ 2	4
Los Angeles, Calif.	4,745	4,661	4	4	0	
San Francisco–						
Oakland, Calif.	4,584	4,477	5	6	− 1	1
Pittsburgh	4,583	4,506	6	5	+ 1	1
St. Louis, Mo.	4,546	4,251	7	9	− 2	4
Philadelphia–						
Camden	4,506	4,384	8	7	+ 1	1
Boston, Mass.	4,200	4,300	9	8	+ 1	1
Baltimore, Md.	3,983	3,919	10	10	0	
Total						14

* From *Bulletin 1097* (revised), U. S. Bureau of Labor Statistics, June, 1953.

The basic quantity needed, Σd^2, is derived as indicated in Table 9-12. Given this quantity and N, the number of cities, we have

$$r_r = 1 - \frac{84}{10^3 - 10}$$
$$= + 0.9152$$

It is clear from formula (9.35) that r_r will be $+ 1$ if the rankings of cities based on the two variables are identical throughout. For then each d will be zero, and Σd^2 will be zero. It may be shown that when the rankings are exactly inverse r_r will be $- 1$. Thus, as for r, r_r may fall between $+ 1$ and $- 1$, being 0 when there is no relation between the two rankings.

Kendall's Coefficient. Some difficulties are faced in basing inferences and tests of significance upon r_r, because its sampling distribution for certain values of N is not known. For this reason special interest attaches to an alternative measure of rank correlation developed by M. G. Kendall. Since the sampling distribution of this measure, τ (tau) is known, it is more generally satisfactory than r_r for purposes of inference.

We may illustrate the computation and use of tau with reference to Bureau of Labor Statistics data for a sample of twelve United States cities defining estimated family budgets and average weekly earnings in manufacturing industries. These are given in Table 9-13. Required calculations are based on the ranks that are given in columns (4) and (5) of that Table. It will be convenient, for purposes of reference, to present these ranks as rows, as below, with the ranking of column (4) in the first row, that of column (5) in the second:

Family budget	1	2	3	4	5	6	7	8	9	10	11	12
Weekly earnings	3	4	1	5	2	11	9	6	7	8	10	12

TABLE 9–13

Estimated Family Budget for Four Persons and Average Weekly Earnings of Production Workers in Manufacturing Industries for Each of Twelve Cities in 1951

(1) City	(2) Estimated family budget*	(3) Average weekly earnings in manufacturing†	(4) Rank on basis of family budget	(5) Rank on basis of average weekly earnings in manufacturing
New Orleans, La.	$3,812	$53.20	1	3
Mobile, Ala.	3,969	54.95	2	4
Scranton, Pa.	4,002	48.27	3	1
Savannah, Ga.	4,067	55.59	4	5
Manchester, N. H.	4,090	51.84	5	2
Buffalo, N. Y.	4,127	73.76	6	11
Portland, Ore.	4,153	70.89	7	9
Memphis, Tenn.	4,190	58.22	8	6
Denver, Colo.	4,199	63.08	9	7
Baltimore, Md.	4,217	64.35	10	8
Seattle, Wash.	4,280	72.60	11	10
Milwaukee, Wis.	4,387	74.79	12	12

* This budget, prepared by the Bureau of Labor Statistics, is the estimated dollar cost, as of October, 1951, of maintaining a family of four (husband, wife, and two children) at a level of adequate living. It does not represent what such a family actually spends.

† From *Employment and Earnings*, U. S. Bureau of Labor Statistics, May, 1954.

As a basic measure of the degree of concordance of two such rankings as those given in Table 9-13 and in the text directly above, Kendall uses a quantity S (standing for *score*). S has two components. The first of these is a positive quantity, P, derived from standings in the second ranking (i.e., those in the second row above) which are in the "right" order, that is, which correspond in order to the standings in the first row. Correspondence, or agreement, in ranking does not necessarily mean identity of ranking. The standard ranking in the first row above is in order of increasing family budgets. As one moves from left to right in the rankings of the first row, average family budgets increase. Therefore the ranking of any two cities in the second row corresponds to the first-row ranking if the city on the right has higher average weekly earnings than the one on the left. ("Right" and "left" refer, of course, to the relative positions of the two entries in the second row of rankings given above.) Thus the first entry, "3," in the second row designates New Orleans. Of the cities that are to the right of New Orleans in the second row entries, 9 exceed New Orleans in average weekly earnings. This represents a contribution of 9 to the value of P. Similarly, there are 8 cities to the right of entry "4," Mobile, that exceed Mobile in average weekly earnings; 9 to the right of entry "1," Scranton, that exceed Scranton; 7 to the right of entry "5," Savannah, that exceed Savannah, etc. (In deriving these numbers for a given city the investigator does not go back to the figures for weekly earnings; he merely counts the number of entries in the second row with rankings that exceed the ranking of the given city.) P is the sum of the positive measures of this sort that may be derived from the rankings in the second row above (or in column (5) of Table 9-13). In detail, we have

$$P = +9 +8 +9 +7 +7 +1 +2 +4 +3 +2 +1 +0 = +53$$

This total, + 53, may be viewed as a measure of the degree of concordance, or agreement, between the two rankings.

The second component of S is a negative quantity, Q, derived from those standings in the second row of rankings given above that are *inverse* to the order of the natural integers in the first row. Thus starting with the entry "3" for New Orleans, we find to the right of it 2 lower rankings, "1" and "2" (standing respectively for Scranton and Manchester). These lower rankings mean, of course, that Scranton and Manchester had lower average weekly earnings than New Orleans, although their estimated family budgets were higher. This is an inverse relationship between the budget and weekly earnings rankings. We have here a contribution of − 2 to the total score. Similarly, there are 2 cities to the right of the entry for Mobile, "4," that have lower rankings; none to the right of the entry for Scranton, "1"; 1 to the right of the entry for Savannah, "5"; etc. Thus Q is built up:

$$Q = -2 -2 -0 -1 -0 -5 -3 -0 -0 -0 -0 -0 = -13$$

The desired total score is the sum of P, defining positive agreement between the rankings, and of Q, defining disagreement, or inverse relations, between the rankings. In the present case

$$S = P + Q = + 53 + (- 13) = + 40$$

The desired abstract measure of degree of relationships between the two rankings is given by

$$\tau = \frac{S}{\frac{1}{2}N(N - 1)} \tag{9.36}$$

$$\tau = \frac{+ 40}{\frac{1}{2}12(12 - 1)} = \frac{+ 40}{66} = + 0.606$$

Kendall's coefficient is $+ 1$ when the two rankings are identical throughout, $- 1$ when they are inverse.[23] It will equal zero when there is no relation between the two rankings.

Tests of Significance of Rank Order Coefficients

We have referred briefly above to problems of inference that are faced in using coefficients of rank correlation. Such problems arise, primarily, in determining whether a given coefficient provides evidence of a significant degree of correlation, in the population, between the attributes on which paired rankings have been based.

Sampling Errors of Spearman's Coefficient. Coefficients of rank correlation, r_r, derived from large samples drawn from a universe for which ρ_r is zero are distributed normally, or effectively so. For the standard deviation of such a distribution of r_r's we have

$$s_{r_r} = \frac{1}{\sqrt{N - 1}} \tag{9.37}$$

This may be applied in testing the null hypothesis when N is large, say 25 or more, and when there are no ties in the rankings of either variable.

For small samples the distribution of r_r is not normal. Kendall (Ref. 78, I, 396-7; Ref. 80, 142) gives tables that may be used in

---

[23] The maximum absolute value of S, which will come when the rankings are identical or exactly inverse, will equal $\frac{1}{2}N(N - 1)$, the denominator of the expression for tau. It is worth noting, too, as a convenient check on the count, that the absolute sum of P and Q, taken without regard to sign, will always equal $\frac{1}{2}N(N - 1)$.

determining the significance of the Spearman coefficient when $N < 9$. For sample sizes between 9 and 25, drawn from uncorrelated parent populations, the distribution of r_r is not known. We should note, also, that the distributions of r_r for samples drawn from correlated parent populations (i.e., $\rho_r \neq 0$) have not been established. Thus there are important areas of indeterminacy in basing inferences on the Spearman coefficient.

Sampling Errors of Kendall's Coefficient. A test of the significance of a given τ is based, for convenience, on the corresponding value of S. When N is greater than 10 the distribution of S, for samples drawn from a universe in which paired rankings are not correlated, may be regarded as normal. The variance of such a distribution (which is, of course, the square of the standard error of S) is a function of N. It is given[24] by

$$s^2_{sc} = \frac{1}{18} N(N-1)(2N+5) \qquad (9.38)$$

In testing S for significance by means of this measure a correction for continuity should be applied. This correction is needed because, in using the normal distribution as an approximation to the exact distribution of S, we are replacing what is in fact a discontinuous distribution (S being a discrete variable) by the continuous normal distribution. The approximation may be improved by reducing the observed value of S by 1, if S is positive, by increasing the observed value of S by 1 if S is negative. (This correction is made only in applying the significance test; the S that is used in deriving τ is uncorrected.)

For the sample of twelve cities represented in Table 9-13 τ is equal to $+0.606$; S is equal to $+40$; S(corrected) is $40-1$, or 39; N is 12. For the variance of S we have, from formula (9.38)

$$s^2_{sc} = \frac{1}{18}(12 \times 11 \times 29) = 212.67$$

and

$$s_{sc} = 14.58$$

In testing the null hypothesis we should use S corrected for

---

[24] See Kendall, Ref. 80, Chapter 5. We should note that formula (9.38) applies to cases in which there are no ties in either ranking. For modifications required when ties are present, see Kendall, Ref. 80, Chapters 4 and 5.

continuity. The general test, then, for samples in which N exceeds 10, is of the form

$$T = \frac{S(\text{corrected}) - 0}{s_{sc}} = \frac{39 - 0}{14.58} = 2.67$$

Here we express the observed value of S (as corrected) as a deviation from the null value, 0, and divide the deviation by the standard error of S. The resulting T, which is to be interpreted as a normal deviate, equals 2.67. Since a deviation as great as this, or greater, would occur less frequently than 1 time out of 100 if chance alone were operative, the null hypothesis may be rejected. The evidence of Table 9-13 indicates that there is significant correlation between rankings of cities based on the cost of maintaining a four-person family and rankings based on average weekly earnings in manufacturing.

The distribution of S derived from samples for which N is 10 or less may not be treated as normal. The above procedure is not applicable to such cases. However, Kendall has established the distributions of S, for values of N from 4 to 10, and has prepared a summary table for use in tests of significance applied to such small sample results. (Kendall, Ref. 80, Appendix Table 1). Thus, for tests of significance, based on S (or τ) the full range of values of N is covered. For this reason Kendall's measures of rank correlation represent a distinct advance over Spearman's, where problems of inference are involved.

Coefficients of rank correlation, with other nonparametric measures, have a considerable range of usefulness. Their freedom from assumptions concerning the nature of population distributions gives them special validity in situations not infrequently encountered in handling economic and other social data. Series ordered in time, which are of special concern in economic analysis, represent one promising area of use for such methods. Some of these uses will be touched upon at later points.

REFERENCES

Clark, C. E., *An Introduction to Statistics*, Chap. 9.

Croxton, F. E. and Cowden, D. J., *Applied General Statistics*, Chap. 22.

Deming, W. E., *Statistical Adjustment of Data*, Chap. 4.

Dixon, W. J. and Massey, F. J. Jr., *Introduction to Statistical Analysis*, Chap. 11.

Ezekiel, M., *Methods of Correlation Analysis*, 2nd ed., Chaps. 3, 5, 7, 18.

Fisher, Sir Ronald (R. A.), *Statistical Methods for Research Workers*, 11th ed., Chap. 6.

Freeman, H. A., *Industrial Statistics*, Chap. 3.

Freund, J. E., *Modern Elementary Statistics*, Chaps. 13, 14.

Goulden, C. H., *Methods of Statistical Analysis*, 2nd ed., Chaps. 6, 7.

Hoel, P. G., *Introduction to Mathematical Statistics*, 2nd ed., Chap. 7.

Hotelling, H., "New Light on the Correlation Coefficient and Its Transforms," *Journal of the Royal Statistical Society*, Series B, Vol. 15, No. 2, 1953.

Kendall, M. G., *The Advanced Theory of Statistics*, 3rd ed., Vol. I, Chaps. 14, 16.

Kendall, M. G., *Rank Correlation Methods*.

Lewis, E. E., *Methods of Statistical Analysis in Economics and Business*, Chap. 12.

Mather, K., *Statistical Analysis in Biology*, 2nd ed., Chap. 8.

Rider, P. R., *An Introduction to Modern Statistical Methods*, Chap. 4.

Riggleman, J. R. and Frisbee, I. N., *Business Statistics*, 3rd ed., Chap. 12.

Snedecor, G. W., *Statistical Methods*, 4th ed., Chaps. 6, 7.

Spurr, W. A., Kellogg, L. S. and Smith, J. H., *Business and Economic Statistics*, Chap. 17.

Tippett, L. H. C., *The Methods of Statistics*, 4th ed., Chaps. 8, 9.

Treloar, A. E., *Elements of Statistical Reasoning*, Chaps. 7, 8, 9.

Walker, H. M. and Lev., *Statistical Inference*, pp. 230-258, 278-287.

Waugh, A. E., *Elements of Statistical Method*, 3rd ed., Chaps. 11, 15.

Yule, G. U. and Kendall, M. G., *An Introduction to the Theory of Statistics.* 14th ed., Chaps. 9, 10, 11, 15.

The publishers and the dates of publication of the books named in chapter reference lists are given in the bibliography at the end of this volume.

CHAPTER 10

The Analysis of Time Series: Secular Trends

The preceding sections have dealt with distributions of observations organized on the basis of frequency of occurrence. We have been concerned with patterns of variation, and with methods appropriate to inductive generalization and the testing of hypotheses when the variation present reflects the play of random factors. When data are organized in such frequency distributions the order, in time, of the various observations is neglected, as having no bearing on the problems at issue. Thus when a coin is tossed there is no reason for distinguishing the tenth throw from the second. We turn now to procedures employed when the chronological order in which observations are made is of the essence of the problems being studied—when our interest lies in variation over time. This is obviously the case in the study of biological growth; it is true for the physicist investigating variations in radioactivity over time. It is true, also, of many of the central problems faced in the social and economic sciences, and in business administration. Changes in birth rates and death rates, changes in national income, changes in prices and in the physical volume of production, variations in sales and in profits—in all these the time sequence is crucial.

Movements in Historical Variables

Time series, or historical variables as Schumpeter has called them, are subject to the play of a diversity of forces. Random factors are present, as with the frequency series discussed above,

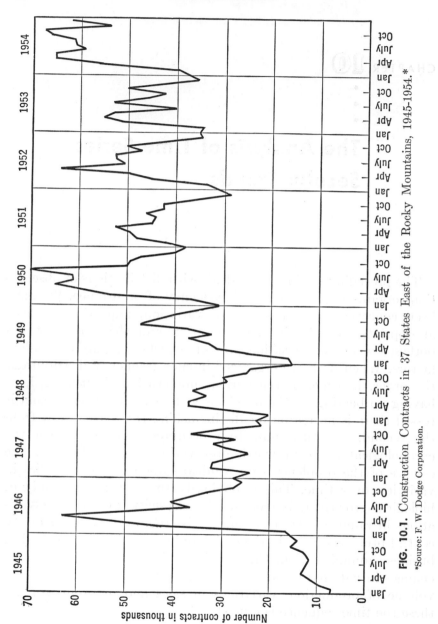

FIG. 10.1. Construction Contracts in 37 States East of the Rocky Mountains, 1945-1954.*

*Source: F. W. Dodge Corporation.

but nonrandom factors are present too, and often dominate the behavior of the observations. The presence of nonrandom factors, indeed, gives rise to the special problems faced in the analysis of time series. Techniques suitable to the study of random variation are not appropriate in dealing with patterns of variation due to specific nonrandom factors.

A graphic representation of observations on a historical variable reveals, usually, a succession of discontinuous changes from month to month or year to year. If we are dealing, for example, with number of construction contracts awarded, by months, we have the record plotted in Fig. 10.1. The entry for any one month will be the resultant of many impinging factors—the plans of diverse private builders, the state of employment, construction programs of governmental units of all sorts, the time of year and the state of the weather, the supply of materials and the level of costs, the business situation, prevailing or impending strikes, the existence of peace or war, etc. In studying a historical series of this sort it is usually desirable to classify these diverse factors into categories that are significant for the purpose in hand and that correspond to realities in the field of study. Any such classification must be, in part at least, arbitrary. It will be affected by the preconceptions of the investigator, by the immediate objects of his study, and by the theoretical framework he has set up. Obviously, if the classification employed is to be useful these preconceptions and this framework must be in harmony with the processes to which the observations relate. Having set up such a classification the investigator seeks to decompose the observations into elements corresponding to the classes he has set up. The statistical procedures to be discussed in this and the two following chapters have as their central objective such "decomposition."

The forces affecting historical variables have been classified as nonrecurring or recurring; as evolutionary, periodic, or random. There has been introduced, also, the notion of structural change— a change, which may be sudden or progressive, in the relations among the elements of a system. Most commonly employed, and perhaps most generally useful in dealing with individual series, is a classification that distinguishes secular, seasonal, cyclical, and random components.

In speaking of the secular component, or the *secular trend*, of a historical variable we use the term secular in a sense relating to the ages, to long periods of time. Secular forces are those that determine the long-term movements of the series, movements that may reflect persistent growth, persistent decline, or successive stages of growth and decline in evolutionary, irreversible development. The concept of secular change entails notions of regularity, of essential continuity. Frequent and sudden changes either in absolute amounts or in rates of increase or decrease are inconsistent with the idea of secular trend. It is true that there may be changes in trend, changes due to the interjection of a new element or the withdrawal of an old one. But, essentially, the secular trend of a series of observations ordered in time is conceived of as a smooth, continuous process underlying the irregularities of month-to-month or year-to-year change that characterize most historical variables in the social and economic fields.

Seasonal variations are found in many historical series for which quarterly, monthly, or weekly values are obtainable. Railroad freight traffic, fire losses, the consumption of many commodities, department store sales, employment, and many other such variables are marked by seasonal swings repeated with minor variations (and sometimes with progressive changes) year after year. Such variations are definitely periodic in character, with a constant twelve-month period.

Less markedly periodic, but recurring, nevertheless, with considerable regularity are the *cyclical fluctuations* that are found in many economic and social series. Prices, wages, the volume of industrial production and of trade, marriage rates, trading on the Stock Exchange, and most series related to the activities of individual business enterprises are affected by the swings of business through alternating periods of expansion and contraction. The length of such periods may vary, but observable sequences of change during these cycles have in the past been sufficiently regular in pattern to render them capable of systematic study.

Entangled with these more or less irregular movements are the effects of accidental and irregular factors—the movements we think of as *random*. In time series analysis this category is usually a catch-all for the consequences of catastrophic events, such as earthquakes, wars, floods, and conflagrations, as well as for the effects of countless minor events equally fortuitous though less violent in their incidence. Such events influence the value of a variable at any stated date, modifying the effects of long-term movements and of seasonal and cyclical factors. The observed value at any time is the resultant of the play of all these forces.

The problem of decomposition. When an investigator analyzes a series in time he is usually interested in some one of these types of change. Is there a recurring seasonal pattern in the production of lumber? What is it? What is the pattern of change in the volume of industrial production during business cycles? What has been the character of development in the output of electric power over the last century? The investigator would like to dissociate the movements of immediate interest from all other movements that shape the observed behavior of the series in question. This is the task of decomposition. It will be noted that a fundamental problem is faced here: How are the constituent elements blended together to make up the historical series that is actually recorded? Are cyclical fluctuations superimposed upon an underlying trend that would be there if there were no cycles? Are seasonal fluctuations in turn superimposed upon a trend-cycle composite? Or are cycles superimposed upon a trend-seasonal composite? Are random factors added to the trend-cycle-seasonal composite? Reverting to secular movements: Is the trend a purely mental construct? Does growth come in fact by forward leaps and lesser retrogressions, rather than by smooth and continuous evolution? We shall have more to say about some of these questions at a later stage. At this point we may merely note that the questions raised are largely unanswerable. We don't know how the forces of historical change interact to yield the series we have observed. Whatever process of decomposition we may employ rests on certain assumptions about the manner in which the effects of different forces are combined. Some of these assumptions may be more tenable than others. But when we employ a given method we should be aware of the assumptions made.

Distinctive features of time series. Before discussing the details of analytical methods used in this field, we should note two facts that distinguish time-ordered observations of the kind we are here discussing from those we have dealt with in earlier chapters. The first is that the different observations making up a time series are not independent of one another. This is notably true of successive observations. The number of automobiles produced in February, 1955, is not independent of the number produced in January, 1955. This is in sharp contrast, of course, to the independence of outcomes of successive tosses of a coin. Probability calculations that rest on the assumption of independence are not applicable to the closely related observations that make up historical series in the economic and social sciences.

The other fact, also disturbing to one who searches for regularities, is that the variables studied in the social and economic sciences are subject to change, over time, in their population or "universe" characteristics. Business failures, for example, would be materially affected by a change in the law relating to bankruptcies; the introduction of the Federal Reserve System in 1913 changed the whole character of banking in the United States. The implications of this fact are significant. When we draw a sample of black and white balls from an urn and on the basis of the sample estimate the proportion of balls of the two colors in the population we have sampled, we do so in the firm belief that the contents of the urn will not be surreptitiously changed after we have sampled it. If a counterpart of Maxwell's demon were to modify the contents of the urn after we drew the sample, our estimate might not be worth much. But something very like this occurs in the world of human affairs. We study some aspect of group behavior— social or economic—on the basis of observations necessarily localized in time. We then apply to a subsequent period the conclusions we have drawn from the sample observations. But in the meantime social institutions may have changed, economic processes may have been modified, the structure of laws within which men live may have been altered. There is always a demon modifying the contents of the urn from which social scientists and business men draw their samples. The changes resulting may not be important for the purpose a given investigator has in hand. Elements of continuity are present, too. The past is never cut off from the present or the future. But the possibility of significant change is always there, and this means that projection into the future of inferences based upon the study of past patterns, whether of trends, of cycles, or of seasonal movements, is always subject to indefinable margins of error.

The Preliminary Organization of Time Series

The data of time series usually require less preliminary organization than do statistical data that are to be reduced to the form of a frequency distribution. The source, primary or secondary, from which the figures are taken usually presents them in shape for analysis. Certain precautions should be observed, however.

The dates to which the figures apply should be clearly understood and definitely stated. Monthly data may be based upon a single daily figure (as are the price quotations entering into the BLS index of wholesale prices), they may be averages (such as average hourly earnings), or they may be totals for each month (as for figures on cotton consumption). They may be cumulative monthly figures, each item representing the total for the year to date, as in the case of certain coal production data. If average figures are given for a month or year it is important to know how the average has been secured.

Again, it is essential that in any time series there be strict comparability among data for different periods. Any attempt to analyze a series that is not homogeneous must be misleading and futile. Yet such series are not infrequently published. Commodity production or consumption figures published by trade associations and by governmental agencies are sometimes based upon returns from a varying number of reporting concerns. A series of price quotations for different dates may lack comparability because of changes in the unit or grade to which the quotations apply, or because quotations are drawn from different markets. Changes in census classifications may result in lack of comparability of census data. A change in a salesman's territory may alter his returns materially. It is stated that the character of the obligations represented by the United States Steel Corporation's figures for "unfilled orders" has varied from time to time. Records relating to the physical output of a given commodity in different periods may be rendered inaccurate by changes in quality or design. These are examples of faults that may be found in time series, rendering analysis futile. Strict testing is essential before a series be accepted as accurate and homogeneous.

Graphic representation. Normally the first step to be taken in visualizing a series in time and in preparing for further analysis consists of plotting the data. The trend and general characteristics of a series may be most readily apprehended through graphic representation. The data may be plotted on ordinary arithmetic or semilogarithmic paper. The advantages of the latter types for certain purposes have already been explained. The choice in a given case will depend upon the nature of the data and the object of the study. If interest lies in the absolute amount of fluctuations in sales, prices, pig iron production or whatever may be in process of analysis, or in the comparison of absolute differences between series, the ordinary rectilinear chart is to be employed. If percentage variations and the comparison of relative fluctuations are matters of interest, the semilogarithmic representation is preferable. In general, if one is accustomed to the interpretation of this latter type of chart, its use is advisable. A clearer, less-distorted presentation of relations and a more significant comparison of series are generally secured when economic data having time as one variable are plotted on paper with a logarithmic ruling on one axis.

For some purposes the process of studying series in time will have been completed when the data are thus plotted. The general trend may be roughly determined from the chart. The existence of seasonal and other periodic variations may be ascertained. Rough comparisons of trends and fluctuations may be made. All the knowledge thus secured, it should be noted, will be nonquantitative in character, and the comparisons will be tentative and approximative. Even so, such charts enable trends and relations to be much more clearly visualized than do the raw figures, and for some purposes the knowledge thus secured is sufficient, though it lacks precision and accuracy. For other purposes more exact measurement and more refined analysis are required. Certain appropriate methods may be described.

Moving Averages as Measures of Trend

As a first example of a historical variable we may consider the record of number of cars of revenue freight loaded on American railroads. In column (2) of Table 10-1 we have the weekly averages of carloadings, by years, from 1918 to 1953. Since the observations are recorded by years, the seasonal element does not enter in this case. The tabulated figures reflect the play of secular, cyclical, and random factors. Our first task is to seek to define the secular trend.

In Figure 10.2 the data of freight carloadings for the 36-year period have been plotted. Over these years carloadings have been subject to major variations, but a general declining trend is manifest. Several methods are available for arriving at approximations to this trend. By employing moving averages an attempt may be made to eliminate passing fluctuations and to arrive at values

TABLE 10-1

Cars of Revenue Freight Loaded for Class I Railroads
Weekly Averages, by Years, 1918-1953
(thousands of cars)

(1) Year	(2) Original data	(3) Three-year moving average	(4) Five-year moving average	(5) Seven-year moving average	(6) Nine-year moving average
1918	857.5				
1919	804.5	843.2			
1920	867.7	809.5	823.4		
1921	756.2	818.3	843.4	858.3	
1922	830.9	848.3	869.2	876.5	890.5
1923	957.9	907.4	892.7	907.5	905.5
1924	933.4	958.8	945.7	925.4	926.4
1925	985.1	979.9	978.1	959.1	942.8
1926	1021.1	999.7	984.9	985.5	956.9
1927	993.0	1002.1	1001.4	974.7	943.9
1928	992.1	1000.3	980.9	943.4	897.7
1929	1015.9	963.4	919.5	880.1	856.4
1930	882.3	870.9	829.3	814.5	812.9
1931	714.4	712.9	743.3	757.4	766.7
1932	541.9	606.1	658.7	702.2	733.5
1933	561.9	565.7	603.4	656.3	703.8
1934	593.2	587.0	599.4	633.7	656.0
1935	605.8	631.1	635.9	615.3	630.4
1936	694.4	674.9	640.7	631.1	628.7
1937	724.4	668.2	652.5	650.7	658.9
1938	585.7	654.1	671.2	682.1	688.0
1939	652.1	645.7	694.9	713.2	712.7
1940	699.2	721.5	714.8	730.6	738.2
1941	813.3	778.7	760.9	746.4	750.6
1942	823.6	817.7	797.4	777.9	758.4
1943	816.2	824.9	818.8	798.3	788.5
1944	834.8	819.0	815.1	820.7	807.3
1945	806.1	812.0	821.6	821.9	806.3
1946	795.0	819.0	822.6	802.9	799.1
1947	855.8	824.1	793.8	793.1	794.1
1948	821.5	789.3	782.2	785.1	784.6
1949	690.6	753.4	779.0	774.3	773.7
1950	748.1	739.2	753.9	766.0	
1951	778.8	752.5	736.9		
1952	730.5	748.6			
1953	736.6				

that define the influence of the steadily operating secular factor.
If we assume that a definite functional relationship prevails
(empirically at least) between the time factor and the other
variable, an approximation to the trend may be secured by fitting
an appropriate curve to the plotted data. Smoothing the data by

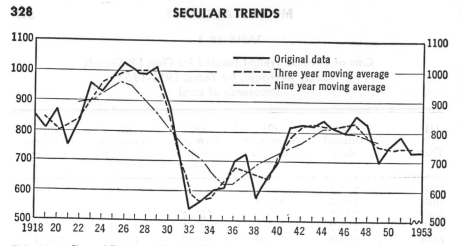

FIG. 10.2. Cars of Revenue Freight Loaded for Class I Railroads: Weekly Averages, by Years, 1918-1953, with Moving Averages (thousands of cars).

hand gives somewhat the same result, the curve being frankly approximative and empirical in character. In certain studies it has been found possible to use one statistical series as base or trend line for another series of homogeneous data.

When a trend is to be determined by the method of moving averages, the average value for a number of years (or months, or weeks) is secured, and this average is taken as the normal or trend value for the unit of time falling at the middle of the period covered in the calculation of the average. Table 10-1 shows the results secured when three-, five-, seven-, and nine-year moving averages are thus computed for freight carloadings for the period 1918-53.

The three-year moving average for 1946 is the average of 1945-6-7, the five-year figure for 1946 is the average of the years 1944-5-6-7-8. The other averages are computed in the same way. In each case the average is centered for the period included; that is, the average is taken to represent the trend value as of the middle of the given period. The employment of an odd number of years simplifies this centering process, though it is not essential that the number be odd. With an even number of years, the figure may be centered by taking a two-year moving average of the moving average first computed. The three- and nine-year moving averages for the entire period are plotted with the original data, in Fig. 10.2.

It is obvious that the effect of the averaging is to give a smoother curve, lessening the influence of the fluctuations that pull the annual figures away from the general trend. The longer the period included in securing each average, the smoother is the curve secured, though there are other factors to consider in deciding upon the length of the period. Certain of these factors may be noted.

Some characteristics of moving averages. Given cyclical fluctuations about a uniform level or about a line ascending with a uniform slope, the length of the cycle and the magnitude of the fluctuations being constant, a moving average having a period equal to the period of the cycle (or to a multiple of that period) will give a straight line, a perfect representation of the trend. Under the same conditions a moving average having a period greater or less than the period of the cycle will give, not a straight line, but a new cycle having the same period as the original, but with fluctuations of less magnitude. The minima and maxima of the cycles thus obtained will not necessarily coincide with the minima and maxima of the original cycles. In general, when such a new cycle is obtained the magnitude of the fluctuations will be less the longer the period on which the average is based.[1]

These propositions may be illustrated by the figures in Table 10-2, arbitrarily chosen. In the first example five figures have been selected which repeat themselves in sequence, fluctuating about a common level.

The moving averages in columns (2) and (3) represent the data with the cycles completely removed. When the period of the average is not equal to the period of the cycle, or to a multiple of that period, the cycle is not removed, as is apparent from the figures in columns (4) and (5).

The conclusions suggested above hold when the cyclical fluctuations take place about any straight line. In Table 10-3 the foregoing data have been employed but with a constant increment of 3. This is equivalent to superimposing the same cycles upon a line with a slope of + 3.

The trend values, with the effect of the cycles completely removed, are secured by taking moving averages equal in period to the cycle or to a multiple of that period. The cycle persists, with the same period but with diminished amplitude, when the average

---

[1] The decrease in the magnitude of the fluctuations is not regular, however, but cyclical.

TABLE 10–2

Illustrating the Application of Moving Averages

(1) Cyclical data	(2) Moving average of 5 items	(3) Moving average of 10 items (centered)	(4) Moving average of 3 items	(5) Moving average of 8 items (centered)
2				
6			$5\frac{1}{3}$	
8	$6\frac{1}{5}$		8	
10	$6\frac{1}{5}$		$7\frac{2}{3}$	
5	$6\frac{1}{5}$		$5\frac{2}{3}$	$6\frac{3}{8}$
2	$6\frac{1}{5}$	$6\frac{1}{5}$	$4\frac{1}{3}$	$6\frac{13}{16}$
6	$6\frac{1}{5}$	$6\frac{1}{5}$	$5\frac{1}{3}$	$6\frac{3}{8}$
8	$6\frac{1}{5}$	$6\frac{1}{5}$	8	$5\frac{3}{4}$
10	$6\frac{1}{5}$	$6\frac{1}{5}$	$7\frac{2}{3}$	$5\frac{11}{16}$
5	$6\frac{1}{5}$	$6\frac{1}{5}$	$5\frac{2}{3}$	$6\frac{3}{8}$
2	$6\frac{1}{5}$	$6\frac{1}{5}$	$4\frac{1}{3}$	$6\frac{13}{16}$
6	$6\frac{1}{5}$	$6\frac{1}{5}$	$5\frac{1}{3}$	$6\frac{3}{8}$
8	$6\frac{1}{5}$	$6\frac{1}{5}$	8	$5\frac{3}{4}$
10	$6\frac{1}{5}$	$6\frac{1}{5}$	$7\frac{2}{3}$	$5\frac{11}{16}$
5	$6\frac{1}{5}$	$6\frac{1}{5}$	$5\frac{2}{3}$	$6\frac{3}{8}$
2	$6\frac{1}{5}$		$4\frac{1}{3}$	$6\frac{13}{16}$
6	$6\frac{1}{5}$		$5\frac{1}{3}$	
8	$6\frac{1}{5}$		8	
10			$7\frac{2}{3}$	
5				

(The items in columns (3) and (5) have been centered by means of a moving average of 2 items.)

is based upon a period not equal to that of the cycle, as is clear from the figures in columns (4) and (5).

When these ideally simple conditions of constant period and amplitude do not exist, the moving average becomes more ambiguous and its interpretation less simple. If the period of the cycle varies, the selection of a period for the moving average is more difficult. In general, a period equal to or greater than the average length of the cycle is to be selected. An average having a shorter period will give a line that is marked by pronounced cycles, these cycles being reduced as the period covered in the calculation of the average increases.

When the amplitude of the cycle varies, the period being constant, a moving average with a period equal to the length of the cycle will give a line of trend marked by minor cycles. The amplitude of these secondary cycles will be a minimum when the period of the average is equal to the period of the cycle (or to a

TABLE 10–3

Illustrating the Application of Moving Averages to a Series with
Linear Trend

(1) Cyclical data	(2) Moving average of 5 items	(3) Moving average of 10 items (centered)	(4) Moving average of 3 items	(5) Moving average of 8 items (centered)
2				
9			$8\frac{1}{3}$	
14	$12\frac{1}{5}$		14	
19	$15\frac{1}{5}$		$16\frac{2}{3}$	
17	$18\frac{1}{5}$		$17\frac{2}{3}$	$18\frac{3}{8}$
17	$21\frac{1}{5}$	$21\frac{1}{5}$	$19\frac{1}{3}$	$21\frac{13}{16}$
24	$24\frac{4}{5}$	$24\frac{4}{5}$	$23\frac{1}{3}$	$24\frac{3}{8}$
20	$27\frac{1}{5}$	$27\frac{1}{5}$	29	$26\frac{3}{4}$
34	$30\frac{3}{5}$	$30\frac{3}{5}$	$31\frac{1}{3}$	$29\frac{11}{16}$
32	$33\frac{1}{5}$	$33\frac{1}{5}$	$32\frac{2}{3}$	$33\frac{3}{8}$
32	$36\frac{1}{5}$	$36\frac{1}{5}$	$34\frac{1}{3}$	$36\frac{13}{16}$
39	$39\frac{1}{5}$	$39\frac{1}{5}$	$38\frac{1}{3}$	$39\frac{3}{8}$
44	$42\frac{1}{5}$	$42\frac{1}{5}$	44	$41\frac{3}{4}$
49	$45\frac{1}{5}$	$45\frac{1}{5}$	$46\frac{2}{3}$	$44\frac{11}{16}$
47	$48\frac{1}{5}$	$48\frac{1}{5}$	$47\frac{2}{3}$	$48\frac{3}{8}$
47	$51\frac{1}{5}$		$49\frac{1}{3}$	$51\frac{13}{16}$
54	$54\frac{1}{5}$		$53\frac{1}{3}$	
59	$57\frac{1}{5}$		59	
64			$61\frac{2}{3}$	
62				

(The items in columns (3) and (5) have been centered by means of a moving average
of 2 items.)

multiple of that period). When these last two irregularities are
combined, and the data are characterized by cycles of varying
amplitude and of varying length, the moving average giving the
most effective representation of the trend is that which has a period
equal to the average length of the cycle, or to a multiple of that
length.

A new factor enters when the trend departs from linearity. If
the underlying trend of a series is concave upward, a moving
average will always exceed the actual trend value; if the reverse
is true, and the trend is convex upward, a moving average will
always be less than the actual trend value.

These conditions are depicted in the following examples. The
figures in Table 10-4 give the values secured when a cycle of
constant period and amplitude, as in column (3), is superimposed
upon a line of trend that is concave upward, i.e., increasing at a

TABLE 10–4

Illustrating the Application of Moving Averages to a Nonlinear Series
(Increasing rate)

(1)	(2)	(3)	(4)	(5)	(6)
				Moving average	True trend
x	x^2	Cyclical data	Col. (2) plus col. (3)	of 5 items in col. (4)	values $(x^2 + 6.2)$
0	0	2	2		
1	1	6	7		
2	4	8	12	12.2	10.2
3	9	10	19	17.2	15.2
4	16	5	21	24.2	22.2
5	25	2	27	33.2	31.2
6	36	6	42	44.2	42.2
7	49	8	57	57.2	55.2
8	64	10	74	72.2	70.2
9	81	5	86	89.2	87.2
10	100	2	102	108.2	106.2
11	121	6	127	129.2	127.2
12	144	8	152	152.2	150.2
13	169	10	179	177.2	175.2
14	196	5	201	204.2	202.2
15	225	2	227	233.2	231.2
16	256	6	262	264.2	262.2
17	289	8	297	297.2	295.2
18	324	10	334		
19	361	5	366		

constantly increasing rate. If the moving average could completely eliminate the effects of the cycle, the values secured from the average would be equal to the average value of the five items in each cycle (6.2) plus the values of the function $y = x^2$, given in column (2).

The values of the moving average are, in this case, in excess of the true trend values, a form of distortion that will always occur with a series of this type.

In Table 10-5 are shown the results of superimposing the same cyclical values upon a line of trend that is convex upward, i.e., increasing at a constantly decreasing rate. In this case, a perfect method of eliminating the cycles would give results equal to the average value of the five items (6.2) plus the values of the function $y = \sqrt{x}$.

In this case the moving average values are consistently too low. The discrepancy is greatest for the lower values of x, as the decrease in the rate of growth is most marked for these values.

TABLE 10–5

Illustrating the Application of Moving Averages to a Nonlinear Series
(Decreasing rate)

(1)	(2)	(3)	(4)	(5)	(6)
					True trend
x	$\sqrt{x}$	Cyclical data	Col. (2) plus col. (3)	Moving average of 5 items	values $(\sqrt{x} + 6.2)$
0	0	2	2.00		
1	1.00	6	7.00		
2	1.41	8	9.41	7.428	7.61
3	1.73	10	11.73	7.876	7.93
4	2.00	5	7.00	8.166	8.20
5	2.24	2	4.24	8.414	8.44
6	2.45	6	8.45	8.634	8.65
7	2.65	8	10.65	8.834	8.85
8	2.83	10	12.83	9.018	9.03
9	3.00	5	8.00	9.192	9.20
10	3.16	2	5.16	9.354	9.36
11	3.32	6	9.32	9.510	9.52
12	3.46	8	11.46	9.658	9.66
13	3.61	10	13.61	9.800	9.81
14	3.74	5	8.74	9.936	9.94
15	3.87	2	5.87	10.068	10.07
16	4.00	6	10.00	10.194	10.20
17	4.12	8	12.12	10.318	10.32
18	4.24	10	14.24		
19	4.36	5	9.36		

Considerations previously reviewed have indicated that a moving average should, in general, be based upon a period at least equal to the period of the cycle, and preferably equal to some higher multiple of that period when the data are at all irregular. The longer the period covered, the greater the stability of the average. But when the underlying trend departs materially from the linear form, following a curve bending upward or downward, the error involved in the use of any moving average increases as the period of the average increases. If a moving average is used in such a case to measure the trend, the period of the average should be the shortest which will serve to average out the cycles; equal, that is, to the average length of one cycle.

In practice, however, these various conditions are found in complicated combinations. The fact that cycles vary in amplitude and length calls for a moving average based upon a fairly long period. The fact that the trend of the data is usually nonlinear calls for a short period average to lessen the upward or downward distortion. A consideration of some importance in practical work is that a moving average can never be brought up to date. The lag is less, of course, the shorter the period covered by the average. The selection of a period in a given case must rest upon a study of the actual data with these various considerations in mind.

It has been assumed in the preceding discussion that the purpose of the moving average is the representation of secular trend. The moving average may be used, also, in smoothing data for the purpose of eliminating random fluctuations. For this purpose a moving average based upon a period shorter than the average length of the cycle should be selected.

Appraisal of moving averages of varying periods. We return now to the data of freight carloadings. A study of the lines marked out by the different moving averages in Fig. 10.2 (p. 328) reveals clear differences between them. The three-year average follows the graph of the original data most closely, as would be expected. The nine-year average marks out the smoothest line of trend, but, on the other hand, departs most widely from the data. This is particularly noticeable from 1923 to 1930 and from 1931 to 1935. The sharp changes in the direction of movement of the original series that came after 1929 and after 1932 account for these departures.

In determining the relative merits of the different moving averages we are aided by the knowledge of the course of business during the period covered. The volume of freight carloadings is a sensitive index of general business conditions, responding immediately to changes in speculative and industrial activity. Major and minor business cycles are reflected in this series. Knowing the number of cycles through which business has passed during the period 1918-53, we may determine which of the moving averages serves best as a standard from which to measure cyclical deviations. In this case we are practically working backward from a known result, a method not always available.

If we take as a starting point in each cycle the year in which revival began, after recession, the following cycles in general business activity may be distinguished:[2]

1919—1921	1932—1938
1921—1924	1938—1946
1924—1927	1946—1949
1927—1932	1949—1954

[2] These dates are based upon the chronology of American business cycles developed by Arthur F. Burns and Wesley C. Mitchell. See Burns and Mitchell, Ref. 13, p. 78.

The cycles marked out by the three-year moving average are too numerous to enumerate. In fact, the deviations from this average are so greatly affected by minor short-term fluctuations that they usually give a poor representation of movements corresponding to cycles in the economy at large. Deviations from the five-, seven-, and nine-year averages mark out the following cycles:

Cycles of deviations from five-year moving averages	Cycles of deviations from seven-year moving averages	Cycles of deviations from nine-year moving averages
1921—1924	1921—1932*	1922—1932*
1924—1927	1932—1938	1932—1938
1927—1932	1938—1945	1938—1946
1932—1938	1945—1949	1946—
1938—1943		
1943—1946		
1946—1949		
1949—		

Differences between the series of cycles thus determined and the reference cycles distinguished by Burns and Mitchell reflect the characteristic features of moving averages. The seven- and nine-year averages fail to reveal short cycles. Neither of these series discloses the two short cycles (1921-24 and 1924-27) that occurred during the "twenties," and that are reflected in the carloadings series. Deviations from the five-year moving averages define these short cycles. On the other hand, this five-year series shows a deviation below the line of trend in 1943, and thus marks off two "cycles" during the one reference cycle of 1938-46 that is recognized in the Burns-Mitchell chronology.

If interest attaches to the shorter swings of business, to cycles with average durations of three to five years, a moving average of relatively short period should be used. A five-year average is appropriate. Averages of longer period define trend movements more faithfully, but may fail to reveal fluctuations properly classified as business cycles. We should refer, however, to recent attempts to establish the reality of long cycles, of nine, eleven, or as many as fifty years in average duration. In the study of such cycles moving averages of corresponding periods would be employed.

In general, the moving average has the prime advantage of flexibility. The representation of secular trend by mathematical

---

* The initial low of each of these cycles is, of course, not clearly marked by deviations beginning only in 1921 or 1922.

curves sometimes involves the breaking up of a period into two or three subdivisions, and the fitting of separate curves to each. This results from changing conditions and sharply changing rates of growth or decline. When such changes occur, the moving average has the merit of flexible adaptation to the new conditions and is often a more effective measure of secular trend than are more pretentious functions.

Simple and weighted moving averages, in varying combinations, have wide uses in the analysis of economic time series. An illuminating discussion of these uses, and of the procedures appropriate to different purposes, is to be found in *The Smoothing of Time Series*, by Frederick R. Macaulay.[3]

Representation of Secular Trends by Mathematical Curves

For many types of data the secular trend may be represented by a mathematical function rather than by a line based upon a moving average. Thus, if the growth (or decline) is by constant absolute increments (or decrements) a straight line will serve as an exact representation of the trend. Or the growth may be by constant percentages, as in the case of capital increase, when a principal sum increases in accordance with the compound interest law. An exponential curve defines such a trend. Where the secular course of a historical variable may be accurately described by a mathematical function, the tasks of analysis, interpretation, and projection may be facilitated by the use of such a function.

A mathematical representation of the trend of a social, economic, or business series is sometimes assumed to define an underlying "law" of development. This is an acceptable view, if we regard a "law" as no more than an observed regularity, and the mathematical expression as a convenient shorthand description of a piece of recorded history. It may be that in time somewhat more firmly based laws of change will be established in the social and economic sciences. Indeed, some students believe that certain mathematical functions do, in fact, define laws of growth that are something more than empirically observed regularities, but the evidence for this view is not yet convincing. For the present it is best to regard a secular trend, whether described by a frankly empirical moving average or by a mathematical function, as no

[3] Ref. 95.

more than an empirically established uniformity, subject to change without notice.

In the practical approach to a problem involving the determination of secular trend the first task is the selection of the appropriate type of curve. This is perhaps the most difficult part of the work; certainly it is the part in which the element of personal judgment enters most directly. For there is no objective rule to follow, no fixed standard by which the most appropriate curve may be selected. Something more will be said on this subject after the characteristics of the chief types of curves and the methods of fitting them have been described. For the present it may be assumed that a curve similar to one of the types described in Chapter 2, or to a related form, has been selected, and that we face the practical task of fitting it to the data.

The problem here is similar to that discussed in the preceding chapter, in considering correlation procedures. There we found that the method of least squares could be used in determining the most probable values of a and b in the equation to a straight line of regression. If the trend function desired in dealing with a given time series is linear, we must get most probable values for the same quantities in an equation of the form $y = a + bx$ (where x is time, and y is the historical variable in question). Customarily, the method of least squares is used in deriving such measures of trend, although the conditions on which that method logically rests are not realized in dealing with time series. For chronologically ordered observations are not independent of one another; deviations from the function to be fitted are likely to be due primarily to nonrandom forces. Thus if we use the method of least squares in fitting a mathematical curve to a series of observations ordered in time we do so on grounds of practicality and expediency. Its use on these terms is defensible, but the limitations attaching to this use of the least squares method reenforce the argument that mathematical trend lines should be viewed as empirically useful functions but not as representations of rationally based laws of historical change.

The least squares procedure in fitting a straight line calls, as we have seen, for the simultaneous solution of two normal equations (see Chapter 9). In handling historical variables the calculations may be simplified somewhat. When the x's are consecutive numbers, as they always are when an unbroken time series is plotted, the origin may be taken at the median value. When the number of observations is odd this will be the middle item, of course. The value of $\Sigma(x)$ will then be zero, and the normal equations become

$$\Sigma(y) = na$$

$$\Sigma(xy) = b\Sigma(x^2)$$

Thus if a time series extends, by years, from 1938 to 1954, the origin may be taken at 1946, the value of x corresponding to 1945 being -1, to 1947, $+1$, and so on. The solution for values of a and b is rendered much easier when the data may be disposed in this way. When there is an even number of years the same process is possible, time (the x-variable) being measured in units of one half year.

Again, when the values of x are consecutive positive numbers starting with one, the values of $\Sigma(x)$ and of $\Sigma(x^2)$ may be easily determined. The sum of the first n natural numbers is equal to $\dfrac{n(n+1)}{2}$. Thus the sum of the numbers from 1 to 5 is $\dfrac{5(5+1)}{2}$, or 15. This term may replace $\Sigma(x)$ in the normal equations. Similarly, the sum of the squares of the first n natural numbers is equal to $\dfrac{2n^3 + 3n^2 + n}{6}$. Thus the sum of the squares of the numbers from 1 to 5 is equal to $\dfrac{250 + 75 + 5}{6} = 55$. This expression may replace $\Sigma(x^2)$ in the normal equations, and we have

$$\Sigma(y) = na + b\left(\frac{n(n+1)}{2}\right) \tag{10.1}$$

$$\Sigma(xy) = a\left(\frac{n(n+1)}{2}\right) + b\left(\frac{2n^3 + 3n^2 + n}{6}\right)$$

It is sometimes easier to work from equations in this form than from those in the form first given. The data for time series may be handled in this way, the years being numbered consecutively, beginning with 1.

Examples of Linear Trends. Figures 10.3 and 10.4 show two historical series to each of which a straight line has been fitted to define secular trend. In Fig. 10.3 are plotted mean annual temper-

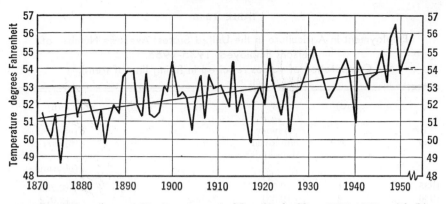

FIG. 10.3. Mean Annual Temperatures in New York City, 1871-1953, with Line of Trend.

atures for New York City for the years 1871-1953. The equation to the trend line, fitted to the data for 1871-1949, is $y = 52.482 + 0.0346x$, where y is temperature in degrees Fahrenheit, and x is time measured in years from an origin at 1910.[4] This provides a good example of the use of a trend line. There has been, apparently, a slow rise in the mean temperature of New York over the last 80 years. The equation cited defines this rise in simple terms, indicating an average annual increase in temperature of 0.0346 degrees Fahrenheit. We may not say that this is a "law" in any fundamental sense. We know of no rational basis for the change, and we have no justification except that of past experience for projecting the observed movement into the future. Yet, as a summary statement of a segment of meteorological history, the equation has obvious utility. Not least, the clear definition of the historical movement suggests problems and stimulates inquiry as to the forces actually at work.

The graph in Fig. 10.4 shows employment in agriculture (family workers plus hired workers) over the years from 1935 to 1953. The procedure employed in fitting a straight line of trend may be illustrated with reference to this series. The observations are given in Table 10-6, together with the values required in the fitting process and the derived trend values. Only the entries in columns (2) to (5) are employed in the calculations.

---

[4] The temperature data are from *Local Climatological Summary, New York City, N Y.*, a publication of the Weather Bureau, U. S. Department of Commerce.

TABLE 10-6

Employment in Agriculture in the United States: Average Number of
Persons Employed, 1935-1953.*
Computation of values required in fitting line of trend.

(1)	(2)	(3) y Persons employed (thousands)	(4) xy	(5) x^2	(6) y_c Trend values (linear) of persons employed (thousands)
Year	x				
1935	1	12,733	12,733	1	12,269
1936	2	12,331	24,662	4	12,072
1937	3	11,978	35,934	9	11,875
1938	4	11,622	46,488	16	11,677
1939	5	11,338	56,690	25	11,480
1940	6	10,979	65,874	36	11,283
1941	7	10,669	74,683	49	11,086
1942	8	10,504	84,032	64	10,889
1943	9	10,446	94,014	81	10,692
1944	10	10,219	102,190	100	10,495
1945	11	10,000	110,000	121	10,298
1946	12	10,295	123,540	144	10,100
1947	13	10,382	134,966	169	9,903
1948	14	10,363	145,082	196	9,706
1949	15	9,964	149,460	225	9,509
1950	16	9,342	149,472	256	9,312
1951	17	8,985	152,745	289	9,115
1952	18	8,669	156,042	324	8,918
1953	19	8,580	163,020	361	8,721
Totals	190	199,399	1,881,627	2,470	

$$N = 19 \qquad \Sigma(y) = 199,399$$
$$\Sigma(x) = 190 \qquad \Sigma(xy) = 1,881,627$$
$$\Sigma(x^2) = 2,470$$

* Family workers plus hired workers.
Source: *Farm Labor*, Agricultural Marketing Service, USDA, Jan. 13, 1954.

The equations to be solved in determining the required constants (see p. 252 above) are of the form

$$\Sigma(y) = Na + b\Sigma(x)$$
$$\Sigma(xy) = a\Sigma(x) + b\Sigma(x^2)$$

Inserting the required values, which are of course derived from the observations, we have

$$199,399 = 19a + 190b$$
$$1,881,627 = 190a + 2470b$$

from which

$$a = 12,465.965$$
$$b = -197.128$$

The equation to the line of best fit is therefore

$$y = 12,466.0 - 197.1x$$

with origin at 1934.

The trend values derived from this equation appear in column (6) of Table 10-6. From inspection of the graph in Fig. 10.4 we

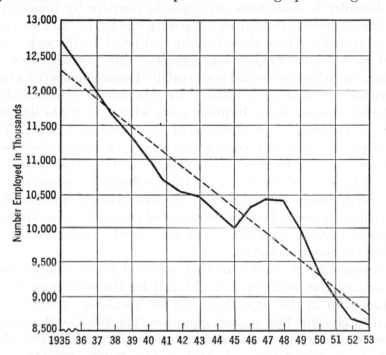

FIG. 10.4. Average Number of Persons Employed in Agriculture in the United States, 1935-1953, with Line of Trend.

conclude that the fitted line provides a good representation of the trend of this series over the period covered. The decline in total agricultural employment has been persistent, broken only by a brief postwar advance. The movement away from agriculture has averaged 197,000 persons a year. The period covered is, of course, a fairly short one. In general our confidence in a fitted trend line as a representation of a secular movement is greater the longer the series of observations. In the present instance we have employed a period marked by fairly rapid mechanization in American agriculture, a fact that gives the trend line of employment a somewhat sounder base than it would have if there were no apparent explanation of the decline noted. (Of course, the decline in agricultural employment goes back beyond 1935, but the movement was accelerated in the middle and late 'thirties.)

Fitting a Polynomial. The discussion above has been confined to the case of linear trend. Such a function frequently defines secular movements accurately, but in many cases it fails to fit the data. This difficulty is sometimes overcome in practice by breaking a series into segments and fitting a separate line to the data for each of these periods. Where there is an actual break in the series, the period as a whole lacking homogeneity, this practice may be justified, but when the period is essentially homogeneous the whole concept of secular trend is violated by this process of subdividing and fitting separate lines. In many cases where a straight line will not fit, a polynomial may represent the trend accurately. The general process of fitting such a curve may be briefly described.

The generalized form of the equation of the type desired is $y = a + bx + cx^2 + dx^3 + \ldots$. For ordinary purposes such a curve should not be carried beyond the second or third power of x. If carried to the second power there are, of course, three unknowns, and three normal equations must be solved simultaneously in securing the required values.

The procedure is similar to that outlined for the linear case. Each observation equation is multiplied by the coefficient of the first unknown in that equation, and the resulting equations are totaled to give the first normal equation. The process is repeated for the two other unknowns, and the three normal equations thus obtained are solved for a, b, and c. The results are the most probable values of these three constants. The following are the general forms which the three normal equations take:

$$\Sigma(y) = na + b\Sigma(x) + c\Sigma(x^2)$$
$$\Sigma(xy) = a\Sigma(x) + b\Sigma(x^2) + c\Sigma(x^3) \qquad (10.2)$$
$$\Sigma(x^2y) = a\Sigma(x^2) + b\Sigma(x^3) + c\Sigma(x^4)$$

As an example of the process, the calculations involved in fitting a power curve of the second degree to the points 1, 2; 2, 6; 3, 7; 4, 8; 5, 10; 6, 11; 7, 11; 8, 10; 9, 9 may be outlined. It is of the greatest practical importance in curve fitting, as in all extensive calculations, that the work be laid out and carried on in a definite and systematic fashion, with each step definitely related to the preceding and succeeding operations. Checks should be introduced wherever possible, as mathematical errors creep into even the most careful work. A tabular arrangement is generally advisable, each operation being revealed and each set of results clearly presented. The data in the present problem may be arranged as in Table 10-7.

TABLE 10–7

Computation of Values Required in Fitting a Polynomial of the Second Degree

x	y	xy	x^2	x^2y	
1	2	2	1	2	$n = 9$
2	6	12	4	24	$\Sigma(x) = 45$
3	7	21	9	63	$\Sigma(x^2) = 285$
4	8	32	16	128	$\Sigma(x^3) = 2,025$
5	10	50	25	250	$\Sigma(x^4) = 15,333$
6	11	66	36	396	$\Sigma(y) = 74$
7	11	77	49	539	$\Sigma(xy) = 421$
8	10	80	64	640	$\Sigma(x^2y) = 2,771$
9	0	81	81	729	
45	74	421	285	2,771	

When the x's are consecutive integers beginning with 1, as in the present case, the values of $\Sigma(x)$, $\Sigma(x^2)$, $\Sigma(x^3)$, and $\Sigma(x^4)$ may be obtained by the use of formulas,[5] or from prepared tables.[6]

Substituting these values in the equations given above, the following normal equations are secured:

$$74 = 9a + 45b + 285c$$
$$421 = 45a + 285b + 2,025c$$
$$2,771 = 285a + 2,025b + 15,333c$$

[5] For convenience of reference we here give the formulas for the sums of the first four powers of the first n natural numbers (repeating two of these from an earlier page):

$$\Sigma n = \frac{n(n + 1)}{2}$$

$$\Sigma(n^2) = \frac{(2n + 1)}{3} \Sigma n$$

$$\Sigma(n^3) = (\Sigma n)^2$$

$$\Sigma(n^4) = \frac{3n^2 + 3n - 1}{5} \Sigma(n^2)$$

[6] See Table XXVIII, Pearson, *Tables for Statisticians and Biometricians.* Values to the sixth power for numbers from 1 to 50 are given in Appendix Table IX of the present volume.

When these equations are solved simultaneously the following values are secured for the three constants:

$$a = -.929$$
$$b = +3.523$$
$$c = -.267$$

The equation of the desired curve is

$$y = -.929 + 3.523x - .267x^2$$

This curve and the nine given points are plotted in Fig. 10.5.

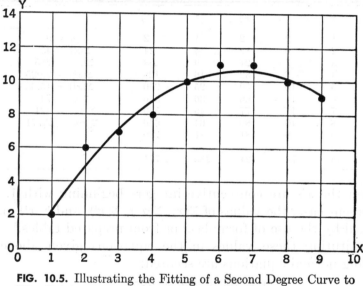

FIG. 10.5. Illustrating the Fitting of a Second Degree Curve to Nine Points.

If the values of x are consecutive, as in the present example, the work of computation is lightened if the mid-value is taken as origin. In this case $\Sigma(x)$ and $\Sigma(x^3)$ are equal to zero, and the normal equations become

$$\Sigma y = na + c\Sigma(x^2)$$
$$\Sigma(xy) = b\Sigma(x^2)$$
$$\Sigma(x^2y) = a\Sigma(x^2) + c\Sigma(x^4)$$

When a polynomial of the third degree, of the form $y = a + bx + cx^2 + dx^3$, is to be fitted to data, four constants must be determined, and four normal equations are necessary. These are of the following form:

$$\left.\begin{array}{l} \Sigma(y) = na + b\Sigma(x) + c\Sigma(x^2) + d\Sigma(x^3) \\ \Sigma(xy) = a\Sigma(x) + b\Sigma(x^2) + c\Sigma(x^3) + d\Sigma(x^4) \\ \Sigma(x^2y) = a\Sigma(x^2) + b\Sigma(x^3) + c\Sigma(x^4) + d\Sigma(x^5) \\ \Sigma(x^3y) = a\Sigma(x^3) + b\Sigma(x^4) + c\Sigma(x^5) + d\Sigma(x^6) \end{array}\right\} \quad (10.3)$$

The solution for four or more constants involves a considerable amount of arithmetical calculation, and there is some question as to the advisability of representing secular trend by equations of this type. With a sufficient number of constants a curve may be fitted that will follow every variation in the data, but such a curve could hardly be taken to represent the long-term trend.[7] Minor departures from a simple uniform trend, linear or otherwise, are to be expected with economic data, but, if a real trend exists, extreme departures from a fairly simple form are rare. If such departures are due to pronounced changes in conditions no single line of trend is likely to be satisfactory, and it is advisable to break the period into parts, with a separate line of trend for each part. "Empirical curves," says Steinmetz, "can be represented by a single equation only when the physical conditions remain constant within the range of the observations." Though this statement relates to the fitting of curves to data from the physical sciences, the general principle applies to economic data.

A Secular Trend of the Second Degree. The production and sales of electric power in recent decades are good examples of series following nonlinear trends. The sales of electric power to ultimate consumers, in the United States, for the years 1937-1953, are plotted in Fig. 10.6. The data, with computations needed for the fitting of a polynomial of the second degree, are presented in Table 10-8.

[7] The famous *razor*, or Law of Parcimony, of William of Occam, which specifies that in explaining things not known to exist the number of entities (here read "constants") should not be increased unnecessarily, has special pertinence to a problem of this sort.

Regarding the employment of potential series of the type indicated for representing empirical curves, Steinmetz states that their use is justified:

1. If the successive coefficients $a, b, c \ldots$ decrease in value so rapidly that within the range of observation the higher terms become rapidly smaller and appear as mere secondary terms.

2. If the successive coefficients follow a definite law, indicating a convergent series which represents some other function, as an exponential, trigonometric, etc.

3. If all the coefficients are very small, with the exception of a few of them, and only the latter ones thus need to be considered.

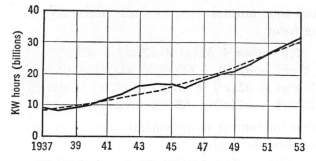

FIG. 10.6. Average Monthly Sales of Electric Power to Ultimate Consumers, 1937-1953, with Line of Trend.*

*Data from Edison Electric Institute.

TABLE 10–8

Sales of Electric Power to Ultimate Consumers, 1937-1953*
(Average monthly sales in billions of kilowatt-hours)
Computation of Values Required in Fitting Line of Trend

(1) Year	(2) x	(3) y (sales)	(4) xy	(5) x^2y
1937	− 8	8.3	− 66.4	531.2
1938	− 7	7.8	− 54.6	382.2
1939	− 6	8.8	− 52.8	316.8
1940	− 5	9.9	− 49.5	247.5
1941	− 4	11.7	− 46.8	187.2
1942	− 3	13.3	− 39.9	119.7
1943	− 2	15.5	− 31.0	62.0
1944	− 1	16.5	− 16.5	16.5
1945	0	16.1	0.0	0.0
1946	+ 1	15.9	+ 15.9	15.9
1947	+ 2	18.1	+ 36.2	72.4
1948	+ 3	20.1	+ 60.3	180.9
1949	+ 4	20.7	+ 82.8	331.2
1950	+ 5	23.4	+ 117.0	585.0
1951	+ 6	26.5	+ 159.0	954.0
1952	+ 7	28.6	+ 200.2	1401.4
1953	+ 8	31.9	+ 255.2	2041.6
		293.1	+ 569.1	7445.5

$$N = 17 \qquad \Sigma(x^4) = 17,544$$
$$\Sigma(x) = 0 \qquad \Sigma(y) = 293.1$$
$$\Sigma(x^2) = 408 \qquad \Sigma(xy) = 569.1$$
$$\Sigma(x^3) = 0 \qquad \Sigma(x^2y) = 7,445.5$$

* Compiled by the Edison Electric Institute.

In the fitting process the origin may be taken at the middle year, to facilitate the calculations. The sums of the second and fourth powers of x may be obtained from prepared tables, or from the formulas cited on p. 343. With the origin at the middle of the period the normal equations required for a fitting of the function $y = a + bx + cx^2$ (see formula 10.2 above) become

$$\Sigma(y) = Na + c\Sigma(x^2)$$
$$\Sigma(xy) = b\Sigma(x^2)$$
$$\Sigma(x^2y) = a\Sigma(x^2) + c\Sigma(x^4)$$

Inserting the appropriate values, we have

$$293.1 = 17a + 408c$$
$$569.1 = 408b$$
$$7{,}445.5 = 408a + 17{,}544c$$

Solving for the constants

$$a = 15.968$$
$$b = +\ 1.395$$
$$c -\ +\ 0.053$$

The required equation is

$$y = 15.968 + 1.395x + 0.053x^2$$

with origin at 1945. This equation is plotted in Fig. 10.6. The smooth growth of total sales of electric power was broken slightly by war and postwar adjustments, but the trend is reasonably well represented by the function employed.

The Use of Logarithms in Curve Fitting. The family of curves described above represents a simple and very useful type. Perhaps of even greater general utility, in the analysis of time series, are curves of a semilogarithmic type. The advantages of plotting many series of data on semilogarithmic or "ratio" paper were explained in an earlier section. A fundamental virtue of this type of plotting is that it presents a true picture of *relative* variations, of *ratios* between magnitudes. Relations of this type are ordinarily of primary interest in the analysis of economic data, and it is logical that determination of trends should proceed on the same basis.

In doing so, we can make use of a group of curves of the same general form as those already described, the one difference being that $\log y$ takes the place of y throughout. That is, the straight line form is $\log y = a + bx$, while the general form for the polynomial series is $\log y = a + bx + cx^2 + dx^3 + \ldots$. The curves secured may be constructed on arithmetic paper, plotting the natural x's and the logarithms of the y's, or natural values of both x's and y's may be plotted on semilogarithmic paper, the logarithmic scale extending along the y-axis. The latter is the simpler method.

To illustrate the procedure, the steps involved in fitting a curve of the type $\log y = a + bx$ will be shown. The trend of petroleum production in the United States from 1936 to 1953 is to be determined. The values needed in the normal equations are derived from Table 10-9. The equations to be solved are of the form

$$\Sigma(\log y) = Na + b\Sigma x$$
$$\Sigma(x \cdot \log y) = a\Sigma x + b\Sigma x^2$$

Substituting the given values we have

$$57.84863 = 18a + 171b$$
$$558.64891 = 171a + 2{,}109b$$

Solving for the constants

$$a = 3.03564$$
$$b = 0.01876$$

The equation to the desired curve is, therefore,

$$\log y = 3.03564 + 0.01876x$$

with origin at 1935.

In fitting this curve by the method of least squares, as is done above, we satisfy the condition that the sum of the squares of the *logarithmic* deviations shall be a minimum. That is, the deviations to which this condition relates are the differences between the logarithms of the observed values and the logarithms of the corresponding trend values. This curve, it should be noted, is not the same as that for which the sum of the squares of the arithmetic (natural) deviations is a minimum.

The substitution in the above equation of the value of x representing any given year will enable the logarithm of the trend or normal value to be calculated. Logarithms thus derived, and the corresponding natural numbers which are the trend values for the various years, are given in columns (6) and (7) of Table 10-9. The trend function is shown graphically in Fig. 10.7, with the original observations. The fit is good.

An equation of this type, defining a linear trend in the logarithms of the dependent variable, has certain distinctive advantages. The

TABLE 10–9

Petroleum Production in the United States, 1936-1953*
(in millions of barrels)
Computation of values required in fitting line of trend

(1) Year	(2) x	(3) y	(4) log y	(5) x log y	(6) log y_c (log of trend)	(7) y_c (computed trend value)
1936	1	1,099.7	3.04127	3.04127	3.05440	1,133.4
1937	2	1,279.2	3.10694	6.21388	3.07316	1,183.4
1938	3	1,214.4	3.08436	9.25308	3.09192	1,235.7
1939	4	1,265.0	3.10209	12.40836	3.11068	1,290.2
1940	5	1,353.2	3.13136	15.65680	3.12944	1,347.2
1941	6	1,402.2	3.14681	18.88086	3.14820	1,406.6
1942	7	1,386.6	3.14195	21.99365	3.16696	1,468.7
1943	8	1,505.6	3.17771	25.42168	3.18572	1,533.6
1944	9	1,677.8	3.22474	29.02266	3.20448	1,601.3
1945	10	1,711.1	3.23328	32.33280	3.22324	1,672.0
1946	11	1,733.4	3.23890	35.62790	3.24200	1,745.8
1947	12	1,857.0	3.26881	39.22572	3.26076	1,822.9
1948	13	2,020.2	3.30539	42.97007	3.27952	1,903.4
1949	14	1,841.9	3.26527	45.71378	3.29828	1,987.4
1950	15	1,973.6	3.29526	49.42890	3.31704	2,075.0
1951	16	2,247.7	3.35174	53.62784	3.33580	2,166.7
1952	17	2,290.0	3.35984	57.11728	3.35456	2,269.4
1953	18	2,360.0	3.37291	60.71238	3.37332	2,362.2
			57.84863	558.64891		

$$N = 18 \qquad \Sigma(\log y) = 57.84863$$
$$\Sigma(x) = 171 \qquad \Sigma(x \cdot \log y) = 558.64891$$
$$\Sigma(x^2) = 2,109$$

* Sources: Bureau of Mines; American Petroleum Institute.

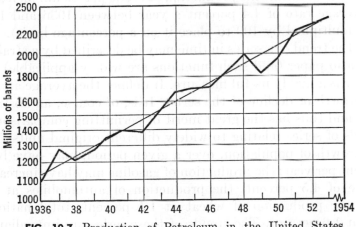

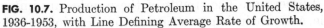

FIG. 10.7. Production of Petroleum in the United States, 1936-1953, with Line Defining Average Rate of Growth.

reader will note that this is the logarithmic form of an equation to a compound interest curve (an exponential curve). This equation was given in Chapter 2 as

$$y = p(1 + r)^x \qquad\qquad (10.4)$$

or

$$\log y = \log p + x \log (1 + r)$$

In the example just given we have used the symbol a for $\log p$ and the symbol b for $\log (1 + r)$, but the equations are identical.

We may readily change to natural numbers the constants in the equation defining the trend of petroleum production from 1936 to 1953. We have

$$\log y = 3.03564 + 0.01876x$$

where 3.03564 is $\log p$ and 0.01876 is $\log (1 + r)$. The natural number corresponding to 3.03564 is 1,085.5. The natural number corresponding to 0.01876 is 1.044. The trend of petroleum production in natural form is, therefore

$$y = 1085.5(1.044)^x$$

with origin at 1935. Subtracting 1 from the constant 1.044 we secure 0.044, which is r, the rate of increase of a series growing in accordance with the compound interest law. (If, on subtracting 1, we have a negative value, the growth is negative, of course.) This measure indicates that the production of crude petroleum increased at an average rate of 4.4 percent a year between 1936 and 1953 (r being multiplied by 100 to place it on a percentage basis).

When the trend of a series in time may be described by a straight line on ratio paper (and such functions are widely applicable) the constant r is a highly useful measure. It defines the average annual rate of growth or decline of the series. It is, of course, an abstract measure and thus has the great merit of permitting comparison of the trends of series relating to widely different original units. The rate of growth of population, over a given period, may have been 1.4 percent per year; the production of gasoline may have increased at a rate of 4.5 percent, the production of automobiles at 4.2 percent, the production of wheat at 1.1 percent, total national income at 1.6 percent. The trends of these series are immediately comparable, and conclusions concerning the direction and character of a nation's development may be drawn. This measure provides a valuable device for the study of social and economic change.[8]

By the use of additional terms a function of the type just discussed may be modified when dealing with a series having a nonlinear trend on ratio paper. The addition of a third constant gives an equation of the type

$$\log y = a + bx + cx^2$$

This is, of course, the counterpart in logarithmic or ratio terms of a polynomial of the second degree in terms of natural numbers. Still further constants may be added—a process that is subject to the reservations already voiced concerning the addition of constants to such equations when natural numbers are employed.

Other Curve Types. The two families of curves described in the preceding sections meet most of the needs of the economic statistician. The trend in most time series may be described by polynomials fitted either to natural numbers or to the logarithms of the data (that is, to the logarithms of the y values; time, the x-variable, is treated in terms of natural numbers in fitting both the above types of curves). These classes constitute flexible and widely applicable curve forms.[9] Attention may be called to several other curve types which have been applied less extensively to time series, but with favorable results in particular cases.

Curves of the ordinary parabolic type ($y = ax^b$) are not generally applicable to economic data in the form of time series, as their use involves the treatment of the time variable as a geometric series. Such a curve, it will be recalled, becomes a straight line on double

---

[8] In any extensive application of this procedure time and labor may be saved by utilizing Glover's mean value table (cf. James W. Glover, *Tables of Applied Mathematics*, George Wahr, Ann Arbor, Michigan, 1923, 468ff.). By the use of this table the compound interest curve may be fitted directly to the natural numbers. All necessary computations are simply and quickly performed.

[9] There are available for fitting higher degree curves of the power series methods that lessen the labor involved, particularly if curves of different degree are to be fitted to the same data. These methods, which reduce the fitting process to a series of simple adding machine operations, are appropriate to extended research projects. Their use is not advisable, however, unless work involving a considerable number of routine operations is contemplated. It is desirable that the student master the basic least squares procedures outlined in the preceding pages, utilizing other methods only when extended computing tasks are undertaken.

For accounts of systematic methods of computing polynomial values and illustrations of the use of orthogonal polynomials see R. A. Fisher (Ref. 50), Fisher and Yates (Ref. 51, pp. 23-25 and Table XXIII for tables to be used in fitting), L. H. C. Tippett (Ref. 160), and M. G. Kendall (Ref. 78, Vol. II).

logarithmic paper. Yet if a curve of this form serves accurately to describe the trend of a given series, its use is justified, empirically.

Such curves may be fitted most readily by employing logarithms and using an equation of the linear type. The equation

$$y = ax^b$$

becomes, in logarithmic form,

$$\log y = \log a + b \log x$$

The equation to the simple exponential curve may be written

$$y = ar^x$$

(The r in this equation is the equivalent of $1 + r$, as given in earlier references.) This equation may be used to define the trend of a series increasing or decreasing in geometric progression. It has been observed that the trends of economic series frequently depart from such a geometric progression by constant magnitudes. By adding this magnitude, in a given case, to the original series (or subtracting it), a modified series with a clear exponential trend may be secured. The trend of the original series may be written

$$y = ar^x - K \tag{10.5}$$

where K is the constant magnitude by which the series departs from a geometric progression. A *modified exponential* curve of this type may give a highly satisfactory representation of trend, in certain cases. The method employed in fitting such a curve is discussed in Appendix F.

Some use has been made, in the interpretation of economic statistics, of the Gompertz curve, the equation to which was originally developed in the actuarial field. The equation is

$$y = ab^{c^x} \tag{10.6}$$

Its use in the analysis of economic statistics has been based upon the argument that there is a general law of growth characteristic of population increase, and that this same type of growth is found in industries in which volume of production is a direct function of the growth of population.

A somewhat similar curve of growth, the "logistic," has been employed by Verhulst, and by Raymond Pearl and Lowell J. Reed in forecasting population growth. This curve has been found to describe the trends of certain social and economic series. Examples of the procedures employed in fitting Gompertz and logistic curves are given in Appendix F.

Determination of monthly trend values. The procedures so far described have dealt with annual measurements only. Having fitted a line or curve to annual data it is frequently necessary to effect a transition to monthly units. Problems involving such monthly measurements are faced in the study of cyclical movements which are discussed in Chapter 12.

The constant a in the trend equation defines the trend value in the year taken as origin. If the annual data employed in the fitting processes are averages of 12 monthly values (e.g., the average price of pig iron in a given year) the constant a measures the trend value for a month centered at the middle of the year covered by the annual figures. If the annual data are aggregates of 12 monthly values (e.g., total production of pig iron in a given year) the constant a must be divided by 12 to obtain the trend value for the month centered at the middle of the year.

If the trend be linear, the constant b in the equation $y = a + bx$ defines the change due to trend over a 12-month period. In interpolating for monthly trend values, the increment (or decrement) from month to month (e.g., from January to February of a given year) is $\frac{b}{12}$, if the annual data employed in the fitting process are averages of monthly values. The increment from month to month is $\frac{b}{144}$ if the annual data are aggregates of monthly values.

The one further step needed is properly to center the monthly trend values. These should, of course, be centered at points of time corresponding to those to which the actual monthly data relate. In averaging, or aggregating, monthly data relating to the middle of each of the 12 months in a calendar year we secure a figure centered at July 1. The month centered at the middle of the year of origin thus centers at July 1. For comparison with actual monthly data, we desire trend values centered at July 15, August 15, etc. At the beginning, therefore, we must add to the trend value for the month centered at the middle of the year of origin $\left(\text{that is, to } a \text{ or to } \frac{a}{12}\right)$ one half of the month-to-month increment (or decrement) that we have obtained from b of the trend equation. This procedure gives us the trend value for the month centered at July 15. This value may be compared with the actual value recorded for that month. The addition to this of the month-to-month trend increment (or decrement) gives trend values for all following months; subtraction gives trend values for all preceding months.[10]

On the Selection of a Curve to Represent Trend

Various types of curves which may be fitted to represent the trend of economic data over a period of time have been described. But which of these many types is to be selected in a given case? Which will give the best standard of "normality" for each of the years covered? Several references to this problem have been made in the preceding sections, but no general principles have been laid down. And, in fact, no general principles can be evoked to answer this fundamental question. There is no absolute test of goodness of fit in such cases. It is largely a matter of personal judgment as to the type of curve which best represents the trend in a given instance, and experience must play a dominant part in such judgments. But certain general considerations are of assistance in selecting the appropriate type of curve.

1. The first step in the selection of a curve type is the plotting of the data. When this has been done, it is frequently possible by inspection to determine the appropriate form. The data may be plotted in four different combinations, of which the first two are of chief importance in dealing with economic material.

a. Natural x, natural y. (That is, plot the given figures on ordinary arithmetic paper.)

b. Natural x, log y. (Plot the x's on the natural scale, and plot the y's on the logarithmic scale; i.e., use semilogarithmic paper.)

c. Natural y, log x. (Plot on semilogarithmic paper, with the x-scale logarithmic.)

---

[10] If the original monthly data relate to the first or last of the month, rather than the middle, a similar correction is needed, but the monthly dates named in the text would be different, of course. If the trend equation is nonlinear, the process of interpolation must be correspondingly modified. For the simple exponential the rate of change from month to month is given by the twelfth root of the year-to-year rate. On general methods of interpolation see *The Calculus of Observations*, by Whittaker and Robinson (Ref. 190).

d. Log y, log x. (Plot on paper with logarithmic ruling on both scales.)

If in any of these cases a straight line trend is denoted, a type of equation which plots as a straight line under the given conditions (see Chapter 2) would be selected. If a linear equation is not appropriate some other simple type may be suggested by the plotted data. In studying such graphs for the purpose of selecting a curve to represent trend, one should be familiar with the curves representing all the simpler equations.

2. The appropriate curve may be determined by a study of the relations between the two variables, x and y. In the simpler cases the following relations hold:[11]

a. If, when the values of x are arranged in an arithmetic series, the corresponding values of y form a geometric series, the relation is of the exponential type, described by the equation

$$y = ab^x$$

b. If, when the values of x are arranged in a geometric series, the corresponding values of y form a geometric series, the relation is of the parabolic or hyperbolic type, described by the equation

$$y = ax^b$$

c. If, when the values of x are arranged in an arithmetic series, the first differences of the corresponding y's are constant, the relation is of the straight line type, described by the equation

$$y = a + bx$$

The differences between successive y values, when x's are arranged in an arithmetic series, are termed "first differences" or "first order differences" and are represented by the symbol Δy. The differences between successive first differences are called "second differences" and are represented by the symbol $\Delta^2 y$.

---

[11] It will be recalled that an arithmetic series changes by a constant absolute increment, while a geometric series changes by a constant percentage.

Differences of higher order are similarly derived. The following table illustrates the formation of differences:

x	y	Δy	$\Delta^2 y$	$\Delta^3 y$
1	11			
2	40	29	32	12
3	101	61	44	12
4	206	105	56	12
5	367	161	68	12
6	596	229	80	12
7	905	309	92	12
8	1,306	401	104	12
9	1,811	505	116	
10	2,432	621		

d. If, when the values of x are arranged in an arithmetic series, the nth differences of the corresponding y's are constant, the relation between the variables is described by a polynomial carried to the nth power of x; that is, by an equation of the type

$$y = a + bx + cx^2 + dx^3 + \ldots + qx^n.$$

Thus, in the example given above, in which the third differences are constant, the relation between x and y would be described by an equation of the form

$$y = a + bx + cx^2 + dx^3$$

When one is selecting a curve to use in the analysis of economic data, he will rarely, if ever, find these tests to be met perfectly. This would happen only when the curve chosen passed through all the plotted points. But data in a given case will generally approximate some one of the conditions described above, and the appropriate type of curve will be indicated.

3. If study of the original data does not render a definite decision possible, several types of curves may be fitted to the data and the decision made by comparing the results. If the equations to the curves being compared contain the same number of constants, a comparison of the root-mean-square deviations about the curves furnishes a valid test of the closeness of the fit within the limits of the data.

The root-mean-square deviation may be readily computed by making use of the following relationship

$$\Sigma(d^2) = \Sigma(y^2) - a\Sigma(y) - b\Sigma(xy) - c\Sigma(x^2y) - \ldots \qquad (10.7)$$

where $\Sigma(d^2)$ is the sum of the squares of the deviations about the line of trend. (The derivation of this equation is explained in Appendix C, in which a generalized form is given.) If the equations do not contain the same number of constants, a test of this sort is invalid and the comparison can only be made by inspection. Personal judgment as to the curve that represents the trend most accurately must be the basis of the decision in such cases.

It should be remembered that the closeness of fit within the limits of the data is not of itself a final criterion. An equation could be secured, having a number of constants equal to the number of points, which would give a curve passing through every point plotted, yet such a curve would not necessarily represent the trend. The concept of a *trend* is of a regular, smooth underlying movement, from which there are deviations, but which marks the long-term tendency of the series. In general, therefore, the curve should be of simple form, if it is to be consistent with the concept of secular trend. This does not mean, however, that a complex trend can be represented by a simple curve that fails to conform to the plotted data.

4. An important question to be answered before the form of curve can be selected relates to the limits within which the line of trend is to be used. If it is to be used only within the limits of the plotted data (i.e., for *interpolation*) one set of considerations governs the choice of a curve. If it is to be projected beyond the limits of the data and used as a basis for the determination of "normal"[12] levels during a subsequent period, other considerations enter. In the former case a reasonable fit to the data is the sole requirement; in the latter case it is necessary, in addition, that the trend of the projection be logical, and consistent with the past record.

---

[12] It is customary to think of the term "normal" as synonymous with "trend value," but we should not forget that "normal" is here used in a conveniently Pickwickian sense. Even in retrospect it is hard to say what was normal in the life of man; to say what will be normal in the future is doubly hazardous. In the *New Yorker's* words, "Normalcy, like love, is old yet ever new. It is the imponderable, haunting element in the statistical pudding. . . . Normalcy is a memory, a wisp, a piece of old lace, a crushed petal between the pages of a book."

The fact should be recognized that projection, or *extrapolation*, represents a guess, justified only on the assumption that a proper line of trend has been fitted and that the same conditions that affected the series in the past will prevail in the future. A change in conditions, the introduction of new elements, renders the projection invalid. When dealing with economic statistics, moreover, it is ordinarily impossible to tell, except in retrospect, when a change has taken place. Conclusions drawn from the projection of a line of trend are always subject to error, therefore. In practical statistical work such projections are made, and are justified on the ground that the most probable course in the future is that which prevailed in the past. Projections into the distant future are, of course, subject to wider margins of error than short-time projections. Lines of trend should be revised from time to time, therefore, as new data become available.

When a projection is to be made, a simple curve with few constants is to be preferred to a more complicated one. A polynomial of the third or fourth degree may give an excellent fit to the data in a given case, but the projection of such curves is inadvisable. It is well to remember, as Perrin has pointed out, that a curve suitable for interpolation may not be at all adapted to extrapolation.

The avoidance of distortion of trend lines by abnormal conditions in the terminal years of the period studied is particularly important when a trend is to be projected.

It seems to be true, in general, that simple curves fitted to the logarithms of the y's give more reliable results when projected than do curves fitted to the natural numbers. In an interesting discussion of this point, Karl G. Karsten has argued that phenomena characterized by a uniform *rate of change* are more likely to maintain their trend than phenomena marked by a uniform *amount of change*. It is the semilogarithmic curves, of course, that best measure *rates* of change.

5. It is frequently true that no one curve will fit a given series during the entire period it is desired to study. This may be due to structural changes in the economy that alter the determinants of growth for the element in question. Thus the industrial revolution, which materially increased the productive powers of the people of Britain in the late eighteenth and nineteenth centuries, paved the way for a substantial advance in the rate of population growth in

the United Kingdom. Such structural changes affect many economic series. By breaking the entire period into sections, appropriate lines of trend may be fitted to the several periods thus marked off. This process may be carried to a quite illogical extreme, however. The concept of trend is of a gradual, long-term change, and the breaking up of a series in order to fit a number of trend lines is contrary to the whole conception. The assumption that a trend has been sharply broken may be justified on occasion, when a real change in underlying conditions is known to have occurred. But when trend breaks are introduced without such rational basis the significance of resulting trend values is of course reduced.

REFERENCES

Burns, A. F., *Production Trends in the United States Since* 1870.

Croxton, F. E. and Cowden, D. J., *Applied General Statistics,* Chaps. 15, 16.

Kendall, M. G., *The Advanced Theory of Statistics*, 3rd ed., Vol. II, pp. 363-387.

Koopmans, T., ed., *Statistical Inference in Dynamic Economic Models*, Chaps. 11, 12 (an econometric approach to the analysis of time series).

Kuznets, S., *Secular Movements in Production and Prices*.

Lewis, E. E., *Methods of Statistical Analysis in Economics and Business*, Chap. 10.

Macaulay, F. R., *The Smoothing of Time Series*.

Mills, F. C., *Economic Tendencies in the United States*.

Riggleman, J. R. and Frisbee, I. N., *Business Statistics*, 3rd ed., Chaps. 14, 15.

Sasuly, M., *Trend Analysis of Statistics: Theory and Technique*.

Schumpeter, J. A., *Business Cycles*, Chap. 5.

Spurr, W. A., Kellogg, L. S. and Smith, J. H., *Business and Economic Statistics*, Chap. 15.

Yule, G. U. and Kendall, M. G., *An Introduction to the Theory of Statistics*, 14th ed., Chap. 26.

The publishers and the dates of publication of the books named in chapter reference lists are given in the bibliography at the end of this volume.

CHAPTER 11

The Analysis of Time Series: Measurement of Seasonal Fluctuations

The measurement of secular trend is but one of the problems connected with the analysis of a series in time. Such series, it has been pointed out, are subject to periodic and semiperiodic fluctuations, seasonal and cyclical in character, and these fluctuations may be objects of major interest to the investigator. We deal in this chapter with the first of these classes of fluctuations.

The pervasiveness of seasonal movements. Seasonal changes in economic series are, of course, true periodicities. The swing of the earth around the sun brings in its wake a host of movements in weather and in harvests, in the flow of goods in domestic and international trade, in the needs and buying practices of consumers, and in the patterns of industrial production that are related to consumer demand, and ramifying consequences of all these.

A few examples will indicate the pervasiveness and amplitude of these movements.[1] Industrial production in the United States reaches a seasonal low in July, a peak in October, the range being from 94 to 103 (where 100 represents the average for the year). Metal mining rises from a low of 72 in January to a high of 121 in June; bituminous coal production is at a low of 75 in July, a peak of 109 in October-November. The production of food and beverages (manufactured products) reaches a low of 91 in February, a high

---

[1] These examples are based on seasonal indexes of the Board of Governors of the Federal Reserve System (see Chapter 14) and of the National Bureau of Economic Research. Such indexes are, of course, subject to change over time.

TABLE 11-1

Incurred Monthly Fire Losses in the United States 1936-1953*
(in thousands of dollars)

	January	February	March	April	May	June	July	August	September	October	November	December	Total
1936	27,730	30,910	29,177	25,785	21,479	20,407	22,357	21,714	20,413	20,439	22,808	30,133	293,353
1937	25,070	28,655	29,319	26,664	21,438	19,525	19,812	19,767	19,350	21,098	23,850	30,173	284,721
1938	27,676	26,473	29,051	25,615	22,917	19,474	20,435	20,821	23,372	24,798	28,659	32,758	302,050
1939	27,615	29,303	30,682	27,061	27,032	24,191	22,468	22,800	22,837	24,300	27,248	27,959	313,496
1940	36,261	34,410	29,789	26,657	23,446	19,506	20,323	20,722	21,198	22,091	23,449	28,617	306,469
1941	26,470	26,102	31,471	29,330	25,637	24,943	23,693	24,122	24,668	30,833	23,822	31,261	322,357
1942	35,565	30,819	30,505	27,960	23,233	22,410	21,000	19,680	20,443	22,621	24,144	36,469	314,849
1943	27,733	33,175	39,214	34,241	29,297	26,854	25,016	29,193	26,488	29,661	31,647	47,716	380,235
1944	38,572	38,280	39,084	34,746	32,815	30,555	32,705	30,638	31,448	32,173	33,847	48,694	423,538
1945	44,865	41,457	40,876	37,950	34,153	34,090	34,054	34,095	32,447	34,470	37,393	49,478	455,329
1946	49,808	51,759	53,252	52,153	46,094	44,240	40,998	40,019	40,256	40,108	44,706	58,094	561,487
1947	57,180	64,247	72,435	68,029	56,545	50,840	49,357	51,359	47,990	54,946	51,346	68,361	692,635
1948	63,010	71,521	74,236	63,751	59,256	54,706	50,955	49,543	49,945	51,845	52,949	69,397	711,114
1949	57,926	62,424	67,218	55,290	54,162	51,787	49,592	50,150	49,678	48,914	53,116	67,279	667,536
1950	58,823	58,340	72,468	61,605	58,765	57,116	52,980	49,878	45,922	49,953	55,790	66,820	688,460
1951	68,686	69,136	71,507	62,965	58,744	56,403	52,220	55,416	53,398	54,660	60,064	68,206	731,405
1952	74,155	69,925	72,254	67,350	62,354	58,585	61,675	56,462	58,949	63,958	65,129	74,127	784,953
1953	76,659	72,706	83,471	67,362	64,239	67,644	74,938	107,713	68,613	68,551	68,064	83,440	903,400

* Compiled by the National Board of Fire Underwriters.

of 114 in September. The consumption of cotton is at a low in July, a high in February, the seasonal amplitude being from 84 to 108. Portland cement production, on the other hand, is at a low of 76 in February, a high of 115 in October. Sales by mail order houses range from a low of 70 in February to a high of 145 in December. Consumer installment credit for purchases from department stores and mail order houses is at a seasonal low of 92 in August and September, a year-end peak of 110 in December, 111 in January. Freight ton-miles on railroads reach a low of 92 in February, a high of 112 in October. And the cold storage holdings of eggs rise from a seasonal low of 4 in February to a high of 192 in July! Some of these are, of course, extreme examples; there are stable series that are virtually unaffected by the march of the seasons. But many social activities and economic processes are affected. Our present concern is with these.

The study of weather and harvest rhythms and of their diverse economic effects can be a rewarding enterprise in its own right, and some few investigations have concentrated attention on them. In the main, however, statisticians seek to define seasonal patterns for the purpose of removing them. The Federal Reserve production index is "adjusted" in this fashion. In the traditional approach in time series analysis, trend and seasonal movements are eliminated in order that "cycles" may be defined. But whether the seasonal patterns are themselves of interest or are to be removed to further other purposes, the first step is to measure them with as much precision as possible.

An Example of the Use of Moving Averages

The figures in Table 11-1, which reflect the month-to-month variations in losses from fire and lightning in the United States, may be used to illustrate the measurement of seasonal fluctuations. The process of measurement begins with the computation of 12-month moving averages. Since the fluctuations to be defined take place within a constant period of 12 months, a moving average may be used with more confidence than when a rhythm of varying length is involved. However, the magnitude of the fluctuations (the *amplitude* of the seasonal swings) may vary somewhat from year to year; moreover, the individual observations to be averaged are affected by random and other nonseasonal factors. Accordingly, the line marked out by the moving averages will not be completely free of seasonal influences, and the deviations from it will not define pure seasonal fluctuations. We may meet these difficulties in part by averaging the ratios of the actual monthly items to the moving averages, by months, and basing indexes of seasonal variation upon these averages.

It is essential, of course, that the moving average, centered, fall at the same date as the original figure with which it is to be compared. This involves a second process of averaging. For example, the monthly totals of fire losses should be considered to be located at the middle of each month. The average of the 12 monthly items for 1936, when centered, falls on July 1. The average of the items from February, 1936, through January, 1937, centered, falls on August 1. To secure a figure comparable with the July 15 average, these two must be averaged. By this process of computing 2-month moving averages from the 12-month averages, comparability with the original figures may be secured. In the actual computations it is simpler to employ moving totals up to the point of final reduction to a properly centered 12-month moving average.

Ratios to Moving Averages. The procedure is illustrated in Table 11-2, which shows the calculations for 2 of the 18 years covered. The 12-month moving totals given in column (3) are centered by means of 2-month moving totals in column (4); dividing by 24, the moving averages given in column (5) are obtained. Expressing the original data in column (2) as ratios to the corresponding averages in column (5), we obtain the figures in column (6).

The derived percentages, showing the relation of actual fire losses, month by month, to the moving averages are given in Table 11-3, for the period 1936-53. These percentages, which are to provide the means by which we compute index numbers of seasonal variation, call for a brief discussion.

The base of each percentage, e.g., 24,335 for July 1936, is an average for 12 months. In the calculation of this average, it is assumed, recurring fluctuations with a period of exactly 12 months will be cancelled out. Thus the average is taken to be free of seasonal movements. The averages will, however, move with the long-term trend, if there is one. They will reflect periodic movements, such as business cycles, that run their courses in periods exceeding 12 months in length. Deviations from the moving

TABLE 11–2

Showing the Calculation of 12-Month Moving Averages of Monthly Fire
Losses and of the Ratios of Actual Fire Losses to Moving Averages
(Fire losses in thousands of dollars)

(1) Year and month	(2) Amount of loss	(3) 12-month moving total	(4) 2-month moving total of col. (3)	(5) Col. (4) ÷ 24	(6) Ratio of col. (2) to col. (5)
1936					
January	27,730				
February	30,910				
March	29,177				
April	25,786				
May	21,479				
June	20,407				
July	23,357	293,353	584,046	24,335	.9187
August	21,714	290,693	579,131	24,130	.8999
September	20,413	288,438	577,018	24,042	.8490
October	20,439	288,580	578,038	24,085	.8486
November	22,808	289,458	578,875	24,120	.9456
December	30,133	289,417	577,952	24,081	1.2513
1937					
January	25,070	288,535	574,525	23,938	1.0473
February	28,655	285,990	570,033	23,751	1.2065
March	29,319	284,043	567,023	23,626	1.2410
April	26,664	282,980	566,619	23,609	1.1294
May	21,438	283,639	568,320	23,680	.9053
June	19,525	284,681	569,402	23,725	.8230
July	19,812	284,721	572,048	23,835	.8312
August	19,767	287,327	572,472	23,853	.8287
September	19,350	285,145	570,022	23,751	.8147
October	21,098	284,877	568,706	23,696	.8904
November	23,850	283,829	569,137	23,714	1.0057
December	30,173	285,308	570,565	23,773	1.2692

Columns (3) to (6) must, of course, be blank for the first six months of 1936. Data for the last six months of 1935 would be needed to compute moving totals for January–June 1936. Entries for 1937 are complete, since 1938 data were available and have been used. Table 11-2 is a portion of the work table covering the full eighteen years.

averages, deviations which make the percentages in Table 11-3 exceed or fall below 100, are taken to be due primarily to seasonal movements. If the seasonal pattern were perfectly repetitive, and if no other forces affected the percentages, the figures for any one month, say December, would all be identical, and any one of them could be taken as an index of December's seasonal movements. It is clear that they are not identical. The December percentages range from a low of 104.8 in 1939 to a high of 142.5 in 1943. Various forces other than seasonal do in fact affect fire losses in each month of the year. Random factors play an important role

TABLE 11-3

Percentage Relations of Incurred Fire Losses to 12-Month Moving Averages, Centered, 1936-1953

	January	February	March	April	May	June	July	August	September	October	November	December
1936							91.9	90.0	84.9	84.9	94.6	125.1
1937	104.7	120.6	124.1	112.9	90.5	82.3	83.1	82.9	81.5	89.0	100.6	126.9
1938	116.3	110.9	120.6	105.0	92.6	77.7	81.2	82.3	91.8	96.9	111.0	125.0
1939	104.3	110.0	114.9	101.5	101.7	91.9	84.8	84.3	83.9	89.4	100.9	104.8
1940	137.4	131.3	114.3	102.9	91.4	76.5	80.9	85.0	87.9	91.0	95.8	115.4
1941	105.2	102.5	122.3	111.7	96.3	83.2	87.0	86.7	88.2	110.6	85.9	113.6
1942	130.3	114.1	114.5	107.0	90.1	86.1	81.0	76.6	78.2	84.5	88.5	131.6
1943	98.8	115.8	133.9	114.8	96.3	86.0	77.8	89.0	80.2	89.8	95.3	142.5
1944	113.6	111.5	112.9	99.5	93.4	86.7	92.0	85.2	87.0	88.5	92.6	132.5
1945	121.4	111.5	109.4	101.2	90.5	89.9	89.2	87.9	81.7	84.4	89.2	115.5
1946	114.3	117.4	119.2	115.3	100.7	95.3	87.0	83.5	81.7	79.1	86.3	110.6
1947	107.6	119.1	132.3	122.1	99.9	88.7	85.1	87.8	81.5	93.5	87.4	115.9
1948	106.4	120.8	125.4	107.7	100.2	92.4	86.3	84.7	86.4	90.7	93.6	123.4
1949	103.3	111.4	111.9	98.9	97.1	92.9	88.8	90.2	89.4	87.2	94.0	118.2
1950	102.7	101.6	126.6	107.8	102.6	99.5	91.6	85.1	77.8	84.6	94.4	113.1
1951	116.4	116.7	119.6	104.4	96.8	92.6	85.4	90.2	86.8	88.6	94.4	109.5
1952	118.1	110.6	113.8	105.1	96.4	89.9	94.1	85.9	88.9	95.8	96.8	110.1
1953	112.3	102.5	113.6	90.9	86.4	90.3						

in the incidence of fires; they may cause any month in a given year to be well below or well above the figure that might be expected on the basis of past experience. It is unlikely that the trend of fire losses is exactly reflected in the long-term movements of the 12-month moving averages; to the extent that the trend is not so defined, the monthly percentages of Table 11-3 will depart from 100. It is, similarly, unlikely that cyclical fluctuations in fire losses are fully embodied in the moving averages; the percentages of Table 11-3 will be affected by any discrepancy of this sort.

For these various reasons we find considerable variation among the percentages for each month of the year. The degree of variation is revealed in Fig. 11.1, a multiple frequency table showing the scatter of the percentages falling in each of the twelve months. There is, of course, an obvious escape from the difficulties presented by variation within a given month. We may average the 17 items for January, the 17 for February, etc. This procedure has an excellent rational justification. We may assume that the *seasonal force* is fairly constant in its influence upon fire losses in, say, the month of August. Losses in that month tend always to be low. But *random factors* will sometimes work to make the losses in a given month low, sometimes high. So, also, will *cyclical divergences* from 12-month moving averages, since the averages may be expected to be below the cyclical norm in some years, above in others. Trend divergences can conceivably offer greater difficulties; moving averages may consistently fall below or exceed trend values, if the true trends are nonlinear with persistent upward or downward curvature.[2] With this one exception, we should expect the effects of nonseasonal influences to be such as would be cancelled out, in the long run, by averaging the percentages for a given month. The persistent influence of the seasonal movement would be dominant, and would determine the location of the average for that month. The trend factor would be disturbing only if the series being studied were nonlinear, with considerable curvature.

That there is a seasonal pattern in fire losses is clearly shown by Fig. 11.1. Although there is considerable variation in some months, losses are persistently high from December to March, fall from March to August, remain low through the fall months, and rise again in December. The existence of such a pronounced pattern

[2] See pp. 331-3.

Relatives	Jan.	Feb.	Mar.	Apr.	May	June	July	Aug.	Sept.	Oct.	Nov.	Dec.
142 - 144.9												|
139 - 141.9												
136 - 138.9	|											
133 - 135.9			|									
130 - 132.9	|	|	|									||
127 - 129.9												
124 - 126.9		|||										|||
121 - 123.9	|		|	|								|
118 - 120.9	|	|||	|||									|
115 - 117.9	||	|||		|								|||
112 - 114.9	|||	|	卌|	||								||
109 - 111.9		卌|	||	|						|	|	|||
106 - 108.9	||			|||								
103 - 105.9	||||			|||								|
100 - 102.9	|	|||		|||	||||						||	
97 - 99.9	|			||	||	|					|	
94 - 96.9					||||	|	|			||	卌|	
91 - 93.9					|||	卌	|||		|	||	||	
88 - 90.9				|	|||	||||	||	||||	|||	卌|	||	
85 - 87.9					|	|||	卌	卌||	||||	|	|||	
82 - 84.9						|	||	卌	||	||||		
79 - 81.9							|||		卌	|		
76 - 78.9						||	|	|	||			

FIG. 11.1. Frequency Distributions: Monthly Incurred Fire Losses Expressed as Relatives of Corresponding 12-Month Moving Averages.

gives us confidence that the seasonal index numbers to be derived will be significant of real changes within the year.

Means and Medians of Ratios to Moving Averages. Various methods are employed in seeking to obtain a representative and accurate index figure for each month of the year. Of the conventional averages, the arithmetic mean and the median are appropriate. Averages of these types, for each of the 12 months, are given in Table 11-4, with corresponding adjusted measures. The

TABLE 11-4

Indexes of Seasonal Variation in Fire Losses. Arithmetic Means and Medians Computed from Ratios to 12-Month Moving Averages

(1) Month	(2) Arithmetic means	(3) Arithmetic means, adjusted	(4) Medians	(5) Medians adjusted
January	112.54	112.9	112.3	113.2
February	113.43	113.7	111.5	112.4
March	119.37	119.7	119.2	120.2
April	106.39	106.7	105.1	106.0
May	95.46	95.7	96.3	97.1
June	88.94	89.2	89.9	90.7
July	86.31	86.5	86.3	87.0
August	85.72	86.0	85.2	85.9
September	84.58	84.8	84.9	85.6
October	89.91	90.2	89.0	89.8
November	94.37	94.6	94.4	95.2
December	119.63	120.0	115.9	116.9
Average	99.72	100.0	99.17	100.0

adjustment is needed because the average of the 12 monthly means (or the 12 monthly medians) will seldom be exactly 100; there is rarely a complete cancelling out of the effects of nonseasonal forces. Thus for the arithmetic means in column (2) of Table 11-4 the average is 99.72. Since the monthly seasonal indexes are designed to show how a given annual total of fire losses would be divided among the 12 months, if seasonal forces alone were operative, the average of the 12 seasonal indexes should be exactly 100. The simple adjustment needed is made, in this case by multiplying each of the items in column (2) by the reciprocal of 99.72. The adjusted measures in column (3) will then average 100. (Two decimal places are used in the calculations, but the final indexes are carried to but one decimal place.) A similar adjustment is made for the medians of the original monthly percentages.

Both sets of adjusted indexes show a wide range of variation in fire losses, within the year. September falls to some 15 percent below the average monthly loss for the year; March and December mark seasonal peaks, from 17 to 20 percent above the yearly average. That this is a consistent pattern is clearly shown by the frequency distributions in Fig. 11.1.

The two sets of seasonal indexes agree very closely. The differences between them fall within a range of less than 2 percent, except for December, a month of considerable dispersion in fire losses. Each of the two types has its merits and demerits. The mean is affected by the values of all the measurements available for each month. It may, however, be unduly affected by exceptional cases. Thus a conflagration would swell fire losses in a given month to a quite unrepresentative figure. A seasonal index for that month might be misleading were the exceptional figure included in its calculation. The median, which avoids this danger, has its own drawbacks. It is subject to material changes in value by the addition or withdrawal of one or two entries, unless there is a definite concentration in the monthly distributions. Since the choice of an average is conditioned in part upon the character of the distribution of observations within given months, the tabular summary given in Fig. 11.1 can be made to serve as a very useful guide.

Positional Means. Use is often made of a third method of computing seasonal indexes, a method that combines many of the advantages of both mean and median. This involves the taking of an arithmetic mean of the central items in each monthly array of percentages. When there is an odd number of cases in each monthly distribution, this may be the mean of the three or five central observations; when the number is even, the middle four or six observations may be averaged. (The measures should be derived, of course, not from the frequency distributions, but from arrays of the original items.) Such a "positional average" is unaffected by extreme values, and is likely to be more stable than the median, i.e., less affected by the addition or removal of one or more items. In Table 11-5 are given indexes of seasonal variation in fire losses obtained by using such positional averages.

The indexes given in columns (3) and (5) of Table 11-5 trace out the same general pattern of seasonal variation that was defined by the indexes in Table 11-4. It is to be noted, however, that the in-

TABLE 11-5

Indexes of Seasonal Variation in Fire Losses
Positional Means based upon Ratios to Moving Averages

(1) Month	(2) Arithmetic mean of 3 central items	(3) Col. (2) adjusted	(4) Arithmetic mean of 5 central items	(5) Col. (4) adjusted
January	111.18	112.3	110.84	111.8
February	112.37	113.5	112.86	113.9
March	116.20	117.3	116.50	117.5
April	105.70	106.7	105.84	106.8
May	96.33	97.3	95.80	96.7
June	90.00	90.9	90.12	90.9
July	86.23	87.1	86.16	86.9
August	85.40	86.2	85.58	86.3
September	85.07	85.9	84.78	85.5
October	89.00	89.9	89.06	89.8
November	94.33	95.2	94.38	95.2
December	116.53	117.7	117.68	118.7
Average	99.03	100.0	99.13	100.0

dexes derived by averaging central items come between the extremes obtained from simple arithmetic means and medians for the month of December. The positional means have clear merit. In general, they are to be preferred to either the arithmetic mean or the median when the arrays of monthly relatives show any considerable degree of dispersion.

Other methods. The preceding example has illustrated the use of ratios to moving averages in defining patterns of seasonal variation. A somewhat similar method employs ratios to trend values. Such ratios are tabulated, for the different months of the year, in the manner shown in Fig. 11.1. Seasonal indexes are then obtained by averaging, exactly as in handling ratios to moving averages. The use of trend ratios is in general less satisfactory than the use of moving averages, and is not now generally employed. For the deviations from trend will reflect cyclical, random, and seasonal fluctuations, and the averaging of ratios to trend must be trusted to remove the full influence of cycles, as well as random effects. Since this removal can seldom if ever be achieved, the resulting indexes of seasonal variation are not too trustworthy. Still a third method of measuring seasonal movements rests on graphic procedures, utilizing the special advantages of ratio (or semilogarithmic) paper. The interested student will find an explanation of this method in Spurr, Kellogg, and Smith (Ref. 150).

We must note that not all series of observations recorded by months (or other subdivisions of the year) are marked by seasonal variation. In each case the investigator must assure himself that in making adjustments for seasonal movements he is correcting for truly repetitive fluctuations in the original series. The processes described in the preceding pages will almost always give monthly means of ratios to 12-month moving averages that vary, for the months of the year; the play of random factors will assure this. But the fact that the indexes thus obtained vary from month to month is no guaranty that a true seasonal pattern exists. Rational considerations, together with an orderly pattern of seasonal movements in such a presentation as that illustrated by the multiple frequency table in Fig. 11.1, will often be sufficient warrant for accepting a set of seasonal indexes as significant. (The observations should, of course, cover a number of years—eight to twelve may be thought of as a minimum, although working statisticians familiar with their materials sometimes base seasonal indexes on a record covering as few as five years.) When such considerations can be supplemented by such objective tests as are discussed in Chapter 16, the case for acceptance is of course stronger.

Changes in Seasonal Patterns

The basic seasonal impulses that are generated by the annually recurring rhythms of weather remain fairly constant over time, although there are slow secular changes in weather (see Fig. 10.3) and variations from year to year in the intensity of winter cold and summer heat. The derived patterns of economic behavior are by no means constant, however. Changes in seasonal patterns may be abrupt; they may be slow, but progressive in character; they may be gradual but irregular. Abrupt changes come, for example, when a national economy makes a swift transition from peace to war, or from war to peace. Evolutionary or secular changes in pattern may come with slow alterations in trade practices, in production procedures, or in consumption habits. The displacement of the open car by the closed car brought such a progressive modification in the seasonal pattern of automobile sales. The irregular changes may be due to a host of minor factors, or may be related to a definable cause. Thus the price of an agricultural product may follow one seasonal pattern in years of high production and quite a different pattern in years of low production. Shifts in the dates of annual automobile shows may affect the seasonal distribution of automobile sales. Patterns of retail sales in some fields vary with changes in the date of Easter. For these reasons the statisticians may never regard a seasonal pattern as fixed. Continuing checks are needed; these may lead to the use of new seasonal adjustments every five or ten years, or even more frequently. (Note, for example, the many shifts made between 1947 and 1952 in the seasonal adjustments in components of the Federal Reserve Index of Industrial Production.)[3]

When the change in a seasonal pattern is evolutionary, the progressive change in the index for each month may be measured separately. Thus when ratios to moving averages have been obtained, all the January items may be plotted chronologically, say from 1937 to 1953. If there is a progressive change in the January ratios, this movement may be defined by an appropriate line of trend. The trend value for January, 1937, is a first approximation to the January seasonal index for 1937; the trend value for January, 1938, provides a similar approximation to the seasonal index for January, 1938, and so on for January of each of the other years covered. All February ratios are treated in the same way, trend values for February of each year then providing first approximations to the February seasonal indexes. Similar procedures give corresponding measures for each of the other months of the year. The preliminary seasonal indexes for the 12 months of each year must then be adjusted to make their average equal to 100, just as was done with the preliminary indexes for fire losses cited above.

The key operation in this procedure is the determination of the trends of the ratios for the various months of the year. Careful study of the plotted figures for each month is, of course, a first step. The investigator may then decide to fit a mathematical function by least squares. A simple straight line is a useful form, if the secular movement for the given month is marked by regular increments or decrements in absolute terms. Alternately, a moving average of five or seven terms may be employed, or a free-hand

[3] *Federal Reserve Bulletin*, September, 1953, pp. 54-5.

curve may be drawn through the plotted points for a single month. Moving averages have been employed by the National Bureau of Economic Research in handling changing seasonals; the free-hand method has been extensively used by the Research Division of the Board of Governors of the Federal Reserve System in dealing with seasonal changes in elements of their production index.

Testing a Shift in Seasonal Pattern. In dealing with shifts in seasonal patterns the investigator faces the omnipresent play of random factors. These will bring about some variation from year to year in the apparent seasonal movements of even the steadiest of series. We need here, therefore, some means of distinguishing significant from nonsignificant variations. The methods of rank correlation discussed in Chapter 9 may be used in applying such a test. Observations to be used are presented in Table 11-6.[4]

The figures in column (2) of Table 11-6 are ratios of the type shown above in column (6) of Table 11-2. These are ratios for the month of December, arranged in chronological order. They show,

TABLE 11–6

Data for Testing an Apparent Shift in Seasonal Pattern
December Employment in Construction Work in North Dakota, 1940-1951
Ratios to 12-Month Moving Average, Centered

(1) Year	(2) Ratio of employment in December to 12-month moving average	(3) Rank	(4) Natural integers
1940	0.445	1	1
1941	0.668	4	2
1942	0.524	2	3
1943	0.663	3	4
1944	0.695	5	5
1945	0.763	7	6
1946	0.902	12	7
1947	0.795	9	8
1948	0.781	8	9
1949	0.875	10	10
1950	0.877	11	11
1951	0.747	6	12

[4] This interesting example of a nonparametric test applied in time-series analysis is cited, with permission, from a doctoral dissertation by K. A. Middleton on *The Estimation of Monthly Labor Force Employment and Unemployment Data for States* (filed in the Columbia University Library).

obviously, that construction employment in December was in each year below the annual average. Severe winter weather tends, of course, to curtail such activity. If, over a period of 12 years, no real shift had occurred in the seasonal standing of December, in volume of employment in construction, we should expect the ratios in column (2) of Table 11-6 to stand in random order, when ranked in order of size and listed chronologically, as in column (3) of that table. There is, however, some indication of a progressive increase in the December ratios—an increase that would mean an advance in December employment in construction, relatively to the other months of the year. There is some reason to think that this advance has in fact occurred with the development of improved all-weather construction materials and techniques. But we need an objective test. Can the ranking in column (3) be considered random, or does it manifest a progressive increase in the December ratios?

The test takes the form of a comparison of the ranks given in column (3) with the natural integers given in column (4). If the rankings in column (3) are random, correlation will be zero, within sampling limits. Kendall's coefficient of rank correlation is well adapted for use in testing this null hypothesis (see Chapter 9, pp. 312-7 above, for details of the measures employed in this test).

From the rankings given in Table 11-6, we have

$$S = 40$$
$$s_{sc} = 14.60$$

where s_{sc} is the standard error of S. Does the observed value of S deviate significantly from an assumed population value of zero? The sample is large enough to warrant the assumption that S is distributed normally, after correction for continuity. We have, therefore, for the normal deviate,

$$T = \frac{39 - 0}{14.60} = 2.67$$

Judging this result on the conservative 1 percent level, we must reject the null hypothesis. Positively, this means that the data of Table 11-6 provide evidence of a progressive change in the seasonal ratios for December.

Electronic Computations in Seasonal Analysis. A recent development in the work of the U. S. Bureau of the Census promises to extend and materially improve processes of seasonal analysis. A systematic procedure is now available for using Univac, one of the high-speed electronic computers, in the construction of seasonal indexes and in the testing of these indexes for significance. The operation is an adaptation of the ratio-to-moving-average method, using positional means, that was explained in the preceding pages. The derived measures are moving indexes—devised, that is, to take account, year by year, of true changes in seasonal patterns. The method is accurate, expeditious, and inexpensive in terms of machine time. Computations for a monthly series covering 10 years, with tests of the significance of the seasonal pattern and of the validity of the adjustments, can be completed in about one minute, at a cost of about two dollars.[5] Although the average investigator will not have such equipment at his disposal, its use in a central federal agency will mean that all basic economic and social series can be readily tested for seasonality, and adjusted, if adjustment is required.

REFERENCES

Burns, A. F. and Mitchell, W. C., *Measuring Business Cycles*, pp. 43-55.

Croxton, F. E. and Cowden, D. J., *Applied General Statistics*, Chaps. 17, 18.

Federal Reserve System, Board of Governors, *Federal Reserve Bulletin*, Dec. 1953, pp. 1260-1264.

Joy, A. and Thomas, W., "The Use of Moving Averages in the Measurement of Seasonal Variations," *Journal of the American Statistical Association*, Sept. 1928.

Kuznets, S., *Seasonal Variations in Industry and Trade*.

Lewis, E. E., *Methods of Statistical Analysis in Economics and Business*, Chap. 11.

Mendershausen, H., "Methods of Computing and Eliminating Changing Seasonal Fluctuations," *Econometrica*, July 1937.

Riggleman, J. R. and Frisbee, I. N., *Business Statistics*, 3rd ed., Chap. 16.

Shiskin, J., "A New Multiplicative Seasonal Index," *Journal of the American Statistical Association*, Dec., 1942.

Spurr, W. A., Kellogg, L. S. and Smith, J. H., *Business and Economic Statistics*, pp. 356-376.

Yule, G. U. and Kendall, M. G., *An Introduction to the Theory of Statistics*, 14th ed., Chap. 26.

The publishers and the dates of publication of the books named in chapter reference lists are given in the bibliography at the end of this volume.

[5] For an explanation of this innovation, with a full example of seasonal analysis by electronic means, see "Seasonal Computations on Univac," by Julius Shiskin, *The American Statistician*, February, 1955.

CHAPTER **12**

: : :

The Analysis of Time Series:
Cyclical Fluctuations

We deal in this chapter with the problems faced in identifying and measuring cyclical fluctuations in historical variables. Major interest in many economic and social studies is attached to these cyclical changes, and their measurement is regarded by many as the central task in time series analysis.

Our interest here is in cyclical fluctuations in individual time series. These are, obviously, not unrelated to cycles in the economy at large. Indeed, cyclical changes in the majority of economic series that reveal such movements conform with varying leads or lags and with varying amplitudes to broad cyclical swings in the general economy.[1] But every economic and social series has its own pattern of behavior over time. Our task is to identify cyclical patterns that are unique to individual series. The data thus provided may serve the needs of those who are concerned only with given series—with cyclical movements of interest rates, of wholesale prices, of automobile sales—or they may contribute to an understanding of the complex patterns of cycles in general business.

[1] In interpreting cyclical movements of individual series we should bear in mind the nature of cycles in the general economy. The characteristics of these general movements have been set forth by Burns and Mitchell: "Business cycles are a type of fluctuation found in the aggregate economic activity of nations that organize their work mainly in business enterprises; a cycle consists of expansions occurring at about the same time in many economic activities, followed by similarly general recessions, contractions, and revivals which merge into the expansion phase of the next cycle; this sequence of changes is recurrent but not periodic; in duration business cycles vary from more than one year to ten or twelve years; they are not divisible into shorter cycles of similar character with amplitudes approximating their own." (Burns and Mitchell, Ref. 13)

Residuals as "Cycles"

A method of cycle analysis long associated with the name of Warren Persons (Ref. 127) may be illustrated with reference to the data of pig iron production in the United States for the period 1926-1953. (Annual averages for this series, for the full period of 28 years, are given in Table 12-1. Monthly data for twelve selected years are cited in Table 12-2, column 2.) The essence of this procedure is the "elimination" of the trend and seasonal components of a given series in time; the residual movements are viewed as acceptable approximations to the cyclical component which is the object of interest. The residue will, of course, also contain

TABLE 12–1

Pig Iron Production in the United States, 1926-1953[*]
(Daily average, in thousands of gross tons)

(1) Year	(2) Actual output	(3) Estimate of normal output based on exponential trend
1926	107.0	65.4
1927	99.3	67.7
1928	103.3	70.2
1929	115.8	72.7
1930	86.1	75.4
1931	50.2	78.1
1932	23.8	80.9
1933	36.1	83.9
1934	43.6	86.9
1935	57.6	90.1
1936	83.6	93.4
1937	100.4	96.7
1938	51.4	100.3
1939	86.3	103.9
1940	114.5	107.7
1941	136.7	111.6
1942	146.3	115.6
1943	150.5	119.8
1944	151.1	124.2
1945	132.6	128.7
1946	110.8	133.3
1947	145.2	138.2
1948	148.1	143.2
1949	132.8	148.4
1950	160.0	153.8
1951	174.2	159.4
1952	151.6	165.2
1953	185.6	171.2

[*] Monthly data for this series, going back to 1877, will be found in *Historical Statistics of the United States*, 1877-1945, U. S. Bureau of the Census, 332-3.

elements reflecting the play of random factors. Account is taken of these (they may, indeed, be smoothed out to some extent) in interpreting the results of the analysis.

The first task is that of fitting an appropriate line of trend to the series that is to be analyzed. This, of course, is a crucial operation, since the assumptions that are made in the selection and fitting of a trend line will have great influence on the final measures that are taken to define patterns of cyclical behavior. We shall comment later on this matter. At this stage of the presentation we shall assume that a suitable function has been selected, for fitting to data covering an appropriate period of time. Although monthly data will be used in the analysis, it is usually desirable to fit a trend to annual data, with subsequent interpolation for monthly trend values.

Trend and seasonal components. In Fig. 12.1 we have plotted the annual pig iron production figures for the years 1926-1953, together with an exponential curve fitted to the data. The reader will note that the annual figures used are averages of daily output. The equation to the trend function (which is of the family $y = ar^x$,) is $y = 65.35537 (1.0363)^x$, with origin at 1926.[2] The value of r indicates that this series increased, during the 28 years here covered, at an annual average rate of 3.63 percent. As will be clear from the graph and from a comparison of the actual and trend values given

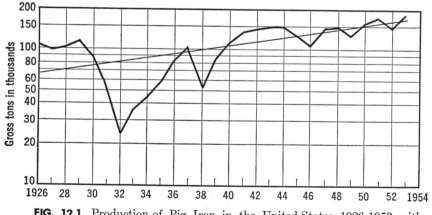

FIG. 12.1. Production of Pig Iron in the United States, 1926-1953, with Line of Trend (Daily Average).

[2] Such a function, as we have seen in Chapter 10, may be fitted by least squares, after putting the equation in the logarithmic form $\{\log y = \log a + (\log r)x\}$. We have here made use of Glover's Tables in the simplified procedure referred to in the footnote on p. 351 above.

in Table 12-1, the actual changes from year to year show wide departures from this average rate; the period covered was a disturbed one. But the underlying movement of pig iron production over these years conforms reasonably well to the indicated trend.

Examination of the monthly figures on the production of pig iron indicates that there was a fairly consistent seasonal pattern from 1926 to 1938 (earlier years are not here included), but no consistent pattern for the years since then. Accordingly, we shall make adjustments for seasonal movements for the earlier period only. (The seasonal indexes for this period are given in Table 12-2, below).

The Measurement of Cyclical Fluctuations. There remains the task of combining the measurements of secular trend and seasonal variation to secure measurements of cyclical changes in pig iron production. A suitable procedure is illustrated in Table 12-2. Since the process is the same from year to year (except for differences due to the application or nonapplication of a seasonal correction) the illustration is limited to 12 years, for 4 of which seasonal adjustments are made. In column (2) of Table 12-2 we have the actual output of pig iron by months. For the 4 years, 1935-38, a constant seasonal correction is made for each of the 12 months by dividing the actual output for that month by the seasonal index (in ratio form). Thus for January, 1935, the actual daily average output of 47.7 thousand tons becomes 48.2 after the seasonal adjustment. Since January is normally low, in seasonal terms (index = .99), the effect of the adjustment designed to eliminate the seasonal movement is of course to increase the output figure. For March, on the other hand, the seasonal index is high (1.11). Adjustment of the actual output of 57.1 thousands of tons for March, 1935, gives an adjusted figure of 51.4 thousand tons. The seasonally adjusted measures, represented by the symbol A_a, are given in column (4) of Part I of Table 12-2, for the period January 1935-December 1938. Part II of Table 12-2 covers the eight years 1946-53. For these years no seasonal adjustment is made. In subsequent operations we shall use the actual output in column (2) of this part of the table as equivalent to the seasonally adjusted output in Part I of the table.

The next step is to express the actual output (seasonally adjusted where necessary) as a deviation from trend. Monthly trend values, obtained by interpolation from annual trend values, are given in

TABLE 12–2 PART I

Illustrating the Analysis of a Series in Time: Pig Iron Production, 1935-38
(Daily average, in thousands of gross tons)

(1) Year and month	(2) Actual output	(3) Seasonal index (as ratio)	(4) Seasonally adjusted output (A/S)	(5) Trend value	(6) Deviation of seasonally adjusted output from trend	(7) "Cycles" in pig iron output
	A	S	A_a	T	$A_a - T$	$\dfrac{A_a - T}{T} \times 100$
1935						
January	47.7	.99	48.2	88.6	− 40.4	− 45.6
February	57.4	1.03	55.7	88.9	− 33.2	− 37.3
March	57.1	1.11	51.4	89.2	− 37.8	− 42.4
April	55.4	1.09	50.8	89.4	− 38.6	− 43.2
May	55.7	1.06	52.5	89.7	− 37.2	− 41.5
June	51.6	1.00	51.6	90.0	− 38.4	− 42.7
July	49.0	.93	52.7	90.2	− 37.5	− 41.6
August	56.8	.94	60.4	90.5	− 30.1	− 33.3
September	59.2	.94	63.0	90.8	− 27.8	− 30.6
October	63.8	.98	65.1	91.0	− 25.9	− 28.5
November	68.9	.98	70.3	91.3	− 21.0	− 23.0
December	68.0	.95	71.6	91.6	− 20.0	− 21.8
1936						
January	65.4	.99	66.1	91.8	− 25.7	− 28.0
February	62.9	1.03	61.1	92.1	− 31.0	− 33.7
March	65.8	1.11	59.3	92.4	− 33.1	− 35.8
April	80.1	1.09	73.5	92.7	− 19.2	− 20.7
May	85.4	1.06	80.6	92.9	− 12.3	− 13.2
June	86.2	1.00	86.2	93.2	− 7.0	− 7.5
July	83.7	.93	90.0	93.5	− 3.5	− 3.7
August	87.5	.94	93.1	93.8	− 0.7	− 0.7
September	91.0	.94	96.8	94.1	+ 2.7	+ 2.9
October	96.5	.98	98.5	94.3	+ 4.2	+ 4.5
November	98.2	.98	100.2	94.6	+ 5.6	+ 5.9
December	100.5	.95	105.8	94.9	+ 10.9	+ 11.5
1937						
January	103.6	.99	104.6	95.2	+ 9.4	+ 9.9
February	107.1	1.03	104.0	95.5	+ 8.5	+ 8.9
March	111.6	1.11	100.5	95.7	+ 4.8	+ 5.0
April	113.1	1.09	103.8	96.0	+ 7.8	+ 8.1
May	114.1	1.06	107.6	96.3	+ 11.3	+ 11.7
June	103.6	1.00	103.6	96.6	+ 7.0	+ 7.2
July	112.9	.93	121.4	96.9	+ 24.5	+ 25.3
August	116.3	.94	123.7	97.2	+ 26.5	+ 27.3
September	113.7	.94	121.0	97.5	+ 23.5	+ 24.1
October	93.3	.98	95.2	97.8	− 2.6	− 2.7
November	66.9	.98	68.3	98.0	− 29.7	− 30.3
December	48.1	.95	50.6	98.3	− 47.7	− 48.5

TABLE 12–2 PART I—Continued

Illustrating the Analysis of a Series in Time: Pig Iron Production, 1935-38

(1) Year and month	(2) Actual output	(3) Seasonal index (as ratio)	(4) Seasonally adjusted output (A/S)	(5) Trend value	(6) Deviation of seasonally adjusted output from trend	(7) "Cycles" in pig iron output
	A	S	A_a	T	$A_a - T$	$\dfrac{A_a - T}{T} \times 100$
1938						
January	46.1	.99	46.6	98.6	− 52.0	− 52.7
February	46.4	1.03	45.0	98.9	− 53.9	− 54.5
March	46.9	1.11	42.3	99.2	− 56.9	− 57.4
April	45.9	1.09	42.1	99.5	− 57.4	− 57.7
May	40.5	1.06	38.2	99.8	− 61.6	− 61.7
June	35.4	1.00	35.4	100.1	− 64.7	− 64.6
July	38.8	.93	41.7	100.4	− 58.7	− 58.5
August	48.2	.94	51.3	100.7	− 49.4	− 49.1
September	56.0	.94	59.6	101.0	− 41.4	− 41.0
October	66.2	.98	67.6	101.3	− 33.7	− 33.3
November	75.7	.98	77.2	101.6	− 24.4	− 24.0
December	71.3	.95	75.1	101.9	− 26.8	− 26.3

TABLE 12–2 PART II

Illustrating the Analysis of a Series in Time: Pig Iron Production, 1946-53
(Daily average, in thousands of gross tons)

(1) Year and month	(2) Actual output	(3) Trend value	(4) Deviation of actual output from trend	(5) "Cycles" in pig iron output
	A	T	$A - T$	$\dfrac{A - T}{T} \times 100$
1946				
January	76.2	131.2	− 55.0	− 41.9
February	36.6	131.6	− 95.0	− 72.2
March	127.4	132.0	− 4.6	− 3.6
April	107.6	132.4	− 24.8	− 18.7
May	70.4	132.8	− 62.4	− 47.0
June	100.6	133.2	23.6	17.7
July	135.5	133.6	+ 1.9	+ 1.4
August	141.1	134.0	+ 7.1	+ 5.3
September	139.5	134.4	+ 5.1	+ 3.8
October	138.7	134.8	+ 3.9	+ 2.9
November	132.0	135.2	− 3.2	− 2.4
December	115.0	135.6	− 20.6	− 15.2

TABLE 12–2 PART II—Continued

Illustrating the Analysis of a Series in Time: Pig Iron Production, 1946-53

(1) Year and month	(2) Actual output	(3) Trend value	(4) Deviation of actual output from trend	(5) "Cycles" in pig iron output
	A	T	$A - T$	$\dfrac{A - T}{T} \times 100$
1947				
January	146.5	136.0	+ 10.5	+ 7.7
February	145.1	136.4	+ 8.7	+ 6.4
March	147.5	136.8	+ 10.7	+ 7.8
April	143.7	137.2	+ 6.5	+ 4.7
May	146.4	137.6	+ 8.8	+ 6.4
June	143.2	138.0	+ 5.2	+ 3.8
July	132.1	138.4	− 6.3	− 4.6
August	141.6	138.8	+ 2.8	+ 2.0
September	142.9	139.3	+ 3.6	+ 2.6
October	155.6	139.7	+ 15.9	+11.4
November	149.3	140.1	+ 9.2	+ 6.6
December	149.1	140.5	+ 8.6	+ 6.1
1948				
January	147.7	140.9	+ 6.8	+ 4.8
February	147.2	141.3	+ 5.9	+ 4.2
March	144.6	141.8	+ 2.8	+ 2.0
April	114.3	142.2	− 27.9	− 19.6
May	146.2	142.6	+ 3.6	+ 2.5
June	148.5	143.0	+ 5.5	+ 3.8
July	141.1	143.5	− 2.4	− 1.7
August	151.4	143.9	+ 7.5	+ 5.2
September	155.0	144.3	+ 10.7	+ 7.4
October	159.0	144.7	+ 14.3	+ 9.9
November	160.7	145.2	+ 15.5	+10.7
December	161.2	145.6	+ 15.6	+10.7
1949				
January	164.9	146.0	+ 18.9	+12.9
February	166.5	146.5	+ 20.0	+13.7
March	167.6	146.9	+ 20.7	+14.1
April	164.6	147.3	+ 17.3	+11.7
May	158.9	147.8	+ 11.1	+ 7.5
June	143.4	148.2	− 4.8	− 3.2
July	120.2	148.7	− 28.5	− 19.2
August	128.9	149.1	− 20.2	− 13.5
September	129.5	149.5	− 20.0	− 13.4
October	17.6	150.0	−132.4	− 88.3
November	81.0	150.4	− 69.4	− 46.1
December	150.7	150.9	− 0.2	− 0.1
1950				
January	152.5	151.3	+ 1.2	+ 0.8
February	133.1	151.8	− 18.7	− 12.3
March	132.5	152.2	− 19.7	− 12.9
April	166.0	152.7	+ 13.3	+ 8.7
May	168.6	153.1	+ 15.5	+10.1
June	167.6	153.6	+ 14.0	+ 9.1
July	169.3	154.1	+ 15.2	+ 9.9
August	166.2	154.5	+ 11.7	+ 7.6
September	169.6	155.0	+ 14.6	+ 9.4
October	170.6	155.4	+ 15.2	+ 9.8
November	160.3	155.9	+ 4.4	+ 2.8
December	164.0	156.4	+ 7.6	+ 4.9

TABLE 12–2 PART II—Continued

Illustrating the Analysis of a Series in Time: Pig Iron Production, 1946-53

(1) Year and month	(2) Actual output	(3) Trend value	(4) Deviation of actual output from trend	(5) "Cycles" in pig iron output
	A	T	$A - T$	$\dfrac{A - T}{T} \times 100$
1951				
January	169.7	156.8	+ 12.9	+ 8.2
February	165.0	157.3	+ 7.7	+ 4.9
March	173.3	157.8	+ 15.5	+ 9.8
April	175.2	158.2	+ 17.0	+ 10.7
May	177.8	158.7	+ 19.1	+ 12.0
June	177.9	159.2	+ 18.7	+ 11.7
July	174.8	159.6	+ 15.2	+ 9.5
August	174.6	160.1	+ 14.5	+ 9.1
September	175.3	160.6	+ 14.7	+ 9.2
October	178.5	161.1	+ 17.4	+ 10.8
November	175.9	161.6	+ 14.3	+ 8.8
December	172.2	162.0	+ 10.2	+ 6.3
1952				
January	174.0	162.5	+ 11.5	+ 7.1
February	178.1	163.0	+ 15.1	+ 9.3
March	181.5	163.5	+ 18.0	+ 11.0
April	155.5	164.0	− 8.5	− 5.2
May	158.2	164.5	− 6.3	− 3.8
June	31.8	165.0	−133.2	− 80.7
July	28.9	165.4	−136.5	− 82.5
August	167.9	165.9	+ 2.0	+ 1.2
September	183.5	166.4	+ 17.1	+ 10.3
October	187.6	166.9	+ 20.7	+ 12.4
November	185.3	167.4	+ 17.9	+ 10.7
December	187.5	167.9	+ 19.6	+ 11.7
1953				
January	189.1	168.4	+ 20.7	+ 12.3
February	187.6	168.9	+ 18.7	+ 11.1
March	192.3	169.4	+ 22.9	+ 13.5
April	185.4	169.9	+ 15.5	+ 9.1
May	189.7	170.4	+ 19.3	+ 11.3
June	189.7	170.9	+ 18.8	+ 11.0
July	187.7	171.4	+ 16.3	+ 9.5
August	186.4	172.0	+ 14.4	+ 8.4
September	184.6	172.5	+ 12.1	+ 7.0
October	187.2	173.0	+ 14.2	+ 8.2
November	180.4	173.5	+ 6.9	+ 4.0
December	166.5	174.0	− 7.5	− 4.3

column (5) of Part I of Table 12-2, in column (3) of Part II. (Interpolation involves, in this case, the application of a month-to-month rate of 1.00298, which is the twelfth root of the annual rate of increase.) The deviations from trend, in absolute terms, appear in column (6) of Part I of Table 12-2, in column (4) of Part II. Finally, we obtain the desired measures by expressing the deviations as percentages of the corresponding trend values (in column (7) of Part I and in column (5) of Part II of Table 12-2). These percentage deviations of seasonally adjusted data from trend (or of actual data from trend, when no seasonal adjustment is necessary) are taken to represent the combined influence of cyclical and accidental factors. (Use is sometimes made of a three- or five-month moving average, or of smoothing by hand, to reduce the effects of accidental factors.) These deviations are often spoken of as "cycles" in the series thus analyzed, but it is well to keep the term in quotation marks, for other than cyclical effects are always present in such measures.

The assumptions implicit in this method of breaking up a time series should be noted. In effect, we assume that the underlying trend gives a basic value, T, which would have been the actual value had there been no random, cyclical, or seasonal effects. The influences of random and cyclical forces are taken to be superimposed, additively, on these trend values, to give the actual values, A, if there is no seasonal pattern in the series in question, or the values A_a if seasonal forces are present. In this latter case, the seasonal factor is assumed to modify A_a for a given month by a constant percentage, plus or minus, to give the observed value for that month. Our process of analysis reverses this procedure, deriving A_a from A, and then measuring the deviation of A_a from an expected value given by the trend function. Other assumptions may be made concerning the manner in which the various forces interact, and these could lead to modifications of the analysis described above. But modification of this part of the procedure would not materially alter the final measurements.

The operations described above are shown graphically in Fig. 12.2. In the upper panel we have the actual monthly data for each of the two selected periods, together with the line of trend. (The trend line was determined, of course, with reference to data for the years 1926-1953; see Fig. 12.1.) The lower panel shows the final measures, the percentage deviations from trend given in the last column of Table 12-2.[3]

---

[3] It is sometimes desirable to reduce the percentage deviations from trend to a form permitting comparison with "cycles" in other time series. As derived, the percentage deviations from trends might have much greater amplitude for one series than for another; without a common denominator comparison would be difficult. The standard deviation can serve as such a common denominator. This is done by expressing the monthly deviations from trend for each series in units of the standard deviation of that series.

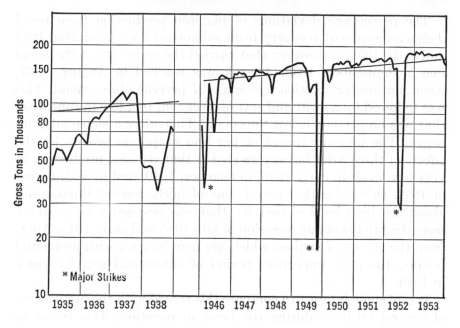

Panel A. Actual Output, with Line of Trend (Daily Average).

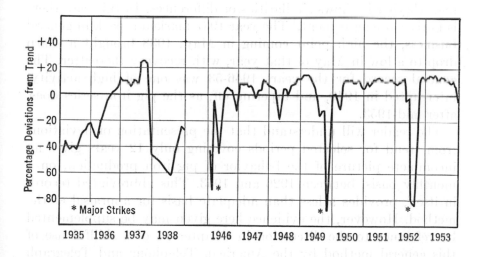

Panel B. "Cycles" in Pig Iron Output: Deviations from Trend (after Seasonal Correction, 1935-1938).

FIG. 12.2. Production of Pig Iron by Months, 1935-1938, 1946-1953.

The percentage deviations of pig iron production from trend define an apparent recovery from subnormal activity during 1935 and early 1936, a recovery that carried the series above the trend line in September, 1936. A peak was reached in August, 1937, when pig iron production was some 27 percent above trend. This was followed by a swift and severe recession, to a low in June, 1938 that was 65 percent below "normal." Thereafter a sharp advance began. The postwar record of pig iron output is broken by the effects of three brief but severe strikes that reduced production to very low levels in early 1946, in October, 1949, and in midsummer of 1952. Otherwise the story is one of fairly modest fluctuations about the high level of activity that was reached with recovery from the brief postwar recession of late 1945 and early 1946. Apart from the effects of strikes, which are here lumped with accidental factors, the only important period of subnormal activity came in 1949.

It is of some interest to compare this record with the movements of general business during the years in question. This is not to suggest that agreement with the broad swings of business is necessary to validate the observed "cycles" in pig iron production for, as we have noted, every series has its own distinctive pattern of behavior. But reference to the general pattern is always reveal-ing, whether it shows similarities or differences. In this case there is fairly close agreement.[4] The year 1937 marked a peak in general business, the high point coming in May; 1938 brought a sharp drop to a low in May of that year, with recovery thereafter. The general record for the years 1946-53 was one of high activity, interrupted in 1949, and tapering off, as the pig iron series does, after mid-1953.

The reader will understand that the presentation of deviations from trend for selected periods covering only 12 years gives an incomplete picture of the behavior of pig iron production, on a monthly basis, between 1926 and 1953. This abbreviated record, in itself, provides a less than adequate basis for appraisal of the method. However, the evidence here given may be supplemented by reference to the discussion in Chapter 14 of a skillful use of this general method by the American Telephone and Telegraph Company, in constructing an index of industrial activity. Special

---

[4] See Table 12-3 below, for dates of cyclical turning points in general business.

attention is called to Fig. 14.2, showing fluctuations of industrial activity in terms of percentage deviations from a computed long-term trend.

Comment on Residuals as "Cycles." The entry in column (7) of Part I of Table 12-2 for March, 1937, indicates that in that month the actual output of pig iron, after seasonal adjustment, was 5 percent above "normal," as defined by the trend function employed in this example. This we have regarded as a measure of the cyclical component in the pig iron series, recognizing that it reflects also the influence of random factors. It is in order at this point to consider more carefully the nature of this and of similar residuals.

Each one of these derived measures is affected, of course, by the choice of a function to define secular trend, by the period employed in fitting a trend line, and by the method (e.g., least squares) used in fitting. It is affected by the choice of a period for the computation of seasonal indexes, by the method used in this computation, and by the investigator's decision to use constant or changing seasonal indexes. It is affected, finally, by the method employed in decomposing the original observation into trend, seasonal, and combined cyclical and random components (i.e., by the assumptions made concerning the way in which the underlying forces interact to yield the actually observed output). With these points in mind, and assuming for the moment that for pig iron production there is a true but to us unknown secular trend, and a true but unknown seasonal pattern, we may list the following as making up the content of such a residual as the one cited above, for March, 1937:

a. A cyclical element;

b. A random component—the resultant of the interplay of all forces other than secular, seasonal, and cyclical;

c. An element representing any errors that may have been made in the definition of the trend;

d. An element representing any errors that may have been made in the determination of the seasonal pattern for the year in question;

e. An element representing any errors made in the decomposition of the original series.

The arbitrary factors contributing to elements (c) and (d) in this list have perhaps already been made clear. The choice of a trend function is in some degree arbitrary; a stated function will yield different trend values for a given month and year depending upon the length of the period to which it is fitted, and the choice of terminal years. Reference to Fig. 12.1 will show that a different fit would have been obtained, with the same function, had the initial year been 1932 instead of 1926.[5]

This means, obviously, that the residuals, and thus the derived "cycles" are similarly affected by the choice of a trend function and of the period used in establishing the fit. Indeed, an investigator will often make his decisions as to function and fitting methods with reference to the cycles that will be defined as a result of the fit. Equally arbitrary are many of the decisions leading to the application of seasonal corrections. Seasonals, indeed are particularly slippery, since seasonal patterns are for many series subject to change without notice. Since the magnitudes of elements (b), (c), and (d) can never be determined, there must always be some uncertainty in the interpretation of the "cycles" that constitute element (a) of the list.

More fundamental is the problem presented by element (e). The method described in this section represents what is in fact a mechanical breakdown of the actual observations. Back of it lies the assumption that the effects of the different forces playing on a series in time are mechanically combined—that a cyclical-random effect is superimposed upon an independent trend, and that this composite is subject to the influence of an independent seasonal.[6] It is not only possible but probable that change over time is not of this nature, that interdependent forces interact to produce an organic amalgam in social and economic development and in the growth or decline of individual series. To attempt mechanically to dissociate the elements of such an amalgam is to do violence to the data that define the results of these interacting forces.

---

[5] We may note that the present fit of the trend line makes 1927 a year of above-normal activity in pig iron production, whereas the National Bureau's chronology of cycles sets a cyclical trough at December of that year (see Table 12-3). That cycle was, however, a very mild one.

[6] If the seasonal adjustment is made by the addition or subtraction of an absolute amount for each month, this implies the independence of the seasonal factor, also. The use of a multiplicative relationship, as in the example above, introduces the assumption of a simple form of dependence, since the absolute size of the correction varies with the magnitude of the base to which it is applied.

There is ample evidence that the factors affecting series in time are in fact correlated. Willard Thorp (Ref. 157) has made the following illuminating observations on the relation of the structure of American business cycles to the trend of wholesale prices:

Period	Trend of wholesale price level	Years of prosperity per year of depression
1790–1815	Prices rising	2.6
1815–1849	Prices falling	0.8
1849–1865	Prices rising	2.9
1865–1896	Prices falling	0.9
1896–1920	Prices rising	3.1

A central aspect of the business cycle—the division of each cycle into phases of prosperity and depression—is fundamentally affected by the trend of the price level. A. F. Burns has remarked on the change in the cyclical pattern of railroad investment as the trend of railroad development was altered. When the pace of railroad growth was rapid, railroad investment tended to lead American recoveries by a substantial interval. As the pace declined, and the industry shifted from an active to a passive role in business cycles, these leads became shorter and finally disappeared. These examples of correlation between trends and cycles may be paralleled by illustrations of relations between seasonal and cyclical patterns. Thus the seasonal and cyclical factors are closely related. For example, the seasonal pattern of steel ingot production during a period of years prior to 1941 was quite different in phases of prosperity and depression. When the steel industry was operating at 95 percent of capacity, the range of steel ingot output, from the lowest month to the highest month of the year, was 11.50 percent of the average for the year; when operations were at 40 percent of capacity, the range from lowest month to highest month was 25.75 percent of the average for the year. The seasonal pattern was accentuated in periods of slack business.[7]

We are justified, therefore, in an attitude of caution toward the results of time series analysis. This is not at all to dismiss the procedures we have discussed, or to reject all derived measures. Trends are real, whether they represent net forward movements (or declines) in wave-like surges and retrogressions, or continuous underlying movements. Seasonal fluctuations are deeply imbedded

[7] Juliber, G. S., "Relation between Seasonal Amplitudes and the Level of Production", *Journal of the American Statistical Association*, Dec. 1941.

in all organic processes. Cycles are demonstrably present in many aspects of social and economic change. The analytical methods we have explained in this and the two preceding chapters represent a rather simple model which helps in the description and understanding of the complex processes of expansion and contraction, of growth and decline. Viewed as approximations, not as rigorously accurate measures, the results obtained by these methods can serve highly useful purposes, whether in research or in practical administration.

Measuring Business Cycles: the Method of the National Bureau of Economic Research

An alternative method of defining patterns of change in the movements of economic time series has been developed by the National Bureau of Economic Research. This method, which is set forth in detail in the monograph by Arthur F. Burns and Wesley C. Mitchell (Ref. 13), is aimed primarily at the study of cyclical fluctuations in time series; its proved fruitfulness makes it an instrument of general statistical interest.

With reference to individual time series the National Bureau procedure aims to answer two sets of questions:

(a) Is there in a given series a pattern of change that repeats itself (with more or less variation) in successive cycles in business at large? If so, what are its characteristics?

(b) Is there in a given series a wave movement peculiar to that series? If so, what are its characteristics?

The questions under (a) are concerned with the behavior of individual series during successive waves of expansion and contraction in the general economy; those under (b) relate to periodic or semiperiodic fluctuations in individual series, without reference to any broader framework. (In identifying these *specific cycles* there is a general reference to cycles in business at large, in that specific cycles must correspond in duration to the National Bureau's concept of business cycles. This means, roughly, a duration of over one year and not over ten or twelve years.) The object sought in answering the second set of questions is very close to the objective of the standard technique discussed in the first part of this chapter.

The questions under (a), however, point to a new and different goal. We shall deal first with these.

The Measurement of Reference Cycles; the Reference Framework. The first step in answering the questions under (a) above is the establishment of a reference framework that marks off the historical troughs and peaks in general business activity. This has been done for four countries—the United States, Great Britain, France, and Germany. The definition of these turning points in economic activity has called for extensive research on the qualitative and quantitative records of business in each of the countries covered. The annals of business, as recorded in contemporary newspapers, trade journals, and other records were exhaustively studied.[8] The provisional reference dates of troughs and peaks set on the basis of this study were checked against extensive compilations of statistical series, were modified, if necessary, and were rechecked as later data became available. The chronology of business cycles thus established for each country provides the reference frame for studying the cyclical behavior of individual time series. This chronology has been worked out on monthly, quarterly, and annual bases, for use with time series given in these time units. The monthly record is, of course, the most revealing, and lends itself to the most accurate analysis. Monthly and annual reference dates for the United States are given in Table 12-3, for the period 1854-1954.[9]

The chronology of business cycles is, of course, of great interest in itself. It indicates that 23 cycles ran their course in the United States between December 1854 and October 1949. The average duration of these reference cycles[10] was 49 months. Periods of expansion averaged 29 months in duration, or 59 percent of the full cycle; periods of contraction were shorter, averaging 20 months, or 41 percent of the full cycle. Individual cycles varied considerably from these averages. Thus in full cycle duration the measures range from 29 months (from a trough in April 1919 to a trough in September 1921) to 99 months (between low points in December

---

[8] See W. L. Thorp, Ref. 157.

[9] For quarterly reference dates for the United States see Burns and Mitchell (Ref. 13, p. 78).

[10] The interval of time falling between dates of successive troughs (alternatively, between successive peaks) is called a *reference cycle*. The term reference cycle is also used as a convenient expression for that portion of an individual time series, such as pig iron production, that falls between such dates.

1870 and March 1879).[11] But our concern at the moment is with the use of this framework in the description of the behavior of individual series.

The Description of Reference Cycle Patterns in Individual Series. Table 12-4 gives the monthly record of railroad freight, in ton-miles, from 1904 to 1953. The first step in analysis is the measurement and "elimination" of seasonal movements in the series, if such movements are present.

The pattern of seasonal variation in freight ton-miles has been subject to change over the 50 years here covered. Heavy traffic has always come in the fall months, with lighter traffic in the winter, but individual months have varied considerably. The seasonal indexes used by the National Bureau for the period 1946-53 are given in Table 12-5, and the method employed in correcting for seasonal variation is there illustrated.

---

[11] The chronology for Great Britain, which has been carried through 1938, shows cycles of somewhat greater average duration than those of the United States.

Reference Dates and Durations of Business Cycles in Great Britain, 1854-1938

Monthly reference dates		Duration in months			Calendar year reference dates	
Peak	Trough	Expansion*	Contraction†	Full cycle	Peak	Trough
	Dec. 1854				1854	1855
Sep. 1857	Mar. 1858	33	6	39	1857	1858
Sep. 1860	Dec. 1862	30	27	57	1860	1862
Mar. 1866	Mar. 1868	39	24	63	1866	1868
Sep. 1872	Jun. 1879	54	81	135	1873	1879
Dec. 1882	Jun. 1886	42	42	84	1883	1886
Sep. 1890	Feb. 1895	51	53	104	1890	1894
Jun. 1900	Sep. 1901	64	15	79	1900	1901
Jun. 1903	Nov. 1904	21	17	38	1903	1904
Jun. 1907	Nov. 1908	31	17	48	1907	1908
Dec. 1912	Sep. 1914	49	21	70	1913	1914
Oct. 1918	Apr. 1919	49	6	55	1917	1919
Mar. 1920	Jun. 1921	11	15	26	1920	1921
Nov. 1924	Jul. 1926	41	20	61	1924	1926
Mar. 1927	Sep. 1928	8	18	26	1927	1928
Jul. 1929	Aug. 1932	10	37	47	1929	1932
Sep. 1937	Sep. 1938	61	12	73	1937	1938

* From trough on preceding line to peak.
† From peak to trough on same line.

TABLE 12–3

Reference Dates and Durations of Business Cycles in the United States, 1854-1954

Monthly reference dates*			Duration in months			Calendar year reference dates		
Initial trough	Peak	Terminal trough	Ex-pansion	Con-traction	Full cycle	Trough	Peak	Trough
Dec. 1854	Jun. 1857	Dec. 1858	30	18	48	1855	1856	1858
Dec. 1858	Oct. 1860	Jun. 1861	22	8	30	1858	1860	1861
Jun. 1861	Apr. 1865	Dec. 1867	46	32	78	1861	1864	1867
Dec. 1867	Jun. 1869	Dec. 1870	18	18	36	1867	1869	1870
Dec. 1870	Oct. 1873	Mar. 1879	34	65	99	1870	1873	1878
Mar. 1879	Mar. 1882	May 1885	36	38	74	1878	1882	1885
May 1885	Mar. 1887	Apr. 1888	22	13	35	1885	1887	1888
Apr. 1888	July 1890	May 1891	27	10	37	1888	1890	1891
May 1891	Jan. 1893	Jun. 1894	20	17	37	1891	1892	1894
Jun. 1894	Dec. 1895	Jun. 1897	18	18	36	1894	1895	1896
Jun. 1897	Jun. 1800	Dec. 1900	24	18	42	1896	1899	1900
Dec. 1900	Sep. 1902	Aug. 1904	21	23	44	1900	1903	1904
Aug. 1004	May 1907	Jun. 1908	33	13	46	1904	1907	1908
Jun. 1908	Jan. 1910	Jan. 1912	19	24	43	1908	1910	1911
Jan. 1912	Jan. 1913	Dec. 1914	12	23	35	1911	1913	1914
Dec. 1914	Aug. 1918	Apr. 1919	44	8	52	1914	1918	1919
Apr. 1919	Jan. 1920	Sep. 1921	9	20	29	1919	1920	1921
Sep. 1921	May 1923	July 1924	20	14	34	1921	1923	1924
July 1924	Oct. 1926	Dec. 1927	27	14	41	1924	1026	1927
Dec. 1927	June 1929	Mar. 1933	18	45	63	1927	1929	1932
Mar. 1933	May 1937	May 1938	50	12	62	1932	1937	1938
May 1938	Feb. 1945	Oct. 1945	81	8	89	1938	1944	1946
Oct. 1945	Nov. 1948	Oct. 1949	37	11	48	1946	1948	1949
Oct. 1949	July 1953†	Aug, 1954†				1949	1953†	1954†

* The following revisions have recently been made in the monthly reference dates: July instead of September 1921; November instead of December 1927; June instead of May 1938.

† Preliminary. No measures of cyclical behavior have been based on the preliminary reference dates, which are subject to revision.

As we have seen on an earlier page, the seasonal adjustment involves merely the division of the original figure for a given month by the seasonal index for that month (with the decimal point shifted two places to the left). Thus for the adjusted figure for January 1948 we divide 51.266 by 0.95, getting 53.96. This seasonal correction, the Bureau is careful to say, is not expected to yield a series that would have been recorded in the absence of seasonal movements. No such decomposition of time series is believed to be possible. But nevertheless such adjustments, where appropriate, are believed to facilitate study and comparison of cyclical movements by giving the investigator measurements in which such movements are more clearly revealed than they are in the original series. The seasonally adjusted series is the subject of the subsequent analysis.

TABLE 12-4

Railroad Freight Ton-Miles, by Months, 1904-1954*

(in billions of ton-miles)

Month	1904	1905	1906	1907	1908	1909	1910	1911	1912	1913	1914	1915	1916	1917	1918	1919
January	14.55	15.69	18.55	19.89	18.03	18.69	20.58	21.17	21.33	26.43	23.93	21.76	28.87	31.51	28.78	31.00
February	14.80	15.24	19.08	20.19	17.71	18.62	21.33	20.81	22.53	26.88	23.12	22.53	29.87	31.76	29.91	28.75
March	14.92	15.66	18.68	20.03	17.38	18.97	21.90	20.49	23.19	25.52	23.61	22.88	30.74	30.01	34.18	26.54
April	14.80	16.38	17.87	20.55	17.23	19.10	22.13	20.66	22.10	24.22	23.48	22.90	29.44	31.06	36.71	27.89
May	14.84	16.53	17.93	21.36	17.02	19.00	21.79	21.16	22.01	25.27	22.17	23.26	27.43	34.95	36.43	30.16
June	14.85	16.70	18.49	21.37	16.98	19.24	21.71	21.16	22.56	25.65	22.33	23.62	26.49	36.40	35.34	
July	14.73	16.55	18.54	21.18	17.61	19.78	21.30	20.69	22.95	24.75	23.08	24.09	27.61	34.85	33.59	
August	14.84	16.65	18.68	21.12	18.02	20.22	21.08	20.82	23.08	24.80	23.10	24.00	28.66	32.29	33.45	
September	15.33	17.08	18.56	20.49	18.37	20.63	21.18	21.22	22.90	24.18	23.22	24.84	28.64	30.22	34.12	
October	15.45	17.20	18.57	20.12	18.73	20.91	20.89	21.16	23.48	24.26	23.13	26.44	28.40	30.01	32.41	
November	15.46	17.48	18.84	19.87	18.61	21.18	20.81	21.12	24.89	24.65	22.14	28.33	29.73	31.13	31.29	
December	15.85	17.89	19.15	18.80	18.72	20.72	21.10	21.33	25.84	24.52	21.68	29.64	30.60	30.84	31.41	

Month	1921	1922	1923	1924	1925	1926	1927	1928	1929	1930	1931	1932
January		23.74	34.02	30.61	33.12	33.65	34.80	32.32	35.26	32.90	27.29	20.40
February		25.45	29.46	32.13	30.56	31.88	33.42	32.14	34.67	31.16	24.55	19.52
March		29.47	35.30	32.97	31.91	35.35	37.62	35.43	36.04	31.65	27.13	21.19
April		22.29	34.79	29.09	30.35	32.93	33.49	32.15	34.92	31.46	25.96	19.06
May		25.06	35.99	30.52	33.16	35.70	36.17	35.62	37.80	32.99	26.90	17.88
June		26.48	34.23	28.76	32.78	35.72	34.83	33.80	36.67	31.16	25.75	16.81
July		24.69	34.52	29.92	34.47	37.93	34.43	35.39	38.10	32.38	27.64	17.10
August	27.53	27.88	36.20	32.63	37.67	39.74	38.16	35.39	41.05	34.04	26.90	18.09
September	27.85	31.67	35.44	35.45	37.99	40.66	39.01	38.57	40.42	33.61	25.72	20.83
October	32.62	36.01	38.28	39.27	40.37	43.93	41.58	44.93	44.03	36.23	27.62	24.15
November	26.85	34.72	34.69	34.76	37.24	40.36	34.28	39.63	35.38	29.62	23.00	19.90
December	23.26	32.81	30.59	33.05	34.91	36.65	31.37	38.59	32.87	26.65	20.66	19.22

Month	1919	1920	1921
January		35.0	29.8
February		33.0	24.9
March	28.8	37.9	26.8
April	28.6	28.6	25.6
May	32.3	37.9	28.2
June	31.9	38.2	28.1
July	34.9	40.4	28.4
August	36.4	42.7	30.4
September	38.7	41.0	30.9
October	40.4	42.6	36.7
November	32.5	37.3	
December	33.4	34.7	

	1933	1934	1935	1936	1937	1938	1939	1940	1941	1942	1943	1944	1945	1946	1947	1948
January	18.01	21.53	22.40	25.04	29.86	23.81	25.56	29.68	32.94	42.96	55.13	60.49	56.81	48.23	53.29	51.27
February	17.31	20.92	21.81	26.31	29.05	21.07	23.11	27.16	31.19	40.81	54.42	59.31	55.42	45.08	48.49	50.20
March	17.37	24.94	24.59	25.30	33.41	23.59	26.03	28.20	37.24	48.25	61.23	62.66	64.38	52.39	56.15	49.83
April	17.79	21.09	21.32	25.22	29.46	20.69	21.66	27.43	28.96	49.95	59.04	60.29	61.37	37.41	50.70	46.48
May	19.81	22.69	22.08	26.91	30.99	21.50	23.29	30.31	39.72	54.25	62.15	64.10	64.18	39.46	56.13	56.40
June	21.54	22.63	23.13	26.23	29.15	21.81	25.88	30.12	40.68	53.85	57.96	61.71	62.53	49.78	53.42	54.92
July	24.10	21.86	20.83	28.31	30.60	23.82	27.26	31.17	42.85	56.96	63.74	62.54	60.68	51.92	51.03	52.73
August	24.14	22.81	23.38	29.17	30.75	25.24	28.73	33.50	45.49	58.63	65.10	64.45	56.79	55.84	58.01	56.31
September	23.83	23.36	25.42	30.21	31.98	26.72	33.36	34.19	44.31	58.16	62.54	61.15	52.66	52.92	56.11	55.42
October	24.18	24.26	28.50	34.08	33.72	30.03	37.29	36.02	47.73	62.16	65.22	63.84	49.78	57.39	61.06	59.06
November	21.75	21.70	25.12	31.12	26.88	26.27	32.55	33.14	42.63	55.98	59.86	59.38	49.77	51.93	56.16	53.27
December	19.95	20.98	23.71	31.03	24.82	25.60	28.69	32.28	41.31	55.04	60.61	57.18	46.29	49.57	54.13	49.40

	1949	1950	1951	1952	1953	1954
January	45.90	39.24	53.85	52.23	48.97	43.75
February	42.51	34.28	45.91	51.46	45.60	41.34
March	44.10	47.88	55.93	53.20	50.77	44.72
April	46.96	46.72	53.97	49.76	50.30	43.52
May	48.01	48.35	56.12	51.72	53.43	46.90
June	45.01	48.98	53.75	45.02	52.69	46.20
July	41.83	49.04	50.57	42.34	51.31	45.06
August	45.33	56.51	57.26	54.14	54.64	
September	41.81	54.94	55.23	55.70	51.94	
October	38.24	58.92	59.44	55.79	54.69	
November	43.33	52.19	54.31	54.35	47.91	
December	42.85	51.46	50.20	49.13	43.54	

* I am indebted to the National Bureau of Economic Research for this compilation, and for the measurements based on it.

The original records used by the National Bureau come from four sources: the Babson Statistical Organization (1866-1922); the American Railway Association (1907-14); the Bureau of Railway Economics and the Interstate Commerce Commission, 1916-24; the Interstate Commerce Commission, 1920-54. Nonrevenue freight is included in the second and third segments, not in the others; this difference does not materially affect the comparability of the segments. The overlaps in Table 12-4 are included for convenience in splicing the separate segments.

TABLE 12–5

Seasonal Correction of Freight Ton-Miles for 1948

	Freight ton-miles actual	Seasonal index	Freight ton-miles seasonally corrected
	(billions)		(billions)
January	51.266	95	53.96
February	50.204	88	57.05
March	49.830	104	47.91
April	46.476	96	48.41
May	56.396	103	54.75
June	54.918	100	54.92
July	52.735	95	55.51
August	56.308	107	52.62
September	55.425	104	53.29
October	59.064	112	52.74
November	53.269	101	52.74
December	49.400	96	51.46

We must next study the behavior of the given series in the framework provided by the dates of troughs and peaks set forth in Table 12-3. It is desirable to do this first graphically, by plotting the seasonally adjusted data (or unadjusted data, if there is no evidence of a seasonal pattern) in this reference frame. Figure 12.3 shows the results of this plotting, for the period 1933-1954. (The graphic record is extended to 1954, although no final reference date beyond the trough at October 1949 had been set when this was written.) The dates of reference troughs and peaks are marked by vertical lines, with phases of general business expansion shown

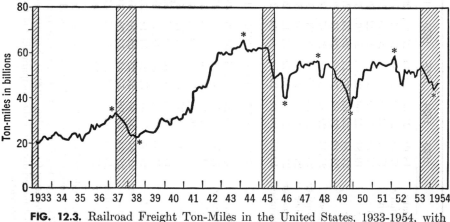

FIG. 12.3. Railroad Freight Ton-Miles in the United States, 1933-1954, with Phases of Reference Contraction and Expansion.

by white areas, phases of business contraction by shaded areas. (The asterisks in Fig. 12.3 mark troughs and peaks in cycles specific to freight ton-miles. These are discussed below.) This graphic portrayal indicates a fairly high degree of conformity of freight ton-miles to cycles in general business. There is, of course, a clearly evident rising trend in the volume of freight carried; this advance has come in successive waves that seem to agree, in general, in the timing of their troughs and peaks with the turning points in business activity in the economy at large. But something more precise than these general impressions is needed if we are to have objective measurements of the behavior of freight ton-miles in this reference framework.

Reference cycle relatives and stage averages. The vertical lines marking successive troughs in general business cut the freight ton-miles series into a number of segments. Each of these segments is spoken of as a "reference cycle" in freight ton-miles—a shorthand expression for "the record of freight ton-miles during a reference cycle." Each segment is a unit of experience in the total behavior of this series over the period covered. These units are to be individually described, in a manner that will permit combination of measures for separate units and comparisons among units.

For the description of a given reference cycle in freight ton-miles —say the cycle that extends from a trough at October 1945 to the next trough at October 1949—the monthly entries for that cycle are first averaged, to obtain the "cycle base." (In this averaging process a weight of one half is given to the observations falling at the initial trough and to those falling at the terminal trough. This is to avoid giving undue weight to troughs, as compared with peaks.) Freight ton-miles for the cycle specified had an average monthly value of 50.52 billions. The separate monthly figures for that cycle are then expressed as relatives of the cycle base. These "reference-cycle relatives" give a complete picture of the pattern of behavior of freight ton-miles during the time segment marked out by the reference cycle troughs at October 1945, and at October 1949. Since their average is 100 they conform to the concept of a cycle as a unit of experience. Because they are in abstract terms they may be compared with similar measures for other cycles. However, the picture they give is too detailed, and comparison of measures for different cycles would be difficult because the number of measures (i.e., monthly relatives) will vary with the durations of reference cycles. For purposes of study it is desirable that each reference-cycle pattern in a given time series be defined by a small number of measures that will summarize its essential features.

This end is achieved by breaking each reference cycle, regardless of duration, into nine stages, for each of which a "stage average" is computed. Stage I marks the initial trough of a given reference cycle; the measure defining the standing of the series at stage I is obtained by averaging reference-cycle relatives for three months centered on the trough. (Thus the measure for stage I in freight ton-miles in the reference cycle that extends from October 1945 to October 1949 is the average of reference-cycle relatives for the three-month period September 1945–November 1945. One month is borrowed from the previous cycle in this averaging process.) Stage V marks the reference-cycle peak; the measure for stage V is the average of reference-cycle relatives for three months centered on the peak. Stage IX marks the terminal trough; the measure for stage IX is the average of reference-cycle relatives for three months centered on the terminal trough. These three stage averages define certain important aspects of a reference-cycle pattern, since they mark the standing of the given series at three important turning points in general business activity. But what happens in the given series in the phase of general business expansion between stages I and V? And what happens during the general contraction between stages V and IX? These may be long phases, covering 50 to 60 months or more, and the investigator needs more details than the three averages cited will provide. Here an arbitrary judgment must be made, as to how much detail is wanted. For its own purposes the National Bureau decided to break the phase of expansion into three equal (or nearly equal) parts, and the phase of contraction into three corresponding parts. For each of these a stage average is constructed. In the expansion phase these are designated stages II, III, and IV; in the contraction phase VI, VII, and VIII.

The expansion phase, which is divided into thirds in these operations, is taken to begin with the month after the trough and to end with the month before the peak. If this time interval is exactly divisible by three there will, of course, be the same number of months in the three stages. If the division gives a remainder of one, this is assigned to the middle stage (III); if a remainder of two, one extra month is assigned to the first third (stage II) and one to the last third (stage IV). For each of these stages the standing of a series in a given reference cycle is measured by the average of the monthly figures falling in that stage. The procedure followed in breaking the contraction phase into thirds and deriving stage averages parallels that described for the phase of expansion.

The use of the method just described, when it is applied to the data of freight ton-miles for a single reference cycle, is illustrated in Table 12-6. The figure 50.52, the monthly average for the full reference cycle, is, of course, the *cycle base* on which the reference-cycle relatives are computed. The stage averages shown in the last column define the behavior of freight ton-miles during the first postwar reference cycle. The pattern marked out by these averages shows a net rise during the phase of reference expansion (between stages I and V) and a net decline during the reference contraction (between stages V and IX). However, there are timing disparities. The initial trough in freight ton-miles came after the trough in general business (i.e., it fell in stage II rather than in stage I), and the peak in freight ton-miles preceded the peak in general business (it came in stage III rather than in stage V).

When operations similar to those exemplified in Table 12-6 are performed for the 10 reference cycles preceding the one just discussed we have, for each of 11 cycles, the stage averages given on lines 1 to 11 of Table 12-7. The separate reference cycle patterns thus defined are shown in Fig. 12.4. For purposes of comparison

TABLE 12–6

Illustrating the Computation of Stage Averages in a Reference Cycle
Freight Ton-Miles, October 1945-October 1949
(Average monthly freight ton-miles: 50.52 billions)

Stage	Period covered	Number of months	Average monthly standing in cycle relatives
I	Sept. 45 – Nov. 45	3	99.5
II	Nov. 45 – Oct. 46	12	96.8
III	Nov. 46 – Oct. 47	12	106.3
IV	Nov. 47 – Oct. 48	12	105.9
V	Oct. 48 – Dec. 48	3	104.3
VI	Dec. 48 – Feb. 49	3	96.4
VII	Mar. 49 – June 49	4	92.6
VIII	July 49 – Sept. 49	3	81.6
IX	Sept. 49 – Nov. 49	3	77.1

TABLE 12–7

Reference-Cycle Patterns: Railroad Freight Ton-Miles, 1904-1949*

Dates of reference cycles			Cycle base	Averages of reference-cycle relatives at nine stages of the cycles								
			I	II	III	IV	V	VI	VII	VIII	IX
			Billions of ton-miles	Three months centered on initial trough		Expansion		Three months centered on peak		Contraction		Three months centered on terminal trough
Trough	Peak	Trough		First third	Middle third	Last third		First third	Middle third	Last third	
	(1)		(2)	(3)	(4)	(5)	(6)	(7)	(8)	(9)	(10)	(11)
1 Aug04	May07	Jun08	18.10	82.7	87.9	98.6	106.2	116.6	116.3	106.1	95.8	95.1
2 Jun08	Jan10	Jan12	20.32	84.7	90.3	93.2	101.2	102.7	106.1	102.6	103.7	106.9
3 Jan12	Jan13	Dec14	23.76	91.5	94.5	96.2	102.2	111.1	106.5	100.9	95.7	92.0
4 Dec14	Aug18	Apr19	29.51	74.1	85.5	101.0	111.5	114.3	112.7	105.8	93.7	95.6
5 Apr19	Jan20	Sep21	33.60	93.0	95.1	102.0	101.0	112.9	111.4	105.9	82.3	86.7
6 Sep21	May23	Jul24	31.06	84.5	86.9	87.2	112.4	120.0	111.2	105.8	102.5	98.3
7 Jul24	Oct26	Dec27	35.36	86.3	93.7	98.8	104.1	106.2	105.8	102.1	99.9	96.5
8 Dec27	Jun29	Mar33	29.72	114.8	118.2	124.1	126.2	127.5	116.0	90.5	66.2	62.5
9 Mar33	May37	May38	25.17	73.8	88.2	91.2	116.3	127.3	119.4	106.0	93.9	90.9
10 May38	Feb45	Oct45	45.33	50.5	61.3	96.1	134.4	135.2	137.3	133.4	116.0	110.9
11 Oct45	Nov48	Oct49	50.52	99.5	96.8	106.3	105.9	104.3	96.4	92.6	81.6	77.1
Average 11 cycles 1904-1949				85.0	90.8	99.5	111.0	116.2	112.6	104.7	93.8	92.0
Average deviation				10.9	8.1	6.4	8.3	8.3	7.0	6.3	9.3	9.3

* In the standard notation of the National Bureau this is Table B1.

they are there plotted on a common axis marking the position of the peak, or stage V, entries.

This chart provides an illuminating portrayal of the patterns of behavior of freight ton-miles in successive reference cycles. In general, freight traffic shows a close correspondence with the major cyclical swings of business at large. There is in all cases a rise in freight volume from stage I to stage V, and in all cases but one a decline in volume from stage V to stage IX. It is clear, however, that the behavior of freight ton-miles during reference cycles shows no absolutely constant pattern. Neither troughs nor peaks in freight volume coincide at all turns with changes in the tide of general business activity. This particular series shows general conformity to the cycles in business at large, but with manifest variations from cycle to cycle.

These variations from cycle to cycle are not without interest, but at this stage of the analysis our concern is with the average behavior of freight ton-miles during cycles in general business. The

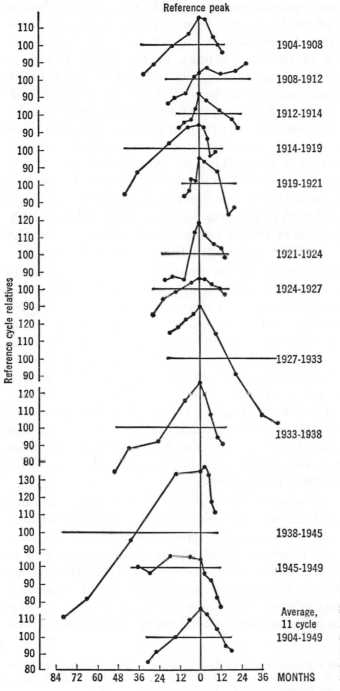

FIG. 12.4.
Patterns of
Successive
Reference Cycles
and Their Average
Pattern, Railroad
Freight Ton-
Miles, 1904-1949.

stage averages for separate cycles in Table 12-7 may be readily combined, since all are in abstract terms. A simple addition of the 11 entries for stage I, and division by 11, gives us 85.0 as the average standing of freight ton-miles at the initial trough of reference cycles; the average for stage II is 90.8; for stage III 99.5, etc. These stage averages are given at the bottom of Table 12-7; they define the average reference cycle pattern for freight ton-miles that is shown graphically as the bottom chart in Fig. 12.4. This average pattern, which is a synthesis of the 11 patterns for individual cycles, is free of the striking irregularities that appear in some of the separate patterns. The movement from trough to peak is quite regular; so is the decline from peak to terminal trough, except for a retardation of the drop between stages VIII and IX. The average behavior of freight ton-miles shows high conformity to the waves of expansion and contraction in general business.

We have noted that the variations of behavior from cycle to cycle, which are concealed in the averages, are of interest to the investigator. A simple measure—the average deviation among the items entering into each stage average—provides a useful indicator of the degree of variation at each stage of the reference cycle. These average deviations are given in Table 12-7, just below the stage averages. We may note that variation from cycle to cycle is greatest at stage I, that it is less at reference cycle peaks than at troughs, and that it is least at stages III and VII. To the student of business cycles this is a highly significant fact, indicating that the tides of freight traffic are most uniform, when we compare cycle with cycle, at the middle stages of general business expansion and of general business contraction.

Interstage rates of change. The National Bureau makes use of a number of derived measures descriptive of the behavior of individual series in the reference-cycle framework.[12] Among the most useful of these are measures of interstage changes, expressed as average monthly rates, in reference-cycle relatives. In deriving each measure of interstage rate of change, the absolute difference between standings in successive stages (as given in Table 12-7) is divided by the number of months between the middle of the first

---

[12] The reader will find full explanations of these measures and many examples of substantive results in *Measuring Business Cycles* by Burns and Mitchell (Ref. 13) and in *What Happens during Business Cycles* by W. C. Mitchell (Ref. 107).

of the two stages and the middle of the second. These rates, for freight ton-miles, are given in Table 12-8.

As is to be expected, there is considerable variation among the rates cited for any given interstage period. Thus the changes between stages IV and V ranged from + 6.0 per month in the 1919-21 reference cycle to − 0.2 per month in the 1945-49 cycle. By averaging the rates for each interstage period we may, in part, eliminate random irregularities. Two sets of derived averages are given at the bottom of Table 12-8. In computing the averages in the first set (unweighted) each measure of interstage change is given the same weight as all others, regardless of whether the interstage interval lasted ten months or three months. In computing those in the second set, the rate for a given interstage interval in a given reference cycle is weighted by the number of months in that interval. (The average number of months in each interval is shown in the table.) Each unweighted measure is

TABLE 12–8

Average Rates of Change per Month from Stage to Stage of Reference Cycles, Railroad Freight Ton-Miles, 1904-1949*

Dates of reference cycles			Rate of change per month in reference cycle relatives from stage to stage of the cycles							
			I–II	II–III	III–IV	IV–V	V–VI	VI–VII	VII–VIII	VIII–IX
				Expansion				Contraction		
			Trough to last third	First to middle third	Middle to last third	Last third to peak	Peak to first third	First to middle third	Middle to last third	Last third to trough
Trough	Peak	Trough	(2)	(3)	(4)	(5)	(6)	(7)	(8)	(9)
	(1)									
1 Aug04	May07	Jun08	+ 0.9	+ 1.0	+ 0.7	+ 1.7	− 0.1	− 2.6	− 2.6	− 0.3
2 Jun08	Jan10	Jan12	+ 1.6	+ 0.5	+ 1.3	+ 0.4	+ 0.8	− 0.5	+ 0.1	+ 0.7
3 Jan12	Jan13	Dec14	+ 1.2	+ 0.5	+ 1.7	+ 3.6	− 1.2	− 0.7	− 0.7	− 0.9
4 Dec14	Aug18	Apr19	+ 1.5	+ 1.1	+ 0.7	+ 0.4	− 1.1	− 2.8	− 4.8	+ 1.3
5 Apr19	Jan20	Sep21	+ 1.0	+ 2.8	− 0.4	+ 6.0	− 0.4	− 0.8	− 3.6	+ 1.3
6 Sep21	May23	Jul24	+ 0.7	0	+ 3.9	+ 2.2	− 3.5	− 1.2	− 0.7	− 1.7
7 Jul24	Oct26	Dec27	+ 1.5	+ 0.6	+ 0.6	+ 0.4	− 0.2	− 0.8	− 0.5	− 1.4
8 Dec27	Jun29	Mar33	+ 1.0	+ 1.1	+ 0.4	+ 0.4	− 1.4	− 1.8	− 1.7	− 0.5
9 Mar33	May37	May38	+ 1.7	+ 0.2	+ 1.5	+ 1.3	− 3.2	− 3.8	− 3.5	− 1.2
10 May38	Feb45	Oct45	+ 0.8	+ 1.3	+ 1.4	+ 0.1	+ 1.4	− 1.6	− 7.0	− 3.4
11 Oct45	Nov48	Oct49	− 0.4	+ 0.8	0	− 0.2	− 4.0	− 1.1	− 3.1	− 2.2
Average 11 cycles 1904-1949			+ 1.0	+ 0.9	+ 1.1	+ 1.5	− 1.2	− 1.6	− 2.6	− 0.8
Average deviation			0.4	0.5	0.8	1.4	1.4	0.8	1.7	1.1
Average int. in mo.			5.7	10.2	10.2	5.7	3.2	5.5	5.5	3.2
Weighted average			+ 1.0	+ 0.9	+ 1.1	+ 0.9	− 1.1	− 1.4	− 2.0	− 0.5

* In the National Bureau's notation, this is Table B2.

accompanied by an average deviation indicative of the degree of uniformity, from cycle to cycle, in the rate of interstage movement.

The weighted averages show relative constancy in the monthly rates of increase in freight ton-miles during the four intervals that make up the phase of expansion. The contraction pattern is less uniform. Recession starts with a drop at the rate of 1.1 percent a month, with acceleration to rates of 1.4 percent and 2.0 percent a month between stages VI and VII and VII and VIII, respectively. The terminal period of contraction in general business, between stages VIII and IX, brings a sharp check to the rate of decline in freight ton-miles, which falls to 0.5 percent a month. (It is convenient to speak of these interstage rates in percentage terms. However, the reader must remember that we are dealing with reference-cycle relatives; the base of each set of relatives is the "cycle base"—the average standing of freight ton-miles in a given reference cycle).

Indexes of conformity to business cycles. We have noted the apparent close conformity of the movements of freight ton-miles to phases of expansion and contraction in general business activity, but this judgment has been based on rather loose impressions given by examination of the tables and charts so far presented. More precise and objective measures of conformity are required. The National Bureau constructs three indexes of conformity for each series—indexes measuring degree of conformity to expansions in general business, to contractions in general business, and to full cycles in general business. To these we now turn.

The data on which conformity measures are based are given in Table 12-9 for freight ton-miles. The time periods here employed are the intervals of reference expansion and of reference contraction. For each reference cycle an entry in column (2) of Table 12-9 measures the difference between the standings of the given series at stages I and V. Referring back to Table 12-7 we note that the stage I standing of freight ton-miles in the reference cycle that ran from August 1904 to June 1908 was 82.7; the stage V standing was 116.6. Subtracting the former figure from the latter we have + 33.9. This appears as the first entry in column (2) of Table 12-9, measuring the total change in freight ton-miles in this phase of expansion. The total change in the succeeding phase of contraction, which is given as the first entry in column (5) of Table 12-9 was − 21.5. This is obtained by subtracting from 95.1 (the standing of freight ton-miles in stage IX of this particular reference cycle) the quantity 116.6 (the stage V standing of the series). For purposes of later calculation it is convenient to reduce the absolute differences given in columns (2) and (5) to monthly averages. This is

TABLE 12–9

Measures of Conformity to Business Cycles
Railroad Freight Ton-Miles, 1904-1949*

Expansion covers stages I–V			Expansions are related to reference expansions						
			Change of reference-cycle relatives during stages matched with					Average change per month for reference contraction minus average change per month for	
Dates of reference cycles			Reference expansion			Reference contraction			Preceding reference expansion (actual difference)	Succeeding reference expansion (sign of difference)
Trough	Peak	Trough	Total change	Interval in months	Average change per month	Total change	Interval in months	Average change per month		
(1)			(2)	(3)	(4)	(5)	(6)	(7)	(8)	(9)
1 Aug01	May07	Jun08	+33.0	33.0	+1.03	−21.5	13.0	−1.65	−2.68	—
2 Jun08	Jan10	Jan12	+18.0	19.0	+0.95	+4.2	24.0	+0.18	−0.77	—
3 Jan12	Jan13	Dec14	+19.6	12.0	+1.63	−19.1	23.0	−0.83	−2.46	—
4 Dec14	Aug18	Apr19	+40.2	44.0	+0.91	−18.7	8.0	−2.34	−3.25	—
5 Apr19	Jan20	Sep21	+19.9	9.0	+2.21	−26.2	20.0	−1.31	−3.52	—
6 Sep21	May23	Jul24	+35.5	20.0	+1.78	−21.7	14.0	−1.55	−3.33	—
7 Jul24	Oct26	Dec27	+19.9	27.0	+0.74	0.7	14.0	−0.09	−1.43	—
8 Dec27	Jun29	Mar33	+12.7	18.0	+0.71	−65.0	45.0	−1.44	−2.15	—
9 Mar33	May37	May38	+53.5	50.0	+1.07	−36.4	12.0	−3.03	−4.10	—
10 May38	Feb45	Oct45	+84.7	81.0	+1.05	−24.3	8.0	−3.04	−4.09	—
11 Oct45	Nov48	Oct49	+4.8	37.0	+0.13	−27.2	11.0	−2.47	−2.60	—
Average 11 cycles 1904–1949			+31.2		+1.11	−24.1		−1.65	−2.76	
Average deviation					0.42			0.78	0.81	
Index of conformity to reference										
Expansion					+100					
Contractions								+82		
Cycles, trough to trough									+100	
Cycles, peak to peak										+100
Cycles, both ways									+100	
Average 7 cycles 1904–14, 1921–38			+27.6		+1.13	−24.2		−1.29	−2.42	
Average deviation					0.33			0.72	0.83	
Index of conformity to reference										
Expansions					+100					
Contractions								+71		
Cycles, trough to trough									+100	
Cycles, peak to peak										+100
Cycles, both ways									+100	

* This is Table B3 in the notation of the National Bureau.

done by dividing each entry in column (2) by the number of months in the corresponding interval of reference expansion, and each entry in column (5) by the number of months in the corresponding interval of reference contraction. Thus we have + 1.11 for the average monthly change in expansion, − 1.65 for the average monthly change in contraction. These averages, which are given in columns (4) and (7) of Table 12-9, are the bases for the computation of conformity measures.

The index of conformity to reference expansions is derived in simple fashion. A credit of + 100 is given for every positive entry in column (4), a debit of − 100 for every negative entry. The sum of these, divided by the number of reference expansions covered by the record, is the desired index. Thus for freight ton-miles we have records for 11 reference expansions. In each of these the average change per month was positive. The index of conformity is given by + 1100 ÷ 11, or + 100. The procedure is the same for reference contractions, except that a negative entry in column (7) represents positive conformity, and yields a credit of + 100 for the given series; a positive entry in column (7) gives a debit, − 100. For freight ton-miles during the 11 contractions covered by the present record we have 10 instances of positive conformity to reference contractions, one instance (the contraction from January 1910 to January 1912) of a rise during reference contraction, which calls for a debit. The sum of the 11 items is + 900. Dividing by 11 we have + 82 as the index of conformity to reference contractions.

It is obvious that these indexes of conformity may range from + 100 to − 100. The first of these figures represents perfect positive conformity. The second, we should note, does not indicate nonconformity; it represents inverse or negative conformity to expansions, or contractions, in general business. Thus for a series such as business failures, which generally declines during periods of expanding business, we should expect a negative index, but this would not denote failure to conform to the movements of business at large. True nonconformity, which would lead to a random assortment of credits and debits of + 100 and − 100 for successive phases of expansion (or contraction), would be represented by a conformity index of zero, or one close to zero.

The conformity indexes for the separate phases of expansion and contraction relate to consistency in *direction* of change. A somewhat different concept of conformity is needed for a full-cycle index. Conformity to the full reference cycle would of course be shown by a rise in the phase of reference expansion followed by a fall during reference contraction. But conformity would also be indicated by a rise during the expansion phase of general business, followed by a rise at a lower rate during the phase of contraction. This is the characteristic cyclical behavior of a series marked by a strong and persistent secular rise. Similarly, there would be full-cycle conformity in behavior marked by a decline in periods of expansion in general business, and by decline at an accelerated rate during contractions in general business. In each of these two cases the individual series shows a clear response to the cyclical movements of business at large, although the response takes the form of a *change in the rate* of advance or decline, rather than a change of direction.

The entries in columns (4) and (7) of Table 12-9 provide a first measure of full-cycle conformity. If we represent the average change per month in a phase of reference contraction by C, and the average change per month in the preceding phase of reference expansion by E_- (the minus sign as subscript indicates that the expansion phase is the one that *precedes* the contraction phase in question) the quantity $C - E_-$ serves as a measure of conformity for a full cycle measured from trough to trough. Thus for the reference cycle running from August 1904 to June 1908 we subtract the entry in column (4) from the entry in column (7), giving

$$C - E_- - - 1.65 - (+ 1.03) - - 2.68$$

which is entered in column (8) of Table 12-9. The entry in column (8) will be negative if the monthly rate of change during contraction is less than the monthly rate of change during the preceding expansion—a condition that represents positive full-cycle conformity. In deriving an index of conformity from the entries in column (8), every minus value counts as + 100, every plus value as − 100. A simple averaging of these entries gives the desired index. Since there are 11 negative values in column (8) of Table 12-9, the index of full-cycle conformity from trough to trough is + 1100 ÷ 11, or + 100.

For series that do not conform perfectly in their expansion and contraction phases, we need a second measure of full-cycle conformity, in which we take account of movements in individual series during cycles that extend from peak to peak of general business activity. If by C we represent the average monthly change in a given series during a stated reference contraction, and by E_+ the average monthly change in that series during the *following* reference expansion, the quantity $C - E_+$ serves as a measure of conformity from peak to peak. This will be a negative quantity if there is change from decline to advance as the series passes from a phase of reference contraction into a phase of reference expansion, if there is deceleration in a rate of decrease, or if there is acceleration of a rate of increase—three conditions that represent conforming response to cycles in general business. It will be a positive quantity under opposite conditions. For the index of full-cycle conformity we actually require only the signs of given differences between C and E_+. These signs, for the peak-to-peak measures, appear in column (9) of Table 12-9. Counting each minus entry as $+ 100$, each plus entry as $- 100$, and averaging, we have the desired index of full-cycle conformity, relating to peak-to-peak movements in individual series. For freight ton-miles this has a value of $+ 100$, representing positive conformity.

In the present instance the indexes obtained from the entries in columns (8) and (9) are identical, but with certain behavior patterns this will not be the case. The general measure of full-cycle conformity employed by the National Bureau is obtained by averaging the trough-to-trough and peak-to-peak indexes. This appears in Table 12-9 as the index of conformity to "cycles, both ways."

In this description of conformity indexes we have dealt with the behavior of individual series during fixed periods—periods marked off by stages I, V, and IX of reference cycles. The investigations of the National Bureau have shown that many individual series may be marked by perfect regularity of response to cyclical movements in general business, but that these regular responses may lead, or lag behind, the turning points of business at large. Thus common stock prices show a high degree of positive conformity to business cycles, but the turning points in such prices usually precede the turning points in general business. Indexes of conformity based on the standard framework marked off by stages I, V, and IX could materially understate the actual degree of conformity found in such a series. Where there is a clear and persistent difference in timing, an additional set of conformity indexes is constructed, using expansion and contraction phases adapted to the timing pattern found in particular series. For common stock prices, for example, the typical period of expansion extended from stage VIII to stage IV of the reference framework, with contraction extending from stage IV to stage VIII. For railroad bond yields the expansion period ran from stage III to stage VI, contraction from stage VI to stage III. The difference between conformity measures derived from the standard framework, ignoring timing differences, and measures taking account of timing differences can be great. Thus for railroad bond yields the index of full-cycle conformity (both ways) in the standard frame is − 16; when timing differences are recognized the corresponding index has a value of + 68.[13]

An indication of a few of the results obtained by the National Bureau in its use of conformity indexes will make clearer the usefulness of these measures. In Mitchell's final study, *What Happens during Business Cycles*, he summarizes conformity measures for the 794 monthly and quarterly series analyzed in the study of cyclical movements in the United States. This is not meant to be a sample completely representative of economic processes; there is unavoidable unevenness of coverage. However, the sample includes series representative of all major sectors of the economy and all phases of economic activity. When conformity indexes for these 794 series are arrayed in order of absolute magnitude (that is, without regard to sign), the following median values are obtained.

	Median
Indexes of conformity to reference expansion	67
" " " " reference contraction	60
" " " " full cycles	78

These indicate a high and significant degree of conformity of economic series to the cyclical fluctuations of business at large. The relative values of the median measures for expansion and contraction phases reflect the generally rising trend characteristic of the American economy over periods covered by these records.

Conformity varies, of course, from sector to sector of the economy. The measures in Table 12-10 reveal significant differ-

---

[13] A detailed account of the measurement of conformity when timing differences are recognized is given in *Measuring Business Cycles* (Ref. 13) pp. 185-197.

TABLE 12–10

Mean Conformity to Business Cycles
Prices and Production in Agricultural and Nonagricultural Industries*

	Prices		Production	
	No. of series	Average Numerical Value of Indexes of Conformity	No. of series	Average Numerical Value of Indexes of Conformity
Agricultural	51	51.6	47	41.8
Nonagricultural industries	96	64.2	141	84.2

* Adapted from *Measuring Business Cycles*, Ref. 13, p. 88, note.

ences. Several economically important conclusions are suggested by this table. Production in agriculture shows the lowest degree of conformity; weather, rather than the state of business, determines output in many agricultural activities. Production in nonagricultural industries shows the highest conformity. Output is controllable at short notice in most of the activities falling in this class; production control is the preferred means of adaptation to changes in market conditions. The prices of nonagricultural products conform less closely to business cycles than does production. Typically, they are more resistant to declines, during business contractions, and are less responsive to the upward push of general expansion. This, of course, is familiar behavior in industries in which "administered prices" are the rule. Finally, we note that the prices of agricultural products are more responsive to cycles in general business activity than is agricultural production. Given a relatively nonconforming output, it is natural that prices should feel the impact of changes in demand.

Other measures given by Mitchell show a wide range of conformity among economic activities. Public construction contracts have an average full-cycle conformity of 32 (computed without regard to sign). For bond yields and other long-term interest rates the average is 66; for bank clearings 83; for private construction contracts 87; for payrolls in durable goods industries 100; and for hours of work per week 100. As presented in their full variety by Mitchell these indexes give a revealing picture of cycles in business, a picture marked by variation in the degree to which individual series participate in these general "cycles" and by diversity in the timing of their individual movements, but a picture, nevertheless, that discloses consistency of pattern and a significant degree of uniformity of movement.

The Description of Specific Cycles. In introducing the methods of the National Bureau we referred to two aspects of its work on cycles. We have studied the first of these—the analysis of the behavior of individual series in a framework set by cyclical turning points in business at large—and now turn to the second. Here we look for evidence of cyclical movements in individual series, and seek to define such movements in a given series, if they are present, in a framework set by the dates of troughs and peaks in that specific series. In place of a single, general framework, which the hypothesis of reference turning points involves, we shall have many frameworks, each defining turning points in cycles specific to a given time series. However, the study of these "specific cycles," as they are termed, is not completely divorced from the assumption that there is something like a common wave movement in general business activity. In searching for specific cycles in individual series the investigator looks for wave movements lasting from over one year to ten or twelve years—movements that correspond, in duration, to the National Bureau's working concept of business cycles. But apart from this general guidance in the selection of appropriate fluctuations the concept of general business cycles does not shape the analysis of specific cycles.

Basically, the method used in defining the characteristics of specific cycles parallels the method outlined for dealing with reference cycles. Monthly data, such as those for freight ton-miles (Table 12-4), are corrected for seasonal variation. The investigator then seeks to define the dates of cyclical troughs and peaks in the corrected series, seeking turning points that mark off cycles lasting more than one year but not more than ten or twelve years. Some subjective judgments must be made here, of course, although specific cyclical movements are clearly defined for many series. There are some series, of course, in which no evidence of cycles can be found. The prices of steel rails, for example, were constant and unchanging over many years in the early parts of this century. But in the Bureau's study of some 830 monthly and quarterly series there were only about 5 percent in which no specific cycles were discernible. Having identified successive troughs and peaks (these are marked by asterisks in Fig. 12.3), the investigator breaks the series into segments marked off by successive troughs. (For series such as bankruptcies, that move inversely to cyclical tides, specific cycle segments are taken from peak to peak.) The monthly observations within each of these segments are then averaged, and the monthly figures are expressed as relatives of the cycle average thus obtained. A nine-stage pattern, corresponding exactly to the nine-stage reference-cycle pattern, is then set up, and stage averages computed from the specific-cycle relatives. These stage averages define a "specific cycle pattern"—that is, the pattern of behavior of the given series within each of the specific cycle segments.

The results of this operation, as applied to monthly data for freight ton-miles between 1904 and 1949, are given in Table 12-11. The first specific cycle recorded for this series extended from a trough in January 1904, through a peak in June 1907, to a trough in June 1908. (The reader will note—see Table 12-7—that the last of these dates happens to coincide with the date of a reference cycle trough, but the other two dates do not coincide with the reference cycle turning points.) In this first specific cycle freight ton-miles rise from a stage I standing of 82.9 (in specific-cycle relatives) to a stage V peak of 120.6, and then fall to a stage IX trough of 97.4. In all, eleven specific cycles in freight ton-miles were identified in the 46 years here covered. Their patterns, as defined by the nine-stage averages, vary of course. To get away from these diversities we may average the measures for each stage, as we did for reference cycles, and thus get measures of the average behavior of the series in question during all the specific cycles observed. This average specific-cycle pattern is defined by the entries in the next to the last line of Table 12-11. It is shown graphically by the broken line plotted in Fig. 12.5. The vertical scale relating to this broken line is in specific cycle relatives, the horizontal scale in months. (The full horizontal distance from T to T—trough to trough—at the top of the diagram is proportionate to the average duration of specific cycles in freight ton-miles.) The average specific cycle pattern shows a fairly regular rise from initial trough to peak, a regular but smaller decline from peak to trough. (The difference between degrees of rise and fall reflects, of course, a secular growth in freight ton-miles over the period covered.) The graph indicates also that the phase of specific-cycle expansion (from T to P on the duration scale) was longer on the

TABLE 12–11

Specific-Cycle Patterns: Railroad Freight Ton-Miles, 1904-1949*

Dates of specific cycles			Averages of specific-cycle relatives at nine stages of the cycles								
			I	II	III	IV	V	VI	VII	VIII	IX
			Three months centered on initial trough	Expansion			Three months centered on peak	Contraction			Three months centered on terminal trough
Trough	Peak	Trough		First third	Middle third	Last third		First third	Middle third	Last third	
	(1)		(2)	(3)	(4)	(5)	(6)	(7)	(8)	(9)	(10)
1 Jan04	Jun07	Jun08	82.9	85.8	98.0	109.2	120.6	117.4	107.0	98.1	97.4
2 Jun08	Apr10	Mar11	85.5	91.5	95.8	104.6	109.1	107.4	104.4	104.6	102.7
3 Mar11	Feb13	Dec14	89.2	90.6	95.1	104.6	113.5	107.6	103.4	98.2	94.4
4 Dec14	Apr18	Mar19	74.0	84.1	99.1	107.9	121.0	118.8	111.0	102.8	93.8
5 Mar19	Feb20	Jul21	91.7	93.0	100.3	103.6	116.4	108.6	107.4	83.7	80.4
6 Jul21	Apr23	Jun24	80.2	85.0	86.6	107.1	120.9	116.0	105.1	108.0	100.1
7 Jun24	Jul26	Dec27	87.3	93.2	97.3	102.4	107.6	106.6	104.1	99.5	96.8
8 Dec27	Aug29	Jul32	109.1	112.4	118.4	120.3	121.0	109.8	91.8	69.2	54.7
9 Jul32	Apr37	May38	69.9	84.4	93.0	114.2	135.1	125.8	111.7	96.6	93.5
10 May38	Feb44	May46	50.3	59.6	82.9	127.9	139.4	133.6	134.2	108.5	95.2
11 May46	Dec47	Oct49	85.1	100.7	106.4	105.7	108.9	103.8	100.3	87.1	76.5
Average 11 cycles 1904–1949			82.3	89.1	97.5	109.8	119.4	114.1	107.3	96.0	89.6
Average deviation			10.0	8.5	6.3	6.0	7.6	7.4	6.4	8.8	10.4

* This is Table A4 in the notation of the National Bureau.

average than the phase of contraction. We shall refer to this point again.

The specific-cycle pattern for freight ton-miles, as plotted in Fig. 12.5, is an average of somewhat diverse movements. How much variation was there, from cycle to cycle, in the behavior of this series? This question is answered by the measures of average deviation given in the last line of Table 12-11. Each stage average, it will be seen, is accompanied by such a measure. There was greatest variation at the trough, when the ebb ceased and the flow began, least variation in the full flood of expansion (stages III and IV) and in midcontraction (stage VII). There was less variation at the peak than at the trough. These are significant facts to the student of cyclical movements.

The solid line in Fig. 12.5 traces the average reference cycle pattern in freight ton-miles, which was discussed in the preceding section. The relation between specific and reference cycles in the present instance is obviously close.

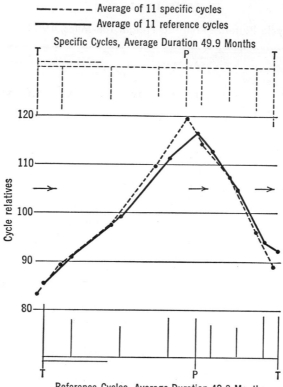

FIG. 12.5. Patterns of Reference and Specific Cycles in Railroad Freight Ton-Miles in the United States, 1904-1949.

The nine black dots connected by lines of dashes in the specific cycle pattern and by solid lines in the reference cycle pattern mark the average standings of freight ton-miles in cycle relatives at the nine stages into which specific and reference cycles are divided.

Source: National Bureau of Economic Research.

The attention of the reader is called to the diversity of information given in graphic form in this figure. We have noted the duration scale for specific cycles, from trough to trough, that is given at the top of the diagram. A parallel scale for reference cycles is at the bottom of the chart. The latter is proportionate in length, to the average duration of reference cycles. The shorter horizontal dotted line at the top, to the left, defines the average deviation of the duration measures for specific cycles, on the duration scale; the corresponding solid line at the bottom of the chart gives the same information for reference cycles in freight ton-miles. The perpendicular broken lines descending from the specific cycle duration scale at the top of Fig. 12.5 are proportionate in length to the average deviations of the measures defining the standings of freight ton-miles at stages I to IX of specific cycles; corresponding perpendicular solid lines at the bottom of the diagram measure the average deviations of freight ton-miles at successive stages of reference cycles. For specific cycles, the measures of average deviations, like those for stage averages, are in specific-cycle relatives; for reference cycles they are in reference-cycle relatives. The arrows in the diagram mark time relations between specific-cycle and reference-cycle turning points. We comment on these below. The use of this standard form of graphic presentation, with a uniform set of scales, enables the user of these charts to grasp quickly the essential features of the cyclical behavior of any given series, and facilitates comparison of measures for different series.

In discussing reference-cycle patterns we have noted the utility of measures of rates of change between cycle stages. Similar rates may be computed for specific cycles. Averages of such rates are given in Table 12-12. Here as in the corresponding table for reference cycles (Table 12-8) we have rates of interstage change, per month, both weighted and unweighted. Each unweighted rate

TABLE 12-12

Average Rates of Change per Month from Stage to Stage of Specific Cycles, Railroad Freight Ton-Miles, 1904-1949*

	Rate of change per month in specific-cycle relatives from stage to stage of the cycles							
	I–II	II–III	III–IV	IV–V	V–VI	VI–VII	VII–VIII	VIII–IX
	Expansion					Contraction		
	Trough to first third	First to middle third	Middle to last third	Last third to peak	Peak to first third	First to middle third	Middle to last third	Last third to trough
(1)	(2)	(3)	(4)	(5)	(6)	(7)	(8)	(9)
Average 11 cycles 1904–1949	+ 1.3	+ 0.9	+ 1.1	+ 2.0	− 1.6	− 1.4	− 1.9	− 1.9
Average deviation	0.6	0.3	0.6	1.1	0.7	1.0	1.2	1.1
Average int. in mo.	5.6	10.2	10.2	5.6	3.3	5.8	5.8	3.3
Weighted average	+ 1.2	+ 0.8	+ 1.2	+ 1.7	− 1.6	− 1.2	− 1.9	− 1.9

* These are summary measures from Table A5, in the National Bureau's notation.

is the simple average of measures of monthly rates of change for a given interstage period during the 11 specific cycles covered by the present record. In getting the weighted average, each constituent measure is weighted by the number of months in the interstage interval to which it relates. Both weighted and unweighted rates indicate a rate of expansion in freight ton-miles that declines after stage II and accelerates thereafter; contraction is retarded slightly after stage VI, but reaches and maintains a high tempo between stages VII and IX.

Timing and duration of specific cycles. To the student of cyclical processes great interest attaches to *sequences of change* at the troughs and peaks of business cycles. Characteristically, business cycles are marked by a series of related movements in employment, production, wholesale and retail sales, inventories, prices, interest rates, and other series dealing with aspects of economic activity. The investigator seeks to define these sequences, and to discover regularities in them.

The National Bureau derives timing measures for individual series by comparing the dates of troughs and peaks of specific cycles with corresponding dates given by the reference-cycle framework. The method is illustrated by the entries in the first five columns of Table 12-13, relating to freight ton-miles. Columns (3) and (5) repeat the reference dates given in Table 12-7. In column (1) are the dates of troughs and peaks in the specific cycles marked out for this series. When the date of a turn in the specific cycle of a series precedes the corresponding reference date, the difference in months is termed a "lead," and is given a minus sign. When the specific-cycle turn follows the corresponding reference date, the difference in months is called a "lag," and is marked by a plus sign. Thus the first entry in column (2) of Table 12-13 is + 1. This refers to the peak in freight ton-miles which came in June 1907, one month after the reference peak of May 1907. The zero entry in column (4) of the same line refers to the June 1908 trough in freight ton-miles, which coincided with the reference trough. The next trough in freight ton-miles came in March 1911, 10 months before the reference trough of January 1912; the entry in column (4) is − 10.

This brief statement describes the procedure appropriate to cases in which specific-cycle turns are clearly related to corresponding reference dates, with no complications arising from inverted

TABLE 12-13

Timing and Duration of Specific Cycles
Railroad Freight Ton-Miles, 1904-1949*

Dates of specific cycles			Lead (−) or lag (+) at				Specific cycles			Percent of duration of specific cycles	
			Reference peak		Reference trough						
			No. of months	Refer- ence date	No. of months	Refer- ence date	Expan- sion mos.	Con- traction mos.	Full cycle mos.	Ex- pan- sion	Con- trac- tion
Trough	Peak	Trough									
	(1)		(2)	(3)	(4)	(5)	(6)	(7)	(8)	(9)	(10)
1 Jan04	Jun07	Jun08	+ 1	5/07	0	6/08	41	12	53	77	23
2 Jun08	Apr10	Mar11	+ 3	1/10	−10	1/12	22	11	33	67	33
3 Mar11	Feb13	Dec14	+ 1	1/13	0	12/14	23	22	45	51	49
4 Dec14	Apr18	Mar19	− 4ᵃ	8/18	− 1ᵃ	4/19	40	11	51	78	22
5 Mar19	Aug20	Jan22	+ 7ᵃ	1/20	+ 4ᵃ	9/21	17ᵃ	17ᵃ	34ᵃ	50ᵃ	50ᵃ
	Apr18	Mar19	− 4	8/18	− 1	4/19		11ᵃ			
6 Mar19	Feb20	Jul21	+ 1	1/20	− 2ᵃ	9/21	11	17	28	39	61
7 Jul21	Apr23	Jun24	− 1ᵃ	5/23	− 1ᵃ	7/24	21ᵃ	14ᵃ	35ᵃ	60ᵃ	40ᵃ
		Jul21			− 2	9/21					
8 Jul21	Apr23	Jun24	− 1	5/23	− 1	7/24	21	14	35	60	40
9 Jun24	Jul26	Dec27	− 3	10/26	0	12/27	25	17	42	60	40
10 Dec27	Aug29	Jul32	+ 2	6/29	− 8	3/33	20	35	55	36	64
11 Jul32	Apr37	May38	− 1	5/37	0	5/38	57	13	70	81	19
12 May38	Feb44	May46	−12	2/45	+ 7	10/45	69	27	96	72	28
13 May46	Dec47	Oct49	−11	11/48	0	10/49	19	22	41	46	54
Average 11 cycles 1904-1949			− 2.2		− 1.4		31.6	18.3	49.9	61	39
Average deviation			3.9		2.9		14.6	6.0	13.7	13	13

ᵃ Excluded from the averages.
* This is an extract from Table A1, in the notation of the National Bureau.

patterns (characteristic of series that decline when general business is expanding, and vice versa), from the interjection of extra specific cycles, from "skipped" cycles (as when a stated series fails to reflect a given reference cycle), or from leads or lags long enough to raise doubts about the timing comparisons that should be made (e.g., is a specific-cycle peak that precedes a given reference peak by 12 months and lags 10 months behind the earlier reference peak to be identified with the earlier or later reference turn?). For the detailed application of the procedures the National Bureau employs in studying timing relations the student should consult the descriptions given in the Burns-Mitchell monograph.[14]

The averages and average deviations given in the last two lines of Table 12-13 are summary measures that define characteristic

[14] Ref. 13, pp. 116-23.

sequences. In deriving such averages the Bureau omits timing measures relating to ambiguous and nonconforming movements of individual series. Only timing measures that may be assumed to be connected with the revivals and recessions of general business are included. The timing averages for freight ton-miles indicate an average lead of 2.2 months in this series at reference peaks, an average lead of 1.4 months at troughs in general business.[15] In view of the size of the average deviations, these measures do not indicate significant departures, in time, from the turns in business activity at large. Although the sequences of change are clouded in many cases, the Bureau's technique has enabled it to define major timing relations of clear economic significance. Thus Mitchell (Ref. 107, pp. 68-75) notes clear leads at reference troughs in new orders for durable goods, construction contracts, security issues, liabilities of commercial failures (an inverted series), stock market transactions and prices of securities, and other series. Many of the same series lead at reference peaks, with new orders for durable goods, construction contracts, series on bank investments and deposits, and stock exchange transactions and prices preceding the down turn in general business by one or two cyclical stages. But, of course, sequences at peaks by no means repeat the patterns of change at troughs.[16]

The specific cycles in any economic series vary in duration, and vary in the relative durations of the phases of expansion and contraction. These aspects of cyclical behavior, which are of obvious interest to the investigator, are defined in columns (6) to (10) of Table 12-13. The specific cycles in freight ton-miles ranged from 28 to 96 months in duration. The average duration was 49.9 months. Typically, the period of expansion constituted 61 percent

[15] The arrows in Fig. 12.5 indicate these average time sequences, when they appear to be regular. For freight ton-miles the arrow drawn from the trough of the average specific-cycle pattern to the trough of the average reference-cycle pattern points from left to right, indicating that in this series revival precedes the trough in general business by more than one month. The arrow from specific-cycle peak to reference-cycle peak points in the same direction, indicating a similar lead at the upper turning point of general business. (When a given series *lags* more than one month behind general business at trough or peak the arrow points to the left. When the average lead or lag is one month or less a vertical arrow is drawn to indicate rough coincidence of average turns.)

[16] G. H. Moore of the National Bureau staff has identified a number of sequences that he believes to be regular enough to warrant their use as indexes of turns in the state of general business. See *Statistical Indicators of Cyclical Revivals and Recessions* (Ref. 110).

of the duration of specific cycles in this series, while contraction made up 39 percent of the full-cycle duration. The measures of average deviation indicate the degree of consistency in these movements, from cycle to cycle.

Amplitudes of specific cycles. Are the cyclical fluctuations found in individual series wide or narrow? To answer this question the National Bureau constructs simple measures of amplitude. These are exemplified in Table 12-14. In the first specific cycle shown for freight ton-miles in this table, the expansion carried the series from a level of 82.9 at the trough centered at January 1904 to 120.6 at the peak centered at June 1907. These standings are given in specific-cycle relatives. The total rise of 37.7 points, given in column (5), is an index of the amplitude of cyclical expansion. From the June 1907 peak freight ton-miles fell to a low of 97.4 at the trough centered at June 1908. The decline of 23.2 points (see column 6) is an index of the amplitude of cyclical fall. Each of these measures may be read as a percentage, the base of the percentages being the average monthly value of freight ton-miles

TABLE 12–14

Amplitude of Specific Cycles, Railroad Freight Ton-Miles, 1904-1949*

Dates of specific cycles			Standing			Total movement			Movement per month		
			At initial trough	At peak	At terminal trough	Rise	Fall	Rise and fall	Rise	Fall	Rise and fall
Trough	Peak	Trough									
	(1)		(2)	(3)	(4)	(5)	(6)	(7)	(8)	(9)	(10)
1 Jan04	Jun07	Jun08	82.9	120.6	97.4	+37.7	−23.2	60.9	+0.9	−1.9	1.1
2 Jun08	Apr10	Mar11	85.5	109.1	102.7	+23.6	− 6.4	30.0	+1.1	−0.6	0.9
3 Mar11	Feb13	Dec14	89.2	113.5	94.4	+24.3	−19.1	43.4	+1.1	−0.9	1.0
4 Dec14	Apr18	Mar19	74.0	121.0	93.8	+47.0	−27.2	74.2	+1.2	−2.5	1.5
5 Mar19	Feb20	Jul21	91.7	116.4	80.4	+24.7	−36.0	60.7	+2.2	−2.1	2.2
6 Jul21	Apr23	Jun24	80.2	120.9	100.1	+40.7	−20.8	61.5	+1.0	−1.5	1.8
7 Jun24	Jul26	Dec27	87.3	107.6	96.8	+20.3	−10.8	31.1	+0.8	−0.6	0.7
8 Dec27	Aug29	Jul32	109.1	121.0	54.7	+11.9	−66.3	78.2	+0.6	−1.9	1.4
9 Jul32	Apr37	May38	69.9	135.1	93.5	+65.2	−41.6	106.8	+1.1	−3.2	1.5
10 May38	Feb44	May46	50.3	139.4	95.2	+89.1	−44.2	133.3	+1.3	−1.6	1.4
11 May46	Dec47	Oct49	85.1	108.9	76.5	+23.8	−32.4	56.2	+1.3	−1.5	1.4
Average 11 cycles 1904–1949			82.3	119.4	89.6	+37.1	−29.8	66.9	+1.2	−1.7	1.4
Average deviation			10.0	7.6	10.4	17.1	13.0	22.7	0.3	0.6	0.3
Weighted average									+1.2	−1.6	1.3

Amplitude of cyclical movements shown by specific-cycle relatives

* This is Table A2 in the notation of the National Bureau.

during the specific cycle that ran from January 1904 to June 1908. The entry in column (7), measuring full-cycle amplitude, is derived from the entries in columns (5) and (6). In general terms, the index of full-cycle amplitude is the change between stages I and V minus the change between stages V and IX, both changes being given appropriate signs. Thus for the first specific cycle shown in Table 12-14, we have

$$\text{Full-cycle amplitude} = +37.7 - (-23.2)$$
$$= 60.9$$

The averages at the foot of Table 12-14 indicate that freight ton-miles rise, on the average, 37.1 points during specific cycle expansions, decline 29.8 points, and have a full-cycle index of amplitude of 66.9. These are abstract measures which may be compared with similar measures for other series, and combined with them.

This same method may be employed in measuring the amplitudes of reference cycles in individual series. Averages measuring swings within the reference-cycle framework will be damped, of course, unless the timing of specific-cycle turns coincides throughout with the turns in general business. For this reason the ratio of the reference-cycle amplitude, for a given series, to its specific-cycle amplitude provides a rough but useful indication of the relation in time between specific cycles and cycles in general business. For freight ton-miles, as we have seen, the full-cycle amplitude of specific cycles is measured by an index of 66.9. The corresponding index for reference cycles is 55.3. (each of these measures is based upon records covering 11 cycles.) The ratio 55.3/66.9, or .83 is relatively high, since specific-cycle turns in freight ton-miles are related fairly closely to the troughs and peaks of the reference chronology.

Because phases of expansion and contraction, and full cycles, vary in duration, it is desirable to reduce the indexes of rise and fall, and of full-cycle amplitude, to monthly rates. These are given in columns (8) to (10) of Table 12-14. Here are measures of the rapidity of rise and of fall, and of full-cycle change, that are for many purposes more revealing than are the indexes of amplitude. It is interesting to note that the most rapid advance in freight ton-miles came in the period from March 1919 to February 1920, and that the most rapid decline came in the contraction between

April 1937, and May 1938. The intensity of these movements would be lost sight of if one studied only the amplitude measures in columns (5) and (6). Weighted averages of the monthly rates (the weights being the number of months to which each of the individual entries relates) supplement the unweighted averages for the entries in columns (8) to (10).

Comment on the Method of the National Bureau. "When you cannot measure what you are speaking about, when you cannot express it in numbers," said Lord Kelvin, "your knowledge is of a meager and unsatisfactory kind." It is a great virtue of the National Bureau procedure that it has brought systematic and comprehensive measurement to the study of business cycles. The battery of measures we have discussed in the preceding pages gives our knowledge of the phenomena of business cycles new precision. Varied aspects of the cyclical behavior of individual economic series—duration, amplitude, timing, conformity to the cyclical swings of general business, and details of characteristic patterns of fluctuation—are defined by this technique. Most of the measures used are abstract numbers that may be compared with similar measures for other series and combined with such measures to permit study of average and aggregative cyclical behavior. These methods constitute a powerful, flexible tool, adapted to the systematic analysis of the complex combinations of regularities and variations that characterize business cycles.

Differences from the traditional approach to the study of cycles that was outlined in the early pages of this chapter are, of course, many. One point of resemblance is that in both methods an attempt is made to remove seasonal fluctuations. Both suffer from the difficulties faced in handling this slippery problem. But in the treatment of secular trends the two procedures are far apart. These are measured and "eliminated," in applying the older method. The National Bureau procedure serves, in effect, to remove intercycle trends, since both reference-cycle and specific-cycle characteristics are defined by relatives for which the mean value of the observations in each cycle is the base. However, the effects of intracycle trends are not removed. If a series is growing this will be manifest by an upward tilt in the average specific-cycle and reference-cycle patterns. The average standing at stage IX will exceed the average standing at stage I. (Differences between averages for other stages will, of course, be correspondingly affected by the secular lift.)

The reverse will be true for a series marked by a secular decline. In thus retaining the secular changes that occur within the limits of each cycle the National Bureau staff believe that they are keeping closer to the reality of cycles than they would if intracycle trends should be removed. The business man making decisions about production and employment sees expansions followed by contractions. In appraising these he makes no sophisticated corrections for trend. A rapidly growing industry provides a stimulus to expansion that a declining industry does not; the secular lift that is the basis for this stimulus should not, in the judgment of the Bureau investigators, be eliminated from the cycle pattern. It is proper to add that the basic tables constructed by the National Bureau include one (not given here) containing detailed measures of secular changes between specific cycles. Thus, although no mathematical trend functions are fitted, secular movements are defined and relevant measures made available for study.

In using the method of the National Bureau the possibility of changes over time in the characteristics of reference and specific cycles must be recognized. An average pattern of cyclical fluctuations in pig iron production, based on data for 18 cycles occurring between 1879 and 1949, would have limited value as a piece of scientific evidence if the cyclical behavior of pig iron production had been significantly modified during this period. More generally, if the characteristics of business cycles at large had been substantially changed—in average duration, in the interrelated patterns of change that make up the broad swings of business activity, in causal relations among constituent elements—over the period covered by available business records, averages for the whole period and conclusions based on such averages would be suspect. If there are significant changes in cyclical patterns when a nation passes from peace to war or from war to peace similar reservations would be called for. The National Bureau has made various probability tests to determine whether such secular or structual changes as have occurred in the character of business cycles have been great enough to discredit the use of averages. The conclusion reached by Burns and Mitchell[17] is that such changes have not invalidated the measures of average behavior they have constructed. However, if there is reason to believe that measures for a single

17 Ref. 13, pp. 412-13.

economic series, or for groups of such series, have been subject to secular or other changes, the averaging process may be adapted to this fact. War cycles may be omitted, if they are believed to be influenced by special forces. The record for a single series may be broken at a date believed to mark a structural change affecting cyclical behavior, and two sets of averages constructed; the hypothesis that there has been a significant change may then be tested. If such precautions are observed, the danger of combining heterogeneous materials in averages or aggregates may be avoided.

The use of a single cycle (reference or specific) as a unit of observation conforms to the view that the cycle is the unit of experience. This practice, which yields a diversity of measures of cyclical behavior, is a distinctive feature of the National Bureau procedure. It permits a variety of groupings and approaches adapted to the purposes of different investigators. Measures of many economic processes during a given reference cycle may be assembled for comparison and combination; measures descriptive of particular processes (e.g., production) in many reference cycles may be combined. In careless hands, however, a method that takes a single cycle as the unit of experience and observation could lead to faulty conclusions. It would be easy, and quite invalid, to assume that the events occurring between stages V and IX of each reference cycle could be completely explained by the events that took place between stages I and V. The economic process is a continuous one. Each cycle and each phase of each cycle is tied to earlier and later events. If we are seeking an explanation of what happened to the economy of the United States between the reference peak at June 1929 and the reference trough at March 1933 we should have to go much farther back in time than to the reference trough at December 1927. The experience we should have to include, if we were tracing the cumulation of events and stresses that led to the contraction of 1929-33, would cover a long stretch of time indeed. To include even the immediately pertinent events in this cumulative process we should have to go back to 1921 or to 1914. Chopping what is essentially a continuous process into segments, as is done in the National Bureau procedure, is a justifiable analytical device, but in the appraisal of evidence and the final formulation of conclusions these isolated portions must be seen as parts of an unbroken chain.

The National Bureau techniques constitute a flexible device for the organization and analysis of measures descriptive of cyclical behavior. The methods have been criticized as having no theoretical underpinning. They are not derived from a definite theoretical construct. This is true, although the methods do rest on certain broad conceptions of the nature of cyclical processes in a modern economy. This separation of techniques from a particular theory is, of course, deliberate. It reflects the view that in scientific research a theoretical construct should not dominate the data. It goes without saying that a research procedure should be adapted to the testing of hypotheses, for without such tests the cumulation of knowledge is impossible. The National Bureau procedure may be used in testing business cycle theories, although the difficulties in the way of conclusive tests are many, in a field in which numerous variables interact in changing combinations. The technique has a final advantage in the diversity of views it affords of cyclical processes, in both microscopic and macroscopic aspects. In revealing both diversity and elements of regularity in cyclical patterns the technique can be germinal of ideas, when used by an alert investigator—a point of merit in any research technique.

Other methods of time-series analysis. A variety of other methods have been used by mathematicians and statisticians in attempting to decompose historical variables into significant components. These methods vary, of course, with the subject matter dealt with, and with the purposes of investigators. Edwin Frickey (Ref. 56; see also review by A. F. Burns, Ref. 11), working from pervasive aggregative cycles that furnish a standard for the study of individual economic series, obtains the secular trends of such series as residuals, after removing variations related to the standard cyclical pattern. The method of serial correlation (entailing the correlation, with varying lags, of the terms in a given time series) has been used to determine the type or types of oscillation inherent in that series (H. Wold, Ref. 194 and Kendall, Ref. 79). When there is reason to believe that a series in time is the sum of a number of harmonic terms (i.e., that the series represents the combination of several elements each characterized by symmetrical fluctuations of constant period) methods of periodogram analysis that have been employed in the natural sciences may be used to break the observed series into its harmonic components (Kendall, Ref. 78). Some methods place special emphasis on the *random* components of time series, and attempt systematic separation of random and nonrandom elements. This is the object of the method of variate differences (see Tintner, Ref. 159). Another approach, involving the concept of stochastic processes, develops more elaborate mathematical models for use in dealing with chronologically ordered observations that contain random (or stochastic) elements (see Hald, Ref. 66). The diversity of methods employed arises, in part, out of the diversity of issues and tasks faced by investigators. In part, however, it reflects the state of our knowledge today. There are probably more unsolved problems in the study of time series than in any other field of statistical practice. Theories and techniques alike are in a developmental stage.

REFERENCES

Burns, A. F., "Frickey on the Decomposition of Time Series," *Review of Economic Statistics*, August 1944.

Burns, A. F. and Mitchell, W. C., *Measuring Business Cycles*, Chaps. 2-8.

Croxton, F. E. and Cowden, D. J., *Applied General Statistics*, Chap. 19.

Frickey, E., *Economic Fluctuations in the United States*.

Hald, A., *The Decomposition of a Series of Observations Composed of a Trend, a Periodic Movement, and a Stochastic Variable*.

Kendall, M. G., *The Advanced Theory of Statistics*, 3rd ed., Vol. II, Chap. 30.

Koopmans, T. C., "Measurement without Theory," (review of Burns and Mitchell, *Measuring Business Cycles*), *Review of Economic Statistics*, Aug. 1947.

Lewis, E. E., *Methods of Statistical Analysis in Economics and Business*, Chap. 11.

Mitchell, W. C., *What Happens During Business Cycles*, Chaps. 1-4, 6.

Persons, W., "Indices of Business Conditions," *Review of Economic Statistics*, Preliminary Vol. 1, 1919.

Riggleman, J. R. and Frisbee, I. N., *Business Statistics*, 3rd ed., Chap. 17.

Schumpeter, J. A., *Business Cycles*, Chap. 5.

Vining, R., "Methodological Issues in Quantitative Economics: Koopmans on the Choice of Variables to be Studied and on Methods of Measurement" (with Reply by Koopmans, and Rejoinder), *The Review of Economics and Statistics*, May 1949.

The publishers and the dates of publication of the books named in chapter reference lists are given in the bibliography at the end of this volume.

CHAPTER **13**

.
.
.

Index Numbers of Prices

The term "index number" has been applied to a number of somewhat similar devices employed in the analysis of statistical series. Index numbers have been most widely used in the study of price changes, but a brief consideration of certain other uses may make clear the essential characteristics of such measures. In its simplest form this name is used for a term in a time series expressed as a relative number. Thus the relative numbers given in columns (3) and (5) of Table 13-1 would be considered index numbers of this simple type.

TABLE 13–1

Examples of Time Series as Relatives (1950 = 100)

(1) Year	(2) U. S. production of crude petroleum (unit: 1,000,000 barrels of 42 gallons each)	(3) Petroleum production relative	(4) Wholesale price of No. 1 dark northern spring wheat Minneapolis Average of average monthly prices per bushel	(5) Wheat price relative
1950	1,974	100.0	$2.41	100.0
1951	2,248	113.9	2.52	104.6
1952	2,290	116.0	2.51	104.1
1953	2,360	119.6	2.53	105.0

The representation of the terms in a time series as relatives, with reference to a fixed base, makes possible a ready comparison of the values for different dates and enables one to follow the movements of the series much more easily than when the data are presented in their original form. Comparison of different series is also facilitated.

Though such relatives have been called index numbers it is better practice to reserve the term for figures that represent the combination of a number of series. The series to be combined may relate to prices, production, consumption, wages, volume of trade, or to any factor subject to temporal variation. (Index numbers have been used also in measuring such geographical differences as arise from variations in living costs from city to city or from country to country.) Quite complex problems may be involved in the construction of any one of these special forms of index numbers, but the essential aim in all cases is to secure a single, simple series that will define the net resultants of the changes occurring in the constituent elements. Our concern in the present chapter is with the procedures used in making index numbers of commodity prices.

Price Movements and Their Measurement: Preliminary Considerations

Price Changes. When price changes are surveyed in detail it is difficult to perceive order, or any definite trend. We find a multiplicity of conflicting movements. The price quotations in Table 13-2, taken at random, are roughly typical of what would be found were the entire field of prices canvassed in order to compare price movements from month to month. All 12 series listed advanced in price over the 15-year period covered by the record. Coffee, showing the greatest rise, was marked by a 12-fold increase in price, hides, at the bottom, by a gain of 13.5 percent. This was, of course, a period that included the inflationary movements of the war and postwar years. A similar period in peacetime would show much less pronounced changes, but the same absence of uniformity in price changes would be found. Each of the thousands of commodities traded in on the markets of any country, or of the world, moves in its own individual way, subject to a variety of influences. Yet it does not act in isolation. In its price movements it affects other commodities, and is affected by them. And, in addition to the forces peculiar to each commodity, there are general forces that act throughout the price system, influencing masses of commodities and services. It is the business of the maker of index numbers to bring order out of this multiplicity of price movements

TABLE 13–2

Commodity Prices at Wholesale*

Commodity	Unit	Price April 1939	Price April 1954	Relative price April 1954 (April 1939 = 100)
CATTLE—				
Fair to choice native steers, Chicago.....Dols. per 100 lbs.		10.55	23.75	225.1
COFFEE—				
Santos No. 4, New York..............Cents per lb......		7¼	89.50	1234.5
COPPER—Electrolytic, New York refinery.Cents per lb......		10.37½	29.87½	288.0
CORN—No. 2 yellow, Chicago..........Dols. per bu......		.48⅞	1.59¼	325.8
COTTON—Middling, ⅞″, New Orleans...Cents per lb......		8.43	32.70	387.9
HIDES—				
Green salted packers, No. 1, heavy native steers, Chicago.....................Cents per lb......		9¼	10½	113.5
HOGS—Good merchantable, pigs and rough stock excluded, Chicago..............Dols. per 100 lbs.		7.15	27.05	378.3
IRON and STEEL—				
Steel scrap, No. 1 heavy melting, Pittsburgh............................Dols. per gross ton		15.50	28.50	183.9
PETROLEUM—Crude, at well Pennsylvania........................Dols. per bbl.....		2.00	3.76	188.0
SUGAR—96° centrifugal, duty paid, N. Y.__Cents per lb......		2.92	6.20	212.3
WHEAT—				
No. 1 northern spring, Minneapolis.....Dols. per bu......		.74⅜	2.33½	313.9
ZINC—Prime western, E. St. Louis.......Cents per lb.,.....		4.50	10.25	227.8

* As compiled from trade sources by *The Guaranty Survey.*

by defining the broad movements that are the net resultant of the diverse forces impinging on prices.

The character of price changes in individual commodities, viewed collectively, is of concern to makers and users of index numbers, for it bears upon the methods that may be used in measuring price movements. In earlier pages of this book, dealing with methods of summarizing quantitative observations, we noted that an average is most meaningful when it represents a distinct central tendency in a mass of relatively homogeneous data. Moreover, the type of average to be employed may vary with the character of the distribution to be represented. We should first, then, determine what the raw materials of the problem are, and study the frequency distributions secured when these raw materials are organized.

Some of the specific purposes served by index numbers of prices are discussed in the following section. At the heart of each of these purposes is the comparison of price quotations for individual commodities at each of two dates. Each pair of quotations measures a change in the price of a single commodity, a change caused by the interplay of many forces. When a great many such price quotations are brought together we have a mass of data representing the interaction of a multitude of forces, some individual and specific in their incidence, some general, affecting the prices of large groups of commodities or of all commodities. What we seek to determine is the net price resultant of all these factors. We seek a measure of the composite effect of the numerous forces that are causing individual prices to rise or fall.

The unit with which we must deal is a single price variation. Whether the statistical methods with which we are familiar may be effectively employed in the organization and analysis of a number of such units depends on the behavior of such units in mass. The following examples illustrate the frequency distributions secured when these data are classified.

Frequency Distributions of Price Relatives. Each price variation is, of course, a ratio, the ratio of the price of a commodity at a given date to the price of the commodity at another date. The ratios may be reduced to a comparable basis by putting them all in the form of relatives, of the type illustrated in preceding examples. In constructing the frequency distribution shown in Table 13-3, the prices at wholesale in 1927 of 670 commodities were expressed as relatives, with the 1926 price as a base in each case.

The frequency polygon representing this distribution appears in Fig. 13.1. For purposes of comparison with similar distributions the figure shows the percentage distribution. The correspondence of this frequency distribution to the standard types portrayed in

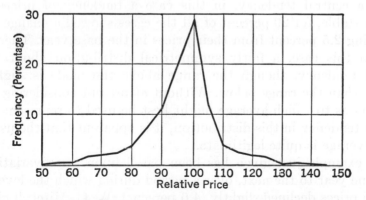

FIG. 13.1. Frequency Polygon: Distribution of Relative Prices of 670 Commodities in 1927 (Average prices in 1926 = 100).

TABLE 13–3

Distribution of the Relative Prices of 670 Commodities in 1927*
(Average prices in 1926 = 100)

Relative prices	Midpoint m	No. of cases f	Percentage of total number of cases
52.5– 57.4	55	1	.1
57.5– 62.4	60	2	.3
62.5– 67.4	65	6	.9
67.5– 72.4	70	7	1.0
72.5– 77.4	75	8	1.2
77.5– 82.4	80	25	3.7
82.5– 87.4	85	50	7.5
87.5– 92.4	90	76	11.3
92.5– 97.4	95	136	20.3
97.5–102.4	100	196	29.3
102.5–107.4	105	83	12.4
107.5–112.4	110	26	3.9
112.5–117.4	115	16	2.4
117.5–122.4	120	14	2.1
122.5–127.4	125	12	1.8
127.5–132.4	130	2	.3
132.5–137.4	135	3	.5
137.5–142.4	140	5	.8
142.5–147.4	145	1	.1
147.5–152.4	150		
152.5–157.4	155	1	.1
		670	100.0

* The 670 commodities included were those employed by the U. S. Bureau of Labor Statistics in the construction of its index of wholesale prices. The original figures, and the relatives, appear in *Bulletin* 473, of that Bureau.

earlier sections is obvious. There is the same marked concentration about a central tendency, in this case a tendency of prices to remain stable, for 29 percent of all the cases showed a change not exceeding 2.5 percent from their prices in the base year. There is also, in this case, a fairly symmetrical distribution about this central tendency, though the range above the mode is slightly greater than the range below. Without at present considering the question as to which average might best be used to represent the central tendency in this distribution, it is apparent that the use of some average is quite legitimate.

The example just given has been based upon price variations from one year to the next, over a period during which the level of general prices declined slightly (4.6 percent). W. C. Mitchell gives a much more comprehensive illustration, based upon the distribution of 5,540 price variations from one year to the next over the period 1890-1913, which shows the same general grouping. The distribution secured by Mitchell is shown in Fig. 4.6 (page 80).

The inertia of prices is most conspicuous when year-to-year price changes are studied. It is therefore advisable to consider the character of price variations over a longer and more disturbed period, that we may learn whether the same type of distribution is obtained. Table 13-4 shows the distribution of 774 price variations,

TABLE 13–4

Distribution of Relative Prices of 774 Commodities in 1933
(Average prices in 1926 = 100)

Relative prices	Midpoint m	No. of cases f	Percentage of total number of cases
10– 14.9	12.5	3	.4
15– 19.9	17.5		
20– 24.9	22.5	1	.1
25– 29.9	27.5	7	.9
30– 34.9	32.5	13	1.7
35– 39.9	37.5	24	3.1
40– 44.9	42.5	28	3.6
45– 49.9	47.5	51	6.6
50– 54.9	52.5	49	6.3
55– 59.9	57.5	50	6.5
60– 64.9	62.5	62	8.0
65– 69.9	67.5	58	7.5
70– 74.9	72.5	93	12.0
75– 79.9	77.5	81	10.5
80– 84.9	82.5	62	8.0
85– 89.9	87.5	67	8.7
90– 94.9	92.5	40	5.2
95– 99.9	97.5	27	3.5
100–104.9	102.5	27	3.5
105–109.9	107.5	11	1.4
110–114.9	112.5	6	.8
115–119.9	117.5	8	1.0
120–124.9	122.5	1	.1
125–129.9	127.5	2	.3
155–159.9	157.5	1	.1
180–184.9	182.5	1	.1
190–194.9	192.5	1	.1
		774	100.0

prices in 1933 being expressed as relatives on a 1926 base. The general level of wholesale prices, it should be noted, declined some 33 percent from 1926 to 1933. The data in Table 13-4 are plotted

FIG. 13.2. Frequency Polygon: Distribution of Relative Prices of 774 Commodities in 1933 (Average prices in 1926 = 100).

in the form of a frequency polygon in Fig. 13.2, the percentage distribution being shown. It will be noted that the distribution is curtailed, the five upper classes being omitted.

The distributions depicted in Figs. 13.1 and 13.2 differ materially. The range of the variations is greater in the second case, a condition naturally to be expected because of the longer period covered. Secondly, a very much smaller percentage of cases is concentrated in the modal group, though there is still a pronounced central tendency. Both distributions, as plotted on the arithmetic scale, are fairly symmetrical, though a few extreme cases extend the actual upper limit of the second distribution. In Fig. 13.1 the concentration about the central tendency is much more marked, and the deviations of individual price ratios from the central tendency are smaller. This distribution resembles one that would be secured from highly accurate physical measurements, or the distribution of shots from a very accurate piece of artillery. The second curve corresponds to one representing less accurate physical measurements, or to the distribution of shots from an old or inaccurate field piece. The modal value occurs less frequently and the deviations from the central tendency are greater. It has been established that the longer the period covered in price comparisons such as those made above, the more pronounced is the tendency shown in Fig. 13.2. The value of the maximum ordinate falls and the range of the distribution increases. The curve becomes flatter and more extended as the time interval increases.

If we were to plot a frequency distribution of 1944 price relatives on 1926 as a base, or of 1954 relatives on the same base, we should expect to find an accentuation of the features we have noted in Fig. 13.2. The wartime distribution, particularly, would be marked by greater skewness than is evident in any of the price distributions referred to above. This point is to be emphasized. A price increase, expressed as a relative, has no upper limit. An increase of 100, 500, 1,000 percent or more is conceivable and possible. (The greatest price increase noted by the War Industries Board in its study of prices during the first world war was one of 4,981 percent, in the case of acetiphenetidin.) But 100 percent is the maximum decline possible, as that would mean that the price of a commodity had fallen to zero. Thus in a period of sharply rising prices positive skewness is characteristic of distributions of price relatives.

In the preceding pages we have briefly considered the character of the raw materials used in index number construction, and have remarked on the nature of the frequency distributions that are obtained when such materials are brought together in quantity. The data we have examined consist of individual price variations, expressed as ratios. When a number of these ratios are assembled a frequency distribution is secured which has points in common with distributions obtained from other collections of quantitative observations. A central tendency, which may legitimately be represented by an average, is apparent in the distribution of price variations. The central tendency is less marked, however, and the deviations from it are more pronounced, the longer the period covered in the price comparison, so that an average becomes less representative as this period increases. In addition, a tendency toward skewness has been noted, and this tendency, we have observed, could be quite pronounced in a period of rising prices. This skewness is due to the fact that we are dealing with ratios that have a definite lower limit and no upper limit.

Some Purposes Served by Index Numbers of Prices. On an earlier page we have said that in obtaining an average of price relatives we are seeking a measure of the composite effect, or net resultant, of the numerous forces that are causing the prices of individual commodities to rise or fall between two dates. A good measure of a clearly defined central tendency in a frequency distribution of price relatives may be taken to define such a net resultant. But this general statement of purpose does not go far enough. The price relatives of what commodities are to be included in such a frequency distribution? To answer this question we must face the question of purpose more directly.

The traditional purpose of the makers of index numbers has been to measure changes in the purchasing power of money. Carli in 1764, Jevons in 1863, Fisher in 1911 thought of their work in these terms. Back of this purpose lies the concept of an average defining a general price level. All commodities and services entering into exchange would be the components of such an average. The prices of all such commodities and services (or a sample fully representative of all) would make up the frequency distribution appropriate to this concept. It is now recognized that such a distribution, which would include commodities at all stages of production and distribution, services to producers and consumers, wages, salaries, rents, profits, taxes, etc., would be heterogeneous in the extreme. For the various elements of the general price system are subject to widely diverse forces. Accordingly, no omnibus measure of changes in prices, in the broadest meaning of that term, is now constructed. Indexes more restricted in scope are more useful to economists, to governmental administrators, and to business men.

The nearest approach to a general price index currently constructed is an index of commodity prices in wholesale markets. In the United States the wholesale price index of the Bureau of Labor Statistics, relating to "the first important commercial transaction for each commodity," is often thought of as measuring changes in the "level of prices," although it covers, in fact, only a portion of wholesale transactions and other markets not at all. But it comprehends a wide range of commodities, and is more inclusive as a measure of price movements than any other current index.[1]

We have referred to the diversity of movements found in the prices of economic goods of all sorts—commodities and services. This diversity is found whether we observe price changes within the year, during cycles of expansion and contraction in general

[1] Reference should be made, however, to the "implicit deflator" of Gross National Product (and to the separate elements of the general deflator) derived by the National Income Unit of the U. S. Department of Commerce in expressing Gross National Product in dollars of constant purchasing power. The "implicit deflator" which is available by years for the period since 1919, is, in effect, a very comprehensive price index, although affected by changes in the composition of the Gross Product as well as by price changes proper. A similar deflator for earlier years was constructed by Simon Kuznets in his measurement of national income.

business, or over longer periods. The student of business cycles and of economic growth knows that these diversities are not haphazard. There are patterns of price change, and in these patterns are found clues to the interacting forces of economic change. A central purpose of index number work today is the measurement of these differing group movements that lead to cyclical and secular changes in the structure of prices. Various classifications of prices are of interest to economists; still others are of concern to business and labor groups and to government officials. The prices of the factors of production (rent, wages and salaries, interest and profit rates), the prices of goods at wholesale and at retail, farm prices, tariff rates—these are among the major classes of contemporary concern. Within the broad category of wholesale prices the U. S. Bureau of Labor Statistics now constructs price index numbers for 15 major commodity groups and for 88 minor groups ranging from grains, milk, coal, and lumber to agricultural machinery, motor vehicles, and radios, television sets, and phonographs. The National Bureau of Economic Research has constructed indexes for raw and manufactured goods, durable and nondurable goods, producer goods and consumer goods, goods of agricultural and of nonagricultural origin, and for other classes of economic interest. Not all sectors of the price system are adequately covered, by any means, but the batteries of group index numbers currently available enable the student to trace shifting price relations in considerable detail.

Closely related to the general purpose just described is measurement of shifts in what may be called the "terms of exchange" of specified economic groups. This is a familiar concept in international trade. Britain's terms of exchange with the rest of the world, as defined by the changing ratio of export prices to import prices, are a matter of central concern to that trading country. The terms of exchange of United States farmers, as measured by the "parity ratio" (the ratio of the prices of farm products, at the farm, to prices paid by farmers for goods purchased), are the basis of federal aid to farmers, and an object of recurring political and economic controversy. Similar terms of exchange are measured by the ratio of wages to the prices paid by consumers, a ratio that affects bargaining over wages, and wage and price regulation in wartime. In increasing degree, special-purpose index numbers are being constructed to define the relations of prices received by specific economic groups to the prices they pay. For any group, or for any individual, this ratio defines a major factor in the economic welfare of that group, or individual. (It is not the only factor, of course. Favorable terms of exchange are of little comfort to a country that cannot sell its products, or to unemployed members of the labor force.)

Another important object in the making of index numbers is that of breaking a change in the aggregate value of a group of commodities into its basic price and quantity components. This purpose may be most readily illustrated with reference to a single commodity. Between 1940 and 1952 the value of raw cotton produced in the United States increased from $621,284,000 to $2,774,-230,000; the amount produced rose from 6,283,000,000 pounds to 7,519,000,000 pounds; the average farm price per pound increased from 9.89 cents to 36.90 cents. Reducing these several changes to relatives, we have

	1940	1952
Quantity of cotton produced, in lbs.	100.0	119.7
Average price of cotton, per lb.	100.0	373.1
Aggregate value of cotton produced	100.0	446.6

The relative numbers measuring the change in total value may be derived either from the aggregate value figures, or by multiplying the quantity relative by the relative measuring the change in unit price. The two processes give the same result. This is always the case when we work with relatives relating to prices, quantities, and values for single commodities. But identity of results is not necessarily found when we work with prices, quantities, and values for groups of commodities. The product of price and quantity indexes may in such cases differ materially from a measure of relative change in values derived directly from the aggregate value figures. When this object—that of breaking a value change (or a value ratio) into consistent price and quantity components—is regarded as of central importance by the maker of index numbers, the methods employed must be adapted to the purpose.

In this brief summary of purposes served by index numbers we have dealt primarily with index numbers of prices. Later we shall deal with problems faced in studying physical quantities. Differences of purpose in the construction of price indexes have some bearing on the choice of technical formulas, a more important bearing on the choice of commodities and determination of the number of commodities to be included in the sample. Technical methods employed are also affected by practical difficulties faced in obtaining data, by computational considerations, and by the time factor in publication of results. For these and other reasons varying methods have been advocated for the construction of index numbers. Differences among methods actually employed, however, are not great today. Although some conflicts of opinion remain, compulsions of practice and an approach to agreement on ends have reduced the differences that prevailed a generation ago.

The practical problems of index-number making in the price field include the choice of commodities (determination of the size and scope of the sample), the obtaining of quotations, and the selection of a method of combining price quotations that will yield a single satisfactory index figure. Our first concern will be the choice of a formula that may be employed in combining price quotations. Alternative possibilities may be illustrated most effectively by the application of a number of methods to the same data. Table 13-5 presents the raw material to which these various methods are to be applied—the average farm prices of twelve leading crops on December 1 of each year from 1929 to 1945. This period, which was marked by the wide price fluctuations brought on first by depression and then by war and inflation, provides a good vehicle for the desired comparisons.

Notation. The symbols to be employed in the computation of index numbers have the following meanings:

p_0': price of a given commodity at time "0" (the base period)

q_0': quantity of same commodity at time "0"

p_1': price of same commodity at time "1"

q_1': quantity of same commodity at time "1"

p_0'': price of second commodity at time "0"

q_0'': quantity of second commodity at time"0"

p_1'': price of second commodity at time "1"

q_1'': quantity of second commodity at time "1"

$\dfrac{p_1'}{p_0'}$: a price relative (relation of price of a given commodity at time "1" to price of same commodity at time "0"; such ratios are usually multiplied by 100 to give the customary relative numbers)

$\dfrac{q_1'}{q_0'}$: a quantity relative

P_{01}: price index for time "1" on time "0" as base

P_{10}: price index for time "0" on time "1" as base

P'_{12}: price index obtained by a base-shifting procedure

Q_{01}: index of physical quantities (produced, exchanged, or consumed) in time "1" (or period "1") on time "0" as base

Q_{10}: index of physical quantities in time "0" on time "1" as base

V_{01}: ratio of aggregate values in time "1" to aggregate values in time "0"; an index of change in the aggregate values of commodities produced, exchanged, or consumed

  L: the Laspeyres formula

  P: the Paasche formula (P with no subscripts will be used as a symbol for the Paasche formula; not to be confused with P_{01}, P_{23}, etc. P with subscripts is used as a general symbol for a price index, the subscripts denoting the years compared.)

  I: the ideal formula

 E_1: a measure of formula error, as shown by the time reversal test

 E_2: a measure of formula error, as shown by the factor reversal test

 D: $L - P$; the difference between results given by the Laspeyres and Paasche formulas; an indication of degree of difference between two regimens

Simple Index Numbers of Prices

In his exhaustive analysis of methods of index number construction Irving Fisher (Ref. 46) distinguishes six fundamental types: the aggregative (or price aggregate), the arithmetic, harmonic, geometric, median, and mode. The latter has never been employed in a practical way, and may be omitted. The characteristics of the five remaining types may be brought out by considering each of them in its simplest form, before examining the more complicated combinations.

Aggregates of actual prices. In the construction of index numbers of the simple aggregative type, commodity prices pertaining to a given date are added; general price changes are measured by comparing the results thus secured for different dates. Using the above symbols

$$P_{01} = \frac{\Sigma p_1}{\Sigma p_0} \tag{13.1}$$

TABLE 13-5

Average Farm Prices, on December 1, of 12 Leading Crops, 1929-1945*

Crop	Unit	1929	1930	1931	1932	1933	1934	1935	1936	1937	1938	1939	1940	1941	1942	1943	1944	1945
Corn	Bu.	.774	.655	.359	.192	.364	.805	.547	.951	.482	.415	.485	.556	.653	.780	1.080	1.060	1.100
Cotton	Lb.	.164	.095	.057	.057	.054	.124	.114	.122	.081	.087	.091	.094	.161	.194	.196	.208	.227
Hay	Ton (sh.)	12.19	12.62	9.05	5.65	8.10	13.72	7.22	10.90	8.76	6.81	7.61	7.39	9.07	10.15	14.85	16.05	15.15
Wheat	Bu.	1.035	.600	.443	.320	.678	.894	.882	1.104	.827	.528	.777	.720	.978	1.073	1.410	1.440	1.535
Oats	Bu.	.426	.315	.230	.134	.304	.525	.256	.463	.289	.234	.334	.320	.431	.458	.760	.678	.691
Potatoes, Wh.	Bu.	1.288	.890	.430	.353	.702	.457	.629	1.021	.521	.580	.700	.535	.800	1.100	1.340	1.465	1.340
Sugar	Lb.†	.038	.033	.032	.029	.032	.029	.031	.038	.032	.029	.030	.029	.035	.037	.037	.038	.038
Barley	Bu.	.544	.389	.353	.201	.407	.778	.376	.844	.507	.356	.430	.411	.546	.600	1.040	.971	1.065
Tobacco	Lb.	.183	.128	.082	.105	.150	.213	.184	.236	.204	.196	.154	.160	.264	.369	.405	.420	.426
Flaxseed	Bu.	2.943	1.398	1.929	.848	1.518	1.653	1.54	1.92	1.81	1.62	1.72	1.40	1.68	2.30	2.84	2.90	2.89
Rye	Bu.	.849	.384	.388	.223	.554	.732	.402	.857	.600	.322	.484	.420	.560	.533	1.045	1.070	1.465
Rice	Bu.	.995	.773	.561	.374	.779	.783	.739	.775	.706	.662	.742	.769	1.351	1.608	1.89	1.77	1.82

† The price of sugar given for each year is the wholesale price of the raw product (96° centrifugal) in the month of December at New York. No figure corresponding to the farm price could be secured for this commodity.

* Source: *Agricultural Statistics*, U. S. Department of Agriculture.

When such index numbers are constructed from the data of Table 13-5 the results in Table 13-6 are secured. The actual aggregates are given in column (2); to facilitate comparison the same figures are reduced to relatives, with the 1929 aggregate as base, in column (3).

TABLE 13–6

Index Numbers of Farm Crop Prices
(Aggregates of actual prices)

(1) Year	(2) Index (aggregate of actual prices)	(3) Index, relative (1929 = 100)
1929	$21.329	100
1930	18.280	86
1931	13.964	65
1932	9.486	44
1933	13.692	64
1934	20.713	97
1935	12.920	61
1936	19.231	90
1937	14.819	69
1938	11.839	56
1939	13.557	64
1940	12.804	60
1941	16.529	77
1942	19.202	90
1943	26.883	126
1944	28.070	132
1945	27.747	130

The results secured by this method of constructing index numbers of prices will be compared shortly with results secured from the same data by other methods. The chief weakness of this type of index number is obvious. This is not an unweighted nor yet an equally weighted index. The influence of each commodity upon the result is dependent upon the price of the unit in which it happens to be traded. In the present index, hay, which is quoted by the ton, is given more weight than all the other 11 commodities combined, with flaxseed second in importance. The index secured by adding the quotations is weighted in an entirely illogical fashion and cannot be accepted as reflecting the course of farm crop prices.

Arithmetic averages of relative prices. Another method employed in the construction of index numbers involves the reduction of each quoted price to a relative, with reference to the price of the same commodity at a certain basic date, these relative figures then being averaged by any of the conventional methods. The example in Table 13-7 illustrates the first phase of this process, data for two years being utilized. The year 1929 is taken as base.

TABLE 13–7

Computation of Relative Prices for the Construction of Index Numbers

(1) Commodity	(2) Unit	(3) Price 1929	(4) Relative	(5) Price 1930	(6) Relative
Corn	Bu.	$ .774	100	$ .655	84.6
Cotton	Lb.	.164	100	.095	57.9
Hay	Ton (sh.)	12.19	100	12.62	103.5
Wheat	Bu.	1.035	100	.600	58.0
Oats	Bu.	.426	100	.315	73.9
Wh. Potatoes	Bu.	1.288	100	.890	69.1
Sugar	Lb.	.038	100	.033	80.8
Barley	Bu.	.544	100	.389	71.5
Tobacco	Lb.	.183	100	.128	69.9
Flaxseed	Bu.	2.843	100	1.398	49.2
Rye	Bu.	.849	100	.384	45.2
Rice	Bu.	.995	100	.773	77.7
			1200		847.3

From these figures the arithmetic averages of relative prices in these two years may be readily computed. The formula for any single relative is $\frac{p_1'}{p_0'}$. When there are N relatives the formula for the index number at time "1" is

$$P_{01} = \frac{\Sigma\left(\frac{p_1}{p_0}\right)}{N} \qquad (13.2)$$

In the present case

$$\text{Index (1929)} = \frac{1,200}{12} = 100$$

$$\text{Index (1930)} = \frac{847.3}{12} = 70.6$$

Index numbers computed in this way for the years 1929 to 1945, inclusive, are shown in column (3) of Table 13-10.

This type of index number is usually termed an "unweighted" index of relative prices. It is weighted, however, just as are the types illustrated in the two examples preceding. The quantity employed as weight in each case is the amount of each commodity which would sell for $100 in the base year. In the preceding example the following quantities have been employed as weights:

Corn	129.2 bu.
Cotton	609.8 lbs.
Hay	8.20 tons
Wheat	96.6 bu.
Oats	234.7 bu.
Potatoes	77.6 bu.
Sugar	2,631.6 lbs.
Barley	183.8 bu.
Tobacco	546.4 lbs.
Flaxseed	35.2 bu.
Rye	117.8 bu.
Rice	100.5 bu.

What has been done, in effect, in the computation of the simple average of relative prices has been to determine the aggregate amount for which the above quantities would sell in each of the eleven years included. At 1929 prices each of the above quantities would sell for $100, the aggregate value being $1,200; at 1930 prices the aggregate value of the above quantities was $847.30. These aggregates, divided by 12, give the index numbers shown in column (3), Table 13-10: 100 for 1929, 71 (70.6) for 1930, etc. Thus the "unweighted average of relative prices" is in fact a weighted aggregate of actual prices. It is equally weighted in the sense that the value of the quantity of each commodity employed as weight was equal to $100 in the base year, 1929.

Medians of relative prices. The median rather than the arithmetic mean may be employed in securing the average of the relative prices for each year. When the relatives in column (6) of Table 13-7 are arranged in order of magnitude the following distribution is secured:

45.2	71.5
49.2	73.9
57.9	77.7
58.0	84.6
69.1	86.8
69.9	103.5

The median of these relatives, 70.7, is the index number for 1930. All the index numbers computed in this way from the medians of relative prices are presented in column (4), Table 13-10.

Geometric averages of relative prices. The geometric averages of the relative prices for the various years may now be computed and the results compared with those secured in the preceding examples. A single relative being represented by the symbol $\dfrac{p_1'}{p_0'}$, the formula for the geometric mean of N relatives is

$$M_g = \sqrt[N]{\frac{p_1'}{p_0'} \times \frac{p_1''}{p_0''} \times \frac{p_1'''}{p_0'''} \times \dots} \qquad (13.3)$$

A geometric mean is generally computed by the aid of logarithms; in this case

$$\text{Log } M_g = \frac{\log\left(\dfrac{p_1'}{p_0'}\right) + \log\left(\dfrac{p_1''}{p_0''}\right) + \log\left(\dfrac{p_1'''}{p_0'''}\right) + \dots}{N} \qquad (13.4)$$

The method of computation may be illustrated for the years 1929 and 1930 (see Table 13-8), the relative prices of the various

TABLE 13-8

Computation of Geometric Averages of Relative Prices

(1) Commodity	(2) Relative price, 1929	(3) Logarithm of figure in col. (2)	(4) Relative price, 1930	(5) Logarithm of figure in col. (4)
Corn	100	2.0	84.6	1.92737
Cotton	100	2.0	57.9	1.76268
Hay	100	2.0	103.5	2.01494
Wheat	100	2.0	58.0	1.76343
Oats	100	2.0	73.9	1.86864
Wh. Potatoes	100	2.0	69.1	1.83948
Sugar	100	2.0	86.8	1.93852
Barley	100	2.0	71.5	1.85431
Tobacco	100	2.0	69.9	1.84448
Flaxseed	100	2.0	49.2	1.69197
Rye	100	2.0	45.2	1.65514
Rice	100	2.0	77.7	1.89042
		24.0		22.05138

$$\text{Log } M_g \ (1929) = \frac{24.0}{12} = 2$$

$$M_g = \text{antilogarithm of } 2 = 100$$

$$\text{Log } M_g \ (1930) = \frac{22.05138}{12} = 1.83761$$

$$M_g = \text{antilogarithm of } 1.83761 = 68.8$$

commodities being repeated from Table 13-7. Averaging the logarithms, and obtaining the corresponding natural numbers, we have 100 as the geometric mean for 1929, 68.8 for 1930.

The results for all the years are summarized in column (5), Table 13-10.

Harmonic averages of relative prices. The characteristics of the harmonic average have been discussed in a preceding chapter. The reciprocal of the harmonic mean, it will be recalled, is the arithmetic mean of the reciprocals of the constituent measures. The constituent items, in the present case, are price relatives of the form $\frac{p_1'}{p_0'}$. The reciprocal of such a relative is $\frac{p_0'}{p_1'}$. The formula for the harmonic mean of N price relatives is, therefore,

$$\frac{1}{H} = \frac{\dfrac{p_0'}{p_1'} + \dfrac{p_0''}{p_1''} + \dfrac{p_0'''}{p_1'''} + \ldots}{N} \tag{13.5}$$

or

$$H = \frac{N}{\Sigma\left(\dfrac{p_0}{p_1}\right)} \tag{13.6}$$

The method of computation is illustrated in Table 13-9.

The index numbers computed in this way for all the years included in the study are shown in column (6), Table 13-10.

In the construction of the five types of index numbers explained above no attempt has been made to use a logical weighting system. All are termed "unweighted" averages, a term which is quite misleading. The first index constructed, based on aggregates of actual prices, is a heavily weighted index number, though the weights are illogical. In the next four the quantities employed as weights are the amounts purchasable for $100 in 1929. The five results are brought together and compared in Table 13-10. In each case the index is given to the nearest whole number. These index numbers are plotted in Fig. 13.3.

Comparison of Simple Index Numbers: The Time Reversal Test. The four averages of relative prices agree much more closely with each other than with the index numbers based on aggregates. For reasons already suggested the latter is quite untrustworthy as a measure of price changes. Of the other index numbers, the arithmetic, geometric, and harmonic means show a consistent

TABLE 13-9

Computation of Harmonic Averages of Relative Prices

(1) Commodity	(2) Relative price, 1929	(3) Reciprocal of figure in col. (2)	(4) Relative price, 1930	(5) Reciprocal of figure in col. (4)
Corn	100	.01	84.6	.01182033
Cotton	100	.01	57.9	.01727116
Hay	100	.01	103.5	.00966184
Wheat	100	.01	58.0	.01724138
Oats	100	.01	73.9	.01353180
Wh. Potatoes	100	.01	69.1	.01447178
Sugar	100	.01	86.8	.01152074
Barley	100	.01	71.5	.01398601
Tobacco	100	.01	69.9	.01430615
Flaxseed	100	.01	49.2	.02032520
Rye	100	.01	45.2	.02212389
Rice	100	.01	77.7	.01287001
		.12		.17913029

$$H(1929) = \frac{12}{.12} = 100$$

$$H(1930) = \frac{12}{.17913029} = 67.0$$

relationship, a fact which follows from the nature of the averages employed. Except in the base year the geometric mean is always less than the arithmetic and the harmonic is always less than the geometric, the amount of difference increasing as the dispersion of prices becomes greater. The median, with only twelve items to be averaged, is somewhat unstable, and its relationship to the other averages is not always a consistent one.

How are we to choose among these varying results? No one of these "unweighted" index numbers is perfect, for weights which have crept in do not measure the relative importance of the various commodities included in the index numbers. But, neglecting for the moment the question of weights, is it possible to test the adequacy of the different methods of measuring changes in the prices as given?

For this purpose Irving Fisher has employed what he terms the "time reversal test." This is merely a test to determine whether a

TABLE 13–10

Index Numbers of Farm Crop Prices, 1929-1945 (1929 = 100)

(1) Year	(2) Aggregates of actual prices (as relatives)	(3) Arithmetic averages of relative prices	(4) Medians of relative prices	(5) Geometric averages of relative prices	(6) Harmonic averages of relative prices
1929	100	100	100	100	100
1930	86	71	71	69	67
1931	65	54	50	52	50
1932	44	39	33	37	35
1933	64	66	66	65	64
1934	97	91	86	86	80
1935	61	68	69	67	65
1936	90	101	100	98	96
1937	69	72	71	70	67
1938	56	60	55	58	57
1939	64	68	69	68	67
1940	60	66	71	64	63
1941	77	92	93	89	86
1942	90	109	102	104	100
1943	126	143	129	138	134
1944	132	143	134	139	136
1945	130	150	145	145	141

given method will work both ways in time, forward and backward. If from 1940 to 1941 sugar should increase from 3 to 4 cents a pound, the price in 1941 would be $133\frac{1}{3}$ percent of the price in 1940, and the price in 1940 would be 75 percent of the price in 1941. One figure is the reciprocal of the other; their product ($1.33\frac{1}{3} \times 0.75$) is unity. Similarly, if a given method of index number construction shows the general price level in one year to be $133\frac{1}{3}$ percent of the level in the preceding year, it should work correctly when reversed; it should show that the price level in the first year was 75 percent of the price level in the second year. When the data for any two years are treated by the same method, but with the bases reversed, the two index numbers secured should be reciprocals of each other. Their product should always be unity. That is, we should have the relation

$$P_{01} \cdot P_{10} = 1$$

where P_{01} is the index for time "1" on time "0" as base, and P_{10} is

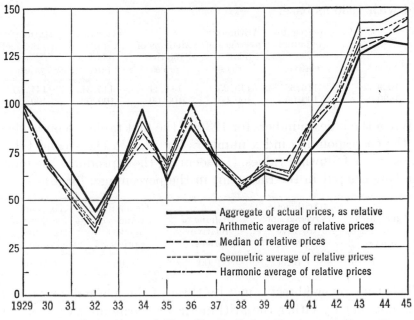

FIG. 13.3. Comparison of Five Simple Index Numbers of Farm Crop Prices, 1929-1945 (1929 = 100).

the index for time "0" on time "1" as base. (In all such expressions as this, the decimal point in the customary price index is assumed to be shifted two places to the left; that is, we deal with ratios, not relatives.) If the product is not unity, there is said to be a *type bias* in the method.

For this error Mudgett (Ref. 113) has used the symbol E_1, where

$$E_1 = (P_{01} \cdot P_{10}) - 1 \qquad (13.7)$$

This will be equal to zero, of course, when the time reversal test is met.

This test may be applied to the methods employed above, using prices for 1929 and 1930. With 1929 as base the following results were obtained

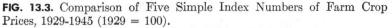

Year	Aggregates of actual prices (as relatives)	Arithmetic averages of relative prices	Medians of relative prices	Geometric averages of relative prices	Harmonic averages of relative prices
1929	100.00	100.00	100.00	100.00	100.00
1930	85.71	70.61	70.73	68.80	66.99

and with 1930 as base:

Year	Aggregates of actual prices (as relatives)	Arithmetic averages of relative prices	Medians of relative prices	Geometric averages of relative prices	Harmonic averages of relative prices
1929	116.68	149.25	141.41	145.31	141.60
1930	100.00	100.00	100.00	100.00	100.00

When the index numbers for 1930 in the first table are multiplied by the corresponding index numbers for 1929 in the second table, we have the following values. (In securing these products the index numbers are put in the ratio, not in the percentage, form.)

Aggregates of actual prices	Arithmetic averages of relative prices	Medians of relative prices	Geometric averages of relative prices	Harmonic averages of relative prices
1.00	1.0539	1.00	1.00	0.9486

This time reversal test is met by three of the methods employed. It is not met by either the arithmetic or harmonic average. For the arithmetic average $E_1 = +0.0539$; for the harmonic average $E_1 = -0.0514$. The former has a distinct upward bias while the harmonic mean shows almost as large an error in the opposite direction. There is, thus, an inherent type bias in both these averages.

Weighted Index Numbers of Prices

Five simple index numbers of prices have been described in the preceding section. With the introduction of weighting the number of possible combinations is greatly increased, but only a few of these types need concern us here.

In the construction of an accurate measure of price changes logical weights must be employed, weights that truly reflect the relative importance of the commodities included. If the weighting problem is ignored haphazard and illogical weights will inevitably be present, whether recognized or not.

The data used in the preceding examples may be utilized to illustrate methods of weighting and to show the effects of varying weights upon index numbers. For present purposes we shall employ weights that define quantities of crops produced or, for certain index types, values of crops produced. The quantities produced during the period 1929-45 are given in Table 13-11.

TABLE 13–11

Annual Physical Production, 12 Crops, 1929-1945

Year	Corn (millions of bu.)	Cotton (millions of bales)*	Hay, tame (millions of short tons)	Wheat (millions of bu.)	Oats (millions of bu.)	White potatoes (millions of bu.)	Sugar† (millions of lbs.)	Barley (millions of bu.)	Tobacco (millions of lbs.)	Flaxseed (millions of bu.)	Rye (millions of bu.)	Rice (millions of bu.)
1929	2,516	14.83	76.02	824.2	1,113	333.4	6,590	280.6	1,533	15.9	35.41	39.53
1930	2,080	13.93	63.71	886.5	1,275	343.8	6,438	301.6	1,648	21.7	45.38	44.93
1931	2,576	17.10	66.99	941.5	1,124	384.3	6,679	200.3	1,565	11.8	32.78	44.61
1932	2,930	13.00	71.77	756.3	1,255	374.7	6,365	299.4	1,018	11.5	39.10	41.62
1933	2,398	13.05	66.30	555.2	736	343.2	6,218	152.8	1,372	6.9	20.57	37.65
1934	1,449	9.64	55.68	526.1	544	406.5	6,680	117.4	1,085	5.7	16.29	39.05
1935	2,299	10.64	78.46	628.2	1,210	378.9	6,641	288.7	1,302	14.9	56.94	39.45
1936	1,506	12.40	62.72	629.9	793	324.0	6,577	147.7	1,163	5.3	24.24	49.82
1937	2,643	18.95	73.27	873.9	1,177	376.4	5,996	221.9	1,569	7.1	48.86	53.42
1938	2,549	11.94	80.40	919.9	1,089	355.8	6,285	256.6	1,386	8.0	55.98	52.51
1939	2,581	11.82	76.38	741.2	958	342.4	7,078	278.2	1,881	19.6	38.56	54.06
1940	2,462	12.57	85.07	813.3	1,245	375.8	7,587	308.9	1,462	30.9	39.98	54.43
1941	2,676	10.74	82.74	943.1	1,181	355.6	6,569	362.1	1,262	32.3	45.36	51.32
1942	3,132	12.82	92.20	974.2	1,350	370.5	5,964	429.2	1,409	41.1	57.67	64.55
1943	3,034	11.43	87.24	841.0	1,138	465.0	6,809	324.2	1,406	51.9	30.45	64.84
1944	3,203	12.23	84.08	1,072.2	1,155	383.1	7,402	278.6	1,957	23.1	25.50	68.16
1945	3,018	9.02	91.57	1,123.1	1,548	425.1	5,319	264.0	1,998	36.7	26.35	70.16

† The figures for sugar represent the total supply available for consumption during twelve months beginning July 1 of the year indicated.
* Bales of 500 lbs., gross weight.

The Laspeyres Formula. The thoroughly illogical results obtained when actual prices, as quoted, are totaled to secure an index number have been pointed out. The same objection cannot be made when the prices are appropriately weighted before the aggregate is taken. If for weights we employ the quantities produced in the base year (at time "0") the formula for the weighted aggregate is

$$L = \frac{\Sigma p_1 q_0}{\Sigma p_0 q_0} \qquad (13.8)$$

This is, in effect, the method employed by the United States Bureau of Labor Statistics, for its index of wholesale prices, though the quantities come from a single year, 1947, while the base of the index is an average of three years, 1947-8-9. The formula for this type of weighted aggregative index is known as Laspeyres' formula, which we shall represent by the symbol L. The method is illustrated in Table 13-12.

TABLE 13–12

Computation of Weighted Aggregates of Actual Prices

(1)	(2)	(3)	(4) Weight (quantity produced 1929, in millions)	(5)	(6)	(7) Weight (quantity produced 1929, in millions)	(8)
Commodity	Unit	Price 1929		Price × weight	Price 1930		Price × weight
		p_0	q_0	$p_0 q_0$	p_1	q_0	$p_1 q_0$
Corn	Bu.	$ .774	2,516	1,947,384,000	.655	2,516	1,647,980,000
Cotton	Lb.	.164	7,089	1,162,596,000	.095	7,089	673,455,000
Hay	Ton(sh.)	12.19	76.02	926,683,800	12.62	76.02	959,372,400
Wheat	Bu.	1.035	824.2	853,047,000	.600	824.2	494,520,000
Oats	Bu.	.426	1,113	474,138,000	.315	1,113	350,595,000
Potatoes, Wh.	Bu.	1.288	333.4	429,419,200	.890	333.4	296,726,000
Sugar	Lb.	.038	6,590	250,420,000	.033	6,590	217,470,000
Barley	Bu.	.544	280.6	152,646,400	.389	280.6	109,153,400
Tobacco	Lb.	.183	1,533	280,539,000	.128	1,533	196,224,000
Flaxseed	Bu.	2.843	15.9	45,203,700	1.398	15.9	22,228,200
Rye	Bu.	.849	35.41	30,063,090	.384	35.41	13,597,440
Rice	Bu.	.995	39.53	39,332,350	.773	39.53	30,556,690
				6,591,472,540			5,011,878,130

The desired index numbers, in the form of relatives, may be computed from the aggregates secured by totaling columns (5) and (8) of Table 13-12. Either year may be taken as the base, and the price aggregate in the other year expressed as a relative of this base. With the 1929 aggregate as base, the index for 1930 is 76.0. Index numbers similarly computed for the other years are given in column (2), Table 13-15.

The Paasche Formula. Another type of weighted aggregate may be constructed, with weights taken not from the base period but from the later period in the given comparison. That is, we may employ q_1 (quantity at time "1") as weight in comparing prices at time "1" with prices at time "0", and employ q_2 (quantity at time "2") as weight in comparing prices at time "2" with prices at time "0." Algebraically, the formula for the index number at time "1" is

$$P = \frac{\Sigma p_1 q_1}{\Sigma p_0 q_1} \tag{13.9}$$

This is known as Paasche's formula. For it we shall use the symbol P. The process of computation is precisely the same as in the preceding example, except that the weights are changed with each successive year. The index numbers secured by this method are given in column (3), Table 13-15.

Averages of Relative Prices. The Laspeyres and Paasche formulas are weighted aggregates of actual prices. The weights employed are *quantities*: Prices multiplied by quantities give the two value aggregates from which each index number is derived. When we average price relatives of the form p_1/p_0, quantities will not serve as weights. The abstract relatives must be weighted by *values*, if the resulting products are to be comparable. For values are in a common dollar unit, while physical quantities may be expressed in a variety of units.

Note on weight bias. If we are comparing prices in years "0" and "1" we may weight each p_1/p_0 relative by the value of the given commodity in the base year, i.e., by $p_0 q_0$, or by the value of that commodity in the given year, i.e., by $p_1 q_1$. Before illustrating the procedure we should note the characteristics of these alternative weighting methods. Irving Fisher (Ref. 46), in an intensive study of weighting, has established that the general effect of weighting by base year values is to give an index number a *downward bias*, while the general effect of weighting by values from the second or given year is to give an index number an *upward bias*. These are not necessary effects, but they are effects usually present because of the patterns customarily found in the related movements of commodity prices and physical quantities.[1]

In the several examples next following we shall deal only with values of quantities produced in the base year, 1929, and in a single given year, 1930. These values are given in the third column of Table 13-13. For weighting purposes they are taken to the nearest million.

Arithmetic averages. In the computation of an index of this type, each relative is multiplied by the appropriate weight, and the sum of the products is divided by the sum of the weights. The process is illustrated in Table 13-13.

The index for 1930, it will be noted, is identical with that secured from the computations illustrated in Table 13-12. That index is a weighted aggregate of actual prices, the weights being the quantities

---

[1] The argument may be briefly summarized: If the price of commodity A rises from year "0" to year "1," the relative p'_1/p'_0 will be greater than 100. If the price of commodity B falls, its relative p''_1/p''_0 will be less than 100. If we assume for the moment that the q's of the two commodities remain unchanged (i.e., that $q_1 = q_0$ in each case) it is clear that base year weight $(p'_0 q'_0)$ for commodity A will be lower than given year weight $(p'_1 q'_1$, which by assumption equals $p'_1 q'_0)$. This means that the price relative for commodity A, which is a high relative (since it exceeds 100), will be given less weight by a system of base year weighting than by a system of given year weighting. In the case of commodity B, for which the price fell, base year weight $(p''_0 q''_0)$ will be higher than given year weight $(p''_1 q''_1$, which by assumption equals $p''_1 q''_0)$. But the price relative p''_1/p''_0 is a low relative, below 100. Base year weighting for this low relative means a higher weight than would given year weighting. Thus the effect of weighting by base-year values is to give a low weight to high relatives, a high weight to low relatives ("low weight" means, of course, lower than would result from given year weighting; "high weight" means higher than would result from given year weighting). In other words, the effects of price increases are underemphasized by base-year weighting, while the effects of price decreases are overemphasized. These two tendencies work in the same direction—toward a lower index than would be had with given year weighting. A similar argument leads to the conclusion that weighting by given year values tends to overemphasize price increases and to underemphasize price declines—both effects working toward a higher index than would be had with base-year weighting.

The conclusions stated rest on the assumption that physical quantities have not changed between year "0" and year "1." If the quantity movements have paralleled the price movements, the "biases" indicated are intensified. On the other hand, movements of quantities and prices in opposite directions over the period covered (negative correlation between quantity and price relatives) will tend to offset the indicated biases, and may, indeed, reverse them. The nature of the weight bias in a particular case will depend, therefore, on the actual behavior of the quantities and prices of commodities included in the index. Over short and medium periods, including business cycles, quantity and price movements are not, in general, inverse for commodities at large. (The inverse movements found in the representations of typical demand and supply curves relate, of course, to assumed static conditions.) Over longer periods, however, inverse movements may prevail. Thus for industrial commodities there was negative correlation between price and quantity movements between 1939 and 1947.

TABLE 13–13

Computation of Weighted Arithmetic Averages of Relative Prices

(1)	(2)	(3)	(4)	(5)	(6)	(7)
Commodity	Relative price 1929	Weight	Relative price × weight	Relative price 1930	Weight	Relative price × weight
Corn	100	$1,947	$194,700	84.6	$1,947	$164,716.2
Cotton	100	1,163	116,300	57.9	1,163	67,337.7
Hay	100	927	92,700	103.5	927	95,944.5
Wheat	100	853	85,300	58.0	853	49,474.0
Oats	100	474	47,400	73.9	474	35,028.6
Potatoes	100	429	42,900	69.1	429	29,643.9
Sugar	100	250	25,000	86.8	250	21,700.0
Barley	100	153	15,300	71.5	153	10,939.5
Tobacco	100	281	28,100	66.9	281	19,641.9
Flaxseed	100	45	4,500	49.2	45	2,214.0
Rye	100	30	3,000	45.2	30	1,356.0
Rice	100	39	3,900	77.7	39	3,030.3
		6,591	650,100		6,591	501,026.6

$$\text{Weighted arithmetic mean (1929)} = \frac{\$659,100}{\$6,591} = 100$$

$$\text{Weighted arithmetic mean (1930)} = \frac{\$501,026.6}{\$6,591} = 76.0$$

(The weights employed are the values of the quantities produced in 1929, in millions)

produced in the base year. An arithmetic mean of relative prices, weighted by values in the base year, is always equal to a relative constructed from such an aggregate.[2]

Harmonic averages. A harmonic average of the relative prices in column (5) of Table 13-13, weighted by 1930 values, gives an index

[2] This may be readily demonstrated algebraically. The value of any commodity in the base year is $p_0 q_0$, while the price relative for a second year is $\frac{p_1}{p_0}$. The weighted mean of such price relatives is equal to

$$\frac{\left(\frac{p_1'}{p_0'} \times p_0'q_0'\right) + \left(\frac{p_1''}{p_0''} \times p_0''q_0''\right) + \left(\frac{p_1'''}{p_0'''} \times p_0'''q_0'''\right) + \cdots}{p_0'q_0' + p_0''q_0'' + p_0'''q_0''' + \cdots}$$

which reduces to

$$\frac{\Sigma p_1 q_0}{\Sigma p_0 q_0}$$

a weighted aggregate of the type mentioned.

of 74.6 for 1930, on the 1929 base. This, it will be noted, is the same as the index yielded by the Paasche formula.[3] Similar measures for the other years covered are given in Table 13-15, column (3).

Geometric averages. The process of computing the weighted geometric mean is identical with that of computing the unweighted geometric mean, except that the logarithm of each relative is multiplied by the given weight and the sum of these weighted logarithms is divided by the sum of the weights, the result being the logarithm of the desired index. The method is illustrated in Table 13-14.

The index for 1930 on the 1929 base is 74.4. Measurements secured for all the years of the period covered are given in column (5), Table 13-15, together with the other weighted index numbers already explained.

How are we to judge of the relative merits of these three index numbers? We may, first, apply the time reversal test which was employed in comparing the five simple index numbers. This test is not met by any of the weighted types we have constructed. The geometric is equally at fault with the others. Though the simple geometric meets the test, the introduction of weighting imparts a bias to the result. Judged by that test alone none of the three is satisfactory. We may next try the second fundamental test that Fisher has developed, which is termed the "factor reversal test."

The Factor Reversal Test. The total value of a given commodity in a given year is, of course, the product of the quantity produced and the price per unit; algebraically, it is equal to $p'q'$. The ratio of the total value in one year to the total value in the preceding year is $\dfrac{p_1'q_1'}{p_0'q_0'}$. If, from one year to the next, both price and quantity should double, the price relative would be 200, the quantity relative 200, and the value relative 400. The total value in the second year would be four times the value in the first year. The value relative would be equal to the product of the price and

---

[3] By a process similar to that illustrated in the preceding footnote, the formula for a harmonic average of relative prices weighted by given year values may be reduced to the Paasche formula

$$\frac{\Sigma p_1 q_1}{\Sigma p_0 q_1}$$

TABLE 13–14

Computation of Weighted Geometric Average of Relative Prices, 1930
(1929 = 100)

Commodity	Relative price, 1930	Logarithm of relative price	Weight	Logarithm of relative price × weight
Corn	84.6	1.92737	1,947	3752.58939
Cotton	57.9	1.76268	1,163	2049.99684
Hay	103.5	2.01494	927	1867.84938
Wheat	58.0	1.76343	853	1504.20579
Oats	73.9	1.86864	474	885.73536
Potatoes, Wh.	69.1	1.83948	429	789.13692
Sugar	86.8	1.93852	250	484.63000
Barley	71.5	1.85431	153	283.70943
Tobacco	69.9	1.84448	281	518.29888
Flaxseed	49.2	1.69197	45	76.13865
Rye	45.2	1.65514	30	49.65420
Rice	77.7	1.89042	39	73.72638
			6,591	12,335.67122

$$\text{Log } M_g = \frac{\Sigma(\log p_1/p_0 \times p_0 q_0)}{\Sigma p_0 q_0}$$

$$= \frac{12,335.67122}{6591} = 1.871593$$

$$M_g = 74.4$$

quantity relatives, a relationship that is obvious in the case of a single commodity.

If, for a number of commodities, we use a given formula in constructing an index of the price change from one year to the next and an index of the quantity change from one year to the next, we should expect the product of the two indexes to be equal to the ratio of the total value of the commodities in the second year to their value in the first year. If the product is not equal to the value ratio there is, with reference to this test, an error in one or both of the index numbers.

As an illustration, we may apply the test to the formula for the first aggregative index constructed, based on the Laspeyres formula $\frac{\Sigma p_1 q_0}{\Sigma p_0 q_0}$. An index of quantities may be computed from this same formula, merely interchanging the q's and the p's; the formula becomes

$$Q_{01} = \frac{\Sigma q_1 p_0}{\Sigma q_0 p_0} \qquad (13.10)$$

The same price factor appears in numerator and denominator,

since we desire to measure only the effect of the quantity change. Substituting the given figures for the twelve farm crops we have, for 1930 on the 1929 base,

$$Q_{01} = \frac{\$6{,}287{,}520{,}870}{\$6{,}591{,}472{,}540} = 0.954$$

In percentage form the index of quantities produced in 1930 is 95.4, with 1929 as base. The corresponding price index, by the same formula, is 76.0. The product

$$P_{01} \cdot Q_{01} = 0.760 \times 0.954 = 0.7250$$

(In securing the product the index numbers are put in ratio, not in percentage form.) That is, if prices have decreased 24.0 percent, while quantities have decreased 4.6 percent, the total value should show a decrease of 27.5 percent.

For the value ratio, derived directly from the sums of the values of the individual commodities for 1929 and 1930, we have

$$V_{01} = \frac{\Sigma p_1 q_1}{\Sigma p_0 q_0} = \frac{\$4{,}690{,}816{,}010}{\$6{,}591{,}472{,}540} = 0.7116$$

As a measure of the magnitude of the error revealed by the factor reversal test we may use the formula proposed by Mudgett (Ref. 113)

$$E_2 = \frac{P_{01} \cdot Q_{01}}{V_{01}} - 1 \qquad (13.11)$$

In the present case $E_2 = +\, 0.0188$. The error is not great, but the formula definitely fails to meet the factor reversal test.

When this test is applied to the second aggregative index, that of Paasche, we secure the following values for 1930, with respect to 1929 as base:

$$P_{01} = \frac{\Sigma p_1 q_1}{\Sigma p_0 q_1} = \frac{\$4{,}690{,}816{,}010}{\$6{,}287{,}520{,}870} = 0.746$$

$$Q_{01} = \frac{\Sigma q_1 p_1}{\Sigma q_0 p_1} = \frac{\$4{,}690{,}816{,}010}{\$5{,}011{,}870{,}130} = 0.936$$

$$P_{01} \cdot Q_{01} = 0.746 \times 0.936 = 0.6983$$

In the computation of E_2 in this case we use, of course, the same V_{01} as in testing the Laspeyres index. For the Paasche formula $E_2 = -\, 0.0187$. Here is an error of the same magnitude as for the Laspeyres index, but in the other direction.

The weighted geometric average also fails to meet this fundamental factor reversal test. With respect to both the geometric index and the aggregates we have, apparently, by the introduction of weights spoiled index numbers which in their simple form were unbiased. Yet weights we must have, if the index numbers are to represent the facts accurately. Neither a simple index nor a weighted form of a simple index will meet the two tests laid down as fundamental. Professor Fisher tested 46 such formulas, of which only 4 (the simple geometric, median, mode, and aggregative) met the time reversal test, and none met the factor reversal test. (The latter test, of course, is applicable only to weighted index numbers).

The "Ideal" Index. A way out of this difficulty is offered by the possibility of "rectifying" formulas in a crossing process, by averaging geometrically formulas that err in opposite directions. Professor Fisher has made exhaustive trials of all possible formulas by this process, finding 13 formulas in all which met both tests. Of these he has selected one as "ideal," from the viewpoint of both accuracy and simplicity of calculation. This ideal index is the geometric mean of the two aggregative types illustrated above. Its formula[4] is

$$I_{01} = \sqrt{\frac{\Sigma p_1 q_0}{\Sigma p_0 q_0} \times \frac{\Sigma p_1 q_1}{\Sigma p_0 q_1}} \tag{13.12}$$

or, using the customary symbols for the Laspeyres and Paasche formulas,

$$I_{01} = \sqrt{L \cdot P} \tag{13.13}$$

This index may be computed readily, in the present instance, from the results already obtained. Thus for 1930 we have

$$\text{Ideal index} = \sqrt{0.760 \times 0.746}$$
$$= 0.753$$

In the customary percentage form this is 75.3.

This index number meets both the time reversal and the factor

---

[4] The same formula was developed independently by Bowley, Pigou, Walsh, Young, and Fisher.

reversal test. For use in the first of these, when year "0" is 1929 and year "1" is 1930, we have from the ideal formula

$$P_{01} = 75.3$$
$$P_{10} = 132.8$$

Hence

$$E_1 = (0.753 \times 1.328) - 1 = 0$$

For the factor reversal test we need, in addition, a quantity index derived from the ideal formula. This is

$$Q_{01} = 94.5$$

From P_{01}, Q_{01}, and the previously derived V_{01} we have

$$E_2 = \frac{(0.753 \times 0.945)}{0.7116} - 1 = 0$$

It is a distinctive feature of the ideal index that it represents a blending of opposing biases. The base-year weighted arithmetic average of relatives (which is the mathematical equivalent of the Laspeyres index) has an upward type bias, a downward weight bias. The given-year weighted harmonic average (the mathematical equivalent of the Paasche index) has a downward type bias, an upward weight bias. The two formulas that embody the opposing type and weight biases are, in the ideal formula, crossed geometrically, i.e., by an averaging process that of itself has no bias. The result is the complete cancellation of biases of the kinds revealed by time reversal and factor reversal tests.

Comparison of weighted index numbers. The ideal index, the two weighted aggregates that enter into its construction, and the geometric mean weighted by values in the base year are given in Table 13-15 for the years 1929 to 1945. The index numbers are plotted in Fig. 13.4.

The wide discrepancies that were found between the various simple index numbers do not appear when the weighted indexes are compared. There are significant differences, but there is none of the erratic behavior of some of the simpler forms.

Of these four types the ideal index probably serves as the best measure of the average price change between 1929 and each of the given years. It is designed, it should be remembered, to measure the change between two stated times, and not for intermediate comparison. The value of the index for 1945, for instance, is

TABLE 13–15

Comparison of Weighted Index Numbers of Farm Crop Prices 1929-1945

(1) Year	(2) Aggregative (weighted by base year quantities) $\dfrac{\Sigma p_1 q_0}{\Sigma p_0 q_0}$	(3) Aggregative (weighted by given year quantities) $\dfrac{\Sigma p_1 q_1}{\Sigma p_0 q_1}$	(4) Ideal index Geometric mean of in- dices in cols. (2) and (3)	(5) Weighted geometric average of relatives (weighted by base year values)
1929	100.0	100.0	100.0	100.0
1930	76.0	74.6	75.3	71.4
1931	49.5	48.3	48.9	47.7
1932	35.9	34.9	35.4	34.0
1933	60.7	60.0	60.3	60.1
1934	94.7	90.3	92.5	91.1
1935	70.0	68.9	69.4	69.1
1936	103.0	100.3	101.6	100.9
1937	66.4	65.3	65.8	64.6
1938	56.5	56.1	56.3	55.5
1939	65.5	65.8	65.6	64.9
1940	66.4	66.3	66.3	65.5
1941	89.7	88.6	89.1	88.4
1942	105.7	104.0	104.8	103.7
1943	136.5	135.8	136.1	134.1
1944	138.2	139.1	138.6	136.6
1945	142.3	143.3	142.8	140.2

determined by the relation between prices and quantities in 1929 and 1945. There is double weighting and the weights vary from year to year. If 1945 is to be compared with 1939 a new index is needed, in which the prices and quantities for 1945 and 1939 alone are included. Direct comparison on the basis of the values for the ideal index given in Table 13-15 is liable to error, because of the weighting system employed.

The circular test. This last point calls for brief comment. If in the use of index numbers interest attaches not merely to a comparison of two years (i.e., to a binary comparison) but to the measurement of price changes over a period of years, it is frequently desirable to shift the base. Thus for any one of the index-number types given in Table 13-15 we might wish to change the base from 1929 to 1939. For many purposes 1939 is a more significant base of comparison for the war years and those following than is 1929. The question at once arises: Would the index derived by this shifting process for a given year, say 1945, on 1939 as base, be

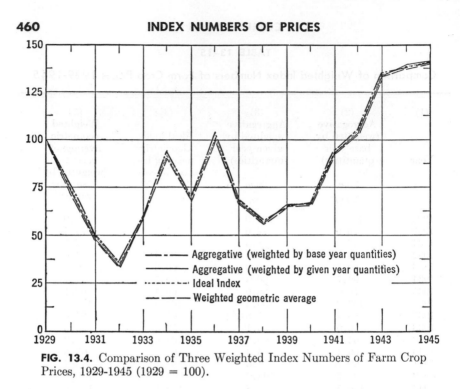

FIG. 13.4. Comparison of Three Weighted Index Numbers of Farm Crop Prices, 1929-1945 (1929 = 100).

equal to the index for 1945 on 1939 as base that would have been obtained had the 1945 index been computed, in the first instance, by the same formula, with 1939 as base? A test of this "shiftability" of base is called the circular test. To exemplify this test we may use the symbol P_{12} for a price index (for year "2" on year "1" as base) derived in the usual fashion for comparison of prices in two specified years, and the symbol P'_{12} for an index derived by a base-shifting procedure. Thus if the original base were year "0," a base-shifting procedure would give us

$$P'_{12} = \frac{P_{02}}{P_{01}} \qquad (13.14)$$

The circular test (which amounts, in fact, to a modification of the time reversal test) is met when $P'_{12} = P_{12}$.

The circular test is not met by the ideal index or by any of the weighted aggregatives with changing weights. The test, as applied to weighted index numbers, is met by an aggregative index with constant weights, and by the geometric mean with constant weights. Thus if we should shift the base from 1929 to 1939, for the indexes in column (5) of Table 13-15, the index for 1945 becomes

216.0 (i.e., 140.2/64.9). This is identical with the index we should have obtained from a geometric average of the individual commodity relatives for 1945, on 1939 as base, using 1929 values as weights. (The weights need not have been drawn from the base of the original index numbers, 1929. Any set of constant weights, used for P' and for P, would yield indexes meeting the circular test, when price relatives are geometrically averaged.)

Summary: alternative formulas. The selection of a formula should be influenced by the results of such tests as those outlined. It will also be affected by the purpose to be served, and by the data available. It is useful here to distinguish the problem faced in a binary comparison—the comparison of prices at two specified dates or for two specified periods—from the task of constructing a continuing series of monthly or annual indexes.

When a single, accurate comparison of just two periods is sought, the case for the ideal index is very strong, provided price and quantity data are available for both periods. This formula comes closest to meeting the difficulties resulting from economic changes. Since it meets the factor reversal test it has the special merit of giving consistent price and quantity indexes. By the use of this formula, that is, it is possible to break a value change into consistent price and quantity components—an objective given top priority by Mudgett (Ref. 113). The second choice would be a modification of the ideal formula recommended by Edgeworth and Marshall, and usually termed the Edgeworth formula. This is

$$\frac{\Sigma(q_0 + q_1)p_1}{\Sigma(q_0 + q_1)p_0} \tag{13.15}$$

It is a simple aggregative index, using as weights the sum of quantities for both base and given years. Thus it takes account of the regimens of both periods. It is a simple, readily constructed measure, giving a very close approximation to the result obtained from the ideal formula. Table 13-16 illustrates the method of computation. The other two formulas here suggested for binary comparisons are those of Laspeyres and Paasche. Either one involves use of weights from a single regimen. Whether these should be selected from the base period (Laspeyres) or taken from the given period (Paasche) will depend on the purpose to be served.

In the construction of a continuing series of index numbers, such as the Bureau of Labor Statistics' series measuring changes in

TABLE 13–16

Computation of Aggregative Index, Weighted by Combined Quantities

(1) Commodity	(2) Unit	(3) Price 1929	(4) Quantity 1929 + quantity 1930 (in millions)	(5) Price 1929 × sum of quantities col. (3) × col. (4)	(6) Price 1930	(7) Price 1930 × sum of quantities col. (6) × col. (4)
Corn	Bu.	$ .774	4,596	$ 3,557,304,000	$ .655	$ 3,010,380,000
Cotton	Lb.	.164	13,747	2,254,508,000	.095	1,305,965,000
Hay	Ton (sh.)	12.19	139.73	1,703,308,700	12.62	1,763,392,600
Wheat	Bu.	1.035	1,710.7	1,770,574,500	.600	1,026,420,000
Oats	Bu.	.426	2,388	1,017,288,000	.315	752,220,000
Potatoes (Wh)	Bu.	1.288	677.2	872,233,600	.890	602,708,000
Sugar	Lb.	.038	13,028	495,064,000	.033	429,924,000
Barley	Bu.	.544	582.2	316,716,800	.389	226,475,800
Tobacco	Lb.	.183	3,181	582,123,000	.128	407,168,000
Flaxseed	Bu.	2.843	37.6	106,896,800	1.398	52,564,800
Rye	Bu.	.849	80.79	68,590,710	.384	31,023,360
Rice	Bu.	.995	84.46	84,037,700	.773	65,287,580
				$12,828,645,810		$ 9,673,529,140

$$\frac{\Sigma(q_0 + q_1)p_1}{\Sigma(q_0 + q_1)p_0} = \frac{\$ 9,673,529,140}{\$12,828,645,810}$$

= 75.4 (index for 1930 on 1929 base, in percentage form)

wholesale prices, the choice of formulas is more restricted. The Paasche, the ideal, and the Edgeworth-Marshall formulas are virtually ruled out, because "given-period" quantity data (i.e., data for the current month or year) are not available for the range of commodities represented by the price quotations used. The formula usually employed in such work is that of Laspeyres, in which base period weights are used, or a modification of Laspeyres employing fixed weights drawn from a year, or other period, other than the base period. The formula for this type of weighted aggregative may be written

$$\frac{\Sigma p_1 q_a}{\Sigma p_0 q_a} \qquad (13.16)$$

where the q_a's represent quantities for the year, or period, "a", which is not the base period. In making its current wholesale price index the Bureau of Labor Statistics uses weights for 1947 (a census year), while the base of the published indexes is the average of 1947, 1948, and 1949. The weighted aggregative represented by the formula cited above is the most generally useful type for a continuing series of index numbers.

A third and very satisfactory index type for a continuing series is the geometric mean of price relatives, weighted by constant-value weights which may or may not come from the base year. The general formula for the logarithm of such a weighted geometric mean is

$$\text{Log } M_g = \frac{\Sigma(\log p_1/p_0)\, p_a q_a}{\Sigma p_a q_a} \qquad (13.17)$$

where p_a and q_a represent the prices and quantities of individual commodities for either the base period or some other period. They must, of course, be constant. The geometric mean is a logical average, when ratios or relative prices are being combined. With fixed weights it is a flexible measure; the base may be shifted at will for it meets the circular test. It does not meet the time or factor reversal tests. If sampling error is a consideration, one must note that the geometric mean is more stable than the ideal, the Laspeyres, or the Paasche indexes. However, since samples of commodities to be used in the construction of index numbers are practically never "probability samples" (i.e., they are not selected by random sampling procedures[4]), this is not a controlling factor.

Changes in Regimen and the Comparison of Price Levels

In the opening pages of this chapter the fact was noted that the degree of dispersion found in frequency distributions of price relatives generally increases with the length of time covered in price comparisons. (Great economic disturbances such as those brought by war may, of course, cause wide dispersion over a short period.) Hence, on statistical grounds, there is justification for the conclusion that the accuracy of well-constructed price indexes is high for measurements extending over a short interval, and becomes progressively lower as the range of time comparison increases. This conclusion now calls for further consideration.

In Laspeyres' formula

$$L = \frac{\Sigma p_1 q_0}{\Sigma p_0 q_0}$$

the price factor alone varies, as between numerator and denominator. The weighting factor q_0 is assumed to relate to a system marked by complete constancy of consumption habits, living

[4] See Chapter 19.

standards, production coefficients, income distribution, and all other nonprice attributes of the economy. This environment, or milieu, for which Sir George Knibbs has used the term "regimen," is taken to be common to the two periods compared. Although the weights we employ may be merely quantities entering into trade, or quantities consumed, they have, in fact, much wider significance. They are assumed to define, directly or indirectly, all the attributes, other than price, of the economic system that prevails at a stated time. If these attributes are held constant as between the two periods compared, then we may expect to measure with accuracy the one factor that does change—the prices of economic goods. The condition we have here assumed is the orthodox one of *ceteris paribus*, the condition that factors other than the one subject to study remain unchanged.

In fact, of course, the regimen does not remain fixed. Changes in tastes and in consumption habits occur; changes in types of goods used as capital equipment take place; incomes shift, and the flow of goods is altered by changes in the distribution of buying power among consuming groups; the very price changes that we seek to measure bring alterations in the demand for given types of goods and in the quantities produced. Of no small moment in the total situation are the changes that occur in the quality of goods that continue to pass by the same trade names. The automobile of 1955 is the same commodity, by name, as the automobile of 1910, but to the average consumer the later model represents quite a different bundle of utilities. Similarly, steel, textiles, locomotives, even the staple articles of diet have undergone important quality changes. A comparison of price levels in 1910 and 1955 that depends for its accuracy on the assumption that all elements of economic life except prices have remained constant is suspect, indeed.

Our difficulties are not removed if we take as the standard of reference the regimen of the second of the two periods compared. This is done in Paasche's formula,

$$P = \frac{\Sigma p_1 q_1}{\Sigma p_0 q_1}$$

The system of consumption standards and all that goes with it may be of modern vintage in this case, but the differences between the regimens of the two periods compared is just as wide. We have not, in fact, held constant nonprice factors, and our measurement of price changes loses in accuracy, as a result.

The method exemplified by the ideal formula, that of employing weighting factors drawn from both periods, represents one attempt at the solution of this problem, but it is far from perfect. The use of quantities drawn from the two regimens does not create a common regimen, the indispensable condition of full accuracy in such comparisons.

The practical procedure in the face of this difficulty is to restrict our comparisons, if high accuracy is required, to periods not widely different in regimen. This will ordinarily mean periods not widely separated in time. Consumption habits, living standards, and technical production methods will be not widely dissimilar in two such periods, and hence the number of identical commodities common to the two periods will be large. Under these conditions considerable confidence may be placed in index numbers measuring average price changes. Comparison of price levels over longer periods may be desired, and may be justified, but the margin of error in the measurements may be expected to increase as the time span extends. Formal precision in weighting and in the selection of acceptable formulas will not provide an escape from the unavoidable difficulties arising out of alterations in the basic conditions of economic life. Real continuity of indexes covering a stretch of years is possible only on the basis of a persisting common regimen.

The regimen changes that come during a short period marked by transition from peace to war, or from war to peace, may be as great as those that come during long periods of peacetime existence, and the same difficulties are faced in measuring price-level changes. Thus all the reservations that attach to the comparison of price levels in years far apart in time attach to comparisons of peacetime and wartime price levels.

The fundamental consideration here is, of course, the magnitude of regimen differences between two stated periods. As an index of this magnitude Mudgett has proposed the quantity D, defined as

$$D = L - P \qquad (13.18)$$

That is, D is the difference between Laspeyres and Paasche indexes. If the regimen defined by the q_0's is very close to that defined by the q_1's, the two indexes will be close together; with widely different regimens the two will be far apart. There is no absolute criterion of "closeness," but the quantity D, considered with reference to the precision desired in a given comparison, gives a basis for accepting or rejecting a given measure. Thus for the Laspeyres and Paasche indexes of farm crop prices for 1945 (on the 1929 base) given in Table 13-15, we have

$$D = 142.3 - 143.3 = -1.0$$

This difference amounts to less than 1 percent. The error attributable to regimen change may be regarded as not serious if an error margin of 1 percent in the desired index is tolerable.

When a continuing series of monthly or annual index numbers is to be made, the problems posed by regimen changes are perplexing. They are, indeed, not open to any completely satisfactory solution. The procedure commonly employed in the face of these difficulties is to construct a series of indexes on a fixed base, with constant weights, but to change the weight base frequently. Thus it is the present intention of the Bureau of Labor Statistics to change the weight base of its wholesale price index every five years, with minor interim adjustments for individual commodities. This device, it is believed, will prevent the constant weights from becoming badly in error.

Chain indexes. The merits of an alternative method, involving the chaining of link relatives, has been very strongly urged by Bruce D. Mudgett (Ref. 113). Link relatives P_{01}, P_{12}, P_{23}, etc., are constructed for successive periods not far apart in time, say for successive years. The comparison of price levels by means of a link relating to two such periods, close together in time and with similar regimens, will be accurate if such an index as the ideal is used. The successive links are then chained, by multiplication, in deriving measures of price change between nonconsecutive periods. Thus we should have

$$P_{02} = P_{01} \cdot P_{12}$$

$$P_{03} = P_{01} \cdot P_{12} \cdot P_{23} = P_{02} \cdot P_{23}$$

Unfortunately there is no clear criterion for choosing between fixed-base and chain indexes. The two methods will give different results in a comparison of nonsuccessive periods; since neither may be accepted as accurate we may not say that the divergence is a measure of the "error" in either index. The fixed-base method clears the gap between year 0 and year n in one jump, assuming an unchanging regimen. The chain method takes account of the regimens of all intervening years. It is argued that we may more effectively bridge a gap between widely dissimilar regimens by this device, allowing our final results to be affected by all the shifts in consumer habits, production coefficients, income levels, income distribution, etc., that have occurred in the years between. But there is no test of the validity of this argument. It is perhaps safe to rest on the fact that there is no accurate method of comparing price levels in periods marked by widely different regimens. Margins of error will be wide, in such comparisons, whatever method of measurement be employed.

The detailed discussion of procedures in the preceding pages has clearly shown that there are some definitely faulty formulas, obviously unsuited for use in the construction of index numbers serving ordinary purposes. Among the better formulas there are some differences in respect of liability to bias and character of data needed, and some variations in sampling reliability. The maker of index numbers will have these in mind in choosing a formula to employ under given conditions. A more important factor in his choice, however, will be the purpose to be served by the index number, the question it is designed to answer. A weighted aggregate of actual prices answers one question definitively. It gives, without equivocation, the aggregate cost of a fixed bill of goods at one period, in relation to the cost of the same bill of goods at another. A geometric mean of relative prices answers another question. It measures with accuracy the average *ratio* of the prices of given commodities at one period to corresponding prices at another period. Some questions (for example, that answered by an unweighted arithmetic average of relative prices) have little if any economic significance. It is because one or two main questions have bulked large in economic discussion that emphasis has been placed upon the finding of a "best" type of index number. Yet the terms "best" and "ideal" are unfortunate, for they imply that some absolute standard exists, with reference to which all formulas may be tested. No such absolute criterion may be applied to the diversity of research problems that call for the construction of index numbers. On the basis of his knowledge of the characteristics of different formulas, the discriminating investigator will choose technical methods adapted to his data and appropriate to his purposes.

Other Problems in the Construction of Index Numbers of Commodity Prices

The preceding section has dealt with the technical problems connected with the averaging of a given set of data in order to secure an index number of price variations. Of equal importance with problems of averaging and weighting are practical questions connected with the gathering of basic data. Since it is impossible to cover the universe of price quotations during a given period, recourse must be had to the method of sampling. In seeking to obtain a representative sample, primary importance attaches to the number of commodities and the character of the commodities to be used in making a given index number.

Commodities to be included. Here again we are confronted with a relation that has already been mentioned, the relation between methods and uses. Decision as to the number of commodities and the kinds of commodities to be included in a given case must rest upon the purpose for which the index is to be constructed. In general, of course, a large sample is better than a small one. The frequency polygon based upon price relatives derived from a large sample will approach more closely to the curve that would represent the universe of price relatives than will that based upon a small sample. Thus, as a measure of general movements of wholesale prices, more confidence may be placed in the present Bureau of Labor Statistics index, which is based on some 2,000 commodity series, than on the Bureau's earlier index, which was based on about 900 price series. A large sample is particularly desirable when group index numbers are to be constructed for small subdivisions of the price universe. Yet index numbers based upon a small number of well-selected quotations must not be ruled out as without value. They can provide at modest expense good approximations to the results that large samples will give for the broad movements of prices. Moreover, for certain special purposes index numbers based upon a limited number of quotations may be preferable. This is particularly true when a "sensitive" index is desired, one that will serve as a forecaster of general price movements rather than as a precise measure of changes in the general price level. Of this type was the Harvard sensitive price index based upon quotations on 13 basic commodities (raw materials). The purposes of such an index are served by the selection of a limited number of commodities the prices of which are subject to extreme fluctuations, rather than by the inclusion of a great many commodities. As a contemporary measure of the same sort we may cite the Bureau of Labor Statistics daily index of spot market prices that includes 22 series. Yet the uses to which an index of this type may be put are limited. The "sluggishness" of the many-commodities index number is a sluggishness which inheres in the price system, and which must be reflected in a faithful index of general prices.

The question of the number of commodities to be included cannot be discussed apart from that of the character of these commodities. The representative character of an index number rests in part upon the number of price series included, but the nature of these series is of even greater importance. For there are highly significant differences in the behavior of the prices of different commodity groups. These groups of prices, their inter-relations, their behavior, their relation to the functioning of the economic system and to the swings of prosperity and depression, are matters of immediate and practical importance to economists and business men.

Since an index number of wholesale prices must rest upon sample quotations, the sample must be representative, must include commodities whose prices are typical of the various elements in the price system. The division into elements for this purpose may be based upon the character of the price changes peculiar to the different groups. Of the groups thus distinguished, the most obvious are those representing different industries. Textile prices and steel prices, leather prices and the prices of chemicals are subject to different influences. Trade depressions and revivals do not affect all industries at the same time or in the same way, so that an index of wholesale prices must include quotations from all important industrial groups. If preponderant influence upon an index is exerted by the prices of products of certain industries, the index, by that much, loses its representative character.

But it is not sufficient that different industries be given appropriate representation in the sample. Differences in price behavior are related to differences of origin (e.g., farm and nonfarm products), to differences of ultimate use (e.g., for capital equipment and for human consumption), to differences in durability, and to differences in the controllability of supply, particularly over short periods. Producer goods differ in their price movements from consumer goods (the latter being goods—raw or fabricated—that are ready for use by final consumers). Fundamental, too are differences in price behavior that are related to differences in degree of fabrication. All these classifications (and others not mentioned) cut across one another, to reveal a universe of commodity prices that is highly heterogeneous in its patterns of price behavior. A thoroughly representative index of wholesale prices should be based, therefore, upon price quotations drawn from these various commodity groups, with weight given to each in proportion to the relative importance in trade of the commodities in each category. The coverage of an index serving a special purpose would, of course, be restricted to groups and to commodities specified with reference to the purpose to be served.

The comparison base. Continuing series of index numbers, of the type represented by the various national indexes of price and living cost monthly or annual measures, are generally published as relatives with reference to some selected year or combination of years as base. The present consensus of opinion is that such a base period should not be too remote in time. Because of regimen change, and of price dispersion that generally increases with time, the margins of error in price comparisons grow as the time period increases. A corollary to this conclusion is that bases should be frequently changed. To hold to a base some 40 years removed in time, as is done in the construction of prices received and paid by farmers (now on the 1910-14 base), intensifies the difficulties of accurate measurement. There is, of course, no stated period at the end of which a base should be changed. International and domestic developments affecting the economic regimen, the availability of new weights, and similar considerations will affect such decisions.

In the practical task of selecting a base period some attention is paid to the state of business during periods that might be chosen. If the base of comparison and the weight base should be a period marked by conditions widely different from those usually prevalent, the accuracy of comparisons with preceding or subsequent periods would be reduced. This is not to say that we should seek as base a period that is to be regarded as "normal." The essence of economic life in modern industrial economies is change. No period provides a standard of normality, with reference to which conditions in subsequent periods may be appraised. In selecting a base for a continuing series of indexes, the index-number maker looks for a period in which conditions are not exceptionally disturbed, but he does not consider that the base serves in any sense as a criterion of what is normal. This statement applies with particular force to relations among commodity prices. These are in constant flux—as they must be in a dynamic world.

A comment may be made on the desirability of standardizing base periods. Numerous index numbers, relating to diverse processes, are now elements of the economic intelligence system of the United States, and of the system of world intelligence that is being slowly developed. When these various indexes are constructed on varying bases they are much less useful than they might be. A definite forward step has been taken in the United States by the Office of Statistical Standards in recommending that the average of 1947, 1948, and 1949 be employed as a standard base period for index numbers constructed by governmental agencies. This is an important beginning in the task of developing a comprehensive battery of comparable measurements covering major economic processes in the United States.

In the preceding pages we have dealt with the general problems that arise in the making of index numbers. In referring to practice we have been concerned primarily with wholesale prices. We now turn briefly to the problems faced in two special fields.[5]

Index Numbers of Consumer Prices

In the literature of index numbers considerable attention is given to the measurement of changes in the cost of living. The term "cost of living" has been an ambiguous one, and remains ambiguous in much current usage. In its most precise sense it involves the determination of the changing money costs of commodity incomes that yield equal real incomes (i.e., satisfactions) at different times or in different places. The ratio of the aggregate money costs, in two situations, of chosen combinations of consumer goods that yield identical aggregate satisfactions would be the desired index of

[5] We do not give here detailed descriptions of methods employed in the construction of particular index numbers. These may be had from the agencies concerned. In the United States the Bureau of Labor Statistics constructs index numbers of wholesale prices and of consumer prices. The Agricultural Marketing Service of the Department of Agriculture constructs index numbers of prices received and paid by farmers, the parity index, and the derived parity ratio. The United Nations' *Monthly Bulletin of Statistics* gives the names of agencies making the chief index numbers of other countries.

living costs in these two situations. (The composition of the market basket of consumer goods may vary, provided only that different combinations yield equivalent satisfactions.) The conditions necessary to perfect accuracy in measuring changes in living costs so defined (conditions that include identical and unchanging want structures, or taste patterns, among all the consumers to whom the measure is to apply) are extraordinarily difficult of attainment. No "true" index of living costs is currently constructed.[6] Contemporary measures that go by that name may be more appropriately regarded as index numbers of prices paid by consumers.

This change in title has, indeed, been made by the U. S. Bureau of Labor Statistics. The full and revealing title of its "Consumer Price Index" is "Index of Changes in Prices of Goods and Services Purchased by City Wage-Earner and Clerical-Worker Families to Maintain their Level of Living."

The customary problems of index-number making are faced in constructing the consumer price index. Price changes must relate to a stated regimen (or to an average of regimens). This regimen is usually defined by weights based upon the expenditures of a representative sample of consumers in a stated period. For the present United States index the weights were derived from a comprehensive survey of consumer expenditures for food, clothing, furniture, and all other goods and services. This survey, made in 1950, included samples of families from the 12 largest urban areas and from a considerable sample of other cities. The "index market basket" as thus established for 1950 was modified to take account of changes occurring between 1950 and fiscal 1951-52, the latter year being the weight base now employed.

The regimen that is assumed to be constant, therefore, is that of the fiscal year 1951-1952. However, the base of comparison is the average of the years 1947-1949. The published index defines the level of consumer prices in given months or years with reference to the average for 1947, 1948, and 1949 as 100. The regimen is represented by a sample of 296 commodities and services. This

---

[6] However, we must note that precision in the measurement of changes in consumer prices has been materially advanced by the explorations of relevant theory. For a lucid discussion of the principles involved see R. Frisch, "Some Basic Principles of Price of Living Measurements," *Econometrica*, Vol. 22, No. 4 (October 1954). The basic theory of cost of living indexes, with an appraisal of the pioneer work of Konus, and of later studies by Staehle, Frisch, Haberler, Wald, Hicks, Allen, and others, is clearly set forth by Ulmer (Ref. 164).

market basket of goods bought by consumers in 1951-52 is assumed to remain the same in quantity and quality. The specifications of individual items are spelled out with precision. Prices for these goods, collected in 46 cities, provide the basic materials for the current index.

The general division of weights in this Consumer Price Index is of interest as an indication of the character of consumer budgets in the United States in the middle of the twentieth century.

Category	Relative importance (percentage)
Food	30
Housing (incl. heat, light, etc.)	32
Apparel	10
Transportation	11
Medical care	5
Personal care	2
Reading and recreation	5
Other goods and services	5
All items	100

We should note that these weights represent national averages. In the detailed work use is made of a set of weights for each of the 46 cities included. The weights for a given city are based on consumer expenditures in that city and in similar cities which it may be taken to represent. In combining measures for separate cities, each city is given a weight proportionate to the wage-earner and clerical-worker population it represents. Worker population weights and family expenditure weights are thus combined in the derivation of the national indexes.

In the construction of the Consumer Price Index the first step is the calculation of an index for the current month (or year) on the preceding month (or year) as base. The formula employed, which utilizes weighted arithmetic averages of relative prices, is equivalent to a modified Laspeyres of the form

$$I_{(i-1)i} = \frac{\Sigma p_i q_a}{\Sigma p_{(i-1)} q_a}$$

where p_i is the price of a given commodity for the current month (or year), $p_{(i-1)}$ is the price of that commodity for the preceding month (or year), and q_a is a quantity weight based on 1951-52 family expenditure patterns. $I_{(i-1)i}$ is a symbol for the price index for period i on the preceding period, $i - 1$, as base. The second step is the shift to the fixed base 1947-49, which we designate period 0. For this operation we have

$$I_{0i} = I_{0(i-1)} \cdot I_{(i-1)i}$$

where I_{0i} is the desired index for period i on period 0 as base, and $I_{0(i-1)}$ is the index for period $i - 1$ (the "preceding period") on the period 0 as base.

The practical difficulties faced in constructing wholesale price indexes are multiplied in the making of consumer price indexes. Regimen changes in a dynamic economy tend to make weight structures out-dated, if not obsolete. Variations in commodity standards, in business practice, and in local customs intensify the problem of obtaining accurate and representative price quotations on goods that may be regarded as unchanging in their specifications. To these working difficulties have now been added responsibilities for administering an instrument on which wage adjustments affecting millions of workers are currently based, and on which important national policy determinations are made. The burden on the Bureau of Labor Statistics is not a light one.

Farm Prices and the Parity Index

A distinctive and important set of special purpose index numbers has been developed in the field of agricultural economics. These measures are of particular interest because since 1933, when the Agricultural Adjustment Act was passed, they have served as instruments of national policy in agriculture. Their current construction and use are determined in part by Congressional action.

This set of indexes is designed to define variations in the terms of exchange of farm producers. They include an index of prices received by farmers for the goods they sell, indexes of prices paid by farmers for items used in family living and in production, and a *parity index* based upon the indexes of prices paid plus interest on indebtedness secured by farm mortgages, taxes on farm real estate, and wages paid to hired farm labor. From the index of prices received and the parity index is derived the *parity ratio*, which serves as a measure of changes in the average purchasing power of farm products.

The index of prices received by farmers is a monthly measure, based upon the prices of about 50 farm products. Prices quoted are those received at points of first sale—local markets or other centers to which farmers deliver their products. Average prices for all grades and qualities are used, without the specifications that define grades in wholesale trade proper. These farm prices, therefore, are not to be identified with the wholesale prices in the great exchanges or in large cities for goods of specified grades that enter into the measures of the Bureau of Labor Statistics. The index is of the weighted aggregative type, with minor modifications to permit changes in weights and in number of commodities included. Weights are based on average quantities marketed; for the current index weights are drawn from the period 1937-1941. The base of the index is the average of the five years January, 1910–December, 1914. Group index numbers are published for crops and for livestock and livestock products, and for 13 smaller subdivisions.

The other member of the exchange or parity ratio for farmers is the composite measure now termed the parity index. Of the three components of the parity index the most important (weight about 44 percent of the total in 1953) is the index of prices paid for items used in family living. This covers prices paid by farmers throughout the nation for consumers' goods. Precise specifications are not defined for these goods; the prices quoted are for the qualities being currently purchased by farmers. The number of price series included was 194 in 1953. Reports are made through mail questionnaires by several thousand retail merchants, both chain store and independent. Weights are based on estimates of the amounts of the various goods and services purchased by farm families. The formula, like that used for the index of prices received, is of the weighted aggregative type. The index base is January, 1910–December, 1914.

The second component of the parity index, with a weight of about 37 percent of the total in 1953, is the index of prices paid for commodities used in farm production. The price series included number 192 (of which 42 are duplicates of series used in the family living index). These series are for such items as feed, seed, livestock, motor vehicles and supplies, fertilizer, and farm machinery. Source of quotations, weight base, index base, and formula are the same as for the index for family living. Both indexes are supplemented by detailed subgroup measures.

With these two indexes of prices paid are combined measures of changes in interest rates, taxes, and wages paid by farmers, to yield the parity index defining changes in the total cost to farmers of the commodities and services they buy. These last three elements taken together accounted in 1953 for about 19 percent of the total parity index. For any month or year the ratio of the index of prices received by farmers to the parity index defines the parity ratio for that period. This ratio is a measure of shifts in the terms of exchange of farmers with the rest of the economy, with reference to the terms prevailing during a base period extending from January, 1910, to December, 1914.

These various measures are given in Table 13-17 for the base period and recent years. As has been indicated, the parity ratio may be thought of as a measure of the purchasing power of an average unit of farm products. In 1953 farmers were receiving, for such an average unit, 158 percent more in current dollars than they were in 1910-14; however, the measures defining changes in the average costs to farmers of goods and services purchased (column

TABLE 13–17

Prices Received and Paid by Farmers, the Parity Index and the Parity Ratio
Selected Years, 1910-1914 to 1954

(1) Year	(2) Prices received by farmers	(3) Prices paid for items used in Family living	(4) Prices paid for items used in Production	(5) Parity index (prices paid, interest, taxes, and wage rates)	(6) Parity ratio (2) ÷ (5)
1910–1914	100	100	100	100	100
1939	95	120	121	123	77
1940	100	121	123	124	81
1941	123	130	130	133	92
1942	158	149	148	152	104
1943	192*	166	164	171	112
1944	196*	175	173	182	108
1945	206*	182	176	190	108
1946	234*	202	191	208	112
1947	275	237	224	240	115
1948	285	251	250	260	110
1949	249	243	238	251	99
1950	256	246	246	256	100
1951	302	268	273	282	107
1952	288	271	274	287	100
1953	258	270	253	279	92
1954	250	274	252	281	89

* Includes certain wartime subsidy payments to farmers.

5), indicate an advance of 179 percent in such costs. The index measuring changes in the real worth, or purchasing power, of an average unit of farm products had fallen from 100, in the base period, to 92 (the ratio of 258 to 279) in 1953—a decline of 8 percent from the "parity" level.

The parity index (column (5) of Table 13-17) is of key importance in the price support program for agricultural products. It is used not only in the derivation of the general parity ratio that has been cited. The parity price of a specific commodity for a given period is obtained by multiplying the base-period price of that commodity by the parity index for the period in question.[7] This parity price provides the basis on which price support levels are determined for that commodity.

The battery of measures relating to prices paid and prices received by farmers are revealing measures of economic change, notable as the products of the most comprehensive attempt ever made to define shifts in the buying and selling relations of a single major group of producers. In this brief summary we have traced certain of the distinctive features of these index numbers. We have noted that the prices received are not prices quoted in the great wholesale centers, but prices realized in first sales by producers. Since they are averages of qualities and grades, and not quotations on commodities of unvarying specifications, their movements may reflect shifts in the average quality of products marketed, as well as price changes proper. This last comment applies with special force to the index of prices paid by farmers. No fixed specifications are set forth here. The prices reported are those for qualities being currently purchased by farmers; if these qualities go up, the movement of the reported price will reflect the improvement in average quality of goods purchased. Thus the index of prices paid for family living, which is in a sense a "cost of living" index for farmers, differs from the consumer price index of the Bureau of Labor Statistics, which uses fixed specifications. The parity index and the consumer price index cover different universes, by different methods.

The period covered by farm price indexes exceeds 40 years—a long stretch of time, for accurate comparison in a dynamic economy. On technical and logical grounds the statistician could wish

---

[7] This statement refers to the so-called "old formula." A "new formula," providing for the use of a moving base period (the ten preceding years) has been written into law.

that a later base of comparison were employed (the 1910-14 base is set, of course, by law). However, the use for recent years of the 1937-41 weight-base (which is soon to be adjusted to take account of postwar patterns of living and production) serves, at least, to introduce comparatively modern weights, and thus sharpens the measures of recent shifts in the farmer's terms of exchange.

Price Index Numbers as Instruments of "Deflation"

Index numbers of prices are used frequently to reduce a monetary series to "real" terms. In one form, this is a process of deflating a series of values expressed in current dollars (or other monetary units). The purpose is to obtain an adjusted series that has been corrected for changes in the worth of the monetary unit. This adjusted series is said to be in "constant dollars," or in dollars of constant purchasing power. The rather loose terminology and practice in this field cover problems of three distinct, although related, types.

Measurement of Shifts in the Terms of Exchange. The measurement of these shifts, which have been spoken of earlier, is not usually thought of as involving deflation, but it is useful to view this as a phase of a broader procedure. In simple terms, we may consider the prices p_a and p_b of Commodities A and B in years 0 and 1:

		Price in	
		Year 0	Year 1
p_a	Actual	$1.00	$1.20
	Rel.	100	120
p_b	Actual	.50	.30
	Rel.	100	60
p_a/p_b		100	200

From the absolute price it is clear that in Year 0, 100 units of Commodity A would exchange for 200 units of Commodity B; in Year 1, 100 units of Commodity A would exchange for 400 units of Commodity B. The terms of exchange had moved in favor of the producers of Commodity A. The shift in these terms is defined by the ratio of the price relatives, which has advanced from 100 to 200.

In general terms we may think of such a relation as the ratio of average unit prices received to average unit prices paid—that is,

P_r/P_p. An increase in this ratio means improvement for the producers represented by P_r. If P_r should be the hourly wage rate for manufacturing workers and P_p the Consumer Price Index, the ratio becomes a measure of changes in "real" hourly wages. If P_r is an index of prices received by farmers and P_p an index of the prices of all goods and services bought by them, the ratio is a measure of the per-unit worth of farm products in terms of goods purchased by farmers—the familiar "parity ratio" previously discussed. If P_r is an index of export prices and P_p an index of prices of goods imported, the ratio P_r/P_p measures changes in the per-unit worth of exports in terms of goods imported. The comparison as thus expressed is always in unit terms (i.e., it measures shifts in purchasing power *per unit* of goods given in exchange). It has significance to the extent that the two index numbers accurately define prices of goods or services that are in fact exchanged. In an exchange system a ratio of this sort has significance, of course, for every individual and every group in the economy, and for every national economy that has dealings with other economies.

Measurement of Changes in Aggregate Purchasing Power. By a simple extension, the measurement of changes in purchasing power may be shifted from a unit to an aggregative basis. If instead of unit prices received we have a series of disposable value aggregates, the aggregate purchasing power of these totals may be derived by deflating the sums by appropriate index numbers of prices paid. If we represent by V_d a disposable value aggregate, by P_p an index of average unit prices paid by those who disburse V_d, and by Q_c the aggregate worth of V_d in terms of goods commanded, the process is given by

$$Q_c = \frac{V_d}{P_p}$$

Numerous examples of this kind of deflation could be cited. If we divide changes in the total wages received by manufacturing workers in given years by appropriate index numbers of consumer prices we have measures of changes in the aggregate real income of these workers. Changes in the real income of farmers may be similarly derived. The essence of this type of deflation is, of course, the division of the value aggregates, or of relatives based thereon, by a price index of the goods and services for which the sums are actually spent.

Conversion of Dollar Sums into Physical Volume Equivalents.
This is the most familiar form of deflation. We may have a series
of annual values of building construction and wish to estimate the
changes in the physical volume of building. Or we may have Gross
National Product for a series of years, in current dollars, and wish
to reduce these sums to terms of constant dollars. Here it is not
the "quantities commanded" by a series of value aggregates but
the physical volume equivalents of these value aggregates that we
wish to estimate. We should like to eliminate the effects of price
changes on these value aggregates, in order to reveal the undis-
torted quantity changes. The heart of this problem lies, again, in
the correct choice of the price index to be used as deflator.

If we are dealing with value aggregates for two years only,
(i.e., if a binary comparison is involved) the best solution of the
problem is given by the ideal index. As we have seen, this index
meets the factor reversal test, i.e., price, quantity, and value index
numbers are mutually consistent. What this means with reference
to the present problem is that when we divide a value index
$\left(\dfrac{\Sigma p_1 q_1}{\Sigma p_0 q_0}\right)$ by a price index constructed from the ideal formula
$\sqrt{\dfrac{\Sigma p_1 q_0}{\Sigma p_0 q_0} \cdot \dfrac{\Sigma p_1 q_1}{\Sigma p_0 q_1}}$, we derive a quantity index constructed by the ideal
formula, $\sqrt{\dfrac{\Sigma q_1 p_0}{\Sigma q_0 p_0} \cdot \dfrac{\Sigma q_1 p_1}{\Sigma q_0 p_1}}$. That is, the derived quantity index has
been weighted by prices representing the regimens of both base
and given years.

Deflation of a value index by a Laspeyres price index (i.e.,
division of $\dfrac{\Sigma p_1 q_1}{\Sigma p_0 q_0}$ by $\dfrac{\Sigma p_1 q_0}{\Sigma p_0 q_0}$) yields a quantity index with price
weights drawn from the second of the two years compared—i.e., a
quantity index constructed by Paasche's formula, $\dfrac{\Sigma q_1 p_1}{\Sigma q_0 p_1}$. Thus, in
effect, this type of deflation shifts the regimen, as we pass from
price to quantity comparisons, from the base year to the given year.
Similarly, deflation of a value index by a Paasche price index (i.e.,
division of $\dfrac{\Sigma p_1 q_1}{\Sigma p_0 q_0}$ by $\dfrac{\Sigma p_1 q_1}{\Sigma p_0 q_1}$) yields a quantity index with price
weights drawn from the base year—i.e., a quantity index con-
structed from Laspeyres' formula, $\dfrac{\Sigma q_1 p_0}{\Sigma q_0 p_0}$. If we are deflating a value

series covering a number of years, and wish to derive quantity indexes that are really weighted by constant base year prices, price indexes with quantity weights drawn from successive "given" years (i.e., Paasche indexes) should be the deflators.[8] This is not a practicable procedure. The usual process is to deflate by a Laspeyres price index, which has the effect indicated above, or by a modified Laspeyres, with q_a weights. The result is a somewhat hybrid type of quantity index, affected by the regimens of base year, given year, and the year a which is the weight base. We face here again, therefore, the difficulties that arise from regimen changes. If these are moderate, the particular manner in which the deflator is weighted does not greatly matter. If regimen changes have been great over the period covered, deflation is inevitably a less accurate process. In general, short-period comparisons of deflated value series will be more accurate than comparisons covering longer periods of time.

We must recognize, of course, that no factoring process of the sort described in the preceding paragraphs actually gives us measures of the quantity changes that would have occurred had there been no price movements. No algebraic manipulation can offset the results of the infinitely complex economic changes that occur over even the shortest period of time. But approximations serve useful purposes, and in such approximations mathematical consistency is desirable. More important than the choice of formula, in such deflation procedures, is the selection of appropriate price quotations in making the deflating index. The commodities and services represented should be those that enter into the value aggregate that is to be deflated. (Here, of course, the situation is quite different from that faced when we are concerned with purchasing power and seek to measure quantity commanded.) Deflation by inappropriate price indexes is one of the commonest sins of economic practice.

The most ambitious task of deflation economists have attempted has been that of reducing national income or national product

---

[8] We may express the conclusions of the preceding argument in a slightly different form. Price and quantity indexes that are mutually consistent, in that their product is equal to the value index, may be constructed by means of Laspeyres and Paasche formulas if the Laspeyres formula is used for one index and the Paasche formula for the other. Thus a base-year weighted Laspeyres price index multiplied by a given-year weighted Paasche quantity index will equal the true value index. The same would be true of a Paasche price index and a Laspeyres quantity index.

estimates, in current dollars, to terms of "constant" dollars. The usual procedure here is deflation in detail, rather than deflation of the grand totals by a single process of division. Deflation in detail involves the construction of deflators for separate components, each deflator being tailored to the task of correcting for price changes in a small segment of the total economy.[9]

An example of the process of deflation. The *Engineering News Record* compiles statistics on heavy engineering contracts awarded in the United States, by months and years. These cover large buildings (industrial, commercial, and public) and other heavy construction projects—highways, waterworks, bridges, etc. For the purpose of reducing the dollar totals for these projects to physical-volume equivalents, an index of building costs and an index of

TABLE 13–18

Actual and Deflated Values of Building Contracts Awarded, 1939-1953

(1)	(2)	(3)	(4)	(5)
Year	Total value of building contracts awarded		Index of building costs†	Index of building volume
	Actual* (in millions of dollars)	Relative		(3) ÷ (4)
1939	1,264	100.0	100.0	100.0
1940	2,190	173.3	102.7	168.7
1941	3,768	298.1	107.1	278.3
1942	6,170	488.1	112.6	433.5
1943	1,817	143.7	115.9	124.0
1944	972	76.9	118.9	64.7
1945	1,485	117.5	121.1	97.0
1946	3,373	266.9	132.8	201.0
1947	3,375	267.0	158.5	168.5
1948	4,145	327.9	174.5	187.9
1949	5,092	402.8	178.2	226.0
1950	9,529	753.9	190.2	396.4
1951	9,457	748.2	202.9	368.8
1952	11,466	907.1	210.5	430.9
1953	9,911	784.1	218.2	359.3

* Contracts for large buildings only are here included. Value minima are given in the *Engineering News Record.* I am indebted to the *Engineering News Record* for the basic data.

† Components of the building cost index include structural steel shapes, Portland cement, lumber, and skilled labor, with appropriate weights.

[9] For details of the work done by the National Income Unit of the U. S. Department of Commerce in deflating Gross National Product see the latest National Income supplement to the *Survey of Current Business.*

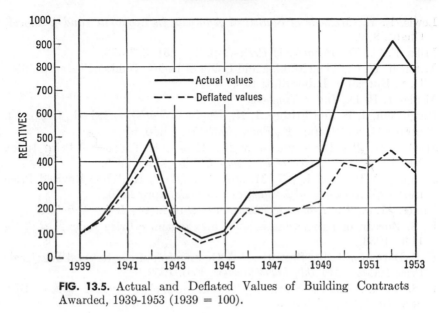

FIG. 13.5. Actual and Deflated Values of Building Contracts Awarded, 1939-1953 (1939 = 100).

construction costs (applicable to nonbuilding projects) have been developed. For the present example we give in Table 13-18 the total value of building contracts awarded in recent years, the index of building costs, and the deflated series that serves as an index of the physical volume of heavy building construction, of the types noted above. Actual and deflated values are shown graphically in Fig. 13.5. Over the 15-year period here covered building costs, as measured by the sample of commodities and services included in the cost index, more than doubled. The appropriate adjustments in obtaining the index of building volume substantially modify the record of contracts awarded, as first given in current dollars.

REFERENCES

Allen, R. G. D., *Statistics for Economists*, Chap. 6.
Croxton, F. E. and Cowden, D. J., *Applied General Statistics*, Chaps. 20, 21.
Fisher, Irving, *The Making of Index Numbers*.
Frisch, R., "Annual Survey of Economic Theory: The Problem of Index Numbers," *Econometrica*, Jan. 1936.
Frisch, R., "Some Basic Principles of Price of Living Measurements," *Econometrica*, Oct. 1954.
Konus, A. A., "The Problem of the True Index of the Cost of Living," *Econometrica*, Jan. 1939.

Lewis, E. E., *Methods of Statistical Analysis in Economics and Business*, Chaps. 8, 9.

Mills, F. C., *The Behavior of Prices*, pp. 219-251, 323-355.

Mitchell, W. C., "The Making and Using of Index Numbers," *Bulletin* 656, U. S. Bureau of Labor Statistics.

Mudgett, B. D., *Index Numbers*.

Riggleman, J. R. and Frisbee, I. N., *Business Statistics*, 3rd ed., Chap. 13.

Simpson, G. and Kafka, F., *Basic Statistics*, Chap. 9.

Staehle, H., "A Development of the Economic Theory of Price Index Numbers," *The Review of Economic Studies*, June 1935.

Stauber, B. R., Koffsky, N. M. and Randall, C. K., "The Revised Price Indexes," *Agricultural Economics Research*, April 1950.

Ulmer, M. J., *The Economic Theory of Cost of Living Index Numbers*.

U. S. Bureau of Labor Statistics, "The Consumer Price Index," *Bulletin* 1140, 1953.

U. S. Bureau of Labor Statistics, "A Description of the Revised Wholesale Price Index," *Monthly Labor Review*, Feb. 1952.

U. S. Bureau of Labor Statistics, "Techniques of Preparing Major BLS Statistical Series," *Bulletin 1168*, Dec. 1954, pp. 63-95.

Waugh, A. E., *Elements of Statistical Method*, 3rd ed., Chap. 14.

Yule, G. U. and Kendall, M. G., *An Introduction to the Theory of Statistics*, 14th ed., Chap. 25.

The publishers and the dates of publication of the books named in chapter reference lists are given in the bibliography at the end of this volume.

CHAPTER **14**

Index Numbers of Production and Productivity

The era between the two world wars, and the decade after World War II, witnessed an extraordinary expansion and refinement of what may be called instruments of economic intelligence. This was notably true in the United States, but this country was by no means alone in this development. The first world war revealed great gaps in our knowledge of economic processes. The information then available on the volume and character of production, production capacity, the size and distribution of national income, the volume and sources of savings, the disposable income of consumers, stocks of goods and their location, and on many other aspects of economic life was of the most fragmentary sort. A striking improvement began with the end of the war. The needs of government, of business, of the banking system, and of other economic elements during the prosperous 'twenties, the depressed 'thirties, the war-torn 'forties, and the cycle-conscious 'fifties stimulated recurrent impressive advances on the statistical front. Among the great gains of these years was the development in this and other countries of comprehensive and accurate indexes of output.

Advances in the measurement of production took place on two fronts. The measurement of total national product and of national income was designed to provide global figures covering all economic activity. These measures in their early form were solely in terms of current monetary units—dollars, pounds, or other. They were, for this country, dollar measures of the performance of the national economy. Concurrently with estimates of national product and income there were developed in the United States a series of index numbers designed to measure in *physical* terms the volume of production in specified fields, and the volume of trade. Here the statistician worked from the beginning with physical units, and sought to construct index numbers free of distortion by the price changes that affect national income and product accounts. These two lines of progress have since merged, to some extent, with the development of methods of deflating national product and some of its elements, correcting, that is, for the effects of price changes. But despite improvement in deflating procedures, index numbers of physical output continue to play major roles as economic indicators in a number of specific fields, notably in measuring industrial production on a monthly or quarterly basis. Our present concern is with the methods employed in the construction of such measures.

Notation. In addition to symbols previously employed (such as Q, Q_{01}, for physical volume indexes, P, P_{01} for price indexes), certain new symbols are introduced in this chapter:

F: a measure of factor input in a productive process

E: all human effort entering into a productive process

M: a measure of man-hours of labor input

N: number of workers employed in the productive process

P_r: a productivity ratio, or productivity index, of the form Q/F, Q/M, or Q/N

R: an index of factor requirements per unit of output; F/Q, M/Q, or N/Q

Q/E: a productivity index in which human effort is the factor input

Q/M: a productivity index measuring output per man-hour of labor input

(Q/E and Q/M may be identical, although the latter expression is sometimes more restrictive)

M/Q: an index of man-hour labor requirements per unit of output

Lower case letters such as q, m, and r may be used to represent output, man-hours of labor input, and labor requirements per unit of output in individual plants or industries or for individual commodities.

The meaning of production indexes. In deriving an index of production for a given sector of an economy the task is that of combining, in some form, a number of measures of output. When such measures are in value terms, as they are when estimates of the national product are built up, the task of combination is simple. All are in dollar units. But when the basic observations are in quantum terms, i.e., in pounds, gallons, bushels, yards, etc., such simple aggregation is impossible. Some common factor must be introduced before a meaningful combination may be effected. The need to introduce some other factor that may serve as a common denominator means that a production index is not a simple aggregate of physical volume data—a significant fact for the understanding of these measures.

It would be gratifying to the economist if the common denominator could be provided by the concept of "utility." If each unit of the diverse products included in a "quantum basket" were the equivalent of a definite number of units of "utility," the same for all consumers, these utility units could be aggregated readily, and movements of the volume of production measured with precision. A Laspeyres index constructed on this basis would be of the form

$$Q_{01} = \frac{\Sigma q_1 u_0}{\Sigma q_0 u_0} \qquad (14.1)$$

where u_0 represents the number of units of utility possessed by a physical unit of a given commodity in the base year. Unfortunately, this procedure is not open to us. "Utility" is an elusive quality of a consumer good. It varies from person to person and is inconstant even for a single consumer. We have no scales for converting physical units into utility equivalents. This means, among other things, that production indexes are not to be interpreted in welfare terms.

The denominators actually available for use in combining physical volume series are two in number—prices and labor time. If we multiply physical volume units by unit prices, we obtain dollar measures that may be combined in value aggregates and compared with similar aggregates for other periods. Alternatively, we may multiply physical volume units by the number of man-hours required for the production of each such unit. The product of each such operation is in man-hours; these man-hour measures may be combined in man-hour totals that may be compared with similar totals for other periods. When unit prices are used to provide the common value denominator, we are, in effect, defining the regimen of the period serving as weight base in terms of its price structure. When man-hours per unit are used to provide the common denominator, we are defining a regimen in terms of the unit labor requirements of the goods entering into the stream of production. In each case the institutions and circumstances of the time (i.e., of the time serving as weight base) place their impress on the production index.

We shall later consider means by which weights are selected and applied in the making of production indexes. The immediate purpose of the preceding discussion is to emphasize the fact that index numbers of physical output are not measures of purely physical change. We cannot abstract from the host of attendant circumstances that make up prevailing regimens. The significance of given output changes depends on the price structure or the structure of unit labor requirements, and each of these in turn reflects a complex economic regimen.

How then are we to regard index numbers of production? They are measures of the physical volume of work done in specified sectors of the economy, this work being measured in terms of quantum output but evaluated (or weighted) with reference to a given regimen, or to some combination of regimens. It is in the evaluation or weighting of the individual production series that we introduce the common denominator that permits aggregation.

It will be useful in the subsequent discussion to distinguish production indexes of four types. First we have *primary* measures, often called unadjusted index numbers. These parallel in construction and in meaning the index numbers of prices considered in the preceding chapter. Secondly, there are seasonally corrected monthly or quarterly measures. These are usually called *adjusted* indexes in the United States; the Statistical Office of the United Nations calls them secondary indexes. A third type, which may be called *trend-adjusted*, is modified by a correction for trend movements, as well as for seasonal fluctuations. As the name suggests, this type is used when the interest of the maker lies in cyclical movements of production or of trade volume. As a fourth type we may distinguish measures of physical output obtained by the deflation of output series originally expressed in value terms. These measures, to which we have referred on earlier pages, we may call *derived* indexes.

Primary Index Numbers of Production

The problems faced in constructing primary production index numbers are essentially the same as those that arise in the making of price indexes. A formula must be decided upon, weights chosen, the coverage of the sample determined, a weight base and a base of comparison selected. We deal briefly with each of these.

Choice of a Formula. For comparing the levels of production at two stated times (i.e., in a binary comparison), the chief formulas available are the Laspeyres, the Paasche, the ideal, the Edgeworth, and the modified Laspeyres (see Chapter 13). In constructing quantity indexes the p's and q's, as used in the price formulas are, of course, transposed. For the Laspeyres production index we have

$$Q_{01} = L = \frac{\Sigma q_1 p_0}{\Sigma q_0 p_0} \qquad (14.2)$$

The Paasche formula becomes

$$Q_{01} = P = \frac{\Sigma q_1 p_1}{\Sigma q_0 p_1} \qquad (14.3)$$

The other forms are correspondingly modified. This reversal of p's and q's means, as was pointed out above, that price weights are used to define a given regimen and to provide a common denominator. Thus the numerator of the Laspeyres formula (14.2) is the aggregate value of the physical amounts produced in time "1," when these physical amounts are multiplied by the unit prices prevailing in time "0." The denominator is the aggregate value of the physical amounts produced in time "0" when these physical amounts are multiplied by the unit prices prevailing in time "0." Numerator and denominator differ only because of *quantity* changes between the two periods.

The choice between formulas for such a binary comparison lies between those weighted with reference to the base-year regimen, to the given-year regimen, to a combination of the two, and to the regimen of a third, possibly intermediate, period. The ideal and the Edgeworth formulas, that combine base-year and given-year regimens, have strong claims, if the necessary data are to be had.

If the difference between base-year and given-year regimens, as measured by $D = L - P$, is slight, choice between the Laspeyres, the Paasche, and one of the combined forms is a matter of convenience. If the regimen difference is great, the hazard of comparison is considerable regardless of formula used.

It is often deemed desirable that a production index and a corresponding price index be consistent in yielding a product equal to a true index of value. The Statistical Office of the United Nations emphasizes this as a general property that a quantity index should possess, and Mudgett regards it as a requirement of first importance. This requirement is met, of course, if the ideal formula is used. It can be met, also, by altering the weight base. Thus if we derive Q_{01} from the Laspeyres formula $\frac{\Sigma q_1 p_0}{\Sigma q_0 p_0}$ and P_{01} from the Paasche formula $\frac{\Sigma p_1 q_1}{\Sigma p_0 q_1}$, their product will be $\frac{\Sigma p_1 q_1}{\Sigma p_0 q_0}$, or V_{01}. The same product will be obtained from a Paasche quantity index and a Laspeyres price index. In practice this requirement is not easy to meet when the given period is a very recent month or year, because of data deficiencies.

A production index may be constructed by weighting quantity data by unit labor requirements, instead of by unit prices. The Laspeyres formula for such an index is

$$Q_{01} = \frac{\Sigma q_1 r_0}{\Sigma q_0 r_0} \tag{14.4}$$

where the r_0 defines the man-hours of labor required, in the base period, to produce a unit of a given product. The numerator and denominator of the measure given above would be aggregates in man-hour terms; since the weighting factor, r_0, is fixed, the difference between numerator and denominator would be a measure of the change from time "0" to time "1" in physical quantities produced. There is much to be said on theoretical grounds for such a production index when the end purpose is the measurement of changes in productivity. However, our present information about unit labor requirements is so scanty that in practice little use can be made of this formula.

The preceding discussion has been concerned with binary comparisons involving production levels in only two periods. The choice of formulas and of weights is more restricted when the problem is that of constructing a series of index numbers designed to keep abreast of current changes. Here the choice really falls between the Laspeyres and a modified Laspeyres formula. The recommendation of the United Nations, which is seeking to standardize international practice, is that the base-weighted Laspeyres index be used for regular monthly or quarterly series of index numbers of industrial (i.e., nonagricultural) production. However, it is recognized that it may be necessary to use fixed weights from a year, or other period, different from the base of comparison of the published series. This alteration means that a modified Laspeyres index $(\Sigma q_1 p_a / \Sigma q_0 p_a)$ would be used. This is the formula currently used by the Board of Governors of the Federal Reserve System. For the FRB index the base of comparison is 1947-49, the weight base 1947. Whatever the base of the fixed weights may be, the conclusion reached in discussing price index numbers holds here also: Fixed base weights should be modified frequently—say every five or at most every ten years in peace times—if the regimen reflected by the weights is not to become seriously out-dated.

Nature of the Quantities and Prices Entering Into a Production Index. The selection of suitable "production" series and weights is a problem of central concern in the making of output indexes. The object is to measure *work done* in each of many farms, mines, factories or industries, to the end that a general index of work done over a given time period may be constructed. Although farms are mentioned here, our chief concern in the present discussion is with nonagricultural production.

Four possible measures may be cited. We may use volume of output as a measure of work done; we may use deliveries; we may use the input of basic materials; or we may use the input of labor time. Each of these has its weaknesses. A count of the numbers of cars produced or of new houses finished in a given month would be unaffected by changes in the amount of work in progress. Moreover where repairs represent a considerable element of current work done, as they would in the construction field, this factor would be left out of a count of new products completed. A record of deliveries of finished products has these same defects and is subject, as well, to inaccuracies due to changes in the stocks of finished goods held by makers. If we measure work done in terms of input of basic materials (as in taking consumption of raw cotton as an index of

total activity in the cotton textile industry) we are open to error
if inventories of materials or of goods in process change materially.
The accuracy of a record of materials input could also be affected
by technical changes that modify the amount of material used per
unit of final product, or by changes in the degree of fabrication of
materials. The perhaps obvious procedure of measuring work done
by a count of man-hours of labor input has the central weakness
of ignoring changes in productivity. If the labor input measure is
adjusted by a coefficient assumed to define current productivity
changes, the danger of error arising out of faults in the coefficient
is faced. Since productivity changes in given factories or industries
are never constant over time, this error can be serious.

In general, production indexes are intended to define changes in
quantum, or physical volume, output; hence the first of the four
measures cited in the preceding paragraph is most relevant. We
must sometimes use other records as approximations to output,
but comprehensive counts of goods produced are the first objective
in the making of these index numbers. Where variations in inventories (of basic materials, of goods in process, or of finished goods),
or changes in technology or in degree of fabrication affect available
records as indications of work done, correction should be made,
if possible.

Since the primary index of production is intended to measure
work done in comparable monthly, quarterly, or annual periods,
correction should be made, also, for circumstances that are obviously distorting. Calendar irregularities that affect the number of
working days per month are the most important of these mechanical difficulties. It is customary, for this reason, to reduce output
records to production per working day or per working week (which
is recommended as standard practice by the United Nations). The
effects of public annual holidays, most of which are regular in their
timing, are generally allowed for in a subsequent correction for
seasonality, which is discussed below.

The p's that enter as weights in the aggregative forms of production index numbers are not, in all cases, the unit prices that are
quoted in the markets. Where the commodity is a basic product
such as iron ore (for which the quoted price covers all work that
has been done on the unit offered for sale), the conventional price
would be used. More frequently, the "work done" in a given
factory or industry takes the form of fabricating raw or partially

finished products. The price of the product of the factory or industry will include the price of materials used plus the value of the net product of the operations performed in the factory or industry. In such a case the p used as a weighting factor should be the value of the *net output* per unit of goods produced. If we are dealing with a manufacturing process what is wanted is the unit "price" of the services of fabrication performed in this operation. Such "prices" are, of course, not usually quoted. However, if the aggregate value of the net output is available, the maker of index numbers may use the value-weighted average of quantity relatives which is the equivalent of the weighted aggregative form. Thus instead of the Laspeyres index he would use the form

$$Q_{01} = \frac{\Sigma\left(\dfrac{q_1}{q_o} \times q_0 p_0\right)}{\Sigma q_0 p_0} \tag{14.5}$$

where $q_0 p_0$ is the aggregate value of the net output of a given product. Or, having the quantities in question, he may secure a "price" per unit of net output by deflating net output in a given period by the number of units produced in that period and then employ the usual aggregative formula.[1]

The familiar "value added" figure given in census records is usually a close approximation to the desired net output for a given industry. Since net output is usually wanted on a factor cost basis, however, certain adjustments may be required to exclude tax payments and costs of business services such as insurance and advertising, and to correct for changes over the census period in quantity of work in progress.

Coverage of Production Index Numbers. No new problems of method are faced in dealing with the scope and coverage of production indexes. There should, of course, be suitable representation of all sectors of the economy which the index purports to cover.

---

[1] In following either of these procedures we are assuming that input quantities (that is, the quantities of materials, fuel, and semifinished products utilized in production) vary proportionately with output quantities. If this is not the case a more accurate index of net output may be derived from the formula

$$\text{Net } Q_{01} = \frac{\Sigma q_1 p_0 - \Sigma q'_1 p'_0}{\Sigma q_0 p_0 - \Sigma q'_0 p'_0}$$

where p' and q' represent prices and quantities of inputs, and p and q represent prices and quantities of products of fabrication, that is, of outputs on a gross basis. On this point see Fabricant (ref. 39) and Geary (ref. 62).

Chief current use of the index number device is made in the field of industrial production. In the recommendations of the U. N. Statistical Office this is taken to comprehend the output of factories, workshops, mines, and handicraft establishments of all sizes, excluding only products of work in the home or farm. This means, in effect, that all nonagricultural production except home-made goods would be included. Very small establishments are excluded on practical grounds. The chief subdivisions of industrial production, as thus defined, are mining, manufacturing, construction, and electric and gas utilities. The Board of Governors of the Federal Reserve System accept this recommendation in principle, but for the present the FRB index is restricted to mining and manufacturing. (An annual physical volume index of agricultural production is constructed in the United States by the Bureau of Agricultural Economics.)

The selection of appropriate groups suitable for international comparisons as well as for domestic purposes has been made possible by the recent development of standard industrial classifications. There is now such an international classification;[2] there is also a widely used classification of the same sort for the United States, developed under the auspices of the Office of Statistical Standards of the Bureau of the Budget, and similar in general structure to the international standard.[3] Following this classification the Board of Governors of the Federal Reserve System constructs group index numbers for 21 manufacturing groups and for 5 mining groups, and for certain combinations of these industrial groups, by appropriate classification of basic monthly series. One classification distinguishes durable from nondurable manufactures. A separate output index, covering major durables weighted by gross values, is designed to measure changes in the supply of such durables entering final consumer markets. Such regroupings of basic industries and products yield index numbers especially adapted for use in the analysis of cyclical and other changes in economic processes.

As to the number of individual series to be included, the United Nations suggest 100 as the minimum, 500 as the maximum. The

---

[2] International Standard Industrial Classification of all Economic Activities, *Statistical Papers Series M*, No. 4, Statistical Office of the United Nations.

[3] *Standard Industrial Classification Manual*, Office of Statistical Standards, Bureau of the Budget.

index of industrial production constructed by the Board of Governors of the Federal Reserve System now includes 175 series.

Comparison Base and Weight Base. The same considerations that favor short-term comparisons in working with index numbers of prices support the case for similar limitations in using production indexes. Considerable regimen changes make fixed weights unrepresentative, and such regimen changes are the rule in a dynamic economy. In its recommendations concerning international practice the U. N. Statistical Office suggests a review and, if necessary, a reweighting of index numbers of industrial production every five years. Such reweighting should be based on censuses or extensive sample surveys of production. Such surveys of the structure of production, made at regular intervals, are essential to accuracy in the measurement of production changes. A corollary of these recommendations is that the comparison base should not be far removed in time. A change every five years, although perhaps desirable, is hardly to be expected in the practical work of index-making agencies. The Federal Reserve Board index is at present issued on the 1947-49 base, which is now standard for the United States. The weight base for this index is 1947.

Fixed weights are a practical necessity in the short-term comparisons for which monthly index numbers are primarily designed. However, such series of current index numbers may well be supplemented by index numbers constructed for the measurement of production changes over longer terms. Annual, biennial, or quinquennial censuses may provide comprehensive and accurate weights suitable for use in "crossed weight" index numbers of the ideal or Edgeworth type (see Chapter 13). These index numbers may then be chained or combined in other ways to provide measurements covering fairly long periods of time. This has been done, in fact, for some years in the United States. The Bureau of the Census and the National Bureau of Economic Research have utilized census data as they became available, in the construction of bench-mark indexes to which current Federal Reserve index numbers have been adjusted. Comprehensive and independently constructed annual measures are currently used for the same purpose in reviewing and adjusting the Federal Reserve Index. Of course, the use of the bench-mark device for purposes of long-term comparison does not solve the fundamental problems raised by regimen changes. But the use of more comprehensive data, more satisfactory weights, and formulas that take some account of regimen shifts makes such index numbers more suitable for long-term comparisons than are the more restricted, fixed-weight monthly indexes.

Seasonally Adjusted Indexes

The volume of production in many industries is subject to seasonal variation. This is obviously the case in agriculture; similar but less extreme variations from month to month are found in metal mining, in coal production, in food and beverage manufacture, and in other manufacturing activities. These seasonal patterns in production are more marked and more regular than are seasonal patterns in commodity prices. For these reasons an adjustment not found desirable in constructing monthly price index numbers is common in the making of monthly production indexes. This adjustment is designed to eliminate movements that are purely seasonal in character, in order that month-to-month changes attributable to the play of other forces may be more clearly defined. Since the purely seasonal element in the total index of industrial production may account for a movement from the seasonal low to the seasonal high of as much as 10 percent, as it does in the Federal Reserve Index, the adjustment is not a minor one.

Actual production changes, including those due to the play of secular, cyclical, seasonal, and random factors are, of course, of central importance. These are measured by a primary, or seasonally unadjusted index. The seasonally adjusted index, where constructed, is a supplementary measure. There is need of both in following economic changes.

Standard methods of measuring seasonal patterns are employed in the construction of seasonally adjusted indexes. The Board of Governors of the Federal Reserve System uses, basically, 12-month moving averages (see Chapter 11). In applying the seasonal correction to a given series, the unadjusted measure for a stated month is divided by the seasonal index for that month, expressed as a ratio (i.e., as 1.10, if the seasonal index is 110). The original measure of production for a given month is thus reduced if the seasonal index for that month is above 1.00, raised if the seasonal index is below 1.00.

The seasonal adjustments may be applied directly to the many individual series entering into the production index, or they may be applied to unadjusted group indexes. The latter is now the procedure employed in making the Federal Reserve Index in the United States. Seasonal adjustments are made directly to each of 26 major group indexes. The seasonally adjusted total index is then obtained by combining the 26 seasonally adjusted group index numbers.[4] This procedure is designed to give flexibility to the seasonal adjustment program, so that revisions designed to allow for shifts in seasonal patterns may be readily made.

The amplitudes of seasonal movements in total industrial production in the United States and in certain of the major sectors of the American economy are indicated by the measures brought together in Table 14-1. These, be it noted, define the seasonal patterns prevailing in 1952. In the main, the patterns remain unchanged from year to year, but in certain industrial sectors shifts occur with some frequency.

TABLE 14–1

Seasonal Factors in Monthly Industrial Production Indexes, 1952
Board of Governors of the Federal Reserve System[*]

	Jan	Feb	Mar	Apr	May	June	July	Aug	Sept	Oct	Nov	Dec
Total Index	99	101	102	100	99	100	94	100	102	103	101	99
Primary Metals	102	104	105	104	102	101	91	95	98	101	100	97
Electrical Machinery	102	105	106	102	99	95	84	97	100	106	104	100
Transportation Equipment	97	102	105	104	101	103	97	99	99	100	97	96
Lumber and Products	90	96	101	105	102	107	94	105	106	105	99	90
Textile Mill Products	101	105	104	100	99	100	86	103	102	102	101	97
Rubber Products	101	104	104	102	99	101	88	96	101	106	102	96
Petroleum and Coal Products	101	100	99	97	98	100	100	102	101	101	101	100
Food and Beverage Manufactures	92	91	92	92	94	102	104	109	114	111	103	96
Bituminous Coal	105	100	100	100	95	98	75	100	104	109	109	105
Anthracite	100	100	92	96	102	106	79	96	105	121	110	93
Metal Mining	72	75	76	101	118	121	119	120	119	113	92	74

[*] From "Revised Federal Reserve Monthly Index of Industrial Production," *Federal Reserve Bulletin*, December, 1953, pp. 54-5.

The abrupt seasonal drop in the total index in July, to a level 6 percent below the average for the year, is a striking example of a sharply changed seasonal pattern. In the unrevised Federal Reserve Index, for which prewar patterns provided most of the seasonal measures, the July seasonal index was 100. The general postwar adoption of industry-wide vacations accounts for the

[4] The seasonally adjusted Federal Reserve indexes of industrial production, as well as the primary or seasonally unadjusted indexes, are published currently in the monthly *Federal Reserve Bulletin*.

difference. This was a change that came suddenly, in contrast to the gradual shifts in seasonal patterns that reflect slowly changing social customs, technologies, and business policies.

An Index of Industrial Activity

In the analysis of time series we have seen that cyclical fluctuations are often the objects of primary interest. This is particularly true in the study of physical volume, for changes in the volume of production and trade are features of fundamental importance in business cycles. Methods have been explained, in the preceding chapters, by means of which we seek to measure the cyclical fluctuations in individual series (fluctuations inextricably entangled with accidental movements of major and minor degree). An obvious next step, in the study of general business conditions, is the construction of a comprehensive index of physical activity adjusted for trend as well as for seasonal movements.

Two somewhat different methods have been employed in making such index numbers. The first entails the fitting of an appropriate line of trend to each of the physical series entering into the general index, the expression of the actual observations as percentages of the corresponding trend values, the seasonal correction of these percentages, and the combination of such adjusted percentages in a general index. The resulting index is in relative terms, but the relatives refer to a hypothetical "normal," not to any fixed base in time. The alternative method calls, first, for the construction of a seasonally adjusted index, similar to that of the Board of Governors of the Federal Reserve System. The secular trend of this index, which will be a composite of the trends of the various constituent series, is determined in the usual way. The final trend-adjusted index is then obtained by expressing the actual monthly values of the general index as percentages of the corresponding trend values of the index.

This latter procedure is well exemplified in an "Index of Industrial Activity" constructed by the Chief Statistician's Division of the American Telephone and Telegraph Company.[5] The elements of this index are monthly data; seasonal corrections are therefore necessary. When these corrections have been made a

[5] This index has been constructed for the use of the staffs of the Bell system companies, and is not available for distribution. It is published here by courtesy of the American Telephone and Telegraph Company.

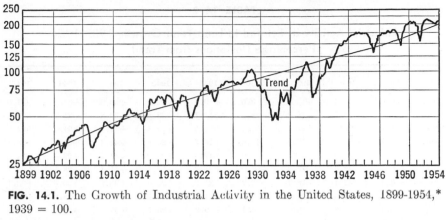

FIG. 14.1. The Growth of Industrial Activity in the United States, 1899-1954,*
1939 = 100.

*Source: American Telephone and Telegraph Company.

general index measuring long-term growth and cyclical-accidental
fluctuations, in combination, is constructed by averaging 25 series,
with appropriate weights.[6] In this form the index, which is not as
yet trend-adjusted, defines the growth of industrial activity in
the United States. It reflects secular factors as well as cyclical-
accidental fluctuations.

This index of growth is shown in Fig. 14.1, for the period
1899-1954. The trend there shown is a modification of an exponential curve fitted to measures of industrial activity per capita of
the population; the modification (by a population index) is designed
to provide a trend line reflecting both the growth of population
and the increase in activity per capita. It will be clear from the
list of series included that this is not an index of production. The
varied series included, among which there are five employment

[6] The following series have been used for the period from 1939 to date:

Metals (weight 30 percent): steel production; copper consumption; lead consumption;
zinc shipments; aluminum, shipments of fabricated products

Textiles (weight 15 percent): cotton consumption; wool consumption; rayon and
acetate production; hosiery shipments

Paper and printing (weight 10 percent): paper production; printing paper production;
newsprint consumption

Lumber production (weight 5 percent)

Food (weight 10 percent): slaughter of cattle; slaughter of hogs; wheat grindings;
corn grindings; malt liquor production

Man-hours in four manufacturing industries (weight 15 percent): chemicals and
allied products; stone, clay, and glass products; petroleum and coal products;
rubber products

Industrial power and man-hours (weight 15 percent): kilowatt hour sales to large
commercial and industrial users; electricity generated by industrial plants;
man-hours in manufacturing industries

TABLE 14–2

Industrial Activity as Related to Long-Term Growth, 1937-1954
Percentage Deviations from Trend

	1937	1938	1939	1940	1941	1942	1943	1944	1945
Jan.	+ 0.6	−38.4	−19.8	− 3.6	+ 9.4	+22.2	+29.9	+31.4	+27.0
Feb.	+ 2.5	−36.7	−18.8	− 8.6	+11.7	+22.4	+30.8	+31.9	+27.5
Mar.	+ 4.5	−36.1	−17.4	−12.6	+14.5	+22.8	+31.1	+31.4	+27.5
Apr.	+ 4.8	−37.0	−19.0	−13.6	+16.7	+23.7	+31.4	+31.4	+26.3
May	+ 5.1	−37.5	−19.6	− 9.9	+19.5	+23.2	+31.7	+29.4	+24.5
Jun.	+ 0.5	−37.6	−17.7	− 5.0	+21.0	+22.7	+31.4	+28.1	+23.1
Jul.	− 0.6	−32.4	−16.9	− 3.2	+21.2	+25.0	+32.2	+28.3	+20.1
Aug.	− 3.4	−28.2	−14.7	− 2.4	+21.1	+25.1	+32.5	+28.3	+12.4
Sep.	− 7.9	−25.8	− 9.6	− 0.4	+19.9	+25.7	+33.8	+27.9	+ 7.1
Oct.	−20.5	−24.2	− 3.2	+ 1.5	+19.3	+27.6	+33.9	+27.5	+ 3.9
Nov.	−33.0	−19.1	− 0.7	+ 3.8	+20.4	+28.3	+33.5	+27.8	+ 5.5
Dec.	−39.5	−20.2	− 1.2	+ 7.2	+21.5	+29.0	+30.5	+28.5	+ 7.2
Avg.	− 7.2	−31.1	−13.2	− 3.9	+18.0	+24.8	+31.9	+29.3	+17.7

	1946	1947	1948	1949	1950	1951	1952	1953	1954
Jan.	+ 0.6	+17.8	+17.7	+12.8	+ 8.5	+17.6	+11.9	+15.7	+ 3.7
Feb.	− 9.8	+18.4	+17.0	+11.1	+ 7.8	+17.3	+13.7	+17.7	+ 3.5
Mar.	+ 2.1	+17.3	+15.7	+ 8.4	+ 7.4	+17.3	+13.5	+19.9	+ 2.5
Apr.	+ 7.6	+17.2	+13.5	+ 5.1	+12.7	+20.4	+ 9.7	+19.4	+ 2.4
May	+ 1.2	+17.0	+15.7	+ 2.4	+14.9	+20.2	+ 7.2	+20.3	+ 2.9
Jun.	+ 4.8	+16.0	+17.6	− 0.3	+15.8	+20.1	− 7.8	+19.9	+ 4.3
Jul.	+11.6	+15.1	+17.9	− 1.3	+17.7	+18.3	−16.4	+18.6	+ 2.1
Aug.	+15.9	+14.9	+17.3	+ 0.5	+18.8	+16.0	+ 3.6	+16.6	− 0.3
Sep.	+15.6	+15.6	+16.6	+ 3.9	+18.3	+14.7	+14.1	+13.6	− 0.2
Oct.	+15.8	+17.7	+16.5	−12.0	+19.0	+12.0	+14.7	+11.5	+ 2.6
Nov.	+17.1	+19.1	+15.4	−10.4	+17.5	+12.6	+16.6	+10.0	+ 5.8
Dec.	+15.4	+18.0	+14.6	+ 3.5	+18.1	+12.2	+15.7	+ 5.3	+ 6.4
Avg.	+ 8.2	+17.0	+16.3	+ 2.0	+14.7	+16.6	+ 8.0	+15.7	+ 3.0

series, are taken to be indicators of "activity," not of physical output.

When each monthly value of the index is expressed as a percentage deviation from trend we have an index of industrial activity as related to long-term growth. Measures in this form are given in Table 14-2, for the period 1937-1954. (This is, of course, only a portion of the period for which the trend line was fitted). The deviations are graphically portrayed in Fig. 14.2. The cyclical-accidental fluctuations in industrial activity in the United States, as represented by the 25 series employed, are traced by the movements of this index.

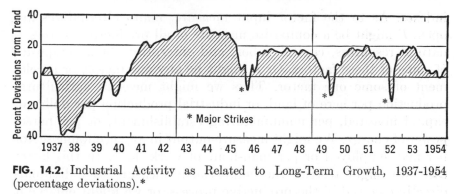

FIG. 14.2. Industrial Activity as Related to Long-Term Growth, 1937-1954 (percentage deviations).*

*Source: American Telephone and Telegraph Company.

The Measurement of Productivity Changes

Changes in productivity, that is, in the effectiveness with which productive factors are applied in the making of economic goods, have contributed mightily to advances in living standards in the United States. But it is not alone as a key element in the long-term growth of a single economy that productivity is studied today. The advancement of productivity among all western nations and in economically underdeveloped regions is sought through the interchange of technicians and of technical information. Productivity has become a central issue in industrial bargaining. The "improvement factor" that is embodied in a number of wage contracts rests upon past and expected productivity gains. For these and other reasons the measurement and interpretation of productivity changes are among the important tasks now falling to the statistician.

The Productivity Ratio. Customary measures of productivity take the form of a ratio in which quantity produced, Q, is set against input of production factors, which we may represent by F. In this form we may call the ratio an index of *productivity* and use for it the symbol P_r. Thus $P_r = Q/F$. Changes in this index define changes in average output per unit of factor input. Inversely, the ratio may be put in the form F/Q which defines factor input per unit of output. We may think of the latter ratio as an index of factor *requirements* per unit of goods produced, and use for it the symbol R. The meaning of either index will depend, obviously, on what is included in the output measure, Q, and in the input measure, F. We have already considered the nature of production indexes. As to the factor input measure, many alternatives are open. F might be a composite measure of all productive factors—natural resources, capital, labor, and enterprise—or a composite of some of these factors. Or F might be any one factor, or an element of some one factor. Thus we might measure agricultural production per acre of land, or industrial production per dollar of capital invested, per manufacturing establishment, or per horsepower of energy. We might measure output in any economic sector per man employed or per man-hour of work done. In this latter case, we might restrict the employment measure to individuals directly engaged in the productive process, or we might enlarge it to include all forms of human effort, supervisory and managerial as well as direct, that enter into a given process of production. Perhaps the most meaningful general form of productivity index would be Q/E, where Q is the output and E represents all human effort entering into the productive process. This form appears commonly as Q/M, where M stands for man-hours of work, the scope of the man-hours measure depending on the purpose of the investigator and the availability of data.

We should emphasize at this point that such measures of productivity carry no causal imputation. If we say that so many bushels of wheat are produced per acre of land, we do not mean that only the services of land enter into the productive process, nor that the land factor is responsible for any gains recorded. Similarly, a measure that sets output against volume of invested capital is not to be taken to mean that the capital factor is responsible for the changes that may occur in the ratio. Again, if an advance is shown by a productivity ratio that sets output against man-hours of work done, this is not to be taken to mean that the gain is to be attributed to the labor factor in production. In all cases the actual factor input is a composite of all agents of production. The human factor uses power, capital equipment, and organizational devices of various sorts in exploiting natural resources to produce economic goods. It is convenient, and meaningful, to measure changes in output with reference to changes in some one component of the factor composite, but it would be a great mistake to assume that this factor operates alone in bringing about a gain or loss. In general, as has been suggested, it is most useful to measure output with reference to the input of human effort. This we shall do in the following discussion. But we must recognize that the effectiveness of this effort varies not alone with the intensity and skill of the human factor, but also with the number and quality of the tools employed, the amount of power utilized, the nature of the productive organization, and other features of the productive process.

It will be useful to distinguish two different methods of obtaining a general index of the effectiveness of productive effort, whether it be of the form Q/M or M/Q. In using one method we work from measures of productivity, or of unit labor requirements, in the factories or industries that are the basic units of study. In the other case we derive productivity indexes from comprehensive measures of output and of labor input covering many commodities or industries. We shall call the first type *directly defined* measures, and the other type *derived* measures.

The Direct Construction of Index Numbers of Unit Labor Requirements. In employing this procedure the statistician works with basic measures of output and of effort input for the individual commodities, establishments, or industries that are to enter into the index. Having the output, q, and the corresponding man-hours of work done, m, for each commodity or industry, he may determine r, the labor requirement per unit of output. This is given, of course, by $r = m/q$. It is essential that m and q be exactly comparable, that is, that q be the product of the effort represented by m. The chief danger of error here is that q may be a gross measure, such as the number of automobiles produced by a given factory, while m is a net measure covering only the final operations in the productive process. The measure m, that is, would not cover the production of the materials and parts embodied in the cars but only the final fabrication. Other possible sources of error, such as failure to allow for changes in work in process, in inventories, etc., have been noted in earlier pages. But when m and q are directly comparable, these and the derived r's provide the statistician with basic materials for the accurate measurement of productivity changes.

The measure of unit labor requirements, r, may be thought of as corresponding to a unit price. In these terms, the formulas available for the construction of index numbers of unit labor requirements (which are reciprocals of productivity measures) correspond to those available for the making of price indexes. If we are to use Laspeyres index, we have

$$R_{01} = \frac{\Sigma r_1 q_0}{\Sigma r_0 q_0} \qquad (14.6)$$

This is a measure of unit labor requirements in time "1" on time "0" as base, the weighting factors being the base period q's. Thus the relative importance of r for each commodity is proportionate to the number of physical units of that commodity produced in the base year. The regimen assumed to be constant is that of the base year, and this regimen is defined by the quantities of the several commodities produced in that year. If we should weight the r's with given year quantities, we should have the Paasche index

$$R_{01} = \frac{\Sigma r_1 q_1}{\Sigma r_0 q_1} \qquad (14.7)$$

The geometric mean of the Laspeyres and Paasche indexes would be the ideal index of unit labor requirements. In all these we are paralleling the measurement of price changes, for unit prices and unit labor requirements are similar measures.

This parallelism extends to the testing of related indexes for mutual consistency. For prices, quantities, and values there is mutual consistency (i.e., the factor reversal test is met) when $PQ = V$, the capital letters standing for the respective index numbers. If we use the symbol M for total man-hours, R for an index of unit labor requirements, and Q for a physical volume index, there is mutual consistency when $RQ = M$. For an individual commodity the relationship $rq = m$ necessarily holds. But the algebraic identity will hold only for an index number formula that meets the factor reversal test. This is true of Fisher's ideal formula, when used in the construction of index numbers of physical output and of unit labor requirements. If we vary the formula, we may derive mutually consistent measures by constructing a Laspeyres index of production and a Paasche index of labor requirements.[7]

That is

$$\frac{\Sigma q_1 r_0}{\Sigma q_0 r_0} \times \frac{\Sigma q_1 r_1}{\Sigma q_1 r_0} = \frac{\Sigma q_1 r_1}{\Sigma q_0 r_0} \qquad (14.8)$$

The product of the production index and the labor requirements

[7] See pp. 480-1 above.

index is a measure of the change in total man-hours of work done. This relationship has a bearing on the problem we face when we derive indexes of productivity, or of unit labor requirements, from indexes of total man-hours and of production.

Derived Index Numbers of Labor Requirements and of Productivity. For an individual commodity $r = m/q$. If the same relationship holds among index numbers relating to many commodities we should have $R = M/Q$. A measure of changes in M is given, of course, by $\Sigma q_1 r_1 / \Sigma q_0 r_0$, the total man-hours of the given year divided by the total man-hours of the base year. If we wish to derive an index R from M/Q, we shall have mutually consistent and compatible measures if we employ an index of production in which the q's are weighted by r's. Thus

$$R = M/Q - \frac{\Sigma q_1 r_1}{\Sigma q_0 r_0} \div \frac{\Sigma q_1 r_0}{\Sigma q_0 r_0} = \frac{\Sigma q_1 r_1}{\Sigma q_1 r_0} \qquad (14.9)$$

This is an index of unit labor requirements, in which the r's are weighted by given year q's.

This process is logically and algebraically satisfactory. The elements of M are of the same order as the elements of Q. The practical difficulty in this procedure has been noted in discussing production indexes. We do not usually have the r's that are employed in constructing the production index. Customarily, in making physical volume indexes, price weights are employed. Using such an index, say of the Laspeyres type, the process of deriving R from M and Q is described by

$$R = M/Q = \frac{\Sigma q_1 r_1}{\Sigma q_0 r_0} \div \frac{\Sigma q_1 p_0}{\Sigma q_0 p_0} \qquad (14.10)$$

It is clear that incommensurable quantities are involved in this derivation. A pure man-hours measure is divided by a price-weighted quantity index. A pecuniary factor has been introduced into the derived index of unit labor requirements.

Although the process just described is disturbing to a purist, it is not entirely without merit. Representation of a given regimen by unit prices, rather than by unit labor requirements, is appropriate for many purposes in dealing with a money economy. When we shift labor from sectors of low value-productivity to sectors of higher value-productivity there is a gain that may properly be included in productivity measures. Accordingly, it is not alone considerations of expediency that lead to the general use of value- or price-weighted production index numbers in deriving measures of unit labor requirements, or of productivity.

It is true today that all comprehensive index numbers of labor requirements and productivity are *derived* measures of the form $P_r = Q/M$ or $R = M/Q$. They are usually obtained by dividing price-weighted index numbers of physical output by measures of changes in the total man-hours of work entering into the given volume of production. (Some indexes define changes in output per man employed, rather than per man-hour of work done. That is, we have $P_r = Q/N$, where N is the number employed.) The prime requirement here is that the components Q and M be truly comparable. The "intrusion of the pecuniary factor" we may accept, and indeed welcome for many purposes, but we may not tolerate material differences in the coverage of the indexes of production and of man-hours.[8]

We should recognize that such derived measures, covering a period of years, are seldom open to unambiguous interpretation, for they are affected by many variables. The quality of goods entering into Q (or more broadly, the product designs of such goods) will vary; the composition of the total Q will certainly change, in respect of kinds of goods included and of the relative shares coming from different manufacturing plants. Changes will occur in the composition of labor input, and in the complex of instruments and organizations used in the productive process. The interaction of these many variables will lead to the net result defined by a productivity index for a given year.

Some Current Measures of Productivity Changes

Current productivity indexes in the United States range from global measures, covering the economy, to measures defining changes in individual plants, or even divisions of a plant. Most of them relate changes in physical output to changes in the input of human effort, measured in man-hours or in man-years, although some efforts have been made to relate productive output to capital

---

[8] Adjustments to correct for inequalities in the coverage of available measures of output and of labor input, which have been made by the National Bureau of Economic Research and by other agencies, are sometimes warranted, although subject to error. For a critical appraisal of such adjustments see Siegel, Ref. 142.

input and to power input. The indexes of broad scope, covering major industries or the economy, are all of the derived type, being subject therefore to the limitations we have just noted. Many of narrower coverage, however, are now built up from careful records of production and man-hour input obtained from individual plants. These, though of limited scope, promise to be of greater analytical value in studies of factors making for productivity gains.

The measures given in Table 14-3 exemplify the global approach. In column (3) are indexes of the real gross national product, by decades, from the late nineteenth century to the middle of the present century. (These are derived from estimates of the gross national product, corrected for price changes.) The indexes of corresponding labor input in column (4) come from estimates of the total employed labor force, by decades, with an adjustment to take account of changes in the length of the average work week. Derived indexes of output per man-hour are given in column (5). The record is one of unbroken advance, but the gains were uneven. The greatest relative increase in output per man-hour came in the decade of the 'twenties—a period of extraordinary advance. The smallest relative gains were made during the decade that spanned the first world war, and in the depressed 'thirties.

TABLE 14-3

Real Gross National Product, Labor Input, and Productivity,
United States, by Decades, 1891-1950*

(1)	(2) Gross national product (billions of 1929	(3)	(4) Total man- hours of labor input	(5) Output per man-hour
Decade	dollars)	(relative)	(relative)	(relative)
1891-1900	294	100.0	100.0	100.0
1901-1910	455	154.8	126.1	122.8
1911-1920	603	205.1	140.5	146.0
1921-1930	838	285.0	145.1	196.4
1931-1940	843	286.7	122.8	233.5
1941-1950	1,493	507.8	180.5	281.3

* From Mills, ref. 103.

Such comprehensive estimates are useful as broad indications of changes in the effectiveness with which productive resources are utilized. By themselves, however, they throw little light on the causal forces behind observed movements of productivity indexes.

For analytical purposes we need intensive field studies, made under controlled conditions, with product design specified, so that the final indexes will measure, essentially, changes in productive efficiency in individual plants. Indexes based on such field studies are given in Table 14-4.

TABLE 14–4

Indexes of Man-hours per Unit of Output, 1939-1950*
Specific Industrial Products

		Man-hours per unit		
(1)	(2)	(3)	(4)	(5)
	Track-laying tractor	Selected types of machine tools		
Year		Direct	Indirect	Total factory
	Total factory labor	factory labor†	factory labor‡	labor
1939	100	100	100	100
1940	99	93	87	90
1941	91	90	89	90
1942	91	86	94	91
1943	95	82	100	92
1944	99	88	115	102
1945	101	89	116	103
1946	105	95	119	108
1947	99	96	122	111
1948	99	98	121	112
1949	97	94	120	108
1950	91	91	115	105

* These indexes (which are here rounded off to the nearest unit) have been constructed by the U. S. Bureau of Labor Statistics. (See Bureau of Labor Statistics, refs. 174 and 177.) For a general statement of the work of the Bureau, covering both secondary source data and field-collected data, see Ref. 173.

† Direct hours of labor input include the work of wage earners engaged directly on production operations, primarily machine operators and assembly workers.

‡ Indirect hours represent functions of time-keeping, shipping and receiving materials, handling, production scheduling, machine set-up, inspection, maintenance, engineering of tools, dies, and gauges, and plant supervision. Where possible, the Bureau excluded from both direct and indirect hours the functions of general accounting, purchasing, personnel relations, welfare services, and developmental engineering. The sum of direct and indirect hours constitutes total factory labor.

The indexes of labor requirements given in column (2) of Table 14-4 relate to three precisely specified types of track-laying tractors. The general record is one of declining unit labor requirements (increasing productivity) in the early years of the war period, followed by rising labor requirements to 1946 and a renewed decline between 1946 and 1950. The information the Bureau compiles concerning conditions in the individual plants from which these records were obtained makes it possible to define with some precision the factors responsible for these changes.

The labor requirement indexes for selected machine tools given in columns (3), (4), and (5) are broader in coverage, since they include types that make up about three quarters of the output, in value terms, of the machine tools industry. (In combining indexes of unit labor requirements for different products, value weights are used.) Here total factory labor is broken into two components—direct and indirect labor. The interesting feature of this record is the sharp divergence of trends in unit labor requirements for direct and indirect labor. A substantial reduction, per unit of product, in the amount of direct labor used in producing machine tools has been paralleled by a material increase in indirect labor. This represents, of course, a major change in factory organization. The net result for the period as a whole was an advance in unit labor requirements, when account is taken of all factory labor. The movement was downward, however, for the last two years covered.

Standing between global estimates of productivity movements in the whole economy and measures based on intensive establishment studies are the indexes given in Table 14-5. These are estimates of productivity changes in four major sectors of the economy. Being based on secondary sources, not on records for individual plants, they suffer from some of the defects noted in discussing economy-wide indexes. However, care has been taken to ensure the reasonable comparability of output and input measures. Although significance should not be attached to minor year-to-year movements of these indexes, they do define with acceptable accuracy broad movements of productivity in the several sectors covered.

The most striking gain in productivity in recent years has been scored in the generation of electric power. Technological advances have here been great. Output per man-hour rose sharply on steam railroads with the increase in volume of traffic that came in the war years, and these gains have been held and in recent years extended. Agriculture, a laggard industry for many generations, opened a new era in the mid-'thirties, as the mechanization movement spread. Recent years have shown continued advance. Productivity gains in mining have been relatively low. Such evidence as we have on productivity in manufacturing industries indicates a gain, since 1939, that exceeds the increase recorded for

TABLE 14–5

Indexes of Productivity in Selected Sectors of the U. S. Economy,
1939-1952*

| Year | Output per man-hour | | | |
	Agriculture	Mining	Steam railroads†	Electric light and power
1939	100	100	100	100
1940	105	102	105	109
1941	110	104	116	123
1942	119	104	140	146
1943	117	102	151	183
1944	121	105	148	191
1945	127	106	140	183
1946	134	107	129	161
1947	133	111	135	167
1948	147	111	133	171
1949	146	109	132	
1950	153	117	150	
1951	151		159	
1952	162		160	

* Sources:
   Index of farm output: U. S. Bureau of Agricultural Economics
   Other indexes: U. S. Bureau of Labor Statistics
† Revenue traffic per man-hour on Class I railroads.

mining, but falls short of the gains cited for the industries listed in Table 14-5.[9]

The accurate measurement of productivity movements is one of the challenging tasks facing statisticians today. It is obvious that we are dealing here with a major dynamic factor in economic life, one that plays a central role in economic growth. Yet only a beginning has been made in the art of measuring such changes. Global indexes, which are almost inevitably rough and inaccurate, are easily constructed. Such measures will continue to be useful, but progress lies in the direction of intensive measurement, for specific products and individual plants and industries. Building

[9] No general index of productivity in manufacturing is available for the period since 1939, although *Bulletin 1046* of the Bureau of Labor Statistics gives indexes for selected manufacturing industries. A period prior to 1939 is covered by Fabricant's index (Ref. 38). One may approximate changes in man-hour output in manufacturing by using the Federal Reserve index of manufacturing production as an output measure, and estimating labor input from Bureau of Labor Statistics' records of manufacturing employment and average length of work week. But these output and input figures are not really comparable; the resulting indexes are of dubious value. The Bureau of Labor Statistics is at present preparing to publish a continuing series of productivity indexes for manufacturing as a whole.

from these we may hope to obtain fuller understanding of the factors that contribute to productivity gains, as well as greater accuracy in defining changes in productive efficiency.

REFERENCES

Anglo-American Council on Productivity, *Final Report*, 1952.

Barger, H., and Schurr, S. H., *The Mining Industries: A Study of Output, Employment and Productivity.*

Barger, H., *The Transportation Industries*, 1889-1946: *A Study of Output, Employment and Productivity.*

Carter, C. F., Reddaway, W. B. and Stone, R., *The Measurement of Production Movements.*

Fabricant, S., *Employment in Manufacturing*, 1899-1939.

Fabricant, S., *The Output of Manufacturing Industries*, 1890-1937.

Federal Reserve System, Board of Governors, "The Revised Federal Reserve Index of Industrial Production," *Federal Reserve Bulletin*, Dec. 1953.

Geary, R. C., "The Concept of the Net Volume of Output with Special Reference to Irish Data," *Journal of the Royal Statistical Society*, Vol. 107, 1944.

Gould, J. M., *Output and Productivity in the Electric and Gas Utilities.*

International Labor Office, "Methods of Labor Productivity Statistics," *Studies and Reports, New Series*, No. 18, Geneva, 1951.

Mills, F. C., "Productivity and Economic Progress," *Occasional Paper 38*, National Bureau of Economic Research, 1952.

Siegel, I., *Concepts and Measurement of Production and Productivity.*

United Nations, Economic Commission for Europe, *Economic Survey of Europe Since the War*, pp. 317-335 (on sources and methods, index numbers of industrial production).

United Nations Statistical Office, "Index Numbers of Industrial Production," *Studies in Methods*, No. 1, 1950.

U. S. Bureau of Labor Statistics, "The Productivity Measurement Program of the Bureau of Labor Statistics," 1950.

U. S. Bureau of Labor Statistics, "Productivity Trends in Selected Industries Through 1950," *Bulletin* 1046, Oct. 1951.

U. S. Bureau of Labor Statistics, *Technical Note on the Measurement of Trends in Output per Man-Hour*, April 1954.

The publishers and the dates of publication of the books named in chapter reference lists are given in the bibliography at the end of this volume.

CHAPTER 15

.
.
.

Chi-Square and its Uses

Marital Status and Saving: An Illustrative Example

A problem that appears in many forms in quantitative work is exemplified by the observations entering into Table 15-1. Here we have summarized information obtained from a survey of consumer finances conducted by the Survey Research Center of the University of Michigan. In this table 3,327 spending units[1] are divided into those headed by single persons and those headed by married persons; they are again divided into those reporting positive savings in the year 1950, and those reporting zero savings or negative savings. This process of classification gives us a 2×2 contingency table[2] containing four subclasses, or cells: single persons who were positive savers in 1950; single persons who were not positive savers; married persons who were positive savers; married persons who were not positive savers. (For convenience I refer to single and married persons; the observations relate of course to spending units headed by such persons.) For each of these we have the observed frequencies given in Table 15-1. Our

---

[1] The terms used by the Survey Research Center are defined as follows:
Spending unit: a group of persons living in the same dwelling and related by blood, marriage or adoption, who pool their incomes for their major items of expense. In some instances a spending unit consists of only one person.
Consumer saving: the difference between current income and the sum of current expenditures for consumption and tax payments. Expenditures to reduce debt are counted as saving, and increases in debt are deducted from saving. Consumption expenditures include expenditures for consumer durable goods except houses, which are regarded as capital assets.

[2] Contingency table is the general term for a two-way classification specifying varying numbers of discrete categories in each of two dimensions.

TABLE 15–1

Observed Frequencies
Two-Way Classification of 3,327 Spending Units, 1950*

Spending units headed by	No. of positive savers	No. of zero savers plus no. of negative savers	Total
Single persons	490	390	880
Married persons	1,552	895	2,447
Total	2,042	1,285	3,327

* This table is based on data from the *Federal Reserve Bulletin*, September 1951, p. 1063. The investigation here recorded was made under the sponsorship of the Board of Governors of the Federal Reserve System.

problem is to determine whether the two principles of classification here employed are independent of one another. Was the fact of saving or nonsaving by spending units in 1950 related to the marital status of the heads of spending units? In dealing with a problem of this sort we set up the hypothesis that in the population of spending units from which this sample was drawn the two principles of classification are unrelated. We test this hypothesis against observations such as those recorded in Table 15-1.

From the hypothesis we are to test we may derive a series of theoretical or "expected" frequencies, i.e., frequencies we should expect to find in the four cells of Table 15-1 if marital status and saving practices were in fact independent, and if the effects of random fluctuations were not present. These expected frequencies may be computed readily from the subtotals in Table 15-1. The process is as follows: Of the 3,327 spending units included in the sample 880, or 26.45 percent of the total, were headed by single persons, while 2,447, or 73.55 percent of the total, were headed by married persons. If marital status had no relation to saving practices, we should expect the 2,042 positive savers to be divided between single and married groups in this same ratio (26.45 to 73.55); similarly, we should expect the 1,285 spending units which are classed as zero or negative savers to be divided between single and married groups in the same ratio. Applying this ratio to each of the column totals we have the expected frequencies that are given in Table 15-2.

The cell frequencies given in Table 15-2 have been computed to reflect the proportions that would be found in a population in

TABLE 15–2

Theoretical Frequencies
Two-Way Classification of 3,327 Spending Units on the Hypothesis
that the Principles of Classification are Independent

Spending units headed by	No. of positive savers	No. of zero savers plus no. of negative savers	Total
Single persons	540.1	339.9	880
Married persons	1,501.9	945.1	2,447
Total	2,042	1,285	3,327

which marital status and saving (or nonsaving) are unrelated. Since they correspond to assumed population proportions, they are unaffected by sampling fluctuations. The observed cell frequencies given in Table 15-1 differ from the expected, or theoretical, frequencies given in Table 15-2. These differences may be due merely to the chance fluctuations that would affect any finite sample; they may, on the other hand, be due to the presence of a real connection between saving tendencies and marital status. In other words, the hypothesis of independence may be false. The problem before us is to determine whether the differences between observed and theoretical cell frequencies are attributable to the play of chance, or whether they are too great to be attributed to chance. In the latter case, the hypothesis of independence must be rejected. Our task, then, is to evaluate these differences.

χ^2: **a Measure of Discrepancies between Observed and Theoretical Frequencies.** The magnitude, in the aggregate, of the differences between the two sets of cell frequencies that appear in Tables 15-1 and 15-2 might be defined in various ways. The quantity we shall here employ is derived by squaring the difference between the members of each pair of observed and theoretical frequencies, dividing each of these squared values by the corresponding expected theoretical frequency, and adding the quotients. The quantity thus obtained was called chi-square by Karl Pearson, who first made use of this measure; it is represented by the symbol χ^2. If we use f_0 for an observed class or cell frequency, and f for an expected or theoretical frequency, we may write

$$\chi^2 = \Sigma\left\{\frac{(f_0 - f)^2}{f}\right\} \qquad (15.1)$$

In the present example, using the observed and theoretical frequencies given in Tables 15-1 and 15-2, we have

$$\chi^2 = \frac{(490\text{-}540.1)^2}{540.1} + \frac{(390\text{-}339.9)^2}{339.9} + \frac{(1552\text{-}1501.9)^2}{1501.9} + \frac{(895\text{-}945.1)^2}{945.1}$$

$$= 4.6473 + 7.3846 + 1.6712 + 2.6558$$

$$= 16.3589$$

It is apparent that χ^2 will be zero if observed and theoretical frequencies are identical throughout. The greater the discrepancies between observation and expectation, the larger will χ^2 be. Its upper limit is infinity. In evaluating the observed χ^2 (for which we may use the symbol χ_0^2) we must determine whether it is of a magnitude that chance might bring about, or whether it is too great to be attributed to the play of random factors. To do this we must know how χ^2 is distributed when, in fact, chance alone is operative in bringing about differences between expectation and observation. Having this information we shall be able to appraise the values of χ^2 obtained in any specific case.

Notation. The following symbols are introduced in this chapter:

χ^2: a measure of the aggregate discrepancy between observed and theoretical frequencies; more generally, a quantity equal to the sum of the squares of n independent normal variates, each having zero mean and unit standard deviation

χ_0^2: an observed value of χ^2

χ_y^2: an observed value of χ^2 after the application of Yates' correction

$\chi_{.01}^2$, $\chi_{.99}^2$, etc.: percentile values of a χ^2 distribution

f_0, f_0': observed frequencies

f, f': theoretical or expected frequencies

n': the number of components of a particular χ_0^2; the number of cells or classes in which f_0 and f are compared

k: the number of linear constraints involved in the derivation of a particular χ_0^2

$n (= n' - k)$: the number of degrees of freedom entering into the calculation of a particular χ_0^2

Empirical Determination of a x^2 Distribution. For present purposes, we shall first derive from empirical data an approximation to the distribution of x^2 that is needed for testing the quantity (16.3589) obtained from the frequencies given in Tables 15-1 and 15-2. We shall then discuss the x^2 distribution in more general terms, and give further illustrations of the uses of this instrument.

In an earlier section (see p. 149) we presented some results from Weldon, derived from 4,096 throws of 12 dice, (a 4, 5, or 6 spot obtained with a single die being counted a success, a 1, 2, or 3 spot a failure). If we may assume that there are no differences among the 12 dice used by Weldon, and that each is flawless, we may obtain from Weldon's results a distribution of x^2 that is relevant to the test we wish to make. For in using Weldon's results we have a set of observed frequencies, we can determine with precision corresponding theoretical frequencies, and on the assumption that the dice were flawless we may attribute the divergence of observed from theoretical frequencies solely to the play of chance. We may thus derive the relative frequencies with which different values of x^2 will occur, when chance alone is operative.[3]

When 12 dice are thrown, a 4, 5, or 6 spot on a single die being counted as a success, the "expected" number of successes on each throw (the most likely outcome) is 6. A deviation from 6 represents a discrepancy between expectation and observation. From the result of each throw of 12 dice a value of x^2 may be computed. Thus, a given throw yields 2 successes and 10 failures. The 2 successes represent a deviation of 4 from the expected value of 6; the 10 failures represent a deviation of 4 from the expected value of 6. (In such an experiment as this there are two components of each value of x^2, even though when one component is given the other is necessarily determined. For the sum of successes and failures must be 12 on each throw.) Substituting these specific values in formula 15.1, we have

$$x^2 = \frac{(2-6)^2}{6} + \frac{(10-6)^2}{6} = 5.333$$

On another trial, with 7 successes and 5 failures, we have

$$x^2 = \frac{(7-6)^2}{6} + \frac{(5-6)^2}{6} = .333$$

[3] If Weldon's dice were not flawless, and if there were in fact differences among them, the approximation to the desired distribution of x^2 would be impaired. But we shall take account of this when we set our empirical results against theoretical models.

On still another trial, giving 6 successes and 6 failures, we have

$$\chi^2 = \frac{(6-6)^2}{6} + \frac{(6-6)^2}{6} = 0$$

The 4,096 throws thus yield 4,096 values of χ^2. Tabulating these with respect to the frequency of occurrence of stated values, we obtain the distribution given in Table 15-3.

TABLE 15–3

Tabulation of 4,096 Observed Values of X^2 ($n = 1$)
(Weldon data)

Value* of x^2 (measuring deviation of observation from expectancy in dice-throwing experiment)	Frequency of occurrence (absolute)	Frequency of occurrence (relative)
0 to .833	2,526	.6167
.833 to 2.167	966	.2358
2.167 to 4.167	455	.1111
4.167 to 6.667	131	.0320
Over 6.667	18	.0044
Total	4,096	1.0000

* The 4,096 values of χ^2 tabulated here constitute a discrete series. The conditions of the experiment are such that the 4,096 observations on χ^2 are distributed among only seven values, ranging from 0 to 12. In order that the observed frequencies of occurrence of stated values of χ^2 may be compared (in a later table) with theoretical frequencies, an uneven class-interval is employed above. Class limits are taken midway between successive values at which the actual observations fall. (The decimal fractions used in the table do not define these limits with full accuracy.) We should note that the restriction of the maximum value of χ^2 to 12 in this illustration is a characteristic of the particular example employed. If more dice than 12 were thrown each time, but with all other conditions unchanged, the maximum value of χ^2 would be higher, and the approximation would be closer.

This table gives us information as to the nature of the discrepancies between theoretical norms and actual results that chance may bring about. For deviations from the expected frequency of successes, 6, may be attributed to the mass of undifferentiated causes we call chance. The magnitude of χ^2 varies, of course, with the degree of deviation. Values of χ^2 not exceeding .833 are most frequent. Higher values of χ^2 occur with decreasing frequency. Only 18 out of 4,096 observed values of χ^2 exceed 6.667. This distribution furnishes us, therefore, with a standard of reference to employ when seeking to determine whether a given discrepancy between theoretical and observed values is attributable to chance, or whether it is too great to be so explained.

This use of the table, as an instrument for determining the probability that given discrepancies between theory and observation are attributable to the play of chance, is facilitated by a somewhat different arrangement. We may set up a table of cumulative values, based upon the tabulation of the 4,096 values of χ^2 obtained in the preceding experiment. These are given in Table 15-4.

TABLE 15–4

Cumulative Relative Frequencies of Occurrence of 4,096 Observed Values of χ^2, with Corresponding Theoretical Frequencies $(n = 1)$

(1) Value of χ^2 (cumulative deviation of observation from expectancy)	(2) Relative frequency of occurrence (Weldon data)	(3) Relative frequency of occurrence (theoretical)
0 or more	1.0000	1.0000
.833 or more	.3833	.3613
2.167 or more	.1475	.1411
4.167 or more	.0364	.0412
6.667 or more	.0044	.0098

The entries in column (2) of this table indicate that in the experiment involving 4,096 throws of dice, a value of χ^2 of 6.667 or more occurs less frequently than 1 time out of 100 (only 44 times out of 10,000, in fact). A value as great as 4.167, however, occurred more frequently than 3 times out of 100. If we interpret these relative frequencies as probabilities, we may obtain from such a table a knowledge of the probabilities corresponding to stated values of χ^2. Here is the instrument we desire, in seeking to determine whether given observations conform closely enough to expectations based on theory, or on working hypotheses we wish to test.

A Test of Independence. With this distribution before us we turn to the appraisal of the results obtained in the study of the marital status and saving behavior of the heads of spending units. The degree of divergence between observed cell frequencies shown in Table 15-1 and the corresponding cell frequencies shown in Table 15-2, which were derived on the assumption that marital status had no relation to saving or nonsaving, is measured by a χ^2 of 16.3589. Could merely random deviations of observed frequencies from assumed (hypothetical) frequencies account for an aggregate divergence as great as this? Using the standard provided by the relative frequencies given in column (2) of Table 15-4 the answer must be no. For these relative frequencies indicate that in only 44 cases out of 10,000 would chance factors yield a value of χ^2 as great as 6.667, or greater. The χ^2 value we have obtained—16.3589—is so improbable, on the assumption that chance alone is operative, that we must rule out that assumption. The hypothesis that the two principles of classification used in Table 15-1 are independent must be rejected. The observations recorded in that table provide strong evidence that saving behavior is related to marital status. Positive saving by single persons is less frequent and positive saving by married persons is more frequent than would be expected on the hypothesis of independence.

For purposes of demonstration the distribution of χ^2 given in column (2) of Table 15-4 has been built up empirically, from Weldon's data. But this distribution, which is subject to errors arising out of flaws in Weldon's dice, to the chance fluctuations that affect any finite sample, and to specific discontinuities arising from the nature of the dice-tossing procedure, is only an approximation to the one we desire. The entries in column (3) of Table 15-4 are free of these limitations. These record the frequencies with which values of χ^2 falling within the limits indicated in column (1) might be expected to occur, on the basis of theory, under the conditions of the present experiment.[4] These entries provide the standard to be employed in determining the significance of the discrepancies between observation and expectation that are found in Tables 15-1 and 15-2. The conclusion we would reach on the basis of the entries in column (3) of Table 15-4 is the same as that based on the entries in column (2). (The approximation given by Weldon's results is, indeed, fairly close to the true theoretical frequencies.)

[4] The theoretical values are from Yule and Kendall, Ref. 199. The entries in column (3) are not, in fact, true frequencies exactly relevant to the observed frequencies in Table 15-1. For the observed frequencies from which any value of χ^2 must be computed are integers; χ^2 is thus a discrete variable with a discontinuous distribution. But when the number of values that χ^2 might take is large, such a discontinuous distribution approaches a smooth curve. The theoretical relative frequencies that would be obtained from the appropriate discontinuous distribution may then be closely approximated by relative frequencies obtained from a smooth distribution function. This is what has been done in deriving the entries given in column (3) of Table 15-4, and in subsequent tables of the χ^2 distribution.

Comments on the Example and the Test

Before discussing the general nature of χ^2, we shall briefly note certain conditions characterizing the data cited above and the procedures employed in making the test.

1. The data define absolute not relative frequencies.
2. The total number of observations is large; the theoretical frequency in each of the four individual cells (Table 15-2) is large.
3. The individual observations making up the sample are independent. The drawings by which we have obtained the entries in the various cells have been random operations.
4. No assumption is made concerning the distribution of members of the population of which our 3,327 observations constitute a sample. In particular, we should note that we make no assumption that the parent population is normally distributed.
5. The quantity χ^2, for the particular example cited, is derived with 1 degree of freedom. If we use n to designate degrees of freedom, n' the number of components of χ^2 (n' is the number of cells in this instance), and k the number of independent restrictions or constraints placed upon the freedom of observed and expected frequencies to vary, we may write

$$n = n' - k$$

In the present instance χ^2 is derived from the entries in 4 cells of Tables 15-1 and 15-2; $n' = 4$. But the observed and expected frequencies are made to agree in three independent respects: (1) N is the same in the two cases. (2) The subtotals or marginal frequencies in the right-hand column of Table 15-2 are made to agree with those in the right-hand column of Table 15-1. Although both the subtotals in the second table agree with those in the first, this agreement represents only 1 independent constraint, since both subtotals are fixed as soon as 1 subtotal and N are defined. (3) The subtotals in the bottom row of Tables 15-2 and 15-1 are made to agree. Here, again, this agreement represents only 1 independent constraint, since N has already been defined.

The effect of fixing N and both sets of subtotals is to leave only one degree of freedom for the cell frequencies, f_0 and f, to differ. That is,

$$n = 4 - 3 = 1$$

We may express this condition in another way by saying that, given the equality of subtotals in Tables 15-1 and 15-2, we are free arbitrarily to specify frequencies in 1 of the 4 cells. For as soon as 1 is set, the other 3 cell frequencies may be derived by subtraction from the subtotals of rows and columns.

The reader should note that the values of χ^2 in Table 15-3, the distribution of which provided the standard used in testing the significance of the observed χ^2 (16.3589), were also derived with 1 degree of freedom. Although there were two components of each of the values of χ^2 derived from Weldon's data (see p. 516), one of these components (say the number of failures) was determined as soon as the other (the number of successes) was given.

As will appear in the later discussion, the form of the χ^2 distribution varies with changes in the degrees of freedom entering into the calculation of χ^2. In testing a given observed value of χ^2 for significance, the test must of course be made with reference to the theoretical distribution of χ^2 having the same degrees of freedom as the observed χ^2.

The χ^2 distribution with $n = 5$. That the distribution of χ^2 varies as n varies is a fact of central importance in the application of the χ^2 test. It will be useful at this point to note the kind of distribution obtained when n is, say, 5, instead of 1 as in the preceding example. Consider the outcome of a throw of 24 dice, account being taken of the frequency of occurrence of each possible result (i.e., the appearance of a 1, 2, 3, 4, 5, or 6 spot). When 24 dice are thrown the "expected" frequencies are 4 one spots, 4 two spots; 4 three spots, etc. In a given throw we obtain the following results:

	Number of spots					
	1	2	3	4	5	6
Observed frequency	2	5	6	4	4	3
Expected frequency	4	4	4	4	4	4

For the results of this throw the value of Chi-square would be given by

$$\chi^2 = \frac{(2-4)^2}{4} + \frac{(5-4)^2}{4} + \frac{(6-4)^2}{4} + \frac{(4-4)^2}{4} + \frac{(4-4)^2}{4}$$
$$+ \frac{(3-4)^2}{4} = 2.50$$

This quantity has 6 components. However, as soon as five are given the sixth is determined, since the total number of events is fixed at 24. There are, then, 5 degrees of freedom in the calculation of χ^2 in this experiment.

If the 24 dice were thrown 1,000 times, we should have 1,000 values of χ^2. A distribution of these could be constructed, similar to that derived empirically for the case in which there was 1 degree of freedom. It would be a different distribution, however, for the change in degrees of freedom has an obvious relation to the magnitude of X^2. The character of the distribution of the values of X^2 that would be obtained in such an experiment is indicated by the entries in Table 15-5. We do not here give empirical values, as in the preceding example. The table shows the theoretical frequencies with which given values of X^2 occur, when 5 degrees of freedom prevail.

TABLE 15–5

Tabulation of X^2, Computed with 5 Degrees of Freedom*

Value of χ^2	Relative frequency of occurrence (theoretical)
0 to 0.999	.0374
1 to 1.999	.1135
2 to 2.999	.1491
3 to 3.999	.1506
4 to 4.999	.1335
5 to 5.999	.1097
6 to 6.999	.0856
7 to 7.999	.0644
8 to 8.999	.0471
9 to 9.999	.0339
10 to 10.999	.0238
11 to 11.999	.0166
12 or more	.0348

* From the table prepared by W. P. Elderton, and given in Pearson, *Tables for Statisticians and Biometricians*.

The χ^2 Distribution: Some General Characteristics

A basic measure with which we have worked in the preceding example is $f_0 - f$, the difference between an observed frequency in a given cell or class and a corresponding theoretical frequency derived from some rational hypothesis. It will be convenient to use the symbol x for the quantity $f_0 - f$. We may conceive of a sampling process, analogous to Weldon's dice throwing, that gives us, with each trial, a measure of f_0 for each of two classes or cells. Given theoretical frequencies f with which to compare the observed frequencies f_0, we may obtain from each trial a measure of the variable x, for each of 2 cells. If the hypothesis from which we obtained the theoretical f's is in fact true, the values of f_0 that we get from repeated sampling operations will, in each cell, be normally distributed about f for that cell.[5] This means that x will be

[5] For in specifying f as the expected frequency in a given cell we are saying that, in drawing a sample of size N from a stated population, the probability that a given individual will fall in that cell is f/N. The probability that a given individual will not fall in that cell is $(N - f)/N$, or $1 - (f/N)$. But these are the conditions that yield a binomial distribution. When the total N is fairly large, and when f/N is not very small, such a distribution will very closely approximate the normal.

normally distributed about a mean of zero. We shall have such a variable x for each of the 2 cells of the table we have constructed. But since one of these variables will be dependent on the other (for each trial the number of "failures" will equal N less the number of "successes"), there will in this two-category case be one independent and normally distributed variable.

In the more general situation, we shall have such a random variable x for each of the n' cells of the contingency table. Not all of these will be independent, because of the constraints introduced. But if there are n degrees of freedom there will be n independent and normally distributed random variables x. It may be shown that the sum of n such independent normal variates will be distributed normally. However, before we added the random variables x that measure the difference between observed and theoretical frequencies in the various cells, these variables were squared. The distribution of the sum of the *squares* of a number of independent normal variates will not be normal; when the squares of n such variates (each with zero mean and unit standard deviation) are added, the distribution of the sum follows the distinctive and important χ^2 form.[6]

We have discussed above the form of the distribution of χ^2 in a single case, when $n - 1$. But the χ^2 distribution, like that of t, consists of many distributions, varying as n varies. If we are to

---

[6] The statement in the preceding footnote may be here carried forward, to illuminate the present point.

The expected frequency f, which is the divisor in formula 15.1 for χ^2, is, for "successes," equivalent to Np, the mean of a binomial distribution. For $f/N = p$, and the product $Np = N(f/N) = f$. For "failures," of which the probability is $q(= 1 - p)$ the theoretical frequency f is equal to Nq. It may be shown that for such a two-category case the two components of χ^2, for which the divisors (the expected values) are Np and Nq, may be combined to give an equation of the type

$$\chi^2 = \frac{(f_0 - Np)^2}{Npq}$$

The numerator of the right-hand member of this equation is the square of a normally distributed variate with mean zero; the denominator is the square of the standard deviation of this variate. (The quantity $\sqrt{Npq}$ is, of course, the standard deviation of a binomial distribution for which p is the probability of a success, q the probability of a failure, and N is the number of independent events in a trial. We are here assuming that the theoretical cell frequencies are sufficiently large so that the binomial distribution may for practical purposes be regarded as normal). Hence the right-hand member as a whole is the square of a normal variate with mean zero and unit standard deviation. If N is large, this quantity has the χ^2 distribution with 1 degree of freedom.

In the extension of the argument to the more general situation, involving more than two categories, probabilities are determined from the multinomial distribution. The general expression for the distribution of χ^2 is derived from the latter.

have an instrument suitable for wide application, we must have knowledge of the sampling distribution of χ^2 under varied conditions. This distribution may be described in mathematical terms, by means of a frequency function that defines the relative frequency with which specified values of χ^2 will occur for any given value of n.[7] These relative frequencies, interpreted as probabilities, enable the investigator to evaluate an observed χ^2. The equation is, however, a somewhat complex one. Alternative and far simpler means of applying the χ^2 test are provided by prepared tables, giving critical values of χ^2 (i.e., values corresponding to probabilities of 0.95, 0.99, etc.) for varying degrees of freedom. For purposes of substantive research, these tables give all the information needed concerning the distribution of χ^2.

Before turning to the use of such tables, it will be helpful to consider the changes that occur in the character of the χ^2 distribution as n varies. As we have seen, χ^2 ranges between zero and infinity, but the manner in which χ^2 is distributed between these two limits varies widely, with variations in the degrees of freedom. This variation is clearly revealed in Fig. 15.1, showing frequency curves for distributions corresponding to n's of 2, 3, 5, and 6. For $n = 2$ the frequency curve decreases steadily. The other curves charted have clearly defined maximum values (in each case at a value of χ^2 equal to $n - 2$). The curves show a fairly rapid approach to symmetry as n increases. The χ^2 distribution tends, indeed, to normality as n tends to infinity—a point to which we shall refer again shortly.

Certain other attributes of the χ^2 distribution may be noted. For any stated number (n) of degrees of freedom, the mean value of the χ^2 distribution will equal that number; i.e., $M = n$. The moments about the mean will be given by

$$\mu_2 = 2n$$

$$\mu_3 = 8n$$

$$\mu_4 = 48n + 12n^2$$

Thus the standard deviation will equal $\sqrt{2n}$. The mode, as we have

[7] This frequency function may be written

$$y = \frac{1}{\left(\frac{n}{2} - 1\right)!} \cdot \frac{1}{2^{n/2}} \left(\chi^2\right)^{(n-2)/2} e^{-\chi^2/2}$$

where n is the number of degrees of freedom.

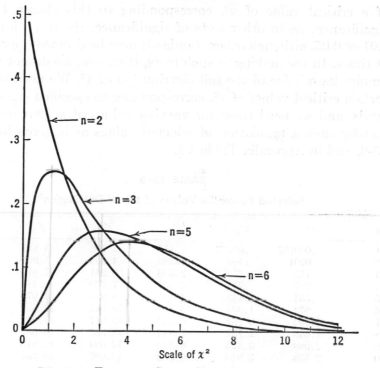

FIG. 15.1. Frequency Curves Showing Distribution of χ^2 for $n = 2, 3, 5, 6$.

indicated, will equal $n - 2$. From the indicated values of mean, mode, and standard deviation it follows that the skewness of a χ^2 distribution will be measured by $\sqrt{2/n}$. (This is Pearson's measure of skewness $(M - M_0)/\sigma$.) These measures relate, of course, to the theoretical distributions that are represented by smooth curves such as those plotted in Fig. 15.1.

On the Application of the χ^2 Test

The Use of Tabulated Percentile Values of χ^2. In the example of a χ^2 test cited on preceding pages we merely noted that the observed value of χ^2 was so great, when set against the relevant χ^2 distribution, that the hypothesis we were testing could not be accepted. If the hypothesis (of independence) had been in fact true, the play of chance could not have brought about so great a value of χ^2. In formal testing we should, however, establish in advance a precise standard for use in accepting or rejecting hypotheses. This involves the selection of a significance level and the determination of a critical value of χ^2, corresponding to this chosen level of significance. As in other tests of significance, the usual levels are 0.01 or 0.05, although other standards may be deemed appropriate at times. In the making of such tests, therefore, we do not usually require knowledge of the full distribution of χ^2. We need to know certain critical values of χ^2, corresponding to specified significance levels, and we need these for varying values of n. Our needs are met by such a tabulation of selected values as is given in Table 15-6, and in Appendix Table VI.

TABLE 15–6

Selected Percentile Values of the χ^2 Distribution*

n	$\chi^2_{.01}$	$\chi^2_{.05}$	$\chi^2_{.50}$	$\chi^2_{.90}$	$\chi^2_{.95}$	$\chi^2_{.99}$
1	.000157	.00393	.455	2.706	3.841	6.635
2	.0201	.103	1.386	4.605	5.991	9.210
3	.115	.352	2.366	6.251	7.815	11.341
4	.297	.711	3.357	7.779	9.488	13.277
5	.554	1.145	4.351	9.236	11.070	15.086
6	.872	1.635	5.348	10.645	12.592	16.812
7	1.239	2.167	6.346	12.017	14.067	18.475
8	1.646	2.733	7.344	13.362	15.507	20.090
9	2.088	3.325	8.343	14.684	16.919	21.666
10	2.558	3.940	9.342	15.987	18.307	23.209
11	3.053	4.575	10.341	17.275	19.675	24.725
12	3.571	5.226	11.340	18.549	21.026	26.217
13	4.107	5.892	12.340	19.812	22.362	27.688
14	4.660	6.571	13.339	21.064	23.685	29.141
15	5.229	7.261	14.339	22.307	24.996	30.578
16	5.812	7.962	15.338	23.542	26.296	32.000
17	6.408	8.672	16.338	24.769	27.587	33.409
18	7.015	9.390	17.338	25.989	28.869	34.805
19	7.633	10.117	18.338	27.204	30.144	36.191
20	8.260	10.851	19.337	28.412	31.410	37.566
21	8.897	11.591	20.337	29.615	32.671	38.932
22	9.542	12.338	21.337	30.813	33.924	40.289
23	10.196	13.091	22.337	32.007	35.172	41.638
24	10.856	13.848	23.337	33.196	36.415	42.980
25	11.524	14.611	24.337	34.382	37.652	44.314
26	12.198	15.379	25.336	35.563	38.885	45.642
27	12.879	16.151	26.336	36.741	40.113	46.963
28	13.565	16.928	27.336	37.916	41.337	48.278
29	14.256	17.708	28.336	39.087	42.557	49.588
30	14.953	18.493	29.336	40.256	43.773	50.892

* This table is reproduced here through the courtesy of R. A. Fisher and his publishers, Oliver and Boyd, of Edinburgh. The entries are taken from Table III of *Statistical Methods for Research Workers*. Column headings are here given as χ^2 percentiles, which correspond to the probability headings given by Fisher. The present table is an abridgment of the original.

The subscripts used in the headings of the several columns indicate percentile values. Thus when we find under $x^2_{.01}$ in the line $n = 5$ a value 0.554, it means that 1 percent of the total area under the curve defining the distribution of x^2 with 5 degrees of freedom will fall to the left of an ordinate erected at 0.554 on the horizontal scale, which is the scale on which x^2 values are recorded. The value of $x^2_{.05}$ for $n = 5$ is 1.145; 5 percent of the area under the curve will lie to the left of an ordinate erected at this point. The 95th percentile, again with 5 degrees of freedom, is 11.070; 95 percent of the area under the curve will lie to the left of an ordinate at this point, and 5 percent of the area will lie to the right. Since these proportionate areas correspond to probabilities, this last statement may be put in this form: With 5 degrees of freedom, the probability that a random value of x^2 from this distribution will equal or exceed 11.070 is 5 out of 100. Figure 15.2 shows the relation of the area of rejection (shown in black) to the total area under the curve for a significance level of 0.05, with $n = 5$.

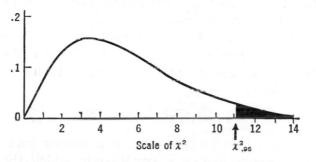

FIG. 15.2. Distribution of x^2 for $n - 5$, with Area of Rejection at .05 Level.

In applying the test in a given case we set the observed value, x^2_0, against the percentile value that corresponds to the chosen significance level, say $x^2_{.99}$. If x^2_0 is less than $x^2_{.99}$, we conclude that the observations are not inconsistent with the hypothesis being tested, which we therefore accept. If x^2_0 is greater than $x^2_{.99}$, we reject the hypothesis. For if the hypothesis should in fact be true, chance would bring about such an observed value of x^2 only 1 time in 100, or less frequently. Given the alternatives of rejecting, or assuming that this rare event has occurred, we prefer to reject the hypothesis. As usually applied, this is a one-tailed test. We are asking whether the discrepancy between observation and expectation is too great to be attributed to chance, and are hence concerned with probabilities represented by the upper tail of the χ^2 distribution. However, as R. A. Fisher has pointed out, suspicion may attach to very low values of χ^2. Thus if χ_0^2 were smaller than $\chi_{.01}^2$ we should have a closeness of agreement between observation and expectation that would be expected, in terms of probabilities, less frequently than 1 time in 100. Such virtual coincidence of observed and theoretical values might occur as a result of chance, but this is so unlikely that we should look for other explanations. The situation suggests an artificial forcing of agreement between hypothesis and observation, such as we might get if the hypothesis were derived from the observations that are used to test the hypothesis. This would, of course, be logically fallacious.

The χ^2 test when n exceeds 30. The selected values of χ^2 in Table 15-6 relate only to distributions for which n is between 1 and 30. For tests involving values of n greater than 30 use is made of the fact that the distribution of the quantity $\sqrt{2\chi^2}$ approximates the normal distribution when n is not small.[8] For n of 30 or more the approximation is acceptably close. The mean of the distribution of $\sqrt{2\chi^2}$ is $\sqrt{2n-1}$, and the standard deviation is equal to 1. Thus the application of a test is simple, for the deviation of $\sqrt{2\chi^2}$ from $\sqrt{2n-1}$ may be interpreted as a normal deviate with unit standard deviation. That is

$$T = \sqrt{2\chi^2} - \sqrt{2n-1} \qquad (15.2)$$

As an example of such a test, consider a comparison of observed and expected frequencies in a situation in which there are 41 degrees of freedom. Let us assume that the observed χ^2 is 72. We then have

$$T = \sqrt{2 \times 72} - \sqrt{(2 \times 41) - 1} = 12 - 9$$
$$= 3$$

The chance of a deviation of three standard deviations from the mean of a normal distribution is so small that we must reject this possibility. We conclude that the divergence of observed from

---

[8] We have already noted that the distribution of χ^2 tends to normality as n increases. However, R. A. Fisher has shown that this tendency is more pronounced for the quantity $\sqrt{2\chi^2}$ than it is for χ^2; thus for a stated value of n we get a better approximation to normality by using the distribution of the former quantity.

expected frequencies in the present instance is too great to be attributed to random factors.

The χ^2 test is applicable to a considerable variety of problems. Whenever, on rational grounds, a set of theoretical frequencies may be derived, for comparison with observed frequencies, this test is appropriate in judging of the significance of discrepancies between the two sets of frequencies. In customary uses of the test theoretical frequencies may be derived on the hypothesis that two principles of classification, applied to the same individual entities, are independent of one another; on the hypothesis that a series of observations, grouped in sets or subsets, are homogeneous in respect of certain definable characteristics (i.e., that the observations relate in fact to entities drawn from the same parent population); on the hypothesis that sample data making up a given frequency distribution are drawn from a population definable by a certain ideal frequency curve. The tests applied in dealing with problems of the three types are termed tests of independence, tests of homogeneity, and tests of goodness of fit.

A *test of independence* has been illustrated by the example with which this chapter opened (see Tables 15-1 and 15-2). This was a special case in that we used a 2×2 table, containing 4 cells, and the problem involved only 1 degree of freedom. The principles of classification might have given us more columns than 2, more rows than 2, and more cells than 4. However, the procedures employed with the larger number of cells would have been the same, except for the use of a different value of n in applying the test. The general relationship from which we may determine n when a test of independence is to be based upon a contingency table containing r rows and c columns is given by $n = (r - 1)(c - 1)$.

A Test of Homogeneity. The Internal Revenue Service has summarized income tax returns received for the year 1951 from 9,036 corporations actively engaged in mining and quarrying. Of these, 4,966 reported net income for that year, while 4,070 reported no net income. That is, approximately 55 percent showed profit for the year, 45 percent showed deficits. Corporations in the major group classed as mining and quarrying are subdivided into five minor groups—metal mining, anthracite mining, bituminous coal and lignite mining, crude petroleum and natural gas production, and nonmetallic mining and quarrying. This question arises: May the 9,036 mining and quarrying corporations be regarded as coming from a single population that is homogeneous with respect to the profitability of operations in 1951, or does the division of corporations into those earning net incomes and those suffering deficits vary significantly from group to group? Data bearing on this question appear in Table 15-7.

TABLE 15–7

Classification of Income Tax Returns for the Year 1951 for Five Classes of Corporations Engaged in Mining and Quarrying, Showing Number Reporting Net Income and Number Reporting No Net Income*

Industrial group	Number of returns showing net income	Number of returns showing no net income	Total number of returns
Metal mining	226	667	893
Anthracite mining	114	117	231
Bituminous coal and lignite mining	912	901	1,813
Crude petroleum and natural gas production	2,436	1,704	4,140
Nonmetallic mining and quarrying	1,278	681	1,959
Total	4,966	4,070	9,036

* Source: Preliminary Report: *Statistics of Income for 1951, Part 2, Corporation Income Tax Returns,* Internal Revenue Service, U. S. Treasury Department, 1954. For definition of terms, see this report.

Of the broad group of corporations engaged in mining and quarrying, 54.96 percent showed a profit in 1951. On the hypothesis that the group, considered as a whole, is homogeneous, we obtain a theoretical frequency for each of the minor groups by taking this percentage of the total number of returns reported for each minor group. That is, the theoretical frequency of success for a given minor group is that to be expected on the assumption that the probability of making a profit in 1951 was, for this group, 0.5496, as it was for all mining and quarrying corporations. Conversely, the probability of failing to make a profit is taken to be 0.4504 for each minor group. Thus for metal mining the theoretical frequency for the "net income" class is given by 0.5496 × 893, which is 491; for the "no net income" class the theoretical frequency is 0.4504 × 893, or 402.

Table 15-8 gives observed and theoretical frequencies, by groups, and outlines the operations that yield χ^2. As in the preceding example, we use the symbols f_0 and f for observed and theoretical frequencies in the "net income" classes. The same symbols, with prime marks, are used for the "no net income" classes. Both elements contribute to the final value of χ^2.

TABLE 15–8

Test of Homogeneity
Comparison of Observed and Theoretical Frequencies, Mining and Quarrying Corporations Classified According to Profitability of Operations in 1951

Industrial group	Corporations showing net income			Corporations showing no net income			Total number of returns
(1)	(2) f_0	(3) f	(4) $\dfrac{(f_0 - f)^2}{f}$	(5) f_0'	(6) f'	(7) $\dfrac{(f_0' - f')^2}{f'}$	(8)
Metal mining	226	491	143.02	667	402	174.69	803
Anthracite mining	114	127	1.33	117	104	1.62	231
Bituminous coal and lignite mining	912	996	7.08	901	817	8.64	1,813
Crude petroleum and natural gas production	2,436	2,275	11.39	1,704	1,865	13.90	4,140
Nonmetallic mining and quarrying	1,278	1,077	37.51	681	882	45.81	1,959
Total	4,966	4,966	200.33	4,070	4,070	244.66	9,036

The discrepancy, in the aggregate, between the observed and theoretical frequencies given in Table 15-8 is measured by the sum of the totals of columns (4) and (7). Thus we have $\chi^2 = 200.33 + 244.66 = 444.99$. This is derived from 10 individual entries in columns (4) and (7), corresponding to 10 comparisons of pairs of observed and theoretical frequencies. There are, however, only 4 degrees of freedom in the computation of χ^2. For it is clear that as soon as we fill in 4 of the 10 cells for which theoretical frequencies are to be determined, the other 6 are fixed, in view of the necessary equality of the marginal totals. In other words, there are 6 constraints, limiting the freedom of observed and theoretical frequencies to differ: The grand totals of the two sets of frequencies must agree; the sums of observed and theoretical frequencies in the "net income" subdivision must be the same (there must also be identity of the sums of observed and theoretical frequencies for the "no net income" subdivision, but this is not an independent condition, since it follows from the equality of the two sets of frequencies for the "net income" subdivision and the equality of the grand totals); for each of 4 minor groups the sums of observed and theoretical frequencies in the "net income" and "no net income" classes must agree (this must also be true for the fifth minor group, but this is not an independent condition; it follows from the other specified conditions). Thus for the degrees of freedom we have

$$n = n' - k = 10 - 6 = 4$$

In testing for significance we set χ_0^2 (444.99) against $\chi_{.99}^2$ if we are working with a 0.01 level of significance. For $n = 4$, $\chi_{.99}^2 = 13.3$. The observed value is much greater than this. Chance alone could not account for the discrepancies between observed and theoretical values. We must reject the hypothesis that the various classes of corporations engaged in mining and quarrying come from a population that was homogeneous in respect of profitability of operations in 1951.

In making a test of homogeneity of the type illustrated, the investigator must be sure that account is taken of frequencies of *nonoccurrence*, as well as occurrence. If we had based the above test on records for corporations showing net income, and had omitted those showing no net income, the result would have been invalid.

A Test of Goodness of Fit. When an ideal frequency curve, whether normal or of some other type, is fitted to an actual frequency distribution, theory and observation are being compared. A test of the concordance of the two (i.e., of goodness of fit) may be made by inspection, but such a test is obviously inadequate. Precision may be secured by employing the χ^2 test. The example in Table 15-9, relating to the distribution of telephone subscribers discussed in Chapter 6, illustrates the procedure.

In such a problem we must specify clearly the hypothesis that is to be tested. In the present instance we set forth, in effect, the following hypothesis: The sample of telephone subscribers for which frequencies are given in column (2) of Table 15-9 has been drawn from a normally distributed population of telephone subscribers having mean 476.96 and standard deviation 147.70. The

TABLE 15-9

Computation of X^2 for Testing Goodness of Fit
Normal Curve of Error Fitted to Distribution of Telephone Subscribers

(1) Class limits	(2) Observed frequency f_0	(3) Theoretical frequency f	(4) $(f_0 - f)$	(5) $\dfrac{(f_0 - f)^2}{f}$
150 and less	10	13.48	− 3.48	.90
150–200	19	16.42	+ 2.58	.41
200–250	38	31.57	+ 6.43	1.31
250–300	50	53.02	− 3.02	.17
300–350	95	79.43	+ 15.57	3.05
350–400	85	106.10	− 21.10	4.20
400–450	115	126.41	− 11.41	1.03
450–500	132	134.31	− 2.31	.04
500–550	144	123.75	+ 20.25	3.31
550–600	116	108.26	+ 7.74	.55
600–650	79	81.85	− 2.85	.10
650–700	54	55.21	− 1.21	.03
700–750	31	33.19	− 2.19	.14
750–800	11	17.81	− 6.81	2.60
More than 800	16	14.19	+ 1.81	.23
	995	995.00	15 groups	$x^2 = 18.07$

population values of mean and standard deviation here given are the sample values; having no other basis for specifying these population parameters, we estimate them from the data of the sample.[9] That is, we impose agreement between observed and theoretical frequencies in these two respects. Since we also make Σf_0 and Σf identical, there are, in all, 3 independent constraints laid upon the observed and theoretical frequencies. Another way of putting this is to say that three constants N, m, and s, have been employed in the process of fitting the ideal curve. Since n', the

---

[9] There is an important theoretical difference between a problem of this sort, in which certain parameters of the hypothetical distribution are estimated from observations included in the sample, and one in which the theoretical distribution is completely specified by the hypothesis. In the latter case none of the parameters need be estimated from the data. (The use of totals and subtotals in calculating theoretical frequencies does not involve the estimation of population parameters.) However, it has been established that the procedures already outlined may be employed when parameters are estimated from actual observations, provided that the number of degrees of freedom is reduced by one unit for each parameter estimated from the sample and provided, also, that the method of maximum likelihood has been employed in estimating the parameters in question. Precautions already noted concerning the minimum size of theoretical cell frequencies should be carefully observed. (See Fisher, Ref. 47, Paper 8 and Cramér, Ref. 23).

number of classes involved in the comparison, is 15, and k, the number of constraints, is 3, we have for degrees of freedom

$$n = n' - k = 15 - 3 = 12$$

It is appropriate to use an 0.05 level of significance in such a test as this.

The derivation of χ^2 from the general formula $\chi^2 = \Sigma\{(f_0 - f)^2/f\}$ is shown in Table 15-9. For the observed value of chi-square we have $\chi_0^2 = 18.07$. Testing for significance, we note from Table 15-6 (or Appendix Table VI) that $\chi_{.95}^2$, the 95th percentile value of χ^2 with 12 degrees of freedom, is 21.0. Since this exceeds χ_0^2, we conclude that the fit is acceptable. The aggregate deviation of observed frequencies from the frequencies corresponding to the fitted normal curve is well within the range of chance fluctuations. The hypothesis that the sample is drawn from a normally distributed parent population is therefore tenable.

One feature of Table 15-9 requires explanation. It will be noted that in the construction of this table the three classes at the lower end of the distribution have been lumped into one, and that the same thing has been done with the six classes at the upper end of the distribution (*cp.* Table 6-3). This is done to avoid the undue magnification of slight differences between the tails of the observed and theoretical distributions. When f, the theoretical frequency, is very small, a relatively slight absolute discrepancy between f_0 and f may serve to swell materially the value of χ^2. (See the statement on p. 522 on the requirement that no one of the cell values of f/N be very small.) A good working rule is that no theoretical cell frequency should be less than 10. Although this rule may be relaxed somewhat when the number of degrees of freedom is 3 or more, 5 may be regarded as the minimum acceptable theoretical frequency in any cell.

The use of χ^2 in testing the fit of theoretical frequency curves is subject to another rather important limitation. In the computation of χ^2 no account is taken of the manner in which discrepancies between f_0 and f are distributed. Yet the distribution of these discrepancies may materially influence our judgment as to the goodness of a given fit. In such an example as that given in Table 15-9, the successive values of $f_0 - f$, counting from the lower limit of the x-scale, might be alternately positive and negative. Something approaching this alternation would be expected if chance factors alone accounted for the differences between observed and theoretical frequencies. But the differences might be distributed otherwise. All the values of $f_0 - f$ below the mode might be positive, while all the values above the mode might be negative. The cumulated discrepancies, as measured by χ^2, might be equal in the two cases, yet far more confidence would attach to a fit marked by alternations of plus and minus deviations than to one in which a series of positive deviations were bunched together on the scale, and negative discrepancies were correspondingly clustered. This limitation serves as a warning against purely mechanical use of the χ^2 test. Examination of the fit, and interpretation of χ^2 in the light of the actual distribution of discrepancies, are required in the application of this test.

In the preceding illustration of a test of goodness of fit, two parameters of the hypothetical normal distribution were estimated from the observations. We took account of this fact by corresponding reductions in the degrees of freedom appropriate to the test. If the hypothesis had fully specified the distribution, without drawing on the sample for estimates of the population mean and standard deviation, this reduction would not have been necessary. In that case only one constraint (growing out of the equality of Σf_0 and Σf) would have been imposed, and we should have lost 1 degree of freedom, not 3.

Yates' Correction for Continuity. We have noted that χ^2 is a discrete variable; the graphic representation of its discontinuous distribution would be a histogram. However, in employing prepared χ^2 tables in applying the usual test, we are using values derived from a smooth distribution function. What we are doing here is analogous to the use of a table of areas under the normal curve to approximate proportions that would be derived from a discontinuous binomial distribution. In both cases the approximation is close, and altogether adequate, when we are dealing with fairly large numbers. The χ^2-test conditions already noted, concerning minimum values of N and of the expected frequencies in individual cells, are related to the requirements of this approximation. In the special case of a 2×2 contingency table the approximation may be improved, and bias arising out of the use of small theoretical frequencies may be reduced, by means of a correction proposed by F. Yates (Ref. 196).

The bias of this situation tends to exaggerate the true values of χ^2. The correction involves the reduction of the deviations of observed from theoretical frequencies, which of course reduces the value of χ^2. The working rule for the application of the correction may be put in these terms: Adjust the observed frequency in each cell of the 2×2 table in such a way as to reduce the absolute deviation of the observed from the theoretical frequency for that cell by $\frac{1}{2}$; adjustments for all the cells are to be made without changing the marginal totals. This operation will increase f_0 by $\frac{1}{2}$ in each of 2 cells, and will reduce f_0 by $\frac{1}{2}$ in each of 2 cells. The correction is not applied in cases in which it would affect the algebraic sign of the deviation of f_0 from f for any one of the 4 cells. In such a case the f_0's, being integers, are as close to the f's as they could be; the aggregate of the observed deviations would not be significant at any level.

The following observed and theoretical frequencies in a two-way classification serve as an example of a test in which Yates' correction may be usefully applied.

	Observed frequencies (f_0)			Theoretical frequencies (f)		
			Total			Total
	12	18	30	18	12	30
	48	22	70	42	28	70
Total	60	40	100	60	40	100

The theoretical frequencies are derived from the marginal subtotals, as in the example given in Table 15-1 and 15-2. If we apply the χ^2 test to the above f_0's and f's, we obtain $\chi_0^2 = 7.1$. Since $\chi_{.99}^2 = 6.635$ for the 1 degree of freedom that we have in such a comparison, the result of the test would be clearly significant at an 0.01 level. We should conclude that the results are inconsistent with the hypothesis that the principles of classification employed are independent. However, with N and f's as small as they are in this example, the correction for continuity is appropriate. Employing the general rule set forth above we should have the following adjusted f_0's:

12.5	17.5	30
47.5	22.5	70
60	40	100

Setting these adjusted frequencies against the theoretical frequencies given above, we obtain $\chi_y^2 = 6.00$ (the subscript y is here used to indicate that Yates' corrections have been applied in obtaining the given value of χ^2). This is smaller than $\chi^2_{.99}$ for 1 degree of freedom. Using an 0.01 standard, we now conclude that the deviations of the observed from the expected frequencies are not clearly significant. The results are not inconsistent with the hypothesis of independence. Since χ_y^2 is the preferred approximation the result of the second test is the one we should accept.

Although Yates' correction is particularly called for when the sample employed in a χ^2 test is small, the correction does not make small N's and f's tolerable. Even when the corrections are to be applied the theoretical frequencies in individual cells should not ordinarily fall below the limits suggested on p. 534. For N's and f's of acceptable size the correction is desirable when observed (uncorrected) values of χ^2 fall near a critical level, for acceptance or rejection. For quite large N's and f's the correction will, of course, have only slight effect on the value of χ^2.

Summary Notes on the Use of χ^2 **in Tests of Significance.** Knowledge of the distribution of χ^2 provides the investigator with a powerful research tool. It is chiefly used in testing hypotheses that provide a set of theoretical frequencies, with which observed frequencies may be compared. Using χ^2, we are able to evaluate discrepancies between observed and theoretical frequencies, and thus to decide whether, on stated levels of significance, the hypotheses in question are to be accepted or rejected. Since χ^2 is derived from observations, it is a statistic and not a parameter (there is no parameter corresponding to it). The χ^2 test is therefore termed *nonparametric*. It is one of the great advantages of this test that it involves no assumptions about the form of the original distributions from which the observations come.

In the preceding discussion we have noted some of the conditions attaching to the use of this tool. We here summarize certain of these, and include other relevant comments.

1. As a test of independence of principles of classification, χ^2 is not a measure of the degree or form of relationship between such principles. It tells us whether two principles of classification are or are not significantly related, without reference to any assumption concerning the form of the relationship. Other

measures (some of which were discussed in Chapter 9) are needed to define degree and nature of relationship.[10]

2. In applying the χ^2 test, the frequencies used must be absolute, not relative. If we know the total N to which given relative frequencies apply, these may of course be changed to absolute frequencies. (The reason for this condition is obvious: The significance of a given divergence of f_0 from f depends on the absolute magnitude of f. The divergence of 4 from 3 may be negligible, the divergence of 400 from 300, which is the same in relative terms, may be highly significant.)

3. The separate observations making up the original sample should be independent of one another.

4. Small theoretical frequencies in individual cells or classes are to be avoided. An f of 10 is regarded as adequate although 5 may be acceptable when n is greater than 2; larger f's give greater precision to the test.

5. The sample size, N, should not be small. An absolute minimum of 50 has been suggested by Yule and Kendall.

6. In making a χ^2 test, the relevant number of degrees of freedom, n, is determined from the relation $n = n' - k$. The symbol n' stands for the number of components of χ^2, which will be equal to the number of cells or classes for which observed and theoretical frequencies are compared. The symbol k stands for the number of independent linear constraints imposed in the given comparison. We have a *constraint* or *restriction* whenever observed and theoretical frequencies are made to agree with one another, in some one respect, in the operations that lead to the calculation of χ_0^2. Thus a constraint is imposed by the equation $\Sigma f = \Sigma f_0$. Two constraints are independent if one does not necessarily entail the other. A constraint is *linear* when the equation that defines it contains no powers of f or of f_0 above the first.

The addition of χ^2 values. It is one of the merits of χ^2 as an instrument of research that independently derived values of χ^2, relating to samples of similar data, may be combined by simple addition to make possible a better (because more comprehensive) test than could be made using the data of any one sample by itself. The sum of the χ^2 values thus combined will itself have a

---

[10] For a discussion of coefficients of contingency which may be used in measuring degree of relationship when nonquantitative principles of classification are employed, see Yule and Kendall, Ref. 199.

χ^2 distribution with degrees of freedom equal to the sum of the degrees of freedom of the separate χ^2 values.

We will suppose that in a period of mild business depression four quite independent samples have been taken of industrial workers. The men covered by each sample are classified two ways, on the basis of employment status, and according to character of goods (durable or nondurable) produced by the industries with which the men are connected. We shall thus have four groups: employed workers producing durable goods, employed workers producing nondurable goods, unemployed men who are normally employed in the production of durable goods, and unemployed men who are normally employed in the production of nondurable goods. There is reason to believe that the incidence of unemployment is heaviest in industries producing durable goods. We test the hypothesis of independence with data from each of the four samples, obtaining the following results:

Sample no.	n	χ^2
1	1	3.75
2	1	3.60
3	1	2.12
4	1	4.20
Total	4	13.67

Results of the tests on samples 1, 2, and 3 are nonsignificant, at the 0.05 level; sample 4 gives a result that is significant at the 0.05 level, but not at the 0.01 level. But the sum, 13.67, tested with n equal to 4, is to be regarded as significant, whether we appraise it with reference to an 0.05 or an 0.01 level of significance. This combining of results in a single inclusive test is appropriate when the samples are independent, and when they may be regarded as drawings from the same parent population.

When χ^2 values are to be added, Yates' correction should not be applied. The addition theorem holds only for uncorrected constituent items.

REFERENCES

Adler, F., "Yates' Correction and the Statisticians," *Journal of the American Statistical Association*, Dec. 1951.

Clark, C. E., *An Introduction to Statistics*, Chap. 8.

Cramér, H., *Mathematical Methods of Statistics*, pp. 233-237, 416-452.

Eisenhart, C., Hastay, M. W. and Wallis, W. A., *Selected Techniques of Statistical Analysis*, Chap. 7.

Fisher, Sir Ronald (R. A.) *Contributions to Mathematical Statistics*, Papers 5, 8.

Fisher, Sir Ronald (R. A.), *Statistical Methods for Research Workers*, 11th ed., Chap. 4.

Goulden, C. H., *Methods of Statistical Analysis*, 2nd ed., Chaps. 15, 16.

Greenwood, E. R. Jr., *A Detailed Proof of the Chi-Square Test of Goodness of Fit*.

Hoel, P. G., *Introduction to Mathematical Statistics*, 2nd ed., Chap. 9.

Kendall, M. G., *The Advanced Theory of Statistics*, Vol. I, Chap. 12.

Lewis, D. and Burke, C. J., "The Use and Misuse of the Chi-Square Test," *The Psychological Bulletin*, Nov. 1949.

Lewis, D. and Burke, C. J., "Further Discussion of the Use and Misuse of the Chi-Square Test," *The Psychological Bulletin*, July 1950.

Mather, K., *Statistical Analysis in Biology*, 2nd ed., Chap. 11.

Rider, P. R., *An Introduction to Modern Statistical Methods*, Chap. 7.

Rosander, A. C., *Elementary Principles of Statistics*, Chap. 28.

Tippett, L. H. C., *The Methods of Statistics*, 4th ed., pp. 126-140.

Walker, H. M. and Lev, J., *Statistical Inference*, Chap. 4.

Yates, F., "Contingency Tables Involving Small Numbers and the χ^2 Test," *Supplement to the Journal of the Royal Statistical Society*, 1, 1934.

Yule, G. U. and Kendall, M. G., *An Introduction to the Theory of Statistics*, 14th ed., Chap. 20.

The publishers and the dates of publication of the books named in chapter reference lists are given in the bibliography at the end of this volume.

CHAPTER 16

The Analysis of Variance

Preliminary Concepts

Statistical method may be regarded as a body of techniques for the study of variation in nature. A systematic procedure for the analysis of variation (or variance), developed by R. A. Fisher, is capable of fruitful application to a diversity of practical problems. A number of the problems previously discussed, particularly those involving relations among variables, may be dealt with most effectively by the instruments Fisher has forged.

At the heart of this procedure lies the comparison of two measures of variation—standard deviations or, more conveniently in most cases, squared standard deviations (i.e., variances). We compare such variances to determine whether they may be regarded as independent estimates of the unknown variance of the same normal parent population. As we shall see, the two variances compared may be derived in a wide variety of ways, for problems of different kinds, but the ultimate question is the same in all cases. Are the two variances compared equal, within sampling limits, or do they differ significantly? If the difference between them is small enough to be attributed to chance, we may accept them as independent estimates of the same population variance. Otherwise, we conclude that the two variances compared do not reflect the play of the same combinations of forces.

Comparison of Standard Deviations: Fisher's z. A simple example will indicate the nature of the test. We may compare the distribution of prices of a sample of 66 preferred stocks, on a stated day, with the distribution of prices of a sample of 66 common stocks, on the same day. The required values are given in Table 16-1.

TABLE 16–1

Comparison of Preferred and Common Stocks in Respect of
Price Variation

	Degrees of freedom (n)	Sum of squares of deviations from mean	Mean square deviation (variance) s^2	Standard deviation s	Common logarithm of standard deviation $\log_{10} s$	Natural logarithm of standard deviation $\log_e s$
Common stocks	65	99,327.28	1,528.112	39.09	1.59207	3.66590
Preferred stocks (seven percent)	65	30,812.20	474.034	21.77	1.33786	3.08056
					Difference =	0.58534

The estimated standard deviation of common stock prices is 39.09
(derived, of course, with $N - 1$ degrees of freedom); that of preferred stock prices is 21.77. We wish to know whether the difference
is attributable to sampling fluctuations. On an earlier page (222)
we discussed a test of the difference between standard deviations,
employing a procedure that is accurate only for large samples. The
test now to be discussed is more precise and more general, being
applicable to small as well as to large samples. We first determine
the coefficient z, the difference between the natural logarithms of
the two standard deviations. That is,

$$z = \log_e s_1 - \log_e s_2 \qquad (16.1)$$

It is to be noted that natural logarithms are to be employed.
Common logarithms on the base 10 may be shifted readily to
natural logarithms on the base e (2.71828) by using the factor
2.3026 as a multiplier. From the entries in the last column of
Table 16-1 we derive 0.58534 as the value of z.

If common and preferred stocks were alike, with respect to the
dispersion of their prices, and if we had sufficiently large samples
so that sampling fluctuations did not affect the measures of
variance, the value of z would be zero. Is the value we have derived
consistent with the hypothesis that the true value of z is zero?
Could sampling fluctuations alone account for a deviation as great
as 0.58534 from a true value of zero? If the derived value of z is
too great to be attributed to sampling fluctuations, the hypothesis

that common and preferred stocks are alike, with respect to the dispersion of their prices, is untenable.

To determine whether the derived value of z is consistent with the hypothesis that its true value is zero, we must know something about the distribution of values of z, if these were computed from many samples drawn under the same conditions. The distribution of z has been defined by R. A. Fisher. Its form in a given case, depends on the values of n_1 and n_2, the degrees of freedom present in deriving the estimated standard deviations. The distribution is normal, or effectively so, when the two n's are both large, or when the two n's are only moderate in size but are equal or nearly so. The standard deviation of a distribution of z's secured under these conditions, or the standard error of z, is a function of the two n's. It may be derived from the relationship

$$\sigma_z = \sqrt{\frac{1}{2}\left(\frac{1}{n_1} + \frac{1}{n_2}\right)} \tag{16.2}$$

In the present example n_1 and n_2 are both equal to 65; s_z, the estimate of the standard error of z is equal to the square root of the reciprocal of 65. We have

$$s_z = \sqrt{0.01538} = 0.124$$

The test of the hypothesis that the true value of z is zero reduces, then, to the question whether a value of 0.58534 is likely to be drawn from a normally distributed population with a mean value of zero and a standard deviation of 0.124. Ninety-nine percent of the observations in such a normal distribution would fall between $+$ 0.319 and $-$ 0.319, that is, between $0 + (2.576 \times 0.124)$ and $0 - (2.576 \times 0.124)$. The observed value of z, which is 0.58534, falls well beyond these limits. It could not be taken, therefore, to represent a chance deviation from zero, and is thus not consistent with the null hypothesis. The dispersion of common stock prices differs significantly from the dispersion of the prices of preferred stocks paying 7 percent dividends.

The reader will note that we have here applied a "two-tailed test" and have therefore used 0.005 points on the two wings of the z distribution. The sum of the segments of the distribution falling beyond these points will make up 1 percent of the total area under the curve, and will represent, in combination, a probability of .01. If we were asking, "Is the dispersion of common stock prices materially greater than the dispersion of preferred stock prices?" we should be dealing with deviations in one direction only, and would use a "one-tailed test"(see above, p. 215). But in the present case we wish to know whether the two standard deviations differ significantly; a minus value of z would be as meaningful to us as a plus value. In such a case we take account of the possibility of a significant deviation in either direction.

When the n's differ in size, and when at least one of them is small, the distribution of z will not be normal. However, the distributions of z for varying values of the n's have been determined by Fisher. Tables giving z values corresponding to selected probabilities for various combinations of the n's have been prepared for the use of investigators.[1] Alternatively, use may be made of a quantity F, which is closely related to z and is somewhat more convenient because it involves natural numbers rather than logarithms. A second example will illustrate this modified procedure in a case in which the n's differ considerably.

Comparison of Variances: the Quantity F. Assume that we have for two cities samples of residence telephone subscribers, classified according to number of calls made in a given year. There are 31 observations in the first city, 121 in the second. As relevant measures, we have

$$n_1 = 30 \qquad\qquad n_2 = 120$$
$$s_1 = 140 \qquad\qquad s_2 = 120$$
$$s_1^2 = 19,600 \qquad\qquad s_2^2 = 14,400$$

We here employ the variances, rather than the standard deviations. May s_1^2 and s_2^2 be regarded as independent estimates of σ^2, the variance of a normal parent population from which the two samples may be assumed to have been drawn? In using F, rather than z, we compare the two measures of variability by setting up a ratio of the two variances.[2] Thus

$$F = s_1^2/s_2^2 \qquad\qquad (16.3)$$
$$= 19,600/14,400 = 1.36$$

F would, of course, be equal to unity were the two variances equal.

---

[1] See R. A. Fisher, Ref. 50, and Fisher and Yates, Ref. 51.

[2] From the derivation of the two quantities it follows that $F = e^{2z}$, and that $z = \frac{1}{2}\log_e F$. Early work in the analysis of variance was done with reference to z. Use is now generally made of the ratio of variances. G. W. Snedecor suggested that this ratio be symbolized by F, in honor of R. A. Fisher.

In the present case we are testing the hypothesis that the true (i.e., population) value of F is unity. Does the value 1.36 represent a divergence from unity that may be attributed to chance, or is it large enough to indicate that factors other than chance are present? To answer this question we must know how F is distributed, when chance alone is operative.

It is clear that the limiting values of F are zero and infinity. The form of the F distribution between these limits depends upon the values of n_1 and n_2, the degrees of freedom present in deriving the estimated variances, s_1^2 and s_2^2. There are thus many distributions of F, these being symmetrical distributions if the n's are equal, skew if the n's are unequal. For n's of 30 and 120, the values in the present example, the distribution of F will be skew. The proportions of the area below stated points on the x-axis of the frequency curve defining this distribution are given in the following summary table:[3]

F	Percentage of area lying below the stated value of F
0.4348	0.5
0.4738	1.0
0.5358	2.5
0.5940	5.0
0.6676	10.0
0.8049	25.0
0.9833	50.0
1.1921	75.0
1.4094	90.0
1.5543	95.0
1.6899	97.5
1.8600	99.0
1.9839	99.5

Since we are asking whether the two variances differ significantly, without reference to which one is the larger or which the smaller, a two-tailed test is again in order. If we are to use an 0.01 standard, the critical values of F are 0.4348 and 1.9839. If the true value of F is unity, the play of chance would bring deviations beyond these limits only 1 time out of 100. The value of F in the comparison of samples of telephone users is 1.36, which is well within the 1 percent limits. The result reveals no significant difference between the two variances.

For tests of this sort we do not need all the details on the F distribution that are given in the above summary table. It is

[3] Derived from "Tables of Percentage Points of the Inverted Beta (F) Distribution," Maxine Merrington and Catherine M. Thompson, *Biometrica*, Vol. 33, pp. 73-88.

enough to have, for the distribution corresponding to a given combination of n's, a few critical values marking off the customary acceptance or rejection limits. A tabulation of such values, for selected combinations of n's, is given in Appendix Table VII.[4] The entries in this table mark the points on the various distributions of F below which will fall 95 percent and 99 percent of the total area (points designated, respectively, $F_{.95}$ and $F_{.99}$). Knowledge of these points (or percentiles) serves the purpose of the investigator in most of the cases that arise in the practical analysis of variance.[5]

[4] This table is taken, with permission, from Snedecor (Ref. 147). Other tables, giving a wider range of F values are available in Fisher and Yates (Ref. 51), and in Merrington and Thompson (see footnote 3).

[5] F and χ^2 are related, a fact that throws light on the nature of the F distribution.

We have

$$\chi^2 = \frac{\Sigma x^2}{\sigma^2} \tag{a}$$

where x is a random variable, normally distributed about mean zero with standard deviation σ (see p. 523)

But since $$s^2 = \frac{\Sigma x^2}{n} \quad \text{(where } n \text{ is } N - 1\text{)}$$

$$\Sigma x^2 = ns^2$$

Hence $$\chi^2 = \frac{ns^2}{\sigma^2} \tag{b}$$

The ratio ns^2/σ^2 has a χ^2 distribution with n degrees of freedom.

From (b)

$$s^2 = \frac{\chi^2 \sigma^2}{n} \tag{c}$$

We have seen that F is the ratio of s_1^2 to s_2^2, these two variances being regarded as independent estimates of σ^2, the variance of a single normal parent population. For the first of these estimates we may write

$$s_1^2 = \frac{\chi_1^2 \sigma^2}{n_1} \tag{d}$$

and for the second

$$s_2^2 = \frac{\chi_2^2 \sigma^2}{n_2} \tag{e}$$

For the ratio of the two

$$F = \frac{s_1^2}{s_2^2} = \frac{\chi_1^2 \sigma^2}{n_1} \div \frac{\chi_2^2 \sigma^2}{n_2}$$

Since σ^2 in the two expressions in the right-hand member above is the same quantity (the variance of a single assumed parent population), we have

$$F = \frac{\chi_1^2/n_1}{\chi_2^2/n_2} \tag{f}$$

Thus F is the ratio of two independent quantities, each having a χ^2 distribution. The ratio of any two such quantities has an F distribution with n's equal to those for the corresponding χ^2 quantities.

An Example of Variance Analysis: Interest Rates

The observations listed in Table 16-2 are averages of interest rates paid on business loans made by member banks of the Federal Reserve System. The rates relate to approximately 100,000 loans made by all classes of member banks to all classes of business borrowers. The survey covered loans outstanding on November 20, 1946. The rates on the loans originally included have here been averaged for various classes of business borrowers, of various sizes. Thus the unit of observation is not the rate on a single loan but the average rate on a group of loans made by a business group having in common certain attributes of size and character of business.[6] The sample we are studying includes 100 of these groups of business borrowers.

TABLE 16–2

Average Interest Rates on Loans made by Member Banks of the
Federal Reserve System to 100 Classes of Business Borrowers
(Percent per annum)

A	B	C	A	B	C
3.0	5.1	4.0	2.5	5.2	2.7
5.2	4.7	3.2	3.7	4.8	2.2
3.5	2.6	4.9	1.9	1.3	3.0
2.0	3.2	4.5	3.3	1.7	1.0
2.9	3.7	5.4	2.0	2.2	2.8
5.5	3.8	2.2	5.4	2.7	1.5
4.2	5.1	4.1	2.7	3.5	3.9
6.1	4.5	2.8	2.1	5.4	5.4
4.5	3.2	4.4	2.5	1.8	2.4
4.4	2.1	2.9	2.2	1.7	3.7
2.5	4.9	1.8	4.3	1.7	4.6
4.1	3.7	4.6	3.3	3.6	2.9
3.8	4.5	2.2	4.2	1.9	1.9
3.3	4.1	5.1	4.0	4.1	4.2
3.8	4.3	4.2	5.0	3.0	3.8
3.5	3.5	3.7	4.9	3.0	1.9
3.8	3.3	1.6	3.0		

The distribution of the observations in Table 16-2 is, within sampling limits, normal. Normality of parent populations is essential to the full accuracy of the methods to be discussed in this chapter.

[6] In obtaining average rates paid by such business groups, each rate was weighted by the dollar value of the loans outstanding at that rate. In averaging the group rates in the present test no weights were used. For the results of the original study see Youngdahl (Ref.198).

Comparison of Estimates of Population Variance: Case I. Our first use of these observations is to illustrate the results we get when we employ different methods of estimating the variance of the population from which the observations come. By random methods we break the 100 observations into three classes designated A, B, and C, in Table 16-2. There are 34 observations in Class A, 33 in Class B, and 33 in Class C. For each of these randomly selected classes we derive the following measures:

Class	N	Mean	Sum of squares of deviations from class mean
A	34	3.6206	40.6556
B	33	3.5424	41.8206
C	33	3.4091	42.4473
Total	100	3.5250	124.9235

If the division of observations into three classes is purely random, as it was intended to be, the differences among the three class means will reflect the play of the same random factors that account for variation within each of the three classes. Thus there are open to us various ways of estimating the magnitude of variations due to these random factors (of estimating, that is, σ or σ^2 of the population from which the 100 observations in the full sample come). The variation within Class A should reflect these forces; so should the variation within Class B, and that within Class C. So also, as we have suggested, should the variation among class means. These are independent estimates. The variation within any one column is independent of the variation within other columns, and the variation between class means is independent of the variation within the several columns.[7] We are not at present interested in differences that may exist among the "within-class" variations in the three classes; therefore we lump these variations to get a single estimate of the degree of variation in the parent population. We thus come down to two independent estimates, one based on the variation between classes, one on the variation within classes.

Since it will be convenient to use F rather than z, we derive

[7] We could, of course, use a measure of variation among the 100 observations in the full sample as another estimate of the population σ or σ^2, but this would not be independent of the measures of variation within classes and between classes. Our present interest centers in variation within and between classes.

estimates of the population σ^2, the variance. For the variance within classes, which we may designate s_2^2, we have

$$s_2^2 = \frac{\text{sum of squares of deviations from class means}}{\text{degrees of freedom for variation within classes}}$$

$$= \frac{\Sigma d_a^2 + \Sigma d_b^2 + \Sigma d_c^2}{(f_a - 1) + (f_b - 1) + (f_c - 1)} \tag{16.4}$$

where the subscripts a, b, and c, denote the classes to which the d's (deviations) and the f's (frequencies) belong. Inserting the appropriate values,

$$s_2^2 = \frac{124.9235}{97} = 1.2879$$

In computing the variance between classes, which we may designate s_1^2, we measure the deviations of the several class means from the grand mean of all the observations, using as weights the numbers of observations in the several classes. Thus

$$s_1^2 = \frac{\text{sum of squares of deviations of class means from grand mean}}{\text{degrees of freedom for variation between classes}}$$

$$= \frac{[(M_a - M)^2 \times f_a] + [(M_b - M)^2 \times f_b] + [(M_c - M)^2 \times f_c]}{\text{number of classes} - 1} \tag{16.5}$$

$$= \frac{[(3.6206 - 3.5250)^2 \times 34] + [(3.5424 - 3.5250)^2 \times 33]}{3 - 1}$$

$$+ \frac{[(3.4091 - 3.5250)^2 \times 33]}{3 - 1}$$

$$= \frac{0.7640}{2}$$

$$= 0.3820$$

Since there are only three class means, there are only two degrees of freedom for variation between class means. The fact that class frequencies must be introduced as weights in the numerator does not affect the degrees of freedom appearing as the denominator.

We now have two variances, s_1^2 and s_2^2, which may be regarded as estimates of an unknown population variance, σ^2. If we are correct in assuming that the same random factors that cause variation within classes are responsible for the observed differences among class means, then s_1^2 and s_2^2 will be equal, within sampling limits.

The hypothesis we are to test is that

$$s_1^2 = s_2^2 = \sigma^2$$

or that

$$F = \frac{s_1^2}{s_2^2} = 1$$

The observed ratio is

$$F = \frac{0.3820}{1.2879} = 0.297$$

Is this value consistent with the hypothesis that the true value of F is unity? The distribution of F that now concerns us is that for which the degrees of freedom are, respectively, 2 and 97. For these values F will have a skew distribution. Points on this distribution that are relevant to a test of significance are given below:

F	Percentage of area lying below the stated value of F $(n_1 = 2; n_2 = 97)$
0.005	0.5
0.01	1.0
0.05	5.0
3.09	95.0
4.83	99.0
5.60	99.5

Since 90 percent of the area under the curve defining the appropriate F distribution will fall between F values of 0.05 and 3.09, it is clear that our observed value, 0.297, is one that might easily have occurred as a result of chance. The variance between classes is smaller than the variance within classes, but the difference is not significant. The results obtained are not inconsistent with the hypothesis that the between-classes variance, s_1^2, and the within-classes variance, s_2^2, are independent and unbiased estimates of σ^2, the variance of the population from which our 100 observations are drawn.

Comparison of Estimates of Population Variance: Case II. In the example just cited we have deliberately sought to obtain random results in variation between classes. Usually this is not the case. A problem of this sort generally arises when we have classified a given set of observations on some principle that, we think, may reveal significant differences in behavior. Then we ask whether the means of the classes set up on the basis of this principle differ more than might be expected if chance factors alone were responsible. To illustrate a procedure of this sort we may employ the same set of interest rates employed above, classified now, however, into rates paid by small business borrowers, rates paid by borrowers of medium size, and rates paid by large business borrowers. On rational grounds we should expect these rates to differ; this expectation is to be checked against the observations. Results of the classification are given in Table 16-3.

TABLE 16–3

Average Interest Rates on Loans by Member Banks of the Federal Reserve System, Classified by Size of Borrower
(percent per annum)

Rates paid by Small Borrowers*	Rates paid by Middle-sized Borrowers†		Rates paid by Large Borrowers‡	
5.4	4.5	3.8	3.0	1.8
5.1	4.1	3.3	2.5	1.9
5.4	4.6	3.8	3.3	2.0
5.1	4.2	3.5	3.0	1.7
5.4	4.4	3.7	2.7	2.2
4.9	4.2	3.3	2.8	1.6
4.5	3.7	2.9	2.1	1.7
4.9	4.3	3.7	2.7	2.2
5.2	4.1	4.2	3.0	2.4
4.7	4.0	3.2	2.2	1.7
4.9	4.1	3.7	2.8	1.8
4.5	3.8	3.2	2.5	2.0
5.0	4.2	3.6	2.7	1.9
5.4	4.6	4.0	3.3	2.1
5.1	4.3	3.5	2.9	2.2
6.1	4.4	4.1	2.9	1.9
5.2	4.3	3.7	3.5	2.6
5.5	4.5	3.8	3.0	2.5
3.8	3.9	3.2	2.2	1.5
4.8	4.0	3.5	3.0	1.9

* With total assets less than $50,000
† With total assets from $50,000 to $750,000
‡ With total assets of $750,000 or more

The means of the rates paid, by classes, and the class N's, are as follows:

		N
Mean rate, small borrowers	5.0450	20
Mean rate, middle-sized borrowers	3.8975	40
Mean rate, large borrowers	2.3925	40
Mean, all rates	3.5250	100

As in the preceding example we now get measures of the variance between classes (s_1^2) and of variance within classes (s_2^2). The corresponding degrees of freedom are n_1 and n_2. The results are set out in Table 16-4.

The two variances in the last column of Table 16-4 are comparable measures of variation between classes and within classes.

TABLE 16–4

Analysis of Variance
Interest Rates paid by Business Borrowers, classified by Size

Variation	Degrees of freedom	Sum of squares	Variance
Between classes	2	103.0605	51.530
Within classes	97	22.6270	0.233
Total	99	125.6875	

We wish to determine whether the variance between the mean interest rates paid by different classes of business borrowers is significantly greater than the variance within these classes, this latter variance being taken to measure the play of the innumerable chance factors that affect interest rates paid by business borrowers. (When we speak of "experimental errors" in the following pages we shall be referring always to the resultants of chance factors that are independent of the principles of classification employed.) The ratio that defines the difference is

$$F = \frac{s_1^2}{s_2^2} = \frac{51.530}{0.233} = 221.1$$

Since we are asking whether the variance in the numerator is significantly greater than the variance in the denominator, we are concerned only with the upper tail of the F distribution. That is, we are to apply a "one-tailed" test. The degrees of freedom in the numerator (n_1) are 2, in the denominator (n_2) 97. Consulting the F table in Appendix VII we find that for $n_1 = 2$ and $n_2 = 80$ the 99th percentile value of F is 4.88; for $n_1 = 2$ and $n_2 = 100$ the 99th percentile is 4.82. For $n_1 = 2$ and $n_2 = 97$ the 99th percentile will be approximately 4.83. Only 1 time out of 100 would the play of chance account for a value of F exceeding 4.83, if the true value were unity. The present F, 221.1, is far in excess of 4.83. We conclude that the observed variances between and within classes cannot be regarded as independent estimates of the same population variance. The variance between classes is significantly greater than the variance within classes. The variation in interest rates paid by business borrowers of different sizes reflects the play of forces other than the chance factors that account for variation within classes.

In tests of this sort it is customary always to construct the F ratio with the variance between classes as the numerator. If F is less than unity, the investigator concludes that there is no indication that special forces are affecting the between-class variation. Only if F is significantly greater than unity does he reject the hypothesis that the true value of F is unity. Thus the usual test is a one-tailed test, employing only $F_{.99}$, the 99th percentile, if rejection is to be on the 0.01 level (or $F_{.95}$ if rejection is to be on the 0.05 level). For this reason the values given in the F table relate only to the upper tails of the various F distributions. If there is occasion to inquire whether a given F ratio is significantly less than unity, the F values for the 1st and 5th percentiles may be readily obtained from the F table as given, for the F distributions are symmetrical in terms of reciprocals.[8]

---

[8] In getting the lower percentage points, the F table is entered with the values of n_1 and n_2 interchanged, i.e., with n_2 counted as degrees of freedom of the numerator, and n_1 as the degrees of freedom of the denominator. For these n's determine from the table the value of F falling, e.g., at the 99th percentage point. The reciprocal of the F value thus obtained will mark the 1st percentage point for the distribution of F corresponding to the original n_1 and n_2. The value of $F_{.05}$ may be obtained in like manner, from the tabled entry for $F_{.95}$.

A simple example will illustrate the method of getting the first percentile. For $n_1 = 4$ and $n_2 = 100$, Appendix Table VII gives 3.51 as the 99th percentile of the F distribution. To obtain the F value of the first percentile, we determine the 99th percentile corresponding to inverted n's, i.e., with the numerator n equal to 100, the denominator n equal to 4. The table gives 13.57. The reciprocal of this, 0.074, is the required first percentile for the distribution of F when the numerator n is 4 and the denominator n is 100.

Notation. At this point it will be helpful to give a summary list of the new symbols already employed in this chapter, or to be employed.

z: the difference between the natural logarithms of two standard deviations

F: the ratio of two variances

$M_a, M_b, \ldots ; M_1, M_2, \ldots$ etc.: arithmetic means of classes $a, b, \ldots,$ 1, 2, ... etc.

$d_a, d_b, \ldots ; d_1, d_2, \ldots$ etc.: deviations from the means of classes $a, b, \ldots, 1, 2, \ldots,$ etc.

$f_a, f_b, \ldots ; f_1, f_2, \ldots$ etc.: frequencies of classes $a, b, \ldots, 1, 2, \ldots$ etc.; also written $N_a, N_b, \ldots ; N_1, N_2, \ldots,$ etc.

$\overline{X}_0$: the observed mean of a given class

$\overline{X}_e$: the estimated mean of a given class

c: number of columns in an analysis-of-variance table

n_i: number of observations in a single column (it is here assumed that the n's vary from column to column)

$\overline{X}_i$: the mean of all the observations in a given column

Q_1: the sum of the squares of the deviations of column means from the grand mean, each deviation weighted by the number of observations in the given column

Q_2: the sum of the squares of the deviations of the individual observations from the respective column means

Q: the sum of the squares of the deviations of the individual observations from the grand mean

Σ': the process of summation applied to the squares of the deviations of individual observations from the mean of a given column

r: number of rows in an analysis-of-variance table (other symbols paralleling those for columns may be used for statistics relating to measurements arranged by rows)

H_r: the null hypothesis relating to the means of rows

H_c: the null hypothesis relating to the means of columns

H_{rc}: the null hypothesis relating to the interaction

$F_{.99}$: the 99th percentile value in a given F distribution; the value of F that will be exceeded only 1 time out of 100 because of the play of chance (other subscripts designate other percentile values)

A standard form. Table 16-4 above is a specific example of an arrangement generally used for the presentation of the calculations involved in the analysis of variance. A suitable standard form for

TABLE 16–5

Standard Form for the Analysis of Variance

(1) Variation	(2) Degrees of freedom	(3) Sum of squares	(4) Mean square
Between classes (columns)	$n_1 = c - 1$	$Q_1 = \Sigma n_i(\overline{X}_i - \overline{X})^2$	$s_1^2 - Q_1/n_1$
Within classes (columns)	$n_2 = N - c$	$Q_2 = \Sigma\Sigma'(X - \overline{X}_i)^2$	$s_2^2 = Q_2/n_2$
Total	$n = N - 1$	$Q = \Sigma(X - \overline{X})^2$	

problems of the type just discussed is shown in Table 16-5. This applies to a classification on a single principle, such as size of business borrower in the interest rate example. Here the classes are columns, as in Table 16-3 above. The entries in the third column of Table 16-5 represent the essential procedures in the analysis of variance, for central interest attaches to the components of Q, the total sum of squares. In a problem of the type represented by Table 16-4 Q is broken into two independent components, Q_1 and Q_2. (Totals are given only for columns (2) and (3) of 16-5; in these columns the entries are additive components of a single sum.) This fundamental relation among the different sums of squares is given by the equation

$$\Sigma(X - \overline{X})^2 = \Sigma n_i(\overline{X}_i - \overline{X})^2 + \Sigma\Sigma'(X - \overline{X}_i)^2 \quad (16.6)$$

In the hypothesis usually tested (that the true value of F is unity) we are assuming that each of the components of the total sum of squares, when divided by the appropriate degrees of freedom, provides an independent estimate of a single population variance, σ^2. If the hypothesis is not true, break-up of the total sum of squares in the manner indicated is designed to reveal the play of distinctive forces, related to the principle of classification employed.

Procedure for computations. The computational procedures to be employed in getting the numerical values required in variance analysis can be simplified by taking advantage of the relationship set forth in Chapter 5. For a series of measurements, X, we have[9]

$$\Sigma(X - \overline{X})^2 = \Sigma X^2 - N(\Sigma X/N)^2 \tag{16.7}$$

or

$$\Sigma(X - \overline{X})^2 = \Sigma X^2 - N\overline{X}^2 \tag{16.8}$$

If we let T (for total) represent ΣX in (16.7) we have a form often more convenient for calculation

$$\Sigma(X - \overline{X})^2 = \Sigma X^2 - T^2/N \tag{16.9}$$

This relationship may be applied in getting the sum of the squared deviations of all observations from the grand mean and, in separate operations, in getting the sum of the squared deviations from the mean of each column. Summation of the observed X's and of the squares of the observed X's provides the basis for the simple calculations needed to get the sum of squares and its components.

The Analysis of Variance with Dual Principles of Classification

In the illustration used above, dealing with interest rates, only one principle of classification was employed. The method of variance analysis is applicable more generally, with observations classified on two, three, four, or more principles. We now deal with an economic example in which two principles of classification are applied. The observations employed are relative numbers measuring the price behavior of 670 commodities, in wholesale markets in the United States, between 1926 and February 1933. The major force affecting these prices over this period was the great recession that reached its trough in 1933. We are concerned with the relative severity of price declines among different classes of goods.

The 670 price relatives (obtained from price quotations compiled by the U. S. Bureau of Labor Statistics) may be classified into those relating to perishable goods (505 in number) and those relating to durable goods (165 in number). The classification has economic significance because of differences in the market conditions, on both supply and demand sides, affecting these classes of goods during a major recession. Again, the 670 observations may be broken down into those relating to raw materials (134 in number) and those relating to manufactured goods (536 in number). Applying the two principles of classification jointly we obtain 4

[9] See footnote p. 119 for the derivation of this relation, using slightly different symbols.

subgroups, perishable raw materials (101 in number), perishable manufactured goods (404 in number), durable raw materials (33 in number) and durable manufactured goods (132 in number). It is to be noted that the ratio of the number of perishable raw materials to the number of perishable manufactured goods, 101:404, is the same as the ratio of the number of durable raw materials to the number of durable manufactured goods, 33:132. It is a necessary condition of the procedure here discussed that the frequencies in the several subgroups be proportional.

Various questions relating to the significance of these principles of classification may be answered with reference to the summary figures given in Table 16-6.

TABLE 16-6

Measurements Relating to the Analysis of the Relative Prices of
670 Commodities for February, 1933
(1926 = 100)

1 Perishable raw materials $N_1 = 101$ $M_1 = 41.663366$ $\Sigma d_1^2 = 31,118.56$	2 Perishable manufactured goods $N_2 = 404$ $M_2 = 62.329208$ $\Sigma d_2^2 = 187,414.21$	I All perishable goods $N_p = 505$ $M_p = 58.196040$ $\Sigma d_p^2 = 253,040.57$
3 Durable raw materials $N_3 = 33$ $M_3 = 65.060606$ $\Sigma d_3^2 = 12,217.88$	4 Durable manufactured goods $N_4 = 132$ $M_4 = 75.719697$ $\Sigma d_4^2 = 31,308.63$	II All durable goods $N_d = 165$ $M_d = 73.587879$ $\Sigma d_d^2 = 46,525.97$
A All raw materials $N_r = 134$ $M_r = 47.425373$ $\Sigma d_r^2 = 56,952.76$	B All manufactured goods $N_m = 536$ $M_m = 65.626866$ $\Sigma d_m^2 = 236,562.35$	All commodities $N = 670$ $M = 61.986567$ $\Sigma d^2 = 329,029.88$

The entries relating to each group and subgroup define the number of commodities included, the mean value of the price relatives for February, 1933, and the sum of the squares of the deviations of the observations in that group from the mean of that group. Thus for perishable raw materials the mean is 41.663366 (indicating an average price decline of 58.34 percent) and the sum of the squares of the deviations of the 101 observations in this group from 41.663366 is 31,118.56. For all commodities the mean is 61.986567, and the sum of the squares of the deviations of the individual items from this mean is 329,029.88. (Extra decimal places are kept in the calculations merely to ensure the formal consistency of numerical results.)

Hypotheses to be tested. In the study of differential price movements among the several classes of goods distinguished in Table 16-6 several different questions interest us: Do the prices of perishable goods and of durable goods differ in their behavior during a major business recession? The means of the two rows (here designated I and II) are relevant to this question. (Differences of this sort, which would here be related to inherent quality factors, are often termed "environmental effects," in the literature on variance analysis.) Do raw material and manufactured goods differ significantly in their price behavior during such a recession? The means of the two columns (here designated A and B) bear upon this question. (Differences related to processes of fabrication would be of the type termed "treatment effects" in the language of variance analysis.) In putting the latter question we are, in effect, asking whether the process of fabrication affects the behavior of commodity prices during a business recession. And here, a further question arises: Does fabrication affect the price behavior of perishable and durable goods in the same degree, or do the prices of these two classes of commodities react differently to fabrication? Such a differential response, if it is present, is termed *interaction*. In seeking answers to these three questions we set up three null hypotheses, for which we may use the symbols presented below:

Hypothesis H_r : the means of the rows do not differ

Hypothesis H_c : the means of the columns do not differ

Hypothesis H_{rc}: there is no interaction

(The hypotheses refer, of course, to population values. We test the hypotheses by determining whether the corresponding sample values differ significantly.)

Components of the Total Sum of Squares. Our first task is to break up the total sum of squares (329,029.88) into components corresponding to the several sources of variation suggested by these hypotheses, obtaining at the same time a component that may be taken to reflect the play of the mass of random factors that are unconnected with the principles of classification employed. This is the "error component," the measure of the magnitude of experimental errors, of fluctuations due to the play of chance.

A sum of squares corresponding to each of the two principles of classification is derived in the manner illustrated in the preceding example. That is, we take the deviation of each class mean from the grand mean, square the deviation and weight by the number of observations in that class. The sum of these weighted squares is the desired component. Thus

Σd^2 between perishable-durable classes

$$= [(58.196040 - 61.986567)^2 \times 505]$$
$$+ [(73.587879 - 61.986567)^2 \times 165]$$

$$= 29,463.31$$

In the same way, we obtain as the sum of squares corresponding to the raw-manufactured division the quantity 35,514.75.

The "error component" of the total sum of squares must be independent of the two principles of classification, for it is to furnish the yardstick to be used in testing the several hypotheses. In the present example we may derive this component most logically from the variation within the four cells numbered 1, 2, 3, and 4 in Table 16-6. Indeed, the dispersion within any one of these cells can provide an estimate of the magnitude of variation due to the play of chance factors. Thus the 101 commodities in Cell 1 are all alike in that they are raw and perishable. The 132 commodities in Cell 4 are all alike in that they are durable and manufactured. The Σd^2 figure for each of these cells measures variability among commodities that are alike in respect of durability and alike in degree of fabrication[10] However, in order to utilize all the information we have, we should combine the sums of squares within the four cells, since no one of them may be taken to provide a better estimate of the "error component" than may be obtained from the others. The process of combination is shown below:

Variability within perishable raw materials group = 31,118.56
Variability within perishable manufactures group = 187,414.21
Variability within durable raw materials group = 12,217.88
Variability within durable manufactures group = 31,308.63
Total variability within cells   262,059.28

[10] This statement may be accepted as accurate for the purpose of the present demonstration. Actually, of course, the distinctions between perishable and durable commodities and between raw and manufactured goods are not clearcut and definite.

The sum 262,059.28, when divided by the appropriate degrees of freedom, may be taken to measure the strength of the forces we lump together as chance, which here means all factors affecting our observations other than those related to the relative durability of commodities or to degree of fabrication of commodities.

The sum of the three components of the total Σd^2 so far distinguished (the variation between perishable-durable classes, between raw-manufactured classes, and within cells) is 327,037.34. Subtracting this from the total sum of squares, 329,029.88, we have a remainder of 1,992.54. This, which may be regarded as the "residual variability between cells" will measure *interaction*, as that term was used above, if interaction is present. If there is no interaction, if the two principles of classification employed are in fact quite independent of one another, the residual variability between cells will reflect the play of chance, alone.

Direct determination of the interaction. The nature of the "interaction component" of the total sum of squares will be clearer, and one of the central assumptions of variance analysis will be brought out, if at this point we derive the interaction sum of squares directly, rather than as a residual. In Table 16-7 we show, for each of the four cells set up by our

TABLE 16–7

Demonstration of Direct Measurement of Interaction, Price Behavior

1 Perishable raw materials	2 Perishable manufactured goods
$\bar{X}_0 = 41.663366$	$\bar{X}_0 = 62.329208$
$\bar{X}_e = 43.634846$	$\bar{X}_e = 61.836339$
$(\bar{X}_0 - \bar{X}_e) = -1.971480$	$(\bar{X}_0 - \bar{X}_e) = +0.492869$
$(\bar{X}_0 - \bar{X}_e)^2 = 3.886733$	$(\bar{X}_0 - \bar{X}_e)^2 = 0.242920$

3 Durable raw materials	4 Durable manufactured goods
$\bar{X}_0 = 65.060606$	$\bar{X}_0 = 75.719697$
$\bar{X}_e = 59.026685$	$\bar{X}_e = 77.228178$
$(\bar{X}_0 - \bar{X}_e) = +6.033921$	$(\bar{X}_0 - \bar{X}_e) = -1.508481$
$(\bar{X}_0 - \bar{X}_e)^2 = 36.408203$	$(\bar{X}_0 - \bar{X}_e)^2 = 2.275515$

$$\Sigma d^2 \text{ (interaction)} = (3.886733 \times 101) + (0.242920 \times 404) + (36.408203 \times 33)$$
$$+ (2.275515 \times 132) = 1992.5384$$

dual principles of classification, the observed mean $\bar{X}_o$ repeated from Table 16-6, and an estimated mean, $\bar{X}_e$. (We need not here employ distinguishing subscripts for the individual cells.) The latter is estimated on the double assumption that the two principles of classification are independent of one another and that the influence of each principle is "additive." Thus we derive $\bar{X}_e$ for perishable raw materials in this fashion: The observed mean of all perishable goods (58.196040) is less by 3.790527 than the observed mean of all commodities (61.986567). On the two assumptions just stated, we should expect the mean of perishable raw materials to differ from the mean of all raw materials (47.425373) by the same absolute amount, i.e., by − 3.790527. This gives us 43.634846 as the expected mean for perishable raw materials. Similarly, we get the expected mean for perishable manufactured goods (61.836339) by subtracting the same amount (3.790527) from the mean of all manufactured goods (65.626866). In the same way, but using an absolute differential of + 11.601312 (= 73.587879 − 61.986567), we get the expected means for the two subclasses of durable goods. In deriving these values we are saying, in effect, that we should expect averages for the perishable and durable components of any class of commodities (obtained by applying a principle of classification that is independent of the perishable-durable principle) to differ in the same direction and by the same absolute amount as the average of all perishable goods differs from the average of all durable goods. This is another way of stating the hypothesis H_{rc}: "There is no interaction between the principles of classification represented by the rows and columns."

Having the values of $\bar{X}_o$ and $\bar{X}_e$ for each cell, we derive the sum of squares representing the interaction from the simple relation

$$\Sigma d^2 \text{ (interaction)} = \Sigma n_i (\bar{X}_o - \bar{X}_e)^2 \tag{16.10}$$

where the n_i's are the numbers of observations within the several cells. Details of the process are shown in Table 16-7. The sum of squares for the interaction is 1992.5384, which is necessarily equal to the value obtained as a residual in earlier calculations.

Tests of Hypotheses. We have now broken into four components the total sum of squares among the 670 commodity price relatives with which we are here concerned. These components are brought together in Table 16-8. The derivation of each has been explained. For the degrees of freedom we have the following general relations (where r stands for number of rows and c number of columns):

$$
\begin{aligned}
DF \text{ between rows} &= r - 1 \\
DF \text{ between columns} &= c - 1 \\
DF \text{ in interaction} &= (r - 1)(c - 1) \\
DF \text{ within cells} &= N - cr \\
DF, \text{ total} &= N - 1
\end{aligned}
$$

The break-up of the total needs little explanation. Within each cell we lose 1 DF; there are cr cells, hence the degrees of freedom for variation within cells will be $N - cr$. In considering the degrees of freedom in the interaction, the student may consider the process by which the interaction sum of squares was obtained, directly. In computing the estimated means for the various cells, use must be made of the means of the columns and the means of rows; hence restrictions are placed on the "freedom" with which estimated cell means may be established, and on the freedom of observed and expected means to differ. In a 2×2 classification, the filling-in of just one cell necessarily fixes the values of the estimated means of the three other cells, since the expected means of cells must be consistent with the column and row means as given. In a 3×3 classification, the establishment of estimated means for just four cells necessarily determines the values for the other five, for the same reason. The relation cited in the summary above defines the interaction degrees of freedom, in general terms.

TABLE 16–8

Components of Variance among Observations Relating to Commodity
Price Movements, 1926—February, 1933
$(1926 = 100)$

(1) Nature of variability	(2) Degrees of freedom	(3) Sum of squares	(4) Variance s^2	(5) F	(6) $F_{.99}$
Between perishable-durable classes	1	29,463.31	29,463.31	74.9	6.68
Between raw-manufactured classes	1	35,514.75	35,514.75	90.3	6.68
Interaction	1	1,992.54	1,992.54	5.06	6.68
Within cells ("experimental error")	666	262,059.28	393.48		
	669	329,029.88			

Using the measures given in Table 16-8 we may now test each of the hypotheses set forth on page 558. Relevant values of F and of $F_{.99}$ are given in columns (5) and (6) of the table. For Hypothesis H_r ("the means of the rows do not differ") we derive the F-ratio $29,463.31/393.48$, which is 74.9. Reference to Appendix Table VII shows that for $n_1 = 1$, $n_2 = 666$, $F_{.99}$ is approximately 6.68. The present value of F is greater than this. The results of the test are not consistent with the null hypothesis. There is a clear indication that the price movements of perishable and durable goods differ during a major recession. In testing H_c ("the means of the columns do not differ"), we use the same error variance, but set it against the variance derived from the means for raw and manufactured goods. Here we have $F = 35,514.75/393.48 = 90.3$. Here, also, we have a clearly significant difference, indicating substantially different patterns of price behavior of raw and manufactured goods in recession.

In testing Hypothesis H_{rc} ("there is no interaction") we again use the variance within cells as the measure of "experimental error," setting it now against the interaction variance. For F we have $1992.54/393.48$, or 5.06. Here, again, $F_{.99}$ has a value of approximately 6.68; $F_{.95}$ is 3.86. If we judge the result with reference to the 1 percent standard we should accept the null hypothesis, and conclude that the residual variability between cells is attributable to the play of chance. Using the 5 percent standard, an investigator would accept the observations as evidence of true interaction. In the present case it would seem reasonable to regard the test as not conclusive, but as providing a strong indication that perishable and durable goods respond differently, in their price behavior, to the process of fabrication. Reference to Table 16-6 will show that among both perishable and durable goods fabrication appears to have reduced susceptibility to price decline under the force of business recession. M_2 is distinctly greater than M_1, and M_4 is greater than M_3. But the influence of fabrication was apparently greater among perishable than among durable goods.

We should note that if the test of the interaction had been clearly consistent with the null hypothesis, it would have been reasonable to combine the interaction variance with the variance within cells to obtain a somewhat more broadly based estimate of the error variance. For such a result would have indicated that the variance derived from the interaction is merely another estimate of the magnitude of variations due to chance. We should do this by adding the sums of squares relating to interaction and to "within-cells" variability, dividing the total by the sum of the corresponding degrees of freedom.

In appraising the results of these several tests of price behavior, we must note that the conditions requisite for the full accuracy of methods of variance analysis are not met by the price data employed (see the later pages of this chapter). There is no indeterminacy about the results of the tests of the two major principles of classification. The observed difference is clearly significant in each case. But when the probabilities are near a critical level, as they are in the test of interaction, the failure of the data fully to meet required conditions calls for special conservatism in interpreting results. All that one may say with confidence about the interaction is that the evidence of differential behavior is strong enough to justify further investigation.

A Test of a Cyclical Pattern

A somewhat different problem in variance analysis is faced when subdivision of the observations by rows and columns gives but one observation in each cell. For we do not then have "within-cell" variance to use as a measure of experimental error. Problems of this sort arise frequently in economic and business research when an investigator wishes to test the significance of a pattern of seasonal behavior, or of a pattern of cyclical movement. The data of Table 16-9, repeated in slightly modified form[11] from Chapter 12, will illustrate a test of this sort.

The meaning of the measurements in Table 16-9 has been explained in Chapter 12. In brief summary, the stage averages in the first line define the standing of railroad freight ton-miles at each of nine stages of the business cycle that extends from the trough at August 1904 to the trough at June 1908. Monthly measures of ton-miles of freight carried have been expressed as relatives of the average of all monthly figures for that particular business cycle, and then averaged for each of the nine stages into which the cycle has been divided. These stages extend from the initial trough (stage I), through three subdivisions of the phase of expansion (stages II to IV) to the peak (stage V), then through three subdivisions of the phase of contraction (stages VI to VIII) to the terminal trough (stage IX). In general, there is a rise from initial trough to peak, a decline from peak to terminal trough, but the patterns vary from cycle to cycle. The averages by cycle stages, given in the last line of Table 16-9, define the average

---

[11] In this presentation stage standings, which were given to one decimal place in Table 12-7, are in whole numbers. This leads to slight differences in the stage averages.

TABLE 16-9

Averages of Reference Cycle Relatives by Cyclical Stages
Railroad Freight Ton-Miles, United States*

Cycle no.	Dates of terminal troughs	I	II	III	IV	V	VI	VII	VIII	IX	Sum	Mean	Sum of squares
					Stage averages of cycle relatives at stage								
1	Aug. 1904–June 1908	83	88	99	106	117	116	106	96	95	906	100.67	92,292
2	June 1908–Jan. 1912	85	90	93	101	103	106	103	104	107	892	99.11	88,894
3	Jan. 1912–Dec. 1914	91	94	96	102	111	106	101	96	92	889	98.78	88,175
4	Dec. 1914–Apr. 1919	74	86	101	111	114	113	106	94	96	895	99.44	90,447
5	Apr. 1919–Sep. 1921	93	95	102	101	113	111	106	82	87	890	98.89	88,898
6	Sep. 1921–July 1924	85	87	87	112	120	111	106	102	98	908	100.89	92,872
7	July 1924–Dec. 1927	86	94	99	104	106	106	102	100	96	893	99.22	88,941
8	Dec. 1927–Mar. 1933	115	118	124	126	127	116	90	66	63	945	105.00	104,411
9	Mar. 1933–May 1938	74	88	91	116	127	119	106	94	91	906	100.67	93,600
10	May 1938–Oct. 1945	51	61	96	134	135	137	133	116	111	974	108.22	113,954
11	Oct. 1945–Oct. 1949	99	97	106	106	104	96	93	82	77	860	95.56	83,016
Sum		936	998	1,094	1,219	1,277	1,237	1,152	1,032	1,013	9,958		1,025,500
Mean		85.09	90.73	99.45	110.82	116.09	112.45	104.73	93.82	92.09		100.59	

* These measurements are used by courtesy of the National Bureau of Economic Research.

behavior of this series during cycles in general business. There appears to be a definite pattern, rising without a break from stage I to stage V, declining without a break from stage V to stage IX. But here, as always in statistical work, we must ask whether the apparent pattern is significant. Within stage I we find averages for individual cycles that vary from 51 to 115, within stage II from 61 to 118, within stage VI from 96 to 137, within stage IX from 63 to 107. This is far from a pattern of uniform behavior. We may not accept the average pattern as significant until we have considered whether the play of chance, alone, might not account for it.

The measures of primary interest to us here are the nine stage averages in the last line of the table. If freight ton-miles were in fact unaffected by the cyclical swings of business in general we should expect that these nine averages would be equal, within sampling limits—that is, that they would depart from equality only to a degree determined by the complex of random factors that affect freight ton-miles. If we can get a suitable yardstick of chance—an error variance—this may be set against a measure of the variation between the averages for the nine cyclical stages to provide us with a test of the significance of the apparent cyclical pattern in freight ton-miles.

It might appear that the variance within columns would serve as the error variance, as it did in the test of interest rates paid by different groups of business borrowers (Table 16-3). But there is an important difference between the "within-column" observations on interest rates and on freight ton-miles. In the interest rate example the distributions of observations within columns were random; for freight ton-miles the arrangement is chronological. In Table 16-9 we have in fact applied two principles of classification. We have a division by columns based on cyclical stages, a division by rows based on time sequence. We have 9 classes by columns, 11 by rows, giving us 99 cells. But in each of these cells there is but one observation. Thus, as we have noted, we can obtain no estimate of the error variance from "within-cell" differences. This means that we can break the total sum of squares into three components, not four, as in the price example (Table 16-6). We shall obtain these components, and then consider how we may best estimate the error variance.

The elements of the total sum of squares and corresponding degrees of freedom are given in Table 16-10. The derivation of the total and of the several components is straightforward. Formula (16.9) on page 556 sets forth the general relation

$$\Sigma(X - \overline{X})^2 = \Sigma X^2 - T^2/N$$

Substituting the relevant values from Table 16-9, we have

$$\Sigma(X - \overline{X})^2 = 1,025,500 - 9,958^2/99 = 23,866$$

as the total sum of squares. For the component representing variation between columns we measure the deviation of each stage average from the grand mean, square, weight by the number of observations in that column, and add. Thus if we represent by Σd_c^2 the sum of squares of deviations of column means from the grand mean, we have

$$\Sigma d_c^2 = 11(85.09 - 100.59)^2 + 11(90.73 - 100.59)^2 + \ldots$$
$$11(92.09 - 100.59)^2$$

$$= 10,555.0962.*$$

---

* An alternative procedure, based on the relations set forth in formula (16.9) will shorten the calculations somewhat. If we represent the various column means by X_i and the corresponding frequencies by n_i we may write

$$\Sigma d_c^2 = \Sigma(n_i\overline{X}_i^2) - T^2/N$$

The first term in the right member of this equation is obtained, of course, by squaring each column mean, multiplying by the number of observations in that column, and adding the products thus obtained. The second quantity is the subtractive term already used in getting the total sum of squares.

By a similar process we obtain the sum of squares representing deviations between cycle averages, which are the means of the rows. We shall use the symbol Σd_r^2 for this subtotal.

$$\Sigma d_r^2 = 9(100.67 - 100.59)^2 + 9(99.11 - 100.59)^2 + \ldots$$
$$9(95.56 - 100.59)^2$$

$$= 1,031.6214.$$

If we now add Σd_c^2 and Σd_r^2, and subtract the sum from the total sum of squares we obtain the third component of this total sum of squares—a residual equal to 12,279.2824 (see (Table 16-10). We may now consider the nature of the variability represented by each of the three components.

TABLE 16–10

Analysis of Variance of Freight Ton-Miles, and Test of
Reference Cycle Pattern

(1) Nature of variability	(2) Number of degrees of freedom (n)	(3) Sum of squares	(4) Variance	(5) F	(6) $F_{.99}$
Between means of cyclical stages	8	10,555.0962	1,319.39	8.60	2.74
Between means of cycles	10	1,031.6214	103.16		
Residuals	80	12,279.2824	153.49		
Total	98	23,866.0000			

The variance between the means of cycle stages—the column means—may reflect the play of chance. However, if freight ton-miles are significantly affected by the cycles in general business that provide the framework within which we have analyzed this series, the differences between the stage averages also reflect these business cycles. The null hypothesis that really interests us in this problem is H_c, which states, in effect, that there is no significant variation between column means. The variance between the means of the 11 cycles represented in Table 16-9—the row means—is due, in the present case, to an arbitrary factor. If each stage average for a given cycle were weighted by the number of months in that stage, the cycle average thus obtained would of necessity be 100. (The stage averages for a given cycle were obtained in the first place by averaging cycle relatives for the months falling in each stage; the base of these relatives is the mean of monthly observations in that cycle.) But since we have used unweighted stage measures in getting the column means (as is generally done in employing this procedure) we must use unweighted measures in getting the corresponding cycle means.[12] Thus the arbitrary factor

---

[12] It would be perfectly possible to employ weighted stage measures in getting both column and row means. A somewhat different cyclical pattern would then be obtained. The argument for the use of unweighted measures is that a single cycle is the unit of observation, and that cycles—and cycle stages—are of equal importance regardless of duration.

representing variability between cycle means must be eliminated before an attempt is made to estimate the error variance. Subtracting this component from the total sum of squares, therefore, as well as the component representing variation between cyclical stages, we have left a residual sum of squares equal to 12,279.2824, and 80 residual degrees of freedom.

This residual corresponds, of course, to the *interaction* discussed in the study of differential price behavior (Tables 16-6 and 16-8). Like the interaction component in that study, the present residual will be affected by any relation that may exist between the principles of classification, as well as by the play of chance. We may use this residual in estimating the error variance only on the assumption that the principles of classification are, in fact, independent. Dependence of principles of classification, or correlation between them, would in this case mean that the pattern of cyclical behavior, in freight ton-miles, has changed progressively with the passage of time. If there has been such a progressive change, its effects will be present in our residual component—and these effects will be nonrandom in character, and thus not suitable for use in an estimate of the error variance. In the price problem (Table 16-6) we were able to test for the presence of systematic or true interaction, for we were able to get an estimate of the error variance from "within-cells" dispersion. Here we have no such possibility, and must decide on rational grounds, or on the basis of other evidence, whether the present residual component can provide an acceptable estimate of the error variance. We may note here that various tests in the course of the National Bureau's studies of business cycles confirm the view that progressive secular changes in reference cycle patterns, although present in particular instances, have been relatively uncommon among American economic series.[13] In the present case, therefore, it seems reasonable to conclude that interaction, if present, is slight, and that the residual does give us an acceptable estimate of experimental error.

We obtain the variance ratio now by setting the variance between stage means against an error variance obtained from the residual. We have $F = 1,319.39/153.49 = 8.60$. For n_1 of 8 and n_2 of 80 the value of $F_{.99}$ is 2.74. The results are not consistent

---

[13] See Burns and Mitchell (Ref. 13) Chapter 10, and conclusions on pages 412-13.

with the hypothesis that there is no significant variation between column means. The evidence points to the existence of a true pattern of cyclical behavior in freight ton-miles.[14]

A test of this sort, it is clear, may also be used in determining whether a pattern of seasonal behavior is significant. Here, again, there is a possibility of true interaction, that is, of progressive change in the seasonal pattern. If such true interaction should be strong, it would dominate the measure of residual variability, and render it unsuitable as a basis for an estimate of the error variance. The possibility of such interaction is almost certainly stronger for seasonal patterns than for cyclical patterns, for in many series seasonal movements seem more likely to change over time than do cyclical movements.

As we have already noted, the application of probability tests to time series is always a somewhat suspect procedure. Hairline decisions can certainly not be made in such cases, for the conditions necessary to true randomness and independence of observations are often absent. For the example here employed the case for a valid inference is reasonably strong. There is no serious departure from requisite basic conditions (see the following section of this chapter), the pattern marked out by the stage averages is systematic and rational, and the margin by which the observed F exceeds $F_{.99}$ is very wide.

In the preceding pages we have given various examples of problems to which the methods of variance analysis may be applied. In the following chapter we shall make further use of these methods in generalizing and sharpening the instruments used in the study of regression and correlation. With the earlier illustrations in mind, we turn now to a brief consideration of the conditions that are assumed to exist if methods of variance analysis are to be properly employed,[15] and to certain other features of this procedure.

[14] We may note that in one respect the evidence in favor of a positive conclusion is stronger than the variance test by itself would indicate. For not only is there variation among the stage averages; there is a systematic pattern—a rise from stage I to stage V, a fall from stage V to stage IX. Variance between stage averages could reflect any form of departure from equality of values. When this departure is systematic, and in a rational pattern, the investigator's confidence in the significance of that pattern can be stronger than a comparison of variances alone might justify.

[15] For a discussion of these assumptions see Eisenhart (Ref. 33).

Some Basic Assumptions in the Analysis of Variance

Distributions of Experimental Errors should be Normal. We have emphasized above the role played by the denominator of the variance ratio. This is the *error variance*, a measure of the magnitude of the experimental errors that reflect the play of chance. It is a necessary condition of the method of variance analysis that the samples from which we derive the error variance come from normally distributed parent populations. Thus in the interest rate example (Table 16-3) the error variance was obtained from the "within-class" variation among rates paid by small borrowers, middle-sized borrowers, and large borrowers. If the present condition is to be met, each of these samples should come from a normal universe. Similarly, in the example based on price relatives (Table 16-6), the observations in each of the four cells should come from normal parent populations. Fortunately, this condition is not an absolute one, although full accuracy of the test is not achieved if it is not met. W. G. Cochran (Ref. 18), appraising various investigations of the effects of non-normality, concludes that for tests of significance no serious error is introduced by non-normality, short of extreme skewness. He suggests, as an approximation, that with non-normality in the experimental errors the true probability corresponding to the 1 percent significance level of the F-table may lie between one half of 1 percent and 2 percent. Corresponding limits for the true probability corresponding to the tabled 5 percent level may fall between 4 and 7 percent. Since the general effect of the non-normality of experimental errors is to lead to the acceptance of too many results as significant, it is reasonable to be conservative in such acceptance if there is doubt as to the normality of the populations sampled.[16]

Experimental Errors should be Homogeneous in their Variance. The error variance that constitutes the denominator of the variance ratio is usually derived from several classes or cells. In Table 16-3 three different classes contributed to the measure of experimental error; in Table 16-6 components of this measure came from four different cells. The present condition is met when these separate components have a common variance. (In technical terms, the

---

[16] The problems presented by non-normal data in variance analysis are discussed by Kendall (Ref. 78, II, 205-15).

columns, rows, or cells from which the error variance is derived should be *homoscedastic*.) This is obviously necessary if the variance that constitutes the yardstick of "chance" is to be accepted as a true measure of the play of purely random factors. For these random factors must be assumed to be the same within all the classes that contribute to a common measure of experimental error. Every observation that enters into this measure must be subject to the play of the same combination of forces. Here, again, this condition is not an absolute one. Extreme heterogeneity of the components of the error variance will distort tests of significance. With modest departures from homogeneity such tests become less sensitive than when the condition is fully met, but are not completely invalidated. Where heterogeneity is suspected, conservatism in the acceptance of results as significant is called for. (A test of the homogeneity of variances is discussed below.)

The Influences Represented by the Principles of Classification should be Additive. In terms commonly used in the literature of variance analysis, treatment effects and environmental effects should be additive. The meaning of this condition was brought out in the direct determination of the interaction in the price example (Table 16-7). We were there concerned with the influence of fabrication on the susceptibility of different classes of commodities to price decline in a major recession. We assumed that this influence was an additive (or subtractive) one, on the scale of natural numbers. In other words, we have assumed that apart from residual (chance) variations the mean of the measurements in any cell (or the value of a single measurement, if there is but one in each cell) could be arrived at by adding to the mean of all observations an absolute amount representing the environmental effect for the subclass in question and an absolute amount representing the treatment effect for that subclass. This general assumption underlies the methods of variance analysis. If the influences should in fact be multiplicative, for example, the usual methods applied to the natural numbers would lead to inaccurate tests and incorrect estimates. For the estimate of error variance will be affected by departures from additivity, as well as by variations proper. This is not always a serious factor, for differences based on additive assumptions may be good approximations to true differences arising from nonadditive effects, if these effects are not of great magnitude (see Cochran Ref. 18). Moreover, transformations of scale (e.g., from the natural to the logarithmic) may provide a means of meeting the additivity condition.

Experimental Errors should be Independent. The observations falling into any of the classes or subclasses from which the error variance is estimated should be independently distributed, as well as normally distributed, about the class, or subclass, mean. In the absence of such independence, estimates of variances can be biased, and tests of significance impaired. Where deliberate design is possible in setting up an experiment involving variance analysis, the effect of independence may be achieved through randomization, but such design is not always possible in dealing with social and economic data. Among the illustrations we have given in this chapter, one may say that in the cycle example the treatment of the original observations in defining stage averages makes for independence of the observations within a given column. However, there is undoubtedly some correlation of observations in both the interest rate and price data used in the examples cited above, but the correlation is not believed to be high. To the extent that it exists, the tests lose in precision.

As has been indicated in the preceding discussion, the conditions requisite to the full accuracy of variance analysis may be relaxed somewhat without invalidating the various tests an investigator may wish to make. But the consequent loss of accuracy means uncertainty in tests of significance, particularly when the variance ratio is close to a critical point on the F-scale. It is often possible to avoid these difficulties through transformations that change the scale on which measurements are recorded. Thus a non-normal distribution of raw data may become normal through the use of a logarithmic scale. The condition of additiveness may be achieved through the same transformation. Bartlett has used a square-root transformation to stabilize the variance of a Poisson distribution. Ranks may be used in place of measurements when the distribution of the latter departs widely from normality. By these and other devices[17] the methods of variance analysis may be made widely applicable in handling observational data.

Proportionality of frequencies. In the discussion of the price problem reference has been made to the proportionality of the cell frequencies. The methods we have illustrated above are applicable,

---

[17] See Bartlett (Ref. 9) for a brief summary of the use of transformations.

in the form demonstrated, only when class frequencies are equal, or proportional. One immediate difficulty arising out of nonproportional frequencies may be pointed out with reference to the data of Table 16-6. It is to be noted that one fifth of all perishable goods are raw materials and one fifth of all durable goods are raw materials. Because of this proportionality, "rawness" influences the measures for perishable and for durable goods in the same degree. If, in fact, nine tenths of the perishable goods had been raw, while only one tenth of durable goods were raw, and if raw materials and manufactured goods differed significantly in price behavior, we should have no true comparison of the difference in price behavior between perishable and durable goods. For the mode of behavior characteristic of raw materials would dominate the measure for perishables, while the behavior characteristic of manufactured goods would dominate the measure for durables. Problems growing out of the nonproportionality of frequencies involve complexities of treatment that cannot be developed here. We may note, however, that there are valid procedures for making homogeneity tests where subclass frequencies are unequal and disproportionate. For discussions of such procedures see Yates (Ref. 195) and Kendall (Ref. 78). Further references are given by Kendall.

Testing the Homogeneity of Sample Variances. We have referred to the basic assumption, in variance analysis, that the experimental errors are homogeneous in their variance. For problems of the kind illustrated above this means that the variances of the several columns, or rows, or cells, that provide the estimate of the error variance are equal, within sampling limits. This is an assumption that often requires verification before an investigator may draw definite conclusions from variance tests. The same problem appears, more generally, whenever a test is to be made of the equality of variances derived from a series of samples. Are the observed differences of an order of magnitude that chance might bring about? Could the samples have come from populations with equal variances? The hypothesis H_0 to be tested may be written

$$\sigma_1^2 = \sigma_2^2 = \sigma_3^2 = \ldots = \sigma_k^2$$

where the several squared sigmas represent the population variances corresponding to a series of measures, $s_1^2, s_2^2, s_3^2, \ldots s_k^2$, derived from k independent samples. The degrees of freedom with which each of these sample variances is computed are $n_1, n_2, \ldots n_k$, respectively. We shall use s_i^2 and n_i as general symbols for these s's and n's.

The test of homogeneity to be illustrated here is due to Bartlett (Ref. 8). It involves the computation of a quantity M/C, the magnitude of which depends upon the degree of variation among the sample variances and upon the several degrees of freedom with which they are estimated. Bartlett has shown that when no one of the sample variances is derived with less than 4 degrees of freedom this quantity is distributed, approximately, in the chi-square distribution, with $k - 1$ degrees of freedom.

The numerator of the ratio M/C is derived as follows:

$$M = n \log_e s_a^2 - \Sigma(n_i \log_e s_i^2) \qquad (16.11)$$

where
$$n = \Sigma n_i$$

and
$$s_a^2 = \frac{\Sigma(n_i s_i^2)}{n}$$

The quantity s_a^2 is merely a weighted mean of the variances s_i^2, the weights being the corresponding degrees of freedom. We may note that if the variances are all equal, n times the logarithm of the weighted mean variance (the first term in the right-hand member of formula 16.11) will be equal to the weighted sum of the logarithms of the individual sample variances (the second term of the right-hand member of formula 16.11) and the value of M will be zero. Its value will increase as the differences among the sample variances increase.

If it is more convenient to work with common logarithms we may perform the initial calculations in those terms, shifting to natural logarithms as a final step by using the multiplier 2.3026. The formula for M then becomes

$$M = 2.3026\{n \log_{10} s_a^2 - \Sigma(n_i \log_{10} s_i^2)\} \qquad (16.12)$$

The distribution of the quantity M is close to that of chi-square with $k - 1$ degrees of freedom.[18] Division of M by the quantity C, which is unity plus a quantity derived from the several measures of degrees of freedom, improves the approximation and renders the test of homogeneity more accurate. For C we have

$$C = 1 + \frac{1}{3(k - 1)}\left\{\Sigma\left(\frac{1}{n_i}\right) - \frac{1}{n}\right\} \qquad (16.13)$$

---

[18] A precise test of the homogeneity of variances may be based on the quantity M alone, using tables prepared by C. M. Thompson and M. Merrington (Ref. 156).

We may illustrate the test of homogeneity with reference to the observations on interest rates paid by small, middle-sized, and large borrowers (Table 16-3). For these borrowers the sample variances were, respectively, 0.2247, 0.1854, and 0.2853. We wish to know whether these results are consistent with the hypothesis that the population variances for the three classes of borrowers are equal. The quantities needed for the several terms in formulas (16.12) and (16.13) above may be obtained from Table 16-11.

TABLE 16–11

Derivation of Quantities Required in Testing
Homogeneity of Variances, Interest Rates

(1) Class of Borrower	(2) n_i	(3) Σd^2 $(= n_i s_i^2)$	(4) s_i^2	(5) $\log_{10} s_i^2$	(6) $n_i \log_{10} s_i^2$	(7) $1/n_i$
Small	19	4.26950	0.2247	-0.64840	-12.31960	0.05263
Medium	39	7.22975	0.1854	-0.73189	-28.54371	0.02564
Large	39	11.12775	0.2853	-0.54470	-21.24330	0.02564
Total	97	22.62700			-62.10661	0.10391

$$s_a^2 = \frac{22.62700}{97} = 0.2333$$

$$n \log_{10} s_a = 97 \times -0.63209 = -61.31273$$

Substituting the required quantities in formula (16-12) above, we have

$$M = 2.3026\{-61.31273 - (-62.10661)\} = 1.82799$$

With similar substitutions in formula (16.13), we have

$$C = 1 + \frac{1}{3 \times 2}(0.10391 - 0.10309) = 1.00014$$

(the quantity 0.10309 is, of course, the reciprocal of 97, the value of n). In the present case the correctional factor C is so small as to be negligible. Applying it, however, we have, for the final approximation

$$M/C = 1.82799/1.00014 = 1.82773$$

The significance of this measure of heterogeneity among variances is to be judged by reference to the distribution of chi-square with $k - 1$ degrees of freedom. In the present example k is 3. A one-tailed test is appropriate here. From Appendix Table VI we note that, with 2 degrees of freedom, the value of $\chi^2_{.95}$ is 5.991.

Chance factors would in 5 cases out of 100 cause chi-square to equal or exceed this value. We conclude that the observations are not inconsistent with the hypothesis that the sample variances for interest rates paid by different classes of borrowers are homogeneous.[19]

F and t. It will have occurred to the reader that one of the major applications of variance analysis represents an extension to several means of the simple test of the difference between two means (see Chapter 8). For such a problem the *t*-test is, indeed, a special case of the *F*-test. In this special case, for which $n_1 = 1$, for F, and the degrees of freedom (n) for t are given by n_2 of the *F*-table, t^2 is equal to F. However, there is a difference between the forms in which the two measures are usually presented, and we must take account of this in comparing them.

It is customary, as we have seen, to use a single tail of the F distribution in variance analysis. Thus for a test at the 1 percent level the critical value is $F_{.99}$. We are concerned with the probability of a deviation in one direction only. With t, however, a two-tailed test is customary. For a *t*-test at the 1 percent level we take account of the possibility of a deviation above or below the mean of the distribution. In this case $P = 0.01$ is the sum of two probabilities, one of 0.005 for a deviation above the mean, one of 0.005 for a deviation below the mean. (Explicitly, the value of $t_{.995}$, defining the point on the *t*-scale above which lies 0.005 of the total area under the curve, is 3.169. Similarly, the value of $t_{.005}$ is 3.169. The sum of 0.005 and 0.005 measures the probability of a deviation of the stated magnitude, or greater, above *or* below the mean.) The relation cited $(F = t^2)$ holds, then, when we speak of F values relating to a single tail of that distribution, of t values that relate to both tails of the t distribution.

A comparison will make the relation clear. For $n = 10$ the value of t corresponding to a P of 0.01 is 3.169 (see Appendix Table III). This P is a two-tailed value, as we have seen. For $n_1 = 1$ and $n_2 = 10$ we note that $F_{.99}$ is 10.04 (Appendix Table VII). This is the value of F to which we should refer in a one-tailed test. The quantities 10.04 and 3.169 stand in the relation indicated, i.e., $F = t^2$.

---

[19] H. O. Hartley has developed a simpler test of the homogeneity of a series of variances, applicable in the special case in which the variances are from samples of uniform size. (See Hartley, Ref. 68). For the use of this test, however, a prepared table is needed. For examples of its application see Walker and Lev (Ref. 186).

REFERENCES

Bartlett, M. S., "The Use of Transformations," *Biometrics*, of the Biometrics Section of the American Statistical Association, March 1947 (transformations considered with special reference to variance analysis).

Clarke, C. E., *An Introduction to Statistics*, Chap. 7.

Cochran, W. G., "Some Consequences when the Assumptions for the Analysis of Variance Are not Satisfied," *Biometrics*, of the Biometrics Section of the American Statistical Association, Mar. 1947.

Cramér, H., *Mathematical Methods of Statistics*, Chap. 36.

Dixon, W. J. and Massey, F. J. Jr., *Introduction to Statistical Analysis*, Chap. 10.

Eisenhart, C., "Some Assumptions Underlying the Analysis of Variance," *Biometrics*, of the Biometrics Section of the American Statistical Association, Mar. 1947.

Eisenhart, C., Hastay, M. W. and Wallis, W. A., *Selected Techniques of Statistical Analysis*, Chaps. 8, 15.

Fisher, Sir Ronald (R. A.), *Statistical Methods for Research Workers*, 11th ed., Chaps. 7, 8.

Freeman, H. A., *Industrial Statistics*, Chap. 2.

Friedman, M., "The Use of Ranks to Avoid the Assumption of Normality Implicit in the Analysis of Variance," *Journal of the American Statistical Association*, Dec. 1937.

Goulden, C. H., *Methods of Statistical Analysis*, 2nd ed., Chaps. 5, 9.

Kendall, M. G., *The Advanced Theory of Statistics*, 3rd ed., Vol. II, Chaps. 23, 24.

Mather, K., *Statistical Analysis in Biology*, 2nd ed., Chap. 6.

Mood, A. M., *Introduction to the Theory of Statistics*, Chap. 14.

Rosander, A. C., *Elementary Principles of Statistics*, Chaps. 29-31.

Snedecor, G. W., *Analysis of Variance*.

Snedecor, G. W., *Statistical Methods*, 4th ed., Chaps. 6, 7.

Tippett, L. H. C., *The Methods of Statistics*, 4th ed., Chaps. 6, 7.

Tippett, L. H. C., *Technological Applications of Statistics*, Chaps. 10, 11.

Walker, H. M. and Lev, J., *Statistical Inference*, pp. 185-228.

Yates, F., "The Analysis of Multiple Classifications with Unequal Numbers in the Different Classes," *Journal of the American Statistical Association*, Mar. 1934.

Yule, G. U. and Kendall, M. G., *An Introduction to the Theory of Statistics*, 14th ed., Chap. 22.

The publishers and the dates of publication of the books named in chapter reference lists are given in the bibliography at the end of this volume.

.

.

.

CHAPTER 17

The Measurement of Relationship:
General Approaches to the Study
of Regression and Correlation

In dealing with correlation in Chapter 9 the discussion was confined to cases in which the relationship between two variables could be defined by a straight line. The coefficient of correlation r is fully accurate and unambiguous in meaning only when such a line gives a good fit to the points representing the paired values of X and Y. In fitting curves to time series, as was explained in an earlier section, we find that in many cases secular trends are nonlinear, and that trend lines of higher degree are needed. The same thing is true when we deal more generally with relations between variable quantities. It is possible to have a high degree of correlation between two variables when a straight line does not describe the relationship. In such a case there would be considerable scatter about the straight line of best fit, and the value of r would be misleadingly low. If a curve representing the real relationship could be fitted, the scatter would be materially reduced and the true correlation could be measured. Our concern in the present chapter is with this more general problem. We shall discuss, first, a procedure for defining nonlinear relationship when a polynomial of the second degree provides a suitable measure of regression. Thereafter we present a systematic approach to the measurement of regression and correlation, using the methods of variance analysis that were developed in Chapter 16.

Notation. The following new symbols will be introduced in this chapter:

i: a sample value of the index of correlation; a measure of degree of correlation when the regression is nonlinear. When written with subscripts, as i_{yx}, the first subscript denotes the dependent variable, the second the independent variable

$\bar{i}$: the index of correlation corrected to take account of the number of constants in the equation of regression

ι (iota): a population value of the index of correlation

s_i: the standard error of the index of correlation

d_{ya}: the deviation of a given observation from the mean of the Y-array in which it falls

d_{my}: the deviation of a given column mean from the mean of all the Y's

A_1: a sum of squares: that component of the variation between arrays that is "explained" by a linear regression function

B_1: a sum of squares: that component of the variation between arrays that is not "explained" by a linear regression function

A_2: a sum of squares: that component of the variation between arrays that is "explained" by a quadratic regression function

B_2: a sum of squares: that component of the variation between arrays that is not "explained" by a quadratic regression function

η (eta): the correlation ratio; when written with subscripts, as η_{yx}, the first subscript denotes the dependent variable, the second the independent variable

$\bar{\eta}$: the correlation ratio corrected to take account of the number of columns (or rows) in the correlation table

Nonlinear Regression

The observations recorded in Table 17-1, which are plotted in Fig. 17.1, are an example of what appears to be nonlinear regression. These observations show the results obtained in the growing of alfalfa on 44 plots of land in California, using varying amounts of irrigation water. The first column of the table gives average yields

TABLE 17-1

Alfalfa Yield and Irrigation
Summary of investigations at Davis, California*
(The figures in the body of the table measure yields, in tons per acre,
in 44 experiments)

	\multicolumn{8}{c}{Inches of irrigation water applied}
	0	12	18	24	30	36	48	60
	2.35	4.31	5.69	6.00	7.53	7.58	8.05	5.55
	2.75	4.78	6.46	6.89	7.97	8.22	8.45	7.25
	2.89	4.84	7.02	7.96	8.32	8.63	8.63	10.17
	3.85	5.83	8.02	8.32	9.43	9.33	8.83	10.70
	5.52	6.51		8.38	9.54	9.38	9.52	
	5.94	7.52		9.96	11.06	12.48	10.62	
Average yield	3.88	5.63	6.80	7.92	8.98	9.27	9.02	8.42	7.48

* Source: Beckett and Robertson, Ref. 10.

per acre on 6 plots to which no irrigation water was applied; the second column gives average yields on 6 plots each of which received 12 inches of irrigation water; etc. Since it is the yield, the Y-variable, that varies in each column while X, the irrigation factor, is fixed for that column, the columns are called Y-arrays, or Y-arrays of type X.

Two regression functions have been fitted to the points plotted in Fig. 17.1. One is a straight line having the equation

$$Y = 5.038 + 0.0886X$$

in which Y represents yield, in tons per acre, and X represents depth of irrigation water applied, in inches. [We should note that in the fitting process the mean of each array is weighted by the number of observations in that array. This implies, merely, that six points are assumed to have coordinates of 0, 3.88 (equal to those of the mean of the first array), that four points are assumed to have coordinates of 18, 6.80 (equal to those of the mean of the third array), etc.] The degree of relationship between the two variables, as described by this line, is indicated by the coefficient of correlation, r, which has a value of $+ 0.69$.

An inspection of the figure indicates that the straight line does not give the best possible fit. It is probable, therefore, that r is not a suitable measure of the degree of relationship between alfalfa yield and depth of irrigation water. (We should have, of course, more objective evidence on these points than is provided by

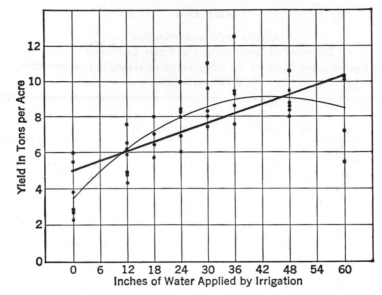

FIG. 17.1. Scatter Diagram Showing the Relation between Alfalfa Yield and Irrigation Water Applied, with Two Lines of Regression.

inspection. Relevant tests of significance are discussed in later sections of this chapter.)

A Quadratic Regression Function. The other regression function in Fig. 17.1 is quadratic—a polynomial of the second degree—fitted by the method of least squares. The equation to this curve is

$$Y = 3.539 + 0.2527X - 0.002827X^2$$

The effect of increasing irrigation upon alfalfa yield appears to be described more accurately by this latter curve than by the straight line, for a law of diminishing returns seems to prevail. The most important result of the study here summarized was the determination of the point at which returns began to diminish—that is, at which alfalfa yield began to fall off. The straight line fails to indicate any such decline.

As the equation of relationship, therefore, we should use the quadratic rather than the linear form. The standard error, $s_{y \cdot x}$, which is a necessary accompanying measure, may be calculated by measuring the deviation of each value from the corresponding computed value, and determining the root-mean-square of these deviations. This procedure is illustrated in Table 17-2. The figures

TABLE 17–2

Comparison of Actual and Computed Alfalfa Yield

(1) Depth of irrigation water	(2) Actual yield	(3) Normal yield as computed from second degree equation	(4) Deviation of actual from normal (2) − (3)	(5)
X	Y	Y_c	d	d^2
0	3.85	3.54	+ .31	.0961
0	5.94	3.54	+2.40	5.7600
0	5.52	3.54	+1.98	3.9204
0	2.75	3.54	− .79	.6241
0	2.89	3.54	− .65	.4225
0	2.35	3.54	−1.19	1.4161
12	4.78	6.16	−1.38	1.9044
12	7.52	6.16	+1.36	1.8496
12	6.51	6.16	+ .35	.1225
12	4.31	6.16	−1.85	3.4225
12	5.83	6.16	− .33	.1089
12	4.84	6.16	−1.32	1.7424
18	7.02	7.17	− .15	.0225
18	5.69	7.17	−1.48	2.1904
18	8.02	7.17	+ .85	.7225
18	6.46	7.17	− .71	.5041
21	6.00	7.98	−1.98	3.9204
21	8.38	7.98	+ .40	.1600
24	8.32	7.98	+ .34	.1156
24	6.89	7.98	−1.09	1.1881
24	9.96	7.98	+1.98	3.9204
24	7.96	7.98	− .02	.0004
30	7.53	8.58	−1.05	1.1025
30	9.54	8.58	+ .96	.9216
30	9.43	8.58	+ .85	.7225
30	7.97	8.58	− .61	.3721
30	11.06	8.58	+2.48	6.1504
30	8.32	8.58	− .26	.0676
36	7.58	8.97	−1.39	1.9321
36	9.33	8.97	+ .36	.1296
36	9.38	8.97	+ .41	.1681
36	8.22	8.97	− .75	.5625
36	12.48	8.97	+3.51	12.3201
36	8.63	8.97	− .34	.1156
48	8.45	9.16	− .71	.5041
48	9.52	9.16	+ .36	.1296
48	8.63	9.16	− .53	.2809
48	8.83	9.16	− .33	.1089
48	10.62	9.16	+1.46	2.1316
48	8.05	9.16	−1.11	1.2321
60	10.17	8.52	+1.65	2.7225
60	7.25	8.52	−1.27	1.6129
60	10.70	8.52	+2.18	4.7524
60	5.55	8.52	−2.97	8.8209
				80.9945

for normal yield which are given in this table are computed from the polynomial equation given above.

Inserting the sum of the squared deviations, as given in column (5) of Table 17-2, in the formula

$$s_{y \cdot x} = \sqrt{\frac{\Sigma d^2}{N}}$$

we have

$$s_{y \cdot x} = \sqrt{\frac{80.9945}{44}} = 1.36$$

The Index of Correlation. We need now the third value, the abstract measure of degree of relationship. In dealing with linear relationship in the preceding chapter we found that such a measure, the coefficient of correlation, could be derived from known values of $s_{y \cdot x}$ and s_y. An analogous measure may be derived in the same way in cases of nonlinear relationship, such as that found in the present problem. Since the term *coefficient of correlation* and the symbol r refer only to cases of linear regression, we may term this general measure the *index of correlation*, and use the letter i to represent it.[1]

As a general formula for the index of correlation we have

$$i_{yx} = \sqrt{1 - \frac{s_{y \cdot x}^2}{s_y^2}} \tag{17.1}$$

The value of $s_{y \cdot x}$ has been derived above.[2] The value of s_y, computed by familiar methods, is found to be 2.27. Substituting in the formula for i, we have

$$i_{yx} = \sqrt{1 - \frac{1.84}{5.19}}$$
$$= 0.80$$

This value is materially greater than that of the coefficient of correlation for the same data. The value of r is $+ 0.69$. These results indicate that the quadratic gives a better fit to the data

---

[1] When this measure was introduced I used the symbol ρ (rho) for it (Ref. 102), and Ezekiel (Ref. 36) used the corresponding capital letter for the index of multiple curvilinear correlation. Since it has now become standard practice to employ Greek letters for population parameters, with ρ representing the parameter corresponding to a sample r, the letter i is here used for the index of correlation. The Greek ι (iota) may be used for the population parameter.

[2] The quantities $s_{y \cdot x}^2$ and s_y^2 are derived by dividing the relevant sums of squares by the same N. That is, there is no reduction of N to take account of degrees of freedom lost. The two mean squares are here to be regarded as descriptive measures.

than does the straight line. We shall later discuss means of determining whether the difference is significant.

We should note that there are two indexes of correlation for a given set of observations. With X dependent the formula becomes

$$i_{xy} = \sqrt{1 - \frac{s_{x \cdot y}^2}{s_x^2}} \qquad (17.2)$$

The first of the two subscripts refers always to the dependent variable, the second to the independent. It is essential that these be shown, for the index would not necessarily be the same with X dependent as with Y dependent.

The significance and the limitations of i should be made clear. Its value depends upon the relation between the scatter about the fitted line and the scatter about the arithmetic mean of the Y's. When the regression is truly linear i and r are identical, r being a special case of i. The limits of i are 0 and 1, a value of 0 indicating that there is no relationship, or that if there is a relationship between the two variables it cannot be described by the particular equation employed. A value of 1 indicates that the relationship, as described by the equation employed, is a perfect one. No positive or negative sign should be attached to i, for the relationship might be positive over part of the range and negative over other parts, as in the alfalfa example given above.

The index of correlation, i, has no clear meaning unless the type of curve to which it applies be named in each case. The meaning of r in this respect is always clear, for it is understood that it relates always to a straight line, but confusion would arise in the case of i unless the type of curve were specifically mentioned.

It is, of course, always possible to secure a curve which will pass through any number of points if the constants in the equation be equal to the number of points. In such a case i would, of necessity, be equal to 1, but this value would have no significance. In any employment of mathematical functions there is this limit of absurdity, when the number of constants is equal to the number of points, and i would merely reflect this absurdity. The ordinary principles of curve fitting must be kept in mind in using such an index as this. It must never be taken to have an absolute significance, standing by itself. Its significance is always relative, referring to the particular function employed. This fact, which is true of every measure of correlation, is frequently overlooked, and fallacious conclusions reached as a result.

A short method of computing the index of correlation. The standard error and the index of correlation were computed by a rather laborious method in the above example, in order that there might be no misunderstanding of their precise meaning. The burden of calculation may be materially reduced, however, by taking advantage of the relationships that were disclosed in dealing with r. For a polynomial of the series

$$Y = a + bX + cX^2 + dX^3 + \ldots$$

the formula for $s_{y \cdot x}$ is derived by a simple extension of that employed in the case of the straight line. As a general formula for a series of this type, we have

$$s_{y \cdot x}^2 = \frac{\Sigma(Y^2) - a\Sigma(Y) - b\Sigma(XY) - c\Sigma(X^2Y) - d\Sigma(X^3Y) - \ldots}{N}$$

$$(17.3)$$

Similarly, the formula for r may be extended to give a general formula for i applicable to any equation of this general type. This formula[3] is

$$i_{yx}^2 = \frac{a\Sigma(Y) + b\Sigma(XY) + c\Sigma(X^2Y) + d\Sigma(X^3Y) + \ldots - Nc_y^2}{\Sigma(Y^2) - Nc_y^2} \quad (17.4)$$

where $c_y = \Sigma Y / N$

In the special case in which the origin is at the mean of the Y's, $\Sigma(y) = 0$ and $c_y = 0$, and the formula reduces to

$$i_{yx}^2 = \frac{b\Sigma(Xy) + c\Sigma(X^2y) + d\Sigma(X^3y) + \ldots}{\Sigma(y^2)} \quad (17.5)$$

The characteristics of the formulas for $s_{y \cdot x}$ and i should be noted. The only values required in securing these measures are the constants in the equation that describes the average relationship, certain values that have been used in the process of fitting and, in addition, $\Sigma(Y^2)$ and c_y^2. Thus, as direct by-products of the fitting process, we have the values of $s_{y \cdot x}$ and i, the two measures which are needed to supplement the regression equation in securing a complete description of the relationship between the two variables

---

[3] See Appendix C for discussion of a general formula for the standard error of estimate. Formula 17.4 is derived from this general formula for $s_{y \cdot x}$.

in question. The equation describes the average relationship. The standard error of estimate, $s_{y \cdot x}$, is a measure of the reliability of estimates based upon this equation, and i is an abstract index of the degree of relationship, in so far as that relationship can be described by the particular curve employed.

The application of these formulas may be illustrated with reference to the problem of alfalfa yield. The following values, derived from the data of Table 17-1 and from the fitting process, are required for this purpose:

$$a = 3.539 \qquad\qquad \Sigma(X^2 Y) = 407,564.64$$
$$b = .252652 \qquad\qquad c_y^2 = 55.9197$$
$$c = -\,.002827 \qquad\qquad \Sigma(Y^2) = 2,688.2268$$
$$\Sigma(Y) = 329.03 \qquad\qquad N = 44$$
$$\Sigma(XY) = 10,271.72$$

Substituting in the formula for the standard error of estimate for a second degree polynomial,

$$s_{y \cdot x}^2 = \frac{\Sigma(Y^2) - a\Sigma(Y) - b\Sigma(XY) - c\Sigma(X^2 Y)}{N} \qquad (17.6)$$

we have

$$s_{y \cdot x}^2 = \frac{2,688.2268 - (3.539 \times 329.03) - (.252652 \times 10,271.72) - (-.002827 \times 407,654.64)}{44}$$

$$= \frac{80.8043}{44}$$

$$= 1.8365$$

$$s_{y \cdot x} = 1.36$$

The index of correlation, for a curve of this type, is computed from the equation

$$i_{yx}^2 = \frac{a\Sigma(Y) + b\Sigma(XY) + c\Sigma(X^2 Y) - Nc_y^2}{\Sigma(Y)^2 - Nc_y^2} \qquad (17.7)$$

Substituting the appropriate values, we have

$$i_{yx}^2 = \frac{146.9557}{2,688.2268 - (44 \times 55.9197)}$$

$$= 0.6452$$

$$i_{yx} = 0.80$$

The value of the index of correlation is influenced by the relation between the number of observations and the number of constants in the equation of relationship. When the two are equal i will have a value of 1. In any case the observed index of correlation tends to exceed the true index because of the flexibility given, in the fitting process, by the constants in the equation of regression. When the number of observations is not large it is advisable to apply a correction for this bias. If we use $\bar{i}$ to represent the corrected value and m to represent the number of constants in the equation of relationship, we may apply a correction in terms of the relation[4]

$$\bar{i}_{yx}^2 = 1 - \left\{(1 - i_{yx}^2)\left(\frac{N-1}{N-m}\right)\right\} \tag{17.8}$$

Inserting the values given in the above example, we have

$$\bar{i}_{yx}^2 = 1 - \left\{(1 - 0.6452)\left(\frac{44-1}{44-3}\right)\right\}$$

$$= 0.6279$$

$$\bar{i}_{yx} = 0.79$$

If, in the application of this test, the quantity in brackets { } exceeds unity, the value of $\bar{i}$ is taken as 0.[5]

These methods of deriving $s_{y \cdot x}$ and i are applicable over a wide field by a simple adaptation of the formulas to the particular equations that may be employed in given instances.

The sampling error of the index of correlation. There is, of course, no one sampling distribution of the index of correlation. There are many, varying as the orders of fitted functions vary, as population values vary and as sample sizes vary. Since these distributions have not been defined with precision, the accurate determination of the standard error of a particular index is not possible. However,

---

[4] From Ezekiel, Ref. 37.

[5] A corresponding correction should be made in the standard error of estimate, when derived from a small number of observations. In this case the correction must raise the unadjusted measure. For this correction Ezekiel gives

$$\bar{s}_{y \cdot x}^2 = s_{y \cdot x}^2\left(\frac{N-1}{N-m}\right)$$

where $\bar{s}_{y \cdot x}$ represents the corrected standard error of estimate.

when samples are large a useful approximation may be derived from the relation

$$s_i = \frac{1 - \iota^2}{\sqrt{N - m}} \tag{17.9}$$

In this formula ι (iota) is the population value (for which we use the sample value as an estimate), m represents the number of constants in the equation of regression. The formula may be used, with the reservations suggested by what has been said, in setting confidence limits for the population value and in tests of significance.[6] For the latter purpose, however, more accurate instruments are provided by methods of variance analysis. The application of these methods to problems of regression and correlation is our concern in the following section.

Variance Analysis in the Measurement of Relationship

The development by R. A. Fisher of the technique of variance analysis provides means for a systematic approach to the study of regression and correlation. In a rational attack upon the problem, in a specific case, it is natural to ask the following questions (with reference to two variables):

1. Do the available observations provide evidence that the two variables are in fact (i.e., apart from chance fluctuations) related in their movements?
2. If we may assume the existence of true correlation, will the simplest possible function—a straight line—acceptably define the regression?
3. If there is correlation, and a straight line is not appropriate as a regression function, will a given second degree function provide an acceptable measure of regression? If such a function is not suitable, will a different function with the same number of constants, or a polynomial of higher degree, give an acceptable fit?

If the answer to the first question is no, the investigator will go no further. If it is yes, he would naturally proceed with the testing of regression functions until he found one that was acceptable. In

---

[6] I should emphasize here that the theory of regression functions of higher degree, and of corresponding measures of correlation, is far less adequately developed than is the theory of linear regression and correlation. Accordingly, while such nonlinear functions and measures may be descriptively useful, generalization from them must be imprecise.

doing so, bearing in mind Occam's razor (see footnote p. 345), he would seek the simplest function that is acceptable on rational grounds and that conforms to the actual observations. It is a great virtue of the method of variance analysis that it permits this systematic approach, providing instruments for testing the hypotheses that the investigator propounds, successively, as he proceeds with his study.

The method employed in applying to a typical correlation problem the method of analysis based on comparison of variances may be illustrated with reference to the data of alfalfa yield previously studied (see Table 17-1). The average yield of alfalfa in the 44 experiments there recorded was 7.48 tons per acre. But there was rather wide variation among the results. The sum of the squares of the deviations of the 44 observations from the mean is 228.33. This total, which we shall represent by Q (see Table 16-5), sets our problem. We should like to find reasons for the variation it represents.

Testing for the Existence of Correlation. The observations are set up in Table 17-1 in a form suited to the testing of hypotheses concerning possible relations between alfalfa yield and applications of irrigation water. The data are arranged in eight arrays, classified according to the depth of irrigation water applied. This depth varied from 0 to 60 inches. Variations in yield appear to be associated with variations in amount of water applied. As a basis for our procedure we set up, first, the hypothesis that there is no such association. To test this hypothesis, we may break the sum that measures the total variation of yields into two parts measuring, respectively, the variation within arrays and the variation between arrays.

To determine the total *variation within arrays*, the deviation of each observation from the mean of the array in which it falls is measured. The sum of the squares of these deviations, for all the arrays, is the desired total. Thus, in the first array of Table 17-1, the mean is 3.88 tons. The deviation of the first observation, 2.35, from this figure, is -1.53; its square is 2.3409. The deviation of the second observation, 2.75, is -1.13; its square is 1.2769. Determining in similar fashion the deviations of the four other observations in that array from the mean of the array, squaring these, and adding the six squared values, we have 11.5320 as the sum of the squares of the deviations in the first array. Performing similar calculations for the seven other arrays and adding the eight sums thus secured, we have a figure of 76.39. This is the total variation within arrays. We shall refer to this as component Q_2 of the total variation (see Table 16-5). If we use the symbol d_{ya} to represent the deviation of a given observation from the mean of the Y-array in which it falls, Σ' to indicate summation within a given column, and Σ to indicate over-all summation, $Q_2 = \Sigma\Sigma'd_{ya}^2$.

In determining the total *variation between arrays*, the deviations of the means of the various arrays from the mean of all the observations are measured and squared, and the weighted sum of these squares is secured. Weights are based upon the number of observations in the several arrays. Thus the mean of the first array, 3.88 deviates from the mean of all the observations, 7.48, by -3.60; the square of this is 12.9600. Multiplying by 6 (the number of observations in the first class), we have 77.7600. Securing similar weighted figures for the seven other arrays, and adding, we have 151.94 as the variation between arrays. This is component Q_1 of the total variation. Using the notation of the standard form given in Table 16-5, $Q_1 = \Sigma n_i(\overline{Y}_i - \overline{Y})^2$. It will be convenient to let d_{my} represent the deviation of a given column mean from $\overline{Y}$ and to write $Q_1 = \Sigma d_{my}^2$, it being understood that suitable weights (n_i) were employed before summation.

In breaking the total sum of squares, 228.33, into two components equal, respectively, to 76.39 and 151.94, we have distinguished variations in yield that are definitely not related to differences in depth of irrigation water applied, from variations in yield that may or may not be related to irrigation differences.[7] Within the first array, including six experiments on plots to which no irrigation water was applied, yields varied from 2.35 tons to 5.94 tons per acre. The total variation within this array (the sum of the squares of the deviations from the mean of the array) amounted to 11.5320. Since the irrigation factor was constant, this sum measures variation which is completely independent of changes in irrigation. This is true also of the figure 76.39, measuring total variation within all the eight arrays set up in Table 17-1. Differences in soils and innumerable minor factors combined to create variation within these arrays. The figure 76.39 measures the play of that host of undefined forces to which we give the name *chance*.

---

[7] The procedure here employed follows that exemplified in Table 16-4, and given in standard form in Table 16-5.

The one specific factor that does not affect this figure is irrigation. We have measured this component of total variation in such a way that irrigational differences do not enter.

Irrigational differences do enter definitely into the variation between arrays. Indeed, it may be the dominant factor in this variation, which is measured by the figure 151.94. But of this we cannot be sure. For the means of the eight arrays differ among themselves not only because of differences in the amounts of irrigation water applied to the different plots. To differences in yields due to the irrigation factor are added differences due to the innumerable other forces that influence alfalfa yield, the forces we lump together as chance. For chance factors affect the means of the various arrays, and so affect the variation between arrays, just as they affect the variation within arrays. As the experiment was designed, the influence of irrigational differences is present only in the variation between arrays, but the influence of "chance" is present in both the variation within arrays and the variation between arrays.

In this fact is found the key to our problem, and the instrument for testing the null hypothesis. For, in so far as chance alone is operative, the variation between arrays would be expected to be of the same order of magnitude as the variation within arrays. The figures we have so far examined indicate that the variation between arrays is greater than the variation within arrays. But this may be a purely fortuitous result. The apparent increase of yield with increased irrigation may be entirely a chance phenomenon, similar to a run of heads in tossing a coin. This we must test. We must determine whether the forces responsible for variation between arrays are the same as the forces responsible for variation within arrays.

The hypothesis we shall test, and which may of course be disproved, is that the forces responsible for variation between arrays are the same as the forces responsible for variation within arrays; in other words, that there is no association between depth of irrigation water applied and alfalfa yield. The test to be applied has been described in Chapter 16. We compare the two measures of variation, to determine whether they are of the same order of magnitude.

It will be clear (see Table 16-5) that there are 7 degrees of freedom for variation between the columns of Table 17-1, 36 for variation within columns. Subsequent steps in testing for the existence of correlation are set forth in Table 17-3. It is obviously variation within arrays (Component Q_2) that provides us with the error variance, the yardstick that defines the magnitude of variations we may attribute to the play of chance. Variance between arrays, 21.71, is distinctly greater than the error variance, 2.12, but we require an objective test for the proper appraisal of the difference. The variance ratio F is 21.71/2.12, or 10.24. This is far greater than 3.18, the 99th percentile value of F for $n_1 = 7$, $n_2 = 36$ (see Appendix Table VII). If we are testing the present null hypothesis with reference to a 1 percent level of significance, the hypothesis must be rejected. Chance alone could not bring so great a departure from an F value of 1. The forces responsible for

TABLE 17–3

A Test of the Existence of Correlation: Alfalfa Yield and Irrigation Water

(1) Nature of variability	(2) Degrees of freedom	(3) Sum of squares	(4) Variance s^2	(5) F	(6) $F_{.99}$
	(n)				
Between arrays					
Component Q_1	7	151.94	21.71		
Within arrays					
Component Q_2	36	70.39	2.12	10.24	3.18
	—	——			
	43	228.33			

variation between arrays could not be the same as those responsible for variation within arrays. Which leaves us with the positive conclusion that alfalfa yield and depth of irrigation water are related.

It will be noted that in the above test we have made no assumptions as to the form of the relationship, whether linear, quadratic, or other. We have asked whether there is correlation, the regression function being undefined, and have concluded that there is.

Testing the Hypothesis of Linear Relationship. It is now in order to identify an acceptable regression function that will define in quantitative terms the relationship between alfalfa yield and depth of water applied to alfalfa plots. We may do this by testing, in turn, various hypotheses concerning the form of this function, until we secure one with which the observations are not inconsistent.

We shall start with the hypothesis that there is a linear relationship between alfalfa yield and depth of irrigation water applied.[8]

The first step in applying the present test is to fit a straight line to the means of the eight arrays shown in Table 17-1. Variation among these means (component Q_1 of the total variation) reflects the presence of correlation between alfalfa yield and irrigation water applied. If the relation between average yield, by classes, and irrigation water applications is perfectly linear, all these class means will fall on a straight line; all the variation between arrays will be accounted for by the hypothesis of a linear relationship.[9] If the relationship is substantially, though not perfectly, linear, the portion of component Q_1 not accounted for by linear regression will be insignificant. If the regression is not truly linear the residue of Q_1 not accounted for (i.e., the scatter of the means of the arrays about the straight line of regression) will be too great, and some other hypothesis concerning the character of the relationship between alfalfa yield and irrigation water applied must be employed.

A straight line fitted by the method of least squares to the means of the eight arrays is shown in Fig. 17.1 on page 582. The equation to this line, as we have seen, is $Y = 5.038 + 0.0886X$, where Y is alfalfa yield in tons per acre and X is depth of irrigation water applied, in inches. In Table 17-4 are given the values of the means of the various arrays, and the corresponding computed values, as derived from the straight line of regression.

It is clear from the graph and the table that the fit of the straight line to the means of the arrays is not perfect. The inadequacy of the fit is measured by the sum of the squared deviations of the class means from the corresponding computed values (each squared deviation being weighted by the number of observations in the given class). This sum, 44.79, to which we may refer as B_1, is one component of Q_1, the variation between arrays. It is that portion

---

[8] Each hypothesis tested should be rational, acceptable on logical grounds. If we are thinking of general relationships, prevailing over the entire range of possible observation, the assumption of a straight-line relationship between alfalfa yield and amount of irrigation water applied is not tenable. For it is not to be expected that increased irrigation will increase yield without limit. In the present case we test the hypothesis of a linear relationship in order that the demonstration of procedure may be systematic and complete, although that hypothesis is not a rational one, even within the range of the present observations.

[9] This is not to say that r would equal unity under these conditions. There would still be variation within classes that would not be related to irrigation differences.

TABLE 17–4

Alfalfa Yield and Depth of Irrigation Water
(Class means and values based on linear relationship
$Y = 5.038 + .0886X$)

(1) Inches of water (class)	(2) No. of obser- vations	(3) Mean yield of class	(4) Estimated yield, linear relationship (tons)	(5) Difference between mean yield of class and estimated yield	(6)	(7)
				$(\overline{Y}_p - y_c)$		
	f	$\overline{Y}_p$	y_c	d	d^2	fd^2
0	6	3.88	5.04	−1.16	1.3456	8.0736
12	6	5.63	6.10	− .47	.2209	1.3254
18	4	6.80	6.63	+ .17	.0289	.1156
24	6	7.92	7.16	+ .76	.5776	3.4656
30	6	8.98	7.70	+1.28	1.6384	9.8304
36	6	9.27	8.23	+1.04	1.0816	6.4896
48	6	9.02	9.29	− .27	.0729	.4374
60	4	8.42	10.36	−1.94	3.7636	15.0544
						44.7920

of the variation between arrays that is not accounted for by the hypothesis of a linear relation between yield and irrigation water.

The method of deriving the other component of Q_1 is shown in Table 17-5. The sum 107.15, to which we may refer as A_1, is that component of the variation between arrays which is accounted for by the hypothesis of linear regression. The items in column (3) of Table 17-5 differ from 7.48, the mean of all the observations, for the reason suggested by the hypothesis. We assume that they differ because, with increased applications of water, yield increases in a manner defined precisely by the equation $Y = 5.038 + 0.0886X$. The sum of these variations, 107.15, represents, on this assumption, the full effect on alfalfa yield of variations of irrigation applications.

The total of the two sums of squares to which we have referred as A_1 and B_1 is equal to 151.94, or Q_1, the sum of squares between arrays. Working on the hypothesis that the variables with which we are dealing stand in a linear relationship, we have broken the component Q_1 of the total variation into two portions. One of these (A_1) measures the variation between arrays that is accounted for by the linear hypothesis; the other (B_1) measures the variation

TABLE 17–5

Computation of Variation in Alfalfa Yield Attributable to Irrigation
Differences on the Hypothesis of Linear Regression

(1)	(2)	(3)	(4)	(5)	(6)	(7)
Inches of water	No. of observations	Estimated yield, linear relationship (tons)	Mean yield, all observations	Difference between mean yield and yield estimated on linear hypothesis		
				$(y_c - \overline{Y})$		
	f	y_c	$\overline{Y}$	d	d^2	fd^2
0	6	5.04	7.48	−2.44	5.9536	35.7216
12	6	6.10	7.48	−1.38	1.9044	11.4264
18	4	6.63	7.48	− .85	.7225	2.8900
24	6	7.16	7.48	− .32	.1024	.6144
30	6	7.70	7.48	+ .22	.0484	.2904
36	6	8.23	7.48	+ .75	.5625	3.3750
48	6	9.29	7.48	+1.81	3.2761	19.6566
60	4	10.36	7.48	+2.88	8.2944	33.1776
						107.1520

between arrays that is not accounted for by that hypothesis. We should expect some departure from linearity in a sample such as ours, even though it were drawn from a universe marked by a perfect linear relationship. But there are limits to the deviations that might reflect fluctuations of sampling. The question we now face is whether B_1 is small enough to be accepted as the resultant of random factors, or whether it is so large as to represent a breakdown of our hypothesis.

In our earlier discussion we noted that component Q_2 of the total variation measured the influence of a host of random forces affecting alfalfa yield, forces other than the irrigation factor. Q_2, therefore, serves as an index of the magnitude of random forces, and hence as a standard defining the probable limits of sampling fluctuations, in so far as these are present in component Q_1. We may use Q_2, which relates to variation within arrays, as a yardstick in determining whether B_1 is attributable to fluctuations of sampling, or whether it is too large to be so explained.

In comparing components Q_2 and B_1 account must be taken of the number of degrees of freedom present in each. This has already been established for Q_2. The following tabular summary of the operations just performed may help to explain the relations involved for B_1.

Nature of variability	No. of degrees of freedom	Sum of squares	Variance
Between arrays, due to linear regression (Component A_1)	1	107.15	
Deviations of class means from straight line of regression (Component B_1)	6	44.79	7.47
Total variation between arrays (Q_1)	7	151.94	

The seven degrees of freedom entering into Q_1 are divided, one to component A_1 and six to component B_1. That the points on a straight line vary from one another with 1 degree of freedom is clear from a consideration of the linear equation $y = a + bx$. The values of y may differ because of the presence of the coefficient b, which defines the slope. If b were zero, the equation would define a horizontal line, with values of y constant. It is the slope that constitutes the one degree of freedom among points defined by a linear equation. With respect to B_1, we are dealing with eight points, to which a straight line has been fitted. If there were but two points both of them would lie on the line; there would be no possibility of deviation. With three points, one degree of freedom to deviate is introduced; with eight points there are six degrees of freedom. The degrees of freedom to deviate from any fitted curve are obviously equal to the number of points to which the curve is fitted, less the number of constants in the equation to that curve.

Dividing 44.79 by 6 we may secure, then, the value of the variance (the mean square) comparable to the variance of component Q_2. A test of our hypothesis again reduces to a comparison of variances. This appears in Table 17-6.

TABLE 17–6

A Test of the Hypothesis of Linear Relationship

(1) Nature of variability	(2) Degrees of freedom n	(3) Variance s^2	(4) F	(5) $F_{.99}$
Deviations of means from line of regression (Component B_1)	6	7.47		
Within arrays (Component Q_2)	36	2.12	3.52	3.35

The variation within arrays reflects the play of random factors, independent of irrigation. The force of these factors is indicated by a variance of 2.12. If similar random factors, independent of irrigation, were responsible for the deviations of the means of the eight arrays from the straight line of regression, we should expect the variance that measures such deviations to be of the same order of magnitude. Actually it is much greater, 7.47. But we cannot say, from inspection, that the difference between the two variances is not due to fluctuations of sampling. An accurate test is needed. The entries in columns (4) and (5) of Table 17-6 give us the basis of such a test. Less frequently than 1 time out of 100 would chance account for a value of F as great as the one observed. We conclude, therefore, that random forces, of the type responsible for variation within arrays, are not responsible for the deviations of the means of the eight arrays from the straight line of regression. These deviations are too great to be consistent with the hypothesis that there is a linear relationship between alfalfa yield and depth of irrigation water. This equation fails to account, adequately, for the observed variation between arrays.

Testing the Hypothesis of Curvilinear Relationship. We may now test the hypothesis that a polynomial of the second degree $(Y = a + bX + cX^2)$ defines the relation between alfalfa yield and depth of irrigation water applied. The procedure is identical with that followed in the case of the straight line. By the method of least squares we determine the best values of the constants in an equation of the desired form. The curve is fitted to the means of the eight arrays, each weighted by the number of observations in that array. The derived equation, which was discussed in the early pages of this chapter, is $Y = 3.539 + 0.2527X - 0.002827X^2$. The curve appears graphically in Fig. 17.1; the computation of the sum of the squared deviations from it is shown in Table 17-7.

The inadequacy of the fit is measured this time by the figure 4.61, the sum of the squared deviations from the power curve of the second degree. This sum, to which we may refer as B_2, is a component of Q_1, the variation between arrays. It is the portion that is not accounted for by the hypothesis of curvilinear relationship, of the type assumed, between alfalfa yield and irrigation water applied. The other component of Q_1, is derived by the method indicated in Table 17-8.

We may designate by A_2 the sum 147.32. This is the component

of the variation between arrays that is accounted for by the
hypothesis of a relationship defined by a second degree curve. The
items in column (3) of Table 17-8 differ from the mean of all the

TABLE 17–7

Alfalfa Yield and Depth of Irrigation Water
(Class means and values based on a polynomial of the second degree)

(1)	(2)	(3)	(4)	(5)	(6)	(7)
Inches of water (class)	No. of obser- vations	Mean yield of class (tons)	Estimated yield, from equation (tons)	Difference between mean yield of class and esti- mated yield		
	f	$\overline{Y}_p$	y_c	$\overline{Y}_p - y_c$ d	d^2	fd^2
0	6	3.88	3.54	$+$ .34	.1156	.6936
12	6	5.63	6.16	$-$ .53	.2809	1.6854
18	4	6.80	7.17	$-$ .37	.1369	.5476
24	6	7.92	7.98	$-$ .06	.0036	.0216
30	6	8.98	8.58	$+$ .40	.1600	.9600
36	6	9.27	8.97	$+$ .30	.0900	.5400
48	6	9.02	9.16	$-$ .14	.0196	.1176
60	4	8.42	8.52	$-$ .10	.0100	.0400
						4.6058

TABLE 17–8

Computation of Variation in Alfalfa Yield Attributable to Irrigation
Differences on the Hypothesis of Non-Linear Regression

(1)	(2)	(3)	(4)	(5)	(6)	(7)
Inches of water	No. of obser- vations	Estimated yield, equation of second degree	Mean yield, all obser- vations			
	f	y_c	$\overline{Y}$	$y_c - \overline{Y}$ d	d^2	fd^2
0	6	3.54	7.48	-3.94	15.5236	93.1416
12	6	6.16	7.48	-1.32	1.7424	10.4544
18	4	7.17	7.48	$-$ .31	.0961	.3844
24	6	7.98	7.48	$+$ .50	.2500	1.5000
30	6	8.58	7.48	$+1.10$	1.2100	7.2600
36	6	8.97	7.48	$+1.49$	2.2201	13.3206
48	6	9.16	7.48	$+1.68$	2.8224	16.9344
60	4	8.52	7.48	$+1.04$	1.0816	4.3264
						147.3218

observations, on our present assumption, because alfalfa yield varies with increased applications of water in a manner defined by the equation

$$Y = 3.539 + 0.2527X - 0.002827X^2$$

We have again broken Q_1, the total variation between arrays, into two components, A_2 representing the influence of the irrigation factor, working in accordance with a definite law, and B_2 representing random factors, or random factors combined with the irrigation factor. (The irrigation factor enters into B_2 to the extent that the hypothesis in question fails to take account of the true relation between alfalfa yield and depth of water applied.) This is, of course, a different division of Q_1 from that resulting from the application of a linear hypothesis. The present division may be set down in summary.

Nature of variability	No. of degrees of freedom	Sum of squares	Variance
Between arrays, due to regression of second degree (Component A_2)	2	147.32	
Deviations of class means from curve of regression (Component B_2)	5	4.61	.92
Total variation between arrays (Q_1)	7	151.93	

The seven degrees of freedom entering into Q_1 are now divided, five to component B_2 and two to component A_2. The reasons for this allocation of the degrees of freedom are similar to those presented in discussing the linear hypothesis. As regards B_2, the item now of chief concern to us, it is clear that when a curve defined by an equation with three constants is fitted to eight points there are five degrees of freedom to deviate from that curve.

Dividing 4.61 by 5 we secure .92, the value of the variance comparable to the variance of Q_2. For again we must use a criterion based on Q_2, in determining the limits within which variation due to random factors, independent of irrigation, may play. We come again to a comparison of variances (Table 17-9).

In this case the degree of deviation from the curve of regression defined by the polynomial of the second degree is actually less than the deviation within arrays, which serves as our yardstick. The value of F is less than unity. Without further test we may say that

TABLE 17–9
A Test of the Hypothesis of Curvilinear Relationship

(1) Nature of variability	(2) Degrees of freedom n	(3) Variance s^2	(4) F
Deviation from second degree curve of regression (Component B_2)	5	.92	
Within arrays (Component Q_2)	36	2.12	0.43

the results are not inconsistent with the hypothesis that the second degree equation we have employed defines acceptably the relationship between alfalfa yield and depth of irrigation water applied. The departures from the curve of regression may be attributed to chance.

In following this general procedure it is necessary to test different hypotheses (i.e., different functions) only until the difference between the variance defined by component Q_2 and the variance defining departures from the curve of regression be small enough to be attributed to the play of chance. Thus, if a P of .05 constitutes our standard, the variance ratio given in Table 17-9 might be as great as 2.48 (see Appendix Table VII) without leading to rejection of the hypothesis being tested. It could be as great as 3.58 if our standard of significance were a P of .01. A rather exceptionally close fit by the second degree curve we have employed gives us a value of F below unity.

We have arrived, then, at a hypothesis concerning the relation between alfalfa yield and depth of irrigation water applied, with which observed facts are not inconsistent. Our observations, be it noted, do not establish the truth of this hypothesis. Other hypotheses might be equally tenable, and perhaps even more closely in accord with the facts.[10] All that we can say is that the observed facts do not disprove the hypothesis. If the hypothesis is tenable on rational grounds, we have reached a conclusion upon which we may rest, for the time.

[10] We could, of course, fit a curve of still higher degree, the equation to which might contain four constants, or more, instead of the three constants in the equation actually employed. The deviations from this curve of higher degree would be smaller than from the curve of second degree, and F would be correspondingly smaller. It is a principle of scientific procedure, however, to employ the simplest acceptable function. Needless complexities, whether in the form of unnecessary assumptions or of unnecessary constants in an equation of relationship, are rigorously avoided.

A Summary View of Measures of Relationship

In opening the preceding discussion of the use of variance analysis in the measurement of relationship, we noted that our problem was posed by the fact of variation in alfalfa yields, as reported from experiments on 44 plots of land. The magnitude of this variation is measured by the sum of the squared deviations of the yields of the individual plots from the grand mean (a sum derived from $\Sigma(X - \overline{X})^2$, or Σd^2). This sum is 228.33. We have broken up this total in various ways, in the course of the testing process just described. In now recapitulating these steps, in slightly different order, we shall relate the measures employed in the variance analyses to the abstract measures of correlation previously developed and to one additional measure of somewhat the same type.[11]

Components Q_2, A_1, and B_1 of the total variation (see pp. 593 and 597 above) constitute one classification of constituent elements of the total sum of squares, a classification derived from the hypothesis that the relation between alfalfa yield and applications of irrigation water may be described by a straight line. We may call these elements of Classification I (Table 17-10).

TABLE 17–10

Classification I: Component Elements of Total Sum of Squares, Alfalfa Yields
(Linear Hypothesis)

Element	Sum of squares	Measure of correlation
Q_2 : Sum of squares unrelated to irrigation factor (variation within arrays)	76.39	
A_1 : Sum of squares representing variation attributable to irrigation factor on the assumption of a linear relationship (deviation of computed yields from grand mean)	107.15	$r_{yx}^2 = \dfrac{s_{y_c}^2}{s_y^2} = \dfrac{\Sigma d_{y_c}^2/N}{\Sigma d_y^2/N}$ $= \dfrac{\Sigma d_{y_c}^2}{\Sigma d_y^2} = \dfrac{107.15}{228.33} = 0.4693$ $r_{yx} = +0.69$
B_1 : Sum of squared deviations of column means from corresponding computed yields (variation between columns that is not explained by the linear hypothesis)	44.79	
Q : Total sum of squares	228.33	

[11] See Table 17-1 and Fig. 17.1 for the classified data and the regression functions here referred to.

In Classification I we have broken the total sum of squares (Q) into a portion (Q_2) measuring variation within arrays (which is completely unrelated to the irrigation factor), a portion (A_1) which measures the variation among computed yields (the computed values being given by a specific linear hypothesis), and a portion (B_1) which defines that portion of the variability between columns that is not accounted for by the linear hypothesis. Components A_1 and B_1, it will be recalled, together make up component Q_1, the sum of squares representing variation between classes. In the last column of Table 17-10 we have shown how the coefficient of correlation may be derived as a by-product of the break-up of the total sum of squares. The first expression for r^2 has been given as formula (9.9), on page 268. This coefficient, in squared form, is the ratio of the variance of the computed values of Y to the variance of the observed values of Y. (On an earlier page we have noted that if we may assume Y and X to be causally related, Y being dependent, we may think of r^2 as defining that portion of the variability of Y (as measured by the variance) that is explained by variations in X. If we multiply numerator and denominator of this ratio by N, we have an expression for r^2 as the ratio of Σd_{yc}^2 (the sum of the squares of the deviations of the computed values of Y from $\overline{Y}$) to Σd_y^2 (the sum of the squares of the deviations of the observed values of Y from $\overline{Y}$). But this is merely the ratio of A_1 to Q, the total sum of squares.

In distinguishing elements Q_2, A_2, and B_2 we break up the total sum of squares in a somewhat different fashion. This analysis yields the measures given in Classification II (Table 17-11).

The computations in the new presentation give the index of correlation as a by-product of this particular break-up of the total sum of squares. The quantity s_{yc}^2 again represents the variance of the computed values of Y, but here the computed values are those derived from the polynomial $Y = 3.539 + 0.2527X - 0.002827X^2$ (d_{yc} is, of course, the deviation of one of these computed Y's from $\overline{Y}$.) This quantity measures the variation that is "explained" on the assumption that the quadratic function defines the relationship between yields and applications of irrigation water. The index of correlation may be derived from the ratio of s_{yc}^2 to s_y^2, or from the equivalent ratio of Σd_{yc}^2 to Σd_y^2. This is the ratio of A_2 to Q, the total sum of squares.

We may here draw attention to the elements we have labeled

TABLE 17–11

Classification II: Component Elements of Total Sum of Squares, Alfalfa Yields
(Quadratic hypothesis)

Element	Sum of squares	Measure of correlation
Q_2 : Sum of squares unrelated to irrigation factor (variation within arrays)	76.39	
A_2 : Sum of squares representing variation attributable to irrigation factor on the assumption of a quadratic relationship (deviation of computed yields from grand mean)	147.32	$i_{yx}^2 = \dfrac{s_{y_c}^2}{s_y^2} = \dfrac{\Sigma d_{y_c}^2}{\Sigma d_y^2}$ $= \dfrac{147.32}{228.33} = 0.6452$ $i_{yx} = 0.80$
B_2 : Sum of squared deviations of column means from corresponding computed yields (variation between columns that is not explained by the quadratic hypothesis)	4.61	
Q : Total sum of squares	228.33*	

* The given total and the sum of the component items differ by .01 because of rounding of decimals in the calculations.

B_1 (in Classification I) and B_2 (in Classification II). The variation between columns ($Q_1 = 151.94$) was considered, at the beginning of our analysis, to be due either to the effect of irrigation differences on alfalfa yields, or to the play of chance. In Classification I this variation between columns is broken into a portion (A_1) attributable to irrigation effects on the assumption that the relation is linear, and a portion (B_1) which may be regarded as a measure of the degree to which the linear hypothesis fails to account for all the between-column variation. This failure may reflect the choice of a faulty hypothesis; on the other hand, it may merely reflect the play of chance in between-column variation. Our test (Table 17-6) indicated that the element B_1 was too large to be attributed to chance, and we were led to reject the linear hypothesis.

Similarly, in Classification II, the residual variation B_2 is a measure of the degree to which the quadratic hypothesis fails to account for all the between-column variation. Here again the residual variation might in fact reflect the influence of the irrigation factor on yields, the function chosen being inadequate to define the true relation, or it might be due to chance. Our test (Table 17-9) indicated that residual variation as great as B_2 could easily be due to the influence of random forces. We concluded, therefore, that the observed facts were not inconsistent with the hypothesis that yield is related to irrigation in a manner defined by the specific quadratic equation employed.

The Correlation Ratio. We could, of course, carry further the process exemplified by the analyses shown in Classifications I and II. By fitting polynomials of higher degree (i.e., by adding more constants to the equation of regression) we could further reduce the residual variation. If we should carry this to the point at which the number of constants was equal to the number of columns (8 for the data of Table 17-1) the curve of regression corresponding to this equation would pass through the mean of every column. We should then have the break-up of the total sum of squares that is given in Classification III (Table 17-12). The symbol s_{my}^2 has

TABLE 17–12

Classification III. Component Elements of Total Sum of Squares, Alfalfa Yields Illustrating the Computation of the Correlation Ratio

Element	Sum of squares	Measure of correlation
Q_2 : Sum of squares unrelated to irrigation factor (variation within arrays)	76.39	
Q_1 : Sum of squares representing variation attributable to irrigation factor (total between column variation)	151.94	$\eta_{yx}^2 = \dfrac{s_{my}^2}{s_y^2} = \dfrac{\Sigma d_{my}^2/N}{\Sigma d_y^2/N}$ (17.10)
		$= \dfrac{\Sigma d_{my}^2}{\Sigma d_y^2} = \dfrac{151.94}{228.33} = 0.6654$
		$\eta_{yx} = 0.82$
Q : Total sum of squares	228.33	

been used above to define the variance of the column means about the general mean of the Y's. If we assume that we have a regression function that passes through the mean of each column, each column mean would correspond to a computed value of Y (i.e., to what we have termed Y_c in the previous discussion). Thus s_{my}^2 corresponds to s_{yc}^2 of Classifications I and II. The ratio of s_{my}^2 to s_y^2 (which is equal to the ratio Q_1 to Q, the total sum of squares) is a measure similar to r^2 and i^2, as shown in Classifications I and II. It is termed the *correlation ratio*, and is represented by the symbol η (eta). (The Greek letter eta was used by Karl Pearson for this ratio before the introduction of the convention that Greek letters be used only for population parameters. It is retained here as a symbol for sample values as well as population values of the correlation ratio.)

The reader will note that in Classification III there are only two component elements of the total sum of squares—component Q_2, which measures the variation within columns and component Q_1, which measures the variation between columns. In effect, when we use *eta* as a measure of correlation we are attributing to the independent variable (irrigation, in this case) *all* the between-column variation in the dependent variable (alfalfa yield, in this case). There is nothing corresponding to component B_1 or B_2; no place is left for the role of chance in bringing about yield differences from column to column. *Eta* thus measures the maximum correlation that might exist between two variables. The coefficient r might understate the true correlation, because a straight line failed to define the true relationship; a given index of correlation might similarly understate the actual degree of correlation. But the true correlation could not be greater than that shown by *eta*.

Some characteristics of the correlation ratio. From the formula $\eta_{yx} = s_{my}/s_y$ it is clear that η_{yx} will be zero when there is no variation among the means of the columns of a correlation table. All would lie on a horizontal line passing through the mean of the Y's. When this is true there is obviously no relation between the two variables. *Eta* will be equal to unity when there is no variation within columns (i.e., when component Q_2 of Classification III is zero). In this case, all the variation among the Y's would be between-column variation, and all such variation would be attributed to X. Thus the limits of *eta* are zero and 1.

The correlation ratio never has a negative value. It is possible of course, to determine by inspection of the correlation table whether the relation between two variables is direct, inverse, or varying.

In a conventional correlation table (such as Table 9-7) the observations will be classified by rows as well as by columns. That is, there will be X-arrays as well as Y-arrays. From such a table two correlation ratios may be computed, η_{yx}, corresponding to the measure discussed above, and η_{xy}. As a general formula for the latter we have

$$\eta_{xy} = \frac{s_{mx}}{s_x} \tag{17.11}$$

where s_{mx} is the standard deviation of the means of the several rows about the mean of all the X's. The measure η_{xy} need not, and in general will not, coincide in value with η_{yx}.

Correction of the correlation ratio. The use of η is only possible when the data are numerous, and can be arranged in the form of a correlation table. If a limited number of items should be so arranged, and it chanced that there was but one item in each column, the two measures s_{my} and s_y would be identical and η would necessarily have a value of 1. Computed from a very small number of cases and based on a large number of classes, the correlation ratio would be meaningless.

The raw correlation ratio may be corrected by the method employed on a preceding page for the index of correlation, with m set equal to the number of groups (i.e., to the number of columns, for η_{yx}; to the number of rows for η_{xy}). Thus, if $\bar{\eta}$ be the corrected value, we have

$$\bar{\eta}^2 = 1 - \left\{ (1 - \eta^2) \left(\frac{N - 1}{N - m} \right) \right\} \tag{17.12}$$

In the present instance

$$\bar{\eta}^2 = 1 - \left\{ (1 - 0.6654) \left(\frac{44 - 1}{44 - 8} \right) \right\}$$

$$= 0.6004$$

$$\bar{\eta} = 0.775$$

The reduction from 0.82 to 0.775 is not inconsiderable. When N is very small or m very large, the correction can be substantial.

Relation between the correlation ratio and other measures of correlation. When the relation between two variables is absolutely linear the line running through the means of the columns corresponds, of course, to the line upon which the coefficient of correlation is based. When this is the case η and r have the same value. As the relation between the two variables departs from the linear form the values secured for η and r differ, η being always greater than r. Similarly, if a quadratic function such as that used in the second step of the alfalfa problem passes through the means of all the columns, η and i will be equal. As the actual relationship departs from the quadratic form, the values of η and i will differ, η being always the greater. The reason for these relations will be clear from the argument set forth in presenting Classifications I, II, and III above. Eta, defining maximum possible correlation, sets upper limits for measures of correlation identified with specific functions. In earlier work in this field a test of linearity was based upon the quantity $\eta^2 - r^2$. This quantity would be zero, of course, for a perfectly linear relationship, and would increase in magnitude as the departure from linearity increased. However, the sampling distribution of this quantity does not lend itself to accurate tests of significance. The variance test of the linear hypothesis (Table 17-6) is far more accurate.

The correlation ratio is today of historical rather than of practical interest. As an upper limit to other measures of degree of correlation, it is a concept that helps toward an understanding of the nature of regression and correlation. But beyond this its uses are limited. Estimates of its standard error are inaccurate and of questionable value for purposes of inference. For the distribution of eta is complex and does not tend toward normality except under very special circumstances. In tests of significance, the more efficient and more soundly based methods of variance analysis have superseded methods utilizing the correlation ratio.

Note on the correlation of time series. The indexes, ratios, and coefficients of correlation treated in this chapter and in Chapter 9 do not exhaust the measures of correlation statisticians have employed in dealing with the diverse problems that arise in research and administration. In closing the present discussion we call attention to correlation procedures used in dealing with the chronologically ordered observations that make up time series.

Direct measurement of the relationship between two time series involves the danger that the correlation revealed will be spurious. If two series, such as the price of bacon and the production of automobiles, were marked by sharply rising secular trends over a given period, the annual or monthly observations on the series would show a high degree of correlation. But such a correlation coefficient would be meaningless, for most purposes. However, correlation measures may be usefully and validly employed in the study of certain aspects of the movements of time series. The relation between cyclical fluctuations in two such series may be of interest to the student of business cycles. For this purpose he may measure the correlation between deviations from suitable trend lines, after seasonal correction. (The trend lines should be of the same order for the two series, i.e., both should be linear, or both should be polynomials of the same degree if the deviations to be correlated are to be strictly comparable.)

Study of the relations between deviations from trend is not limited to the correlation of concurrent items in the two series. It may be desirable to determine whether the cyclical fluctuations in two series coincide in time, or whether cycles in one series consistently precede or lag behind cycles in the other. For this purpose the investigator may first determine r for concurrent observations; he may then compute r for observations that are paired with a constant lag of one month (e.g., the observation on series A for January, 1954, is paired with the observation on series B for February, 1954; the February observation on A is paired with the March observation on B, etc.). Successive pairings, with varying leads and lags, will yield a series of r's. If the largest r is obtained when series A precedes series B by six months, let us say, the investigator concludes that there is a typical six-months interval between "cycles" in series A and "cycles" in series B. The coefficient of correlation is used here to establish *temporal relationship*, rather than the *functional relationship* between variables that may be sought in the usual approach to correlation.[12] There are, of course, possible pitfalls in this use of the correlation coefficient. The chief one is that the temporal relations between cyclical fluctuations in two series may change over time or, which is perhaps more likely, that they may change from phase to phase of the cycle in general business. Thus series A may precede series B in business revivals, but may lag behind series B in business recessions. Conclusions regarding the *average* relationship in time, between these two series, might be quite misleading if the phase relations were markedly different.

Another approach to the measurement of relations between two time series involves the correlation of absolute (or relative) fluctuations from year to year, month to month, or day to day. When

---

[12] This device was first employed by Henry L. Moore in the study of business cycles. The most extensive use of this procedure was made by Warren Persons (Ref. 127). See also Mills, *Statistical Methods*, 1938 edition, Chapter 11.

this is done, no trend lines are fitted. The differences (plus or minus) between successive annual, monthly, or daily observations provide the data that are correlated. The questions that are asked in correlating such paired first differences are, of course, different from those to which the correlation of deviations from trend is directed, and the results will be subject to quite different interpretations.

The coefficient of correlation has been used, also, in studying the internal relations among a given series of chronologically ordered observations, the purpose being to determine the nature of oscillatory movements in the series. Autoregression is the term used for such internal relations among the elements of a series in time. Degree of relationship among observations making up a given series is measured by the *serial correlation coefficient*. In computing a number of such coefficients the observations constituting the series are paired with various lags. We have the serial coefficient of the first order when successive observations are correlated (e.g., pig iron production for January 1955 is paired with pig iron production for February 1955; pig iron production for February is paired with that for March, etc.). A serial coefficient of the second order would involve the pairing of observations with a lag of two months (or years, or days). When a series of such coefficients has been obtained, with lags varying from zero (for which r will be 1, of course) to k, they may be plotted to yield a *correlogram*. (In the correlogram the values of the successive r's are recorded on the Y-axis, the varying values of k (measuring the order) on the X-axis). The pattern traced by the correlogram will indicate the nature of the oscillatory movement characteristic of the series, if there is a true pattern and not merely random change from observation to observation.[13]

REFERENCES

Cramér, H., *Mathematical Methods of Statistics*, Chap. 21.
Croxton, F. E. and Cowden, D. J., *Applied General Statistics*, Chap. 23.
Dean, J., *Statistical Cost Functions of a Hosiery Mill*.
Ezekiel, M., *Methods of Correlation Analysis*, 2nd ed., Chaps. 6, 7.
Fisher, Sir Ronald (R. A.), *Statistical Methods for Research Workers*, 11th ed., Chap. 8.
Goulden, C. H., *Methods of Statistical Analysis*, 2nd ed., Chap. 10.

[13] See Kendall, Ref. 78 and Ref. 79, for an extended treatment of the use of serial correlation procedures in the study of oscillations in time series.

Kendall, M. G., *The Advanced Theory of Statistics*, 3rd ed., Vol. I, pp. 351-362, Vol. II, pp. 402-423.

Schultz, H., *The Theory and Measurement of Demand*.

Tippett, L. H. C., *The Methods of Statistics*, 4th ed., Chap. 11.

The publishers and the dates of publication of the books named in chapter reference lists are given in the bibliography at the end of this volume.

CHAPTER 18

.
.
.

The Measurement of Relationship: Multiple and Partial Correlation

In dealing with methods of defining correlation in the preceding chapters we have been concerned with problems involving only a dependent variable and a single independent variable. We have found, in certain cases, a fairly high degree of correlation between the two variables studied. But it is obvious that economic phenomena are usually affected by more than one factor, that the fluctuations in a single variable may be due to the interaction of many forces. Thus, in the alfalfa example, we studied the effect upon yield of but a single factor, irrigation. But variations in rainfall and temperature must have affected the crops in the different years studied. Similarly, variations in practically every factor dealt with in economic analysis are traceable to more than one cause.[1] If our analysis is to be complete we must employ methods that will enable more than two variables to be handled at a time. We need instruments that will assist us in measuring the relation of a single variable to a combination of two or more other variables and to the individual elements of such a combination. Such instruments may be secured by a simple extension of methods already familiar.

Notation. The symbols used in dealing with interrelations among a number of variables are for the most part obvious modifications of those we have used with two variables. One such modification

---

[1] This should not be taken to mean that the coefficient of correlation establishes or necessarily measures causal relations.

is the use of X with subscripts 1, 2, 3, etc., to represent variables, and the use of corresponding subscripts to the familiar measures of variation, correlation, and regression.

b_{12}: a coefficient of regression relating to an equation in which X_1 is the dependent variable, X_2 the independent variable

$b_{12.34 \ldots n}$: a coefficient of net or partial regression; the coefficient of X_2 in an equation in which X_1 is the dependent variable and X_2, X_3, X_4 . . . X_n are independent variables

$s_{1.2}$: the standard error of estimate of X_1, when estimates are based on X_2; the residual variability of X_1 after account has been taken of the influence of X_2 on X_1

$s_{1.234 \ldots n}$: the standard error of estimate of X_1 when estimates are based on X_2, X_3, X_4 . . . X_n; the residual variability of X_1 after account has been taken of the influence of X_2, X_3, X_4 . . . X_n on X_1; the standard deviation of order n

$\bar{s}_{1.234 \ldots n}$: a value of $s_{1.234 \ldots n}$ corrected to take account of the number of degrees of freedom lost in its computation

p_{12}: the mean product of variables X_1 and X_2

r_{12}: the simple or zero-order coefficient of correlation between X_1 and X_2

$r_{12.34 \ldots n}$: a coefficient of net or partial correlation between X_1 and X_2, the other variables included being X_3, X_4 . . . X_n

$R_{1.234 \ldots n}$: the coefficient of multiple correlation between X_1 and a combination of other variables including X_2, X_3, X_4 . . . X_n

k: the number of independent variables in an equation of multiple regression; the number of degrees of freedom in variation among the computed values of a dependent variable

$\bar{R}_{1.234 \ldots n}$: a value of $R_{1.234 \ldots n}$ corrected to take account of the number of degrees of freedom lost in its computation

$\sigma r_{12.34 \ldots n}$: the standard error of $r_{12.34 \ldots n}$ (the symbol $s r_{12.34 \ldots n}$ is used when the standard error of this coefficient is estimated from sample values)

$\sigma_{R_{1.234} \ldots n}$: the standard error of $R_{1.234} \ldots n$ (the symbol $s_{R_{1.234} \ldots n}$ is used when the standard error of this coefficient is estimated from sample values)

$d_{1.234} \ldots n$: the coefficient of multiple determination; the square of $R_{1.234} \ldots n$

$d_{12.34} \ldots n$: the coefficient of separate determination, approximating the influence of X_2 on X_1 in a situation in which account has also been taken of the influence on X_1 of $X_3, X_4 \ldots X_n$

$_{34} \ldots _n d_{12}$: the coefficient of incremental determination, measuring the contribution of X_2 to an "explanation" of variation in X_1, when X_2 is introduced after account has been taken of the influence on X_1 of the variables $X_3, X_4 \ldots X_n$

β_{12}: a beta coefficient; the coefficient of regression in an equation in which X_1 is dependent and X_2 is independent, both X_1 and X_2 being expressed in units of their respective standard deviations

$\beta_{12.34} \ldots n$: a beta coefficient; the coefficient of X_2 in an equation in which X_1 is the dependent variable and X_2, X_3, $X_4 \ldots X_n$ are independent variables, all variables being expressed in units of their respective standard deviations

A Problem in Multiple Relations: Corn Yield and Temperature Variations

Preliminary Analysis. In Table 18-1 are given figures showing the yield of corn per acre in Kansas from 1890 to 1946, together with the average June, July and August temperatures for each of these years.

It is known that corn yield is affected by the temperature during the growing season. The object of the present study is to determine the precise relation between yield and temperature during each of the three months given, in order to secure a basis for estimating the yield from a knowledge of the temperature. Since certain growing months are more important than others, the relation between temperature and yield may be determined, first, for each of the three months separately.

On the assumption that the relation is linear, the regression function for yield per acre and June temperature will be of the type

$$X_1 = a + b_{12}X_2 \qquad (18.1)$$

The equation describing the relationship between yield per acre and July temperature will be of the type

$$X_1 = a + b_{13}X_3 \qquad (18.2)$$

(In each case X_1 represents average corn yield per acre, for the State, while X_2, X_3, etc., represent the absolute temperature, in degrees Fahrenheit.) Instead of using the symbols Y and X to represent the variables, as in the preceding examples, X_1, X_2, X_3, etc., are employed, X_1 representing in this case the dependent variable. The symbol for the coefficient of regression is, in the first instance above, b_{12}. The subscripts 1 and 2 indicate the variables to which this constant refers, the first subscript always representing the dependent variable (X_1 in the example cited), the second the independent variable (X_2 in the illustration above). These subscripts are necessary to distinguish the different constants when several variables enter into the problem. The meaning is precisely the same as in the former examples when no subscripts were needed because only two variables were dealt with.

Values required for the determination of the constants in formula (18.1) may be computed from Table 18-1. Solving for these constants, we have

$$X_1 = 103.76 - 1.146X_2$$

The value of $s_{1.2}$ may be determined from the formula

$$s_{1.2} = \frac{\Sigma(X_1^2) - a\Sigma(X_1) - b_{12}\Sigma(X_1X_2)}{N} \qquad (18.3)$$

Substituting the given values, and solving for the standard error of estimate, we have

$$s_{1.2} = 6.29$$

The significance of the standard error $s_{1.2}$, as a measure of the reliability of estimates based upon the equation of relationship, has been fully explained. In judging of the usefulness of the equation, $s_{1.2}$ should be compared with s_1 (the standard deviation of X_1) which may be looked upon as a measure of the reliability of

TABLE 18–1

Corn Yield and Temperature in Kansas, 1890-1946*

(1) Year	(2) Average yield per acre, in bushels X_1	(3) Average June temperature X_2	(4) Average July temperature X_3	(5) Average August temperature X_4
1890	15.6	77.6	83.1	76.1
1891	26.7	70.7	74.0	75.1
1892	24.5	73.4	77.5	76.5
1893	21.3	74.7	79.5	73.8
1894	11.2	74.2	77.8	78.0
1895	24.3	71.7	74.9	76.0
1896	28.0	74.1	78.1	78.7
1897	18.0	76.6	80.2	76.0
1898	16.0	75.0	77.7	78.2
1899	27.0	73.9	76.2	80.6
1900	19.0	74.9	77.9	81.0
1901	7.8	77.3	85.0	79.1
1902	29.9	70.9	76.8	78.2
1903	25.6	67.2	78.3	75.3
1904	20.9	70.4	75.6	74.6
1905	27.7	75.5	74.5	78.7
1906	28.9	71.8	73.8	76.3
1907	22.1	72.0	78.4	78.1
1908	22.0	72.1	75.8	76.2
1909	19.9	73.1	78.1	80.1
1910	19.0	72.2	79.5	75.7
1911	14.5	80.5	78.6	76.4
1912	23.0	69.3	79.9	77.4
1913	3.2	74.2	82.1	84.2
1914	18.5	78.2	79.9	78.2
1915	31.0	69.2	74.0	70.1
1916	10.0	70.3	81.2	79.6
1917	13.0	72.8	80.8	73.4
1918	7.1	78.4	78.3	82.3
1919	15.2	72.3	80.2	78.3
1920	26.5	72.8	77.6	72.9
1921	22.2	74.4	79.2	78.6
1922	19.3	75.2	77.0	80.1
1923	21.7	73.3	79.4	78.3
1924	21.7	74.3	75.1	79.0
1925	16.6	77.7	79.7	77.4
1926	11.0	72.5	78.4	79.1
1927	30.0	70.9	76.9	73.1
1928	27.0	67.7	78.1	77.1
1929	17.5	72.2	78.8	78.9

TABLE 18-1—Continued

(1) Year	(2) Average yield per acre, in bushels X_1	(3) Average June temperature X_2	(4) Average July temperature X_3	(5) Average August temperature X_4
1930	12.0	73.1	81.7	80.3
1931	17.5	78.1	80.6	76.1
1932	18.5	74.3	81.8	79.2
1933	11.5	80.5	81.4	76.8
1934	2.8	80.4	87.2	83.3
1935	9.0	70.9	84.1	80.0
1936	4.0	77.5	86.3	85.9
1937	12.0	74.7	81.9	83.9
1938	20.0	73.6	81.4	83.3
1939	13.5	75.8	83.9	78.6
1940	16.0	74.3	82.1	76.1
1941	23.0	72.3	79.5	79.1
1942	28.5	73.0	81.0	76.8
1943	23.0	75.4	80.8	83.4
1944	31.0	76.1	78.0	78.3
1945	24.0	67.8	77.7	78.6
1946	20.0	76.1	81.9	77.6

* The data of corn yield are from *Bulletin 515*, U.S.D.A., and from subsequent annual publications of the U.S.D.A. Temperature data are from reports of the U. S. Weather Bureau for Dodge City, Concordia, and Iola prior to 1936, for Dodge City, Concordia, and Wichita for 1936 and following years.

estimates based upon the arithmetic mean of the variable X_1. For this we have

$$s_1 = 7.20$$

Clearly, the estimates from the equation are more reliable than those based upon the mean. The coefficient of correlation, r, expresses this relationship in abstract terms. We may get this value from the equation

$$r_{12}^2 = \frac{a\Sigma(X_1) + b_{12}\Sigma(X_1X_2) - Nc_1^2}{\Sigma(X_1^2) - Nc_1^2} \qquad (18.4)$$

Solving[2] for r, and giving it the sign of b_{12}, we have

$$r_{12} = -0.4861$$

[2] In this calculation the constants a and b are, for the sake of formal consistency, carried to more places than are given above.

These results indicate a negative correlation, though not a high one, between yield per acre of corn and June temperature in Kansas. Let us see if the estimates could be improved if based upon the temperature in July instead of in June. Solving for the constants in formula (18.2) above, we obtain the relation

$$X_1 = 156.71 - 1.735X_3$$

For the standard error, we have

$$s_{1.3} = 5.06$$

and for the coefficient of correlation

$$r_{13} = -0.7108$$

We have here a closer relation and a better basis for estimates than in the case when June temperature was considered.

Repeating the process for yield per acre and August temperature, we have

$$X_1 = 117.35 - 1.257X_4$$

$$s_{1.4} = 6.15$$

$$r_{14} = -0.5202$$

August temperature, it is evident, also affects the corn yield in Kansas, a low temperature conducing to yield above normal. The relationship is not so close as in the case of July temperature, but it is still significant. What is needed now is some method of combining these three factors, in order that an estimate may be based upon a knowledge of their influence, in combination, upon the yield of corn. The addition or averaging of the temperatures in the three months will not do, for July is obviously more important than either of the other months. We need a method of combination, for purposes of estimation, that will take account of such differences among the independent variables, and of the inter-relations among these variables.

The Estimation of Corn Yield from Three Independent Variables. The estimating or regression equation in the present case will be one in which there is a single dependent variable (corn yield) and three independent variables. It will be of the form

$$X_1 = a + b_{12.34}X_2 + b_{13.24}X_3 + b_{14.23}X_4 \qquad (18.5)$$

When we have the values of the four constants, we may substitute given values of X_2, X_3, and X_4 in the equation and thus get an estimate for X_1 in precisely the same way as when two variables are dealt with. (This method of deriving an estimated value for a dependent variable involves the assumption that the inter-relations among the several variables, when paired, may be adequately defined by straight lines. A comment on this point appears below.) The method of least squares affords the means of solving for the required constants.

The symbols require a word of explanation, as a perfectly simple equation is given a rather ponderous appearance by all the subscripts employed. The symbol b_{12}, it has been explained, represents the coefficient of regression of X_1 on X_2 (i.e., the slope of the line describing their relationship, X_1 being dependent) when these two variables alone are included in the study. The symbol $b_{12.34}$ represents the *coefficient of net regression* of X_1 on X_2. The addition of the subscripts 3 and 4 to the right of the period means, simply, that the variables X_3 and X_4 have been included in the study and the effects of their variations eliminated, in so far as this one constant ($b_{12.34}$) is concerned. This constant measures the weight which must be given to the variable X_2 in an estimate of X_1 based upon the three independent variables, X_2, X_3, and X_4. It will not, of course, be the same as b_{12}, which indicates the weight given to X_2 when an estimate of X_1 is based upon X_2 alone. Similarly the constant $b_{13.24}$, the coefficient of net regression of X_1 on X_3, measures the weight given to X_3 when X_2 and X_4 are also included. Each coefficient represents a single, simple constant, but the subscripts are necessary in order that the precise meaning of this constant may be clear. The subscripts to the left of the period are termed *primary subscripts*, those to the right *secondary subscripts*.

Formation and solution of the normal equations. The first task is the securing of the normal equations required in solving for the constants in the estimating equation given above. Following the usual procedure[3] we have:

$$\text{I} \quad \Sigma(X_1) = Na + b_{12.34}\Sigma(X_2) + b_{13.24}\Sigma(X_3) + b_{14.23}\Sigma(X_4) \quad (18.6)$$

$$\text{II} \quad \Sigma(X_1X_2) = a\Sigma(X_2) + b_{12.34}\Sigma(X_2^2) + b_{13.24}\Sigma(X_2X_3)$$
$$+ b_{14.23}\Sigma(X_2X_4) \quad (18.7)$$

$$\text{III} \quad \Sigma(X_1X_3) = a\Sigma(X_3) + b_{12.34}\Sigma(X_2X_3) + b_{13.24}\Sigma(X_3^2)$$
$$+ b_{14.23}\Sigma(X_3X_4) \quad (18.8)$$

$$\text{IV} \quad \Sigma(X_1X_4) = a\Sigma(X_4) + b_{12.34}\Sigma(X_2X_4) + b_{13.24}\Sigma(X_3X_4)$$
$$+ b_{14.23}\Sigma(X_4^2) \quad (18.9)$$

The given values might be substituted in these simultaneous equations and solutions secured directly for the four constants. It is possible to reduce the number of normal equations by one, however, and thus lessen materially the labor of computation. This is done by using deviations from the arithmetic mean for each variable instead of absolute values, getting rid in this way of the constant term a in the original equation.

If we let A_1, A_2, A_3, etc., represent the arithmetic means of the different variables while x_1, x_2, x_3, etc., represent deviations from the means, we may replace the absolute numbers X_1, X_2, X_3, etc., by their equivalents, $x_1 + A_1$, $x_2 + A_2$, $x_3 + A_3$, etc. Making these substitutions in the normal equations, certain algebraic simplifications are possible which eliminate the first of the normal equations, and reduce the others to the following form:

$$\frac{\Sigma(x_1x_2)}{N} = \frac{\Sigma(x_2^2)}{N}b_{12.34} + \frac{\Sigma(x_2x_3)}{N}b_{13.24} + \frac{\Sigma(x_2x_4)}{N}b_{14.23}$$

$$\frac{\Sigma(x_1x_3)}{N} = \frac{\Sigma(x_2x_3)}{N}b_{12.34} + \frac{\Sigma(x_3^2)}{N}b_{13.24} + \frac{\Sigma(x_3x_4)}{N}b_{14.23}$$

$$\frac{\Sigma(x_1x_4)}{N} = \frac{\Sigma(x_2x_4)}{N}b_{12.34} + \frac{\Sigma(x_3x_4)}{N}b_{13.24} + \frac{\Sigma(x_4^2)}{N}b_{14.23}$$

All the variables in the above equations refer to deviations from the

---

[3] See Appendix C for a discussion of this procedure and of the methods employed in simplifying the normal equations.

respective arithmetic means. Therefore $\dfrac{\Sigma(x_1 x_2)}{N}$ is simply the mean

product of the variables x_1 and x_2, $\dfrac{\Sigma(x_2^2)}{N}$ is s_2^2, etc. Representing the

various mean products by the symbols p_{12}, p_{13}, etc., and inserting the symbols for the squares of the standard deviations, we secure, for the normal equations:

$$p_{12} = s_2^2 b_{12.34} + p_{23} b_{13.24} + p_{24} b_{14.23} \qquad (18.10)$$

$$p_{13} = p_{23} b_{12.34} + s_3^2 b_{13.24} + p_{34} b_{14.23} \qquad (18.11)$$

$$p_{14} = p_{24} b_{12.34} + p_{34} b_{13.24} + s_4^2 b_{14.23} \qquad (18.12)$$

This is the most convenient form for the solution of the normal equations.

From the data, as arranged in Table 18-1, the following values are derived:

$$\Sigma(X_1) = 1{,}090.7 \qquad\qquad \Sigma(X_1^2) = 23{,}822.51$$

$$\Sigma(X_2) = 4{,}209.4 \qquad\qquad \Sigma(X_2^2) = 311{,}390.68$$

$$\Sigma(X_3) = 4{,}519.2 \qquad\qquad \Sigma(X_3^2) = 358{,}794.24$$

$$\Sigma(X_4) = 4{,}454.0 \qquad\qquad \Sigma(X_4^2) = 348{,}539.38$$

$$\Sigma(X_1 X_2) = 79{,}938.04$$

$$\Sigma(X_1 X_3) = 85{,}614.99$$

$$\Sigma(X_1 X_4) = 84{,}591.18$$

$$\Sigma(X_2 X_3) = 333{,}965.04$$

$$\Sigma(X_2 X_4) = 329{,}090.19$$

$$\Sigma(X_3 X_4) = 353{,}366.95$$

$$c_1 = \frac{\Sigma(X_1)}{N}$$

$$= 19.135 \qquad\qquad c_1^2 = 366.15$$

$$c_2 = 73.849 \qquad\qquad c_2^2 = 5{,}453.67$$

$$c_3 = 79.284 \qquad\qquad c_3^2 = 6{,}285.95$$

$$c_4 = 78.140 \qquad\qquad c_4^2 = 6{,}105.86$$

From these values, the quantities necessary for the solution of the normal equations may be readily determined. These quantities are brought together below:

$$s_1^2 = \frac{\Sigma(X_1^2)}{N} - c_1^2$$

$$\frac{23,822.51}{57} - 366.15 = 51.79$$

$$s_2^2 = \frac{311,390.68}{57} - 5,453.67 = 9.32$$

$$s_3^2 = \frac{358,794.24}{57} - 6,285.95 = 8.69$$

$$s_4^2 = \frac{348,539.38}{57} - 6,105.86 = 8.87$$

$$p_{12} = \frac{\Sigma(X_1 X_2)}{N} - c_1 c_2$$

$$= \frac{79,938.04}{57} - 1,413.10 = -10.68$$

$$p_{13} = \frac{85,614.99}{57} - 1,517.10 = -15.08$$

$$p_{14} = \frac{84,591.18}{57} - 1,495.21 = -11.15$$

$$p_{23} = \frac{333,965.04}{57} - 5,855.04 = 4.00$$

$$p_{24} = \frac{329,090.19}{57} - 5,770.56 = 2.95$$

$$p_{34} = \frac{353,366.95}{57} - 6,195.25 = 4.17$$

Substituting in the normal equations, we have:

$$-10.68 = 9.32 b_{12.34} + 4.00 b_{13.24} + 2.95 b_{14.23}$$
$$-15.08 = 4.00 b_{12.34} + 8.69 b_{13.24} + 4.17 b_{14.23}$$
$$-11.15 = 2.95 b_{12.34} + 4.17 b_{13.24} + 8.87 b_{14.23}$$

Solving these simultaneous equations[4] we secure the following values for the constants

$$b_{12.34} = -0.430 \qquad b_{13.24} = -1.295 \qquad b_{14.23} = -0.505$$

---

[4] Any method of solution may be employed. The Doolittle method, described in detail in Appendix C, provides a systematic procedure.

The required equation is, therefore,

$$x_1 = -0.430x_2 - 1.295x_3 - 0.505x_4$$

This is the equation of regression of x_1 on x_2, x_3, and x_4. Any given values of the three independent variables (June temperature, July temperature, and August temperature) may be substituted in this equation, and the most probable value of the dependent variable (corn yield per acre) determined. In the equation as it stands, it should be noted, all the variables are expressed as deviations from their respective arithmetic means. For practical purposes it is advisable to have an equation in terms of the original values. In other words, it is desirable to shift the origin from the point of averages to the zero point on the original scales. This necessitates re-introducing the constant term a.

The value of a may be determined from the equation

$$A_1 = a + A_2 b_{12.34} + A_3 b_{13.24} + A_4 b_{14.23} \qquad (18.13)$$

where the A's represent the respective arithmetic means.[5] Inserting the proper values, we have[6]

$$19.135 = a + 73.849(-0.4303) + 79.284(-1.2948) \\ + 78.140(-0.5053)$$

Solving,

$$a = 193.05$$

The equation of regression in terms of original values is, therefore,

$$X_1 = 193.05 - 0.430X_2 - 1.295X_3 - 0.505X_4$$

Computation of the Standard Error of Estimate. Are estimates based upon this equation any more reliable than those based upon the equations previously derived, each of which referred to a single independent variable? To answer this question the value of the standard error must be computed. This will be represented in the

---

[5] This equation is derived from the first normal equation (formula (18.6) above).

$$\Sigma(X_1) = Na + b_{12.34}\Sigma(X_2) + b_{13.24}\Sigma(X_3) + b_{14.23}\Sigma(X_4)$$

Replacing the absolute numbers X_1, X_2, etc., by their equivalents $x_1 + A_1$, $x_2 + A_2$, etc., we secure

$$\Sigma(x_1) + NA_1 = Na + b_{12.34}[\Sigma(x_2) + NA_2] + b_{13.24}[\Sigma(x_3) + NA_3] + b_{14.23}[\Sigma(x_4) + NA_4]$$

Since $\Sigma(x_1) = 0$, $\Sigma(x_2) = 0$, etc., these values disappear. Dividing through by N we obtain the equation presented above.

[6] The arbitrary origin is at zero on each of the original scales, hence $A_1 = c_1$, $A_2 = c_2$, etc. To ensure greater accuracy in solving for a, the values of the coefficients $b_{12.34}$, $b_{13.24}$, etc., are given to a greater number of decimal places than in the equation of regression.

present case by $s_{1.234}$, the subscripts referring to the single dependent variable (X_1) and the three independent variables. This value may be computed from the formula[7]

$$s^2_{1.234} = s^2_1 - b_{12.34}p_{12} - b_{13.24}p_{13} - b_{14.23}p_{14} \qquad (18.14)$$

Substituting the proper values, we have

$$s^2_{1.234} = 51.79 - 4.5924 - 19.5156 - 5.6307$$
$$= 22.0513$$
$$s_{1.234} = 4.70^*$$

---

* For precise work, when the sample is small, allowance should be made in computing s for the number of constants in the equation of regression. Since there are four constants in the present equation, the 57 observations have but 53 degrees of freedom to deviate from the computed values. Denoting by $\bar{s}$ the corrected value of the standard error of estimate, and by m the number of constants in the equation of regression, Ezekiel (Ref. 37) gives

$$\bar{s}^2 = s^2\left(\frac{N}{N-m}\right)$$

applying this correction to the present measurements, we have

$$\bar{s}^2_{1.234} = 22.0513\left(\frac{57}{57-4}\right)$$
$$= 23.7155$$
$$\bar{s}_{1.234} = 4.87$$

[7] This formula may be derived as follows: Given an equation of the type

$$x_1 = b_{12.34}x_2 + b_{13.24}x_3 + b_{14.23}x_4$$

(in which the variables refer to deviations from the means) each residual may be computed from the equation

$$d = b_{12.34}x_2 + b_{13.24}x_3 + b_{14.23}x_4 - x_1 \qquad (1)$$

Multiplying throughout by d, and adding, we have

$$\Sigma(d^2) = b_{12.34}\Sigma(dx_2) + b_{13.24}\Sigma(dx_3) + b_{14.23}\Sigma(dx_4) - \Sigma(dx_1)$$

but it follows from the method of fitting that

$$\Sigma(dx_2) = 0$$
$$\Sigma(dx_3) = 0$$
$$\Sigma(dx_4) = 0$$

and, therefore, $\Sigma(d^2) = -\Sigma(dx_1)$.   (2)

Multiplying each residual equation (1) by x_1 and adding, we have

$$\Sigma(dx_1) = b_{12.34}\Sigma(x_1x_2) + b_{13.24}\Sigma(x_1x_3) + b_{14.23}\Sigma(x_1x_4) - \Sigma(x^2_1)$$

Substituting the equivalent of $\Sigma(dx_1)$ in equation (2) we secure

$$\Sigma(d^2) = \Sigma(x^2_1) - b_{12.34}\Sigma(x_1x_2) - b_{13.24}\Sigma(x_1x_3) - b_{14.23}\Sigma(x_1x_4)$$

$$s^2_{1.234} = \frac{\Sigma(d^2)}{N} = \frac{\Sigma(x^2_1)}{N} - b_{12.34}\frac{\Sigma(x_1x_2)}{N} - b_{13.24}\frac{\Sigma(x_1x_3)}{N} - b_{14.23}\frac{\Sigma(x_1x_4)}{N}$$

Since the variables refer to deviations from the means, we have

$$s^2_{1.234} = s^2_1 - b_{12.34}p_{12} - b_{13.24}p_{13} - b_{14.23}p_{14}$$

See Appendix C for a general derivation of these relations.

This is to be interpreted just as the standard error of estimate was interpreted in previous cases. The reliability of estimates based upon the mean value of X_1 is measured by s_1, which has a value of 7.20. The reliability of estimates based upon the equation of net regression, when yield is considered as a function of temperature in June, July, and August, is measured by $s_{1.234}$ which has a value of 4.70. It is clear that estimates made from the equation are distinctly more reliable than those based upon a knowledge of X_1 alone. We have by no means accounted for all the factors that are responsible for variability in corn yield, but we have measured and reduced to precise terms the effects of three factors upon the yield of corn per acre in Kansas.

This last statement should not be understood to mean that the equation of multiple regression necessarily defines *all* the influence of these three factors on corn yield. A linear function may only approximate the true relations between dependent and independent variables in a problem of agro-biology of this type; the calendar month may not be the best time-unit to employ in distinguishing strategic periods in the development of a crop; there will be significant variation from year to year in the distribution of temperature within even the best-selected periods of growth; the phases of crop development will vary somewhat in timing from year to year. Errors of these kinds, as well as errors arising from the omission of causal factors other than temperature, are reflected in the standard error of estimate. Wisdom in the selection of functions, time-units, strategic periods, etc., requires some understanding of the ground plan of nature in the particular field of study, as well as competence in the application of statistical techniques. The task of analysis is never purely mechanical.

The Coefficient of Multiple Correlation. We have need now of our third measure, the abstract coefficient of correlation. The value of this coefficient, as we have seen, depends upon the relation between the standard error of estimate and the standard deviation of the dependent variable. It may be computed in the present instance from the formula

$$R_{1.234}^2 = 1 - \frac{s_{1.234}^2}{s_1^2} \tag{18.15}$$

When the relationship between a single dependent variable and several independent variables is being studied, this measure is termed the coefficient of multiple correlation and is represented by the symbol R. The subscript to the left of the period relates to the dependent variable, while those to the right relate to the independent variables. Substituting in this formula the equivalent of $s_{1.234}^2$, we have

$$R_{1.234}^2 = 1 - \frac{s_1^2 - b_{12.34}p_{12} - b_{13.24}p_{13} - b_{14.23}p_{14}}{s_1^2} \quad (18.16)$$

which reduces to[8]

$$R_{1.234}^2 = \frac{b_{12.34}p_{12} + b_{13.24}p_{13} + b_{14.23}p_{14}}{s_1^2} \quad (18.17)$$

Inserting the proper values we have

$$R_{1.234}^2 = \frac{4.5924 + 19.5156 + 5.6307}{51.79}$$

$$= 0.5742$$

$$R_{1.234} = 0.758$$

The correction of R. For the same reason that estimates of the index of correlation derived from samples must be corrected by making allowance for the number of constants in the regression equation, correction must be made in R. For if the number of constants is equal to the number of observations, R will necessarily equal 1. Using $\bar{R}$ to denote the corrected coefficient of multiple correlation and m to denote the number of constants in the equation of regression, Ezekiel gives

$$\bar{R}^2 = 1 - \left\{ (1 - R^2)\left(\frac{N - 1}{N - m}\right) \right\} \quad (18.18)$$

In the present example

$$\bar{R}^2 = 1 - \left\{ (1 - 0.5742)\left(\frac{57 - 1}{57 - 4}\right) \right\}$$

$$= 0.5501$$

$$\bar{R} = 0.742$$

---

[8] The coefficient of multiple correlation may also be derived from the general formula, which refers to an origin at zero on the original scales. This general formula is

$R^2{}_{1.243 \ldots n}$

$$= \frac{a\Sigma(X_1) + b_{12.34 \ldots n}\Sigma(X_1X_2) + b_{13.24 \ldots n}\Sigma(X_1X_3) + b_{14.23 \ldots n}\Sigma(X_1X_4) + \ldots - Nc_1^2}{\Sigma(X_1^2) - Nc_1^2}$$

In later references to this illustration the uncorrected measure is used, though it is to be understood that the corrected measure provides a somewhat closer approximation to the true R than does the uncorrected coefficient.

The coefficient of multiple correlation is an index of the degree of relationship between a single dependent variable and a number of independent variables, in combination. It measures the degree to which variations in the dependent variable are related to the combined action of the other factors. Its significance may be clearer if all the independent variables are looked upon as constituting a single independent series. The coefficient is then seen to be a measure of the relationship between the dependent variable and the independent series, which is precisely what the coefficient of correlation is in the simpler case of two variables. In the multiple case the independent series has several component elements, but this fact does not alter the fundamental nature of the coefficient. No positive or negative sign is attached to R, it should be noted. In the present instance all of the independent variables are negatively correlated with corn yield, and a negative sign might be attached. The correlation could be positive, however, for some of the independent variables, and negative for others. Because of this fact, R is always given without sign. The signs of the constants in the equation of regression indicate which of the independent variables are positively correlated and which are negatively correlated with the dependent variable.

Sampling Errors and Tests of Significance. The sampling error of the coefficient of multiple correlation may be roughly estimated from the formula

$$s_R = \frac{1 - R^2}{\sqrt{N - m}} \tag{18.19}$$

where m is the number of constants in the equation of regression. The use of this formula is subject to serious limitations because of the non-normality of the sampling distribution of R, even for large samples. In determining the significance of R the procedures discussed in Chapter 16 provide a more satisfactory method. The deviations of actual from computed values serve as a yardstick for testing the variability in X_1 that is attributable to X_2, X_3, and X_4, as the relationship is defined by the equation of regression. In common with other correlation problems, this one reduces to a comparison of variances.

The sum of the squares of the deviations of the computed values of X_1 from the mean value of X_1 is 1695.11. If the dependent variable corn yield is in fact unrelated to the several independent variables, this quantity, divided by an appropriate measure of the degrees of freedom present, will provide an estimate of the magnitude of fluctuations in X_1 due to chance. For the computed values of X_1 would in this case vary from the mean of X_1 because of the play of chance, operating with the degrees of freedom given by the several coefficients of regression in the multiple equation of regression. If, on the other hand, there is a real relationship between X_1 and the composite of factors represented by X_2, X_3, and X_4, the variations of computed values of X_1 from the mean of X_1 will reflect the influence of this composite, and will be expected to exceed the values that chance might bring about.

As an estimate of the "error variance," a standard presumed to reflect the play of chance alone, we may use a measure derived from the deviations of observed from computed values of X_1. These residuals, summed and squared, yield a total of 1,256.92. Since there are 57 observations, and since the equation of regression contains four constants, there are 53 degrees of freedom in the deviations from the regression function. The three coefficients of regression (other than the constant a) give three degrees of freedom to variation among the computed values of X_1. We are testing the null hypothesis—i.e., that the two variances compared both define the play of chance, and are therefore to be regarded as estimates of the same quantity. This is a test, in other words, of the hypothesis that there is no correlation between corn yield and the composite of temperature factors represented by the three independent variables. The test takes the following form.

Nature of variability	Degrees of freedom	Sum of squared deviations	Mean square s^2
Variation among computed values	3	1,695.11	565.04
Deviation of observed from computed values	53	1,256.92	23.72
	56	2,952.03	

For s_1^2, the variance to be tested, we have 565.04; for s_2^2, the error variance, 23.72. The variance ratio is

$$F = \frac{s_1^2}{s_2^2} = \frac{565.04}{23.72} = 23.8$$

From the table of the F-distribution (Appendix Table VII) we note that with $n_1 = 3$ and $n_2 = 53$ the 1 percent value of F is about 4.17. The present figure materially exceeds this value. We conclude that R is clearly significant. The variance in corn yield apparently associated with temperature variations is far greater than might be accounted for by the play of chance.

It is sometimes more convenient to derive the variance ratio from the relation

$$F = \frac{R^2(N - k - 1)}{(1 - R^2) k}$$

where k is the number of independent variables in the equation of multiple regression. (If we define R^2 as the ratio of two sums of squares, i.e., as $1,695.11/2,952.03$, this expression for F may readily be identified as the equivalent of the variance ratio.) In the present instance

$$F = \frac{0.5742 (57 - 3 - 1)}{(1 - 0.5742) 3} = 23.8$$

As we have already observed, the application of tests of significance to measures obtained from time series is usually questionable, because of the nonindependence of successive observations. For the weather and yield data here used, however, chance factors play a major part in year-to-year fluctuations, and the usual probability tests may be applied with some confidence.

Comparison of measures of relationship. The degree to which our knowledge of the causes of variation in corn yield has been improved and the reliability of our estimates increased by taking account of the various factors in combination may be more readily appreciated if we bring together the various measures secured in the course of this analysis (see Table 18-2). The initial s_1 of 7.20 has been cut to a value of 4.70 for $s_{1.234}$. This value might be further reduced, and the reliability of estimates correspondingly increased by bringing into the analysis other factors, such as rainfall during the growing months. The method that has been

TABLE 18-2

A Comparison of Certain Measures Pertaining to Corn Yield in Kansas

Basis of estimate	Measure of reliability of estimate	Coefficient of correlation
Arithmetic mean of $X_1 = 19.13$	$s_1 = 7.20$	
$X_1 = 103.76 - 1.146X_2$	$s_{1 \cdot 2} = 6.29$	$r_{12} = -0.4861$
$X_1 = 156.71 - 1.735X_3$	$s_{1 \cdot 3} = 5.06$	$r_{13} = -0.7108$
$X_1 = 117.35 - 1.257X_4$	$s_{1 \cdot 4} = 6.15$	$r_{14} = -0.5202$
$X_1 = 193.05 - 0.430X_2 - 1.295X_3$ $\quad - 0.505X_4$	$s_{1.234} = 4.70$	$R_{1.234} = 0.758$

explained may be extended to cover any number of variables, one equation being added to the set of simultaneous equations for each additional variable introduced. Without setting forth the details of the calculation, we may note the results obtained by adding rainfall in Kansas in June, July, and August (these variables being designated, respectively, X_5, X_6, and X_7) to the three temperature variables already included. The period covered is the same, 1890-1946. In contrast to $s_1 = 7.20$ and $s_{1.234} = 4.70$, we have $s_{1.234567} = 3.89$. The coefficient of multiple correlation is $R_{1.234567} = 0.841$, as compared with $R_{1.234} = 0.758$.

An application of results. Let us illustrate the use of the estimating equation. In the year 1951 the average June temperature in Kansas was 68.9°F, the average July temperature 76.8°F, and the average August temperature 78.2°F. What was the probable corn yield per acre? Substituting these values for X_2, X_3, and X_4 in the equation

$$X_1 = 193.05 - 0.430X_2 - 1.295X_3 - 0.505X_4$$

we have

$$X_1 = 193.05 - (0.430 \times 68.9) - (1.295 \times 76.8) - (0.505 \times 78.2)$$
$$= 24.48.$$

This estimated 1951 yield of 24.48 bushels per acre was very close to the actual yield, which was 24 bushels per acre. The close agreement is, of course, fortuitous, but if underlying conditions have not changed, the actual yield should generally fall within limits of expectation set by the standard error of estimate, $s_{1.234} = 4.70$.

The Measurement of Partial or Net Relations among Variables

The Meaning of Partial Correlation. In the preceding section we sought to determine the degree to which corn yield in Kansas is affected by the temperature in June, July, and August, treating the three independent variables in combination. Our aim has been to measure their combined effect upon corn yield. There is a related problem, which in many studies may be of major importance. This is the determination of the relationship between a dependent variable and a single independent variable in a universe unaffected by variations in other specified variables. Concretely, what would be the effect upon corn yield of variations in July temperature if account were taken of variations in July temperature *after* full account had been taken of the influence on corn yield of variations in June and August temperatures? This is the problem of *net* or *partial correlation.*

It is obvious that if a method could be developed by which two variables could be isolated for separate study, it would add immeasurably to the analytical powers of the social scientist. It would give to the student of social phenomena that power to eliminate irrelevant influences and to concentrate his attention upon a single factor which is possessed by the chemist, for example. In studying the effect of one element upon another the chemist seeks to eliminate all other elements, and the effectiveness of his analysis depends in large part upon the degree to which it is possible thus to isolate the object of immediate interest.

It is not generally possible in economic and social analysis to eliminate all but one of the factors responsible for variations in a given series. The direct and indirect causes of a given social phenomenon are too numerous and too complicated in their interaction for the social scientist ever to hope to emulate the chemist in reducing his problem to terms of but two variables. But, within certain limits, the statistician is able to employ the method of the physical scientist in freeing a stated universe of the effects of changes in certain variables while the effects of variations in another are studied. The methods which make this possible are among the most powerful of the instruments that the student of the social sciences possesses.

The method of partial correlation may be explained with

reference to the problem of corn yield in Kansas. Our object is to determine the net correlation between corn yield and the temperature in each of the three months for which the average temperature is given.

It is important to distinguish between this problem and that faced in the ordinary measurement of relationship between two variables. We have already secured, as a description of the average relationship between corn yield and July temperature, the equation

$$X_1 = 156.71 - 1.735X_3$$

with

$$s_{1.3} = 5.06$$

and

$$r_{13} = -0.7108$$

These measures describe the relationship in question when all other factors are ignored. They are not taken account of. They are merely neglected. It is as though the chemist, in studying the reaction of one element to another, used a test tube containing various impurities, which he made no attempt to remove. The statistician cannot, in general, locate and remove all the "impurities" in his problem, but he should recognize that his measures relate to such uncorrected data.

In seeking to determine the net correlation between corn yield and July temperature we attempt to secure a measure of the correlation which would prevail if other factors might be held constant. We shall take full account of the other factors we have studied, but we shall try to secure a measure influenced only by fluctuations in July temperature, in relation to corn yield.

One possible method of accomplishing this end may be suggested. If one possessed data covering a very long period we might be able to pick out a number of years during which the average temperatures in June and August remained unchanged. Let us say that we could find 30 years in all, during each of which the June temperature averaged 74 degrees and the August temperature 78 degrees. Corn yield and July temperature varied during these years. The relationship between July temperature and corn yield might now be measured, and it would be certain that the results would not be affected by the presence of fluctuations in June temperature and August temperature. Unfortunately, this method of holding certain factors constant cannot be employed. The data are too limited and too varied, in general, to enable us to pick from among them such figures as are appropriate to our purpose. Other methods of arriving at the same end are available, however.

An Illustration of Procedure. As a first step, let us derive the equation defining the relationship between corn yield as dependent variable and June temperature and August temperature as independent variables. This will be of the form

$$X_1 = a + b_{12.4}X_2 + b_{14.2}X_4$$

We solve for the constants exactly as in the preceding example, except that variables X_1, X_2, and X_4 only are employed. The desired equation is

$$X_1 = 157.37 - 0.836X_2 - 0.979X_4$$

We may determine the value of the standard error of estimate from the relation

$$s_{1.24}^2 = s_1^2 - b_{12.4}p_{12} - b_{14.2}p_{14}$$

We secure

$$s_{1.24}^2 = 31.9457$$

$$s_{1.24} = 5.65$$

If corn yield per acre is estimated from June temperature and August temperature the standard error of estimate, or the standard deviation of the remaining variability, is 5.65 bushels. But we know that if corn yield is estimated from June, July, and August temperature, the standard error of estimate, or the standard deviation of the remaining variability, is 4.70 bushels. The measure of remaining or "unexplained" variability is reduced from 5.65 to 4.70 by the addition of July temperature (X_3) to the estimating equation, after account has already been taken of the influence of June temperature (X_2) and August temperature (X_4). The difference between these two measures may be taken to represent a relationship between X_1 and X_3 which is not affected by variations in X_2 and X_4.

We have seen (cf. formula 9.7) that the degree of correlation between a dependent variable (X_1) and an independent variable (X_3) may be defined by the relation

$$r_{13}^2 = \frac{s_1^2 - s_{1.3}^2}{s_1^2} \qquad (18.20)$$

The denominator of the fraction constituting the right-hand member of the equation is s_1^2, the original variability of X_1 as measured by the variance. This same quantity is the first term in the numerator, while the second term, $s_{1.3}^2$, defines the variability of X_1 after account has been taken of the influence[9] of X_3. The whole numerator is thus a measure of the amount by which the variability of X_1 has been reduced by taking account of the influence on X_1 of X_3. When we express this observed reduction in variability, as here measured, as a fractional part of the original variance, we have a measure of the degree of correlation between the two variables, X_1 and X_3. This measure is the square of the familiar coefficient of correlation. In the present problem we have

$$r_{13}^2 = \frac{51.79 - 25.62}{51.79} = 0.5053$$

$$r_{13} = -0.711$$

The coefficient of correlation is given the sign of the corresponding coefficient of regression, in this case b_{13}.

In exactly the same way, we may say that the *net correlation* between X_1 and X_3, when the relationship is not affected by fluctuations in X_2 and X_4, is defined by the relation

$$r_{13.24}^2 = \frac{s_{1.24}^2 - s_{1.234}^2}{s_{1.24}^2} \qquad (18.21)$$

Here the denominator of the right-hand member of the equation $s_{1.24}^2$, defines the variability remaining in X_1 after account has been taken of the influence of X_2 and X_4. This same quantity is the first term in the numerator. The second term defines the variability remaining in X_1 after account has been taken of the influence on X_1 of X_2, X_3, and X_4. *The first and second terms in the numerator differ only because of the presence of correlation between X_1 and X_3*

---

[9] Although it is convenient to use language that implies a causal relationship between the two variables, it is well to remember that an observed correlation does not establish causality.

that is incremental to any correlation that may exist between X_1, *on the one hand, and* X_2 *and* X_4 *on the other.* If the equation

$$X_1 = 193.05 - 0.430X_2 - 1.295X_3 - 0.505X_4$$

gives estimates no more reliable than those derived from the equation

$$X_1 = 157.37 - 0.836X_2 - 0.979X_4$$

then the two terms in the numerator of formula (18.21) will be equal, their difference will be zero, and the value of $r_{13.24}^2$ will be zero. But if the equation containing X_2, X_3, and X_4 as independent variables gives better estimates than does the equation containing only X_2 and X_4, $s_{1.234}^2$ will be smaller than $s_{1.24}^2$. The difference between the two will be a measure of the *incremental* contribution of X_3, when account is taken of X_3 after the relation of X_2 and X_4 to X_1 has been measured. If we express this incremental or net reduction in the variability of X_1 as a fractional part of the variability remaining in X_1 after account had been taken of X_2 and X_4 only, we have a measure of the *net* correlation between X_1 and X_3. Since the measures of variability shown in formula (18.21) are the squares of the respective standard errors, the desired coefficient $r_{13.24}$ is derived by taking the square root of the fraction given by the right-hand member of the equation.

Substituting the appropriate values for the quantities indicated in formula (18.21), we have

$$r_{13.24}^2 = \frac{31.9457 - 22.0513}{31.9457} = 0.3097$$

$$r_{13.24} = -0.557$$

In this case the coefficient of net correlation $r_{13.24}$ is negative, having the same sign as the coefficient of net regression $b_{13.24}$.

The quantity $r_{13.24}$ measures the degree of correlation between X_1 and X_3 when neither one is affected by variations in X_2 and X_4. It may be thought of, equally well, as a measure of the degree to which errors in estimating X_1 are reduced when use is made of X_3, after full account has already been taken of the influence of X_2 and X_4 on X_1.

The meaning of the symbols employed in the above demonstration should be clear from the context. As with the coefficients of net regression, the first of the subscripts to the left of the point (the primary subscripts) refers to the dependent variable; the second of the primary subscripts refers to the single independent variable to which the measure of net correlation applies specifically. The subscripts to the right of the point (the secondary subscripts) indicate the other independent variables in the equation of multiple regression. These other variables are two in number in the present example; there could be one or many. Thus the general formula for the coefficient of net correlation between variables X_1 and X_3 is

$$r_{13.2456 \, \cdots \, n}^2 = \frac{s_{1.2456 \, \cdots \, n}^2 - s_{1.23456 \, \cdots \, n}^2}{s_{1.2456 \, \cdots \, n}^2} \tag{18.22}$$

The variable that is present in the second term of the numerator of the right-hand member and absent in the first term of the numerator is the particular independent variable that is being paired with the dependent variable for the purpose of measuring net relationship.

In a four-variable problem of the type with which we are working the two additional required measures of net correlation (with X_1 dependent throughout) may be derived from the following relations

$$r_{12.34}^2 = \frac{s_{1.34}^2 - s_{1.234}^2}{s_{1.34}^2} \tag{18.23}$$

$$r_{14.23}^2 = \frac{s_{1.23}^2 - s_{1.234}^2}{s_{1.23}^2} \tag{18.24}$$

In each case the numerator of the right-hand member measures the net reduction in the variability of X_1 that is associated with a relationship between X_1 and a single independent variable, account having already been taken of the influence of two other variables. If there is no added contribution, or no incremental relationship, the numerator will be zero, and the coefficient of net correlation will be zero. If the added variable "accounts for" all the remaining variability in X_1, the second term in the numerator (here $s_{1.234}^2$) will be zero and the coefficient of net correlation will be equal to unity. Thus the value of the coefficient of net correlation will vary between zero and one.

The reader will note that the variability with reference to which the "contribution" of an added variable is measured (that is, the denominator of the right-hand member of a formula of the type given above) is not s_1^2, the original variance of X_1, but a measure of the type $s_{1.23}^2$ which defines the variability of X_1 *after* account has been taken of the influence of *previously included* variables. These previously included variables are those represented by the secondary subscripts in the symbol for the coefficient of net correlation.

One further point is to be emphasized. Such measurements as these are *net* only with respect to the variables represented by the secondary subscripts. The coefficient $r_{12.34}$ measures the degree of relation between X_1 and X_2 after account has been taken of the influence on them of variations in X_3 and X_4. There may be many other factors affecting X_1 and X_2; the disturbing influences of such factors have not been eliminated. These other factors still muddy the waters of analysis.

Another Method of Computing Coefficients of Partial Correlation. Obviously a whole series of coefficients of net correlation may be computed in dealing with a number of variables. In deriving a number of such measurements a method may be utilized which differs somewhat from that employed above, and which has certain advantages in the way of systematic arrangement.

A simple coefficient of correlation relating to but two variables is termed a *coefficient of zero order*. Such coefficients are represented by symbols of the type r_{12}, r_{24}, etc. Coefficients of net correlation which relate to two variables, while a single additional variable is held constant, are termed *coefficients of the first order*, and are represented by symbols such as $r_{12.3}$, $r_{24.3}$, etc. Similarly, we may have coefficients of the second, third, fourth, or nth order, depending upon the number of variables held constant while the relationship between a single dependent and a single independent variable is being measured.

It is possible to derive each coefficient of partial correlation from those of the next lower order. Thus a coefficient of the first order may be derived from the relation

$$r_{12.3} = \frac{r_{12} - r_{13} \cdot r_{23}}{(1 - r_{13}^2)^{\frac{1}{2}} (1 - r_{23}^2)^{\frac{1}{2}}} \qquad (18.25)$$

For a coefficient of the second order

$$r_{12.34} = \frac{r_{12.3} - r_{14.3} \cdot r_{24.3}}{(1 - r_{14.3}^2)^{\frac{1}{2}} (1 - r_{24.3}^2)^{\frac{1}{2}}} \qquad (18.26)$$

As a general equation for a coefficient of net correlation of any order,[10] we have

$$r_{12.345 \cdots n} = \frac{r_{12.345 \cdots (n-1)} - (r_{1n.345 \cdots (n-1)} \cdot r_{2n.345 \cdots (n-1)})}{(1 - r_{1n.345 \cdots (n-1)}^2)^{\frac{1}{2}} (1 - r_{2n.345 \cdots (n-1)}^2)^{\frac{1}{2}}} \quad (18.27)$$

Thus it is possible, starting with the zero order coefficients of correlation, to compute all higher order coefficients successively. The mere arithmetic of calculation would be laborious, but certain prepared tables reduce these computations to a minimum.[11] The method may be illustrated, using the data of the preceding problem.

In the present case we require three coefficients of the second order, $r_{12.34}$, $r_{13.24}$, and $r_{14.23}$. These will serve as measures of the net correlation between corn yield and temperature in each of the three critical months. The formula from which the first of these measures may be computed was given above. For the second, we have

$$r_{13.24} = \frac{r_{13.2} - r_{14.2} \cdot r_{34.2}}{(1 - r_{14.2}^2)^{\frac{1}{2}} (1 - r_{34.2}^2)^{\frac{1}{2}}} \quad (18.28)$$

and for the third

$$r_{14.23} = \frac{r_{14.2} - r_{13.2} \cdot r_{43.2}}{(1 - r_{13.2}^2)^{\frac{1}{2}} (1 - r_{43.2}^2)^{\frac{1}{2}}} \quad (18.29)$$

But each of these values may be derived from a slightly different grouping of first order coefficients. We may use the three formulas

$$r_{12.34} = \frac{r_{12.4} - r_{13.4} \cdot r_{23.4}}{(1 - r_{13.4}^2)^{\frac{1}{2}} (1 - r_{23.4}^2)^{\frac{1}{2}}} \quad (18.30)$$

$$r_{13.24} = \frac{r_{13.4} - r_{12.4} \cdot r_{32.4}}{(1 - r_{12.4}^2)^{\frac{1}{2}} (1 - r_{32.4}^2)^{\frac{1}{2}}} \quad (18.31)$$

$$r_{14.23} = \frac{r_{14.3} - r_{12.3} \cdot r_{42.3}}{(1 - r_{12.3}^2)^{\frac{1}{2}} (1 - r_{42.3}^2)^{\frac{1}{2}}} \quad (18.32)$$

By employing both methods in computing each second order coefficient a check upon the calculations is afforded.

[10] It will be noted that in an equation used in computing a coefficient of partial correlation the three r's in the numerator of the right-hand member have the same secondary subscripts, and that these secondary subscripts are *one less* in number than the secondary subscripts of the left-hand member; that the first r in the numerator has the same primary subscripts as the left-hand member; that the second and third r's in the numerator have primary subscripts composed of one of the primary subscripts of the left-hand member plus the missing secondary subscript; that the two r's in the denominator are the same as the second and third r's in the numerator.

[11] J. R. Miner, *Tables of $\sqrt{1 - r^2}$ and $1 - r^2$ for use in Partial Correlation and in Trigonometry*, Johns Hopkins Press, Baltimore, Md., 1922.

Computation of first-order coefficients. The second order coefficients cannot be computed until all necessary first order coefficients have been secured. The necessary equations, of the type

$$r_{12.3} = \frac{r_{12} - r_{13} \cdot r_{23}}{(1 - r_{13}^2)^{\frac{1}{2}} (1 - r_{23}^2)^{\frac{1}{2}}}$$

may be constructed from the general formula for coefficients of partial correlation. Since several of these values must be computed, a systematic arrangement should be employed.

TABLE 18–3

Illustrating the Computation of First Order Coefficients of Partial Correlation
(Kansas corn yield and temperature)

r 0 Order			Product			r 1st Order	
Sub-script	Coef-ficient	$(1 - r^2)^{\frac{1}{2}}$	term of numerator	Whole numerator	Denom-inator	Sub-script	Coef-ficient
12	−.4861		−.3160	−.1701	.6301	12.3	−.2700
13	−.7108	.7034					
23	+.4445	.8958					
14	−.5202		−.3376	−.1826	.6190	14.3	−.2950
13	−.7108	.7034					
43	+.4750	.8800					
24	+.3244		+.2111	+.1133	.7883	24.3	+.1437
23	+.4445	.8958					
43	+.4750	.8800					
13	−.7108		−.2161	−.4947	.7828	13.2	−.6320
12	−.4861	.8739					
32	+.4445	.8958					
14	−.5202		−.1577	−.3625	.8266	14.2	−.4385
12	−.4861	.8739					
42	+.3244	.9459					
34	+.4750		+.1442	+.3308	.8473	34.2	+.3904
32	+.4445	.8958					
42	+.3244	.9459					
12	−.4861		−.1688	−.3173	.8078	12.4	−.3928
14	−.5202	.8540					
24	+.3244	.9459					
13	−.7108		−.2471	−.4637	.7515	13.4	−.6170
14	−.5202	.8540					
34	+.4750	.8800					
23	+.4445		+.1541	+.2904	.8324	23.4	+.3489
24	+.3244	.9459					
34	+.4750	.8800					

The procedure in computing each first order coefficient is simple. Three zero order coefficients are necessary for each calculation. These should be arranged in the table in the order in which they occur in the numerator of the fraction from which the required coefficient is to be computed. The numerator of this fraction is secured by subtracting from the first zero order coefficient the product of the other two. This product term appears in one column of the table. The denominator of the fraction is the product of two terms of the type $\sqrt{1 - r^2}$, derived from the second and third coefficient in each group of three. The tabular arrangement of Table 18-3 permits these computations to be carried forward systematically.

The coefficient $r_{23.4}$ is, of course, identical with $r_{32.4}$; $r_{34.2}$ is identical with $r_{43.2}$, etc. It is unnecessary to duplicate the work of computation with respect to these measures.

Computation of second order coefficients. From these first order coefficients the three required second order coefficients may be secured by methods analogous to those employed above. The computations are shown in Table 18-4. As a check upon the

TABLE 18–4

Illustrating the Computation of Second Order Coefficients of Partial Correlation
(Kansas corn yield and temperature)

r 1st Order			Product			*r* 2nd Order	
Sub-script	Coef-ficient	$(1 - r^2)^{\frac{1}{2}}$	term of numerator	Whole numerator	Denom-inator	Sub-script	Coef-ficient
12.3	−.2700		−.0424	−.2276	.9456	12.34	−.2407
14.3	−.2950	.9555					
24.3	+.1437	.9896					
13.2	−.6320		−.1712	−.4608	.8273	13.24	−.5570
14.2	−.4385	.8987					
34.2	+.3904	.9206					
14.2	−.4385		−.2467	−.1918	.7135	14.23	−.2688
13.2	−.6320	.7750					
43.2	+.3904	.9206					
12.4	−.3928		−.2153	−.1775	.7376	12.34	−.2406
13.4	−.6170	.7870					
23.4	+.3489	.9372					
13.4	−.6170		−.1370	−.4800	.8618	13.24	−.5570
12.4	−.3928	.9196					
32.4	+.3489	.9372					
14.3	−.2950		−.0388	−.2562	.9529	14.23	−.2689
12.3	−.2700	.9629					
42.3	+.1437	.9896					

calculations each required measure is computed from two different combinations of the first order coefficients.

The value of $r_{13.24}$, it will be noted, is the same as that derived from the relation between $s_{1.24}$ and $s_{1.234}$.

The meaning of such coefficients as these was explained in the earlier section dealing with this problem. The following summary of results reveals the gain in knowledge which has resulted from the above analysis.

$$r_{12} = -0.4861 \qquad r_{12.34} = -0.2407$$

$$r_{13} = -0.7108 \qquad r_{13.24} = -0.5770$$

$$r_{14} = -0.5202 \qquad r_{14.23} = -0.2688$$

It is clear that the net effect of June temperature upon corn yield is distinctly less than was indicated by the simple correlation. This is so because there is a positive correlation between temperature in June and temperature in July and August, so that the crude correlation of two variables alone shows June temperature as more important than it really is. For the same reason, all the net coefficients are less than the simple coefficients, though it is still apparent that July temperature is far more important, in relation to corn yield, than the temperature in either of the other months.

The sampling errors of coefficients of partial correlation may be estimated from the same general relations that hold for zero order coefficients, except that the factor $N - 1$ must be further reduced by the number of variables represented by secondary subscripts. Thus for $r_{12.34}$ we have

$$s_{r_{12.34}} = \frac{1 - r_{12.34}^2}{\sqrt{N - 3}} \qquad (18.33)$$

This should be applied with the limitations previously noted for zero order coefficients. There is an assumption of normality concerning the correlated variables; the distributions of the partial coefficients can be badly skewed, particularly with small samples and for population values deviating materially from zero. However, for tests of the null hypothesis, use may be made of the t-distribution, and of Fisher's table for determining the significance of r

(Appendix Table IV), just as for zero order r. In such tests the factor $N - 1$ is reduced by the number of eliminated variates. Finally, by transforming coefficients of partial correlation to z', all the advantages of that shift (see Chapter 9) may be utilized. Here, again, the factor $N - 3$ in the general formula

$$s_{z'} = \frac{1}{\sqrt{N - 3}}$$

is reduced by the number of eliminated variates. Thus this factor would become $N - 5$ for a second order coefficient of the type $r_{12.34}$.

A Measure of Variability. Having these coefficients of net correlation, we may derive by a somewhat different process the familiar measure of residual variability, $s_{1.234 \ldots n}$. This measure, which in its most general form is termed the standard deviation of order n, may be computed from the general equation

$$s^2_{1.23 \ldots n} = s^2_1(1 - r^2_{12})(1 - r^2_{13.2})(1 - r^2_{14.23}) \ldots (1 - r^2_{1n.23 \ldots n-1})$$
$$(18.34)$$

Applying this formula to the results of the study of corn yield, we have

$$s^2_{1.234} = 51.7905\,[1 - (-0.4861)^2]\,[1 - (-0.6320)^2]$$
$$[1 - (-0.2688)^2]$$

$$s^2_{1.234} = 22.0381$$

$$s_{1.234} = 4.69$$

With a difference of one in the second decimal place (due to the rounding of fractions) this is identical with the measure obtained from residuals between observed and computed values of X_1, as calculated from formula (18.14).

Formula (18.34) provides a revealing indication of the manner in which "unexplained" variability is reduced by the addition of successive independent variables to a general equation of regression. We start with s^2_1, the original variability of X_1. When we have taken account of the influence of X_2 on X_1 we have as the remaining variability $s^2_{1.2}$ derived from $s^2_1(1 - r^2_{12})$. If X_2 contributes anything to the explanation of variation in X_1, r_{12} will have a positive value and $s^2_{1.2}$ will be less than s^2_1. We then add X_3; if this variable, coming after X_2, contributes anything to the explanation of variation in X_1, $r_{13.2}^2$ will have a positive value, and $s_{1.23}^2$ will be less than $s_{1.2}^2$. The variable X_4 is then added; if it has a contribution to make, $r_{14.23}^2$ will have a positive value, and $s_{1.234}^2$ will be less than $s_{1.23}^2$. (In the present illustration s_1^2 is equal to 51.79; $s_{1.2}^2$ has a value of 39.55; $s_{1.23}^2$ a value of 23.75; $s_{1.234}^2$ a value of 22.04.) Thus, layer by layer, the onion is peeled. If the addition of variable n should yield a partial r equal to unity, the final factor in formula (18.34) would be zero, and $s_{1.234 \ldots n}^2$ would be zero. All the variation in X_1 would have been "explained." The heart of that particular mystery would have been plucked out.

Formula (18.34) provides a means of computing the coefficient of multiple correlation from the zero order and partial r's. For

$$R_{1.234 \ldots n}^2 = 1 - \frac{s_{1.234 \ldots n}^2}{s_1^2} \tag{18.35}$$

Substituting for the numerator of the right-hand term in formula (18.35) its equivalent from formula (18.34) we obtain an equation which may be put in the form

$$1 - R_{1.23 \ldots n}^2 = (1 - r_{12}^2)(1 - r_{13.2}^2)(1 - r_{14.23}^2) \ldots \\ (1 - r_{1n.23 \ldots (n-1)}^2) \tag{18.36}$$

Beta Coefficients. The several coefficients of regression in an equation of multiple regression are, in effect, weights applied to the different independent variables in estimating the successive values of the dependent variable. Usually these coefficients of regression are not comparable, because the independent factors are expressed in different units, or because they differ in variability. It is often desirable to reduce the coefficients of regression to comparable terms. This may be done by expressing dependent and independent variables alike in units of their respective standard deviations. The coefficients of regression are then called *beta coefficients*, and are represented by the symbols $\beta_{12.34}$, $\beta_{13.24}$, etc. (Since the use of the letter beta for sample values of this particular coefficient is well established, we here depart from the usual rule that Greek letters symbolize population values.)

In terms of a simple two-variable problem, we have

$$x_1 = b_{13}x_3$$

If we change to standard deviation units we must divide both sides of the equation by s_1 and by s_3. This gives

$$\frac{x_1}{s_1 s_3} = \frac{b_{13}}{s_1}\left(\frac{x_3}{s_3}\right)$$

or

$$\frac{x_1}{s_1} = \left(b_{13}\frac{s_3}{s_1}\right)\left(\frac{x_3}{s_3}\right)$$

The desired beta coefficient is, then,

$$\beta_{13} = b_{13}\left(\frac{s_3}{s_1}\right)$$

For the corn yield example, we have

$$\beta_{13} = -1.735\left(\frac{2.95}{7.20}\right) = -0.711$$

This may be taken to mean that with an increase of one standard deviation in X_3 (July temperature), the yield of corn decreased 0.711 of one standard deviation.

These measurements are particularly useful in analyses involving more than two variables. Here the relationships between the beta coefficients and the coefficients of net regression are similar to those indicated for the two-variable problem. Thus

$$\beta_{12.34} = b_{12.34}\left(\frac{s_2}{s_1}\right)$$

$$\beta_{13.24} = b_{13.24}\left(\frac{s_3}{s_1}\right)$$

$$\beta_{14.23} = b_{14.23}\left(\frac{s_4}{s_1}\right)$$

Substituting the required values in these equations, we have

$$\beta_{12.34} = -0.182$$

$$\beta_{13.24} = -0.531$$

$$\beta_{14.23} = -0.209$$

The second of these coefficients may be taken to mean that with an increase of one standard deviation in July temperature, in a situation in which corn yield is unaffected by variations in June or August temperatures, corn yield will decrease by 0.531 of one standard deviation. The other coefficients have similar meanings.

The beta coefficients relate to factors expressed in like units and similar in respect of variability. A fluctuation of one standard deviation in X_2 is thus directly comparable to a fluctuation of one standard deviation in X_3. The coefficients defining the changes in X_1 that are likely to accompany these similar movements in X_2 and X_3 have obvious significance.

Multiple "Determination" and Its Components

In Chapter 9 we have spoken of the interpretation of r^2, as a measure of "determination." This quantity may be derived from the familiar relation

$$r_{12}^2 = \frac{s_1^2 - s_{1\cdot2}^2}{s_1^2},$$

The numerator of the fraction measures the amount by which the variability of X_1 is reduced when account is taken of the influence of X_2 on X_1; the whole fraction measures this reduction as a fractional part of the original variability of X_1. (Variability is measured throughout in terms of the mean square deviation.) If there is a causal connection between X_2 and X_1, with the causal chain running from X_2 to X_1, we may think of this fraction as a measure of the portion of the variability in X_1 that is due to, or is *determined by*, variations in X_2. Thus if s_1^2, the variance of X_1, is 100 and if $s_{1\cdot2}^2$ is 36, r^2 will have a value of 0.64. This may be taken to mean that the variability of X_1 has been reduced by 64 percent by taking account of the influence of X_2 on X_1. The remaining variability of X_1, which is measured by $s_{1\cdot2}^2$ with a value of 36, represents the influence of factors other than X_2.

The interpretation of r^2 as a measure of relative determination is convenient. It is easily understood by a nontechnical person. It is also dangerous, in that the language employed involves an assumption of causality that may be quite unjustified. Throughout the discussion of correlation we have emphasized the fact that the statistical evidence by itself never establishes causality. The statistics define a degree of *co-variation*, but whether causal connections are present or not, and which way they may run if they are present, may not be established from the statistics. Therefore, when r^2 is interpreted as a measure of determination it should be made clear, explicitly, that this interpretation involves the assumption of causality, flowing from the independent to the dependent variable. It should also be clear to one who employs such a measure that the total variability of the dependent variable is being measured, for the purpose in hand, by the mean square deviation, or the variance. The "explained" and "unexplained" portions of the variability are fractional parts of the variance, not of the standard deviation. (The additive relations of the two components will hold only when they are parts of the variance.)

This same usage may be followed, subject to the same qualifications, when several independent variables are employed. The coefficient of multiple correlation, in squared form, may be interpreted as a coefficient of multiple determination. This coefficient is represented by the symbol $d_{1.234 \ldots n}$. Thus for the data of corn yield we have

$$d_{1.234} = R^2_{1.234} = \frac{s_1^2 - s^2_{1.234}}{s_1^2} \tag{18.37}$$

$$= \frac{51.79 - 22.05}{51.79}$$

$$= 0.5742$$

Interpreting this as a coefficient of determination we should say that 57 percent of the variability in corn yield per acre in Kansas is due to variations in temperature during June, July, and August. This is the "explained" portion of corn yield variability. The residual or "unexplained" portion is given by $22.05/51.79$; this is 43 percent of the original variability, as measured by the variance, s_1^2. In this case the assumption of causality has some rational basis. It is not hard to believe that temperature variations during the growing months have a direct influence on the yield of corn.

Coefficients of separate determination. The investigator would like, of course, to break up the total determination, in such a case as that illustrated, by establishing the portions of the total that may be attributed to each of the independent variables. One method involves the computation of coefficients of *separate determination.*[12]

---

[12] See Ezekiel (Ref. 37).

The derivation of these will be clear from the relation

$$d_{1.234} = R^2_{1.234} = \frac{b_{12.34}p_{12} + b_{13.24}p_{13} + b_{14.23}p_{14}}{s_1^2} \qquad (18.38)$$

The numerator of the right-hand member, as we have seen [formula (18.17)] is the equivalent of $s_1^2 - s_{1.234}^2$, the quantity that measures the reduction in the variability of X_1 when account has been taken of the influence on X_1 of X_2, X_3, and X_4. The right-hand member may be broken into three parts, thus

$$d_{1.234} = \frac{b_{12.34}p_{12}}{s_1^2} + \frac{b_{13.24}p_{13}}{s_1^2} + \frac{b_{14.23}p_{14}}{s_1^2} \qquad (18.39)$$

Substituting the appropriate values we have

$$d_{1.234} = \frac{4.5924}{51.79} + \frac{19.5156}{51.79} + \frac{5.6307}{51.79}$$

$$= 0.0887 + 0.3768 + 0.1087$$

$$= 0.5742$$

Rounding out these figures, we have as the components of the coefficient of total determination the three quantities

$$d_{12.34} = 0.09$$

$$d_{13.24} = 0.37$$

$$d_{14.23} = 0.11$$

Each of these coefficients is taken to measure the separate contribution of a given independent variable to the "explanation" of variation in the dependent variable. Thus we should say that variations in June temperature, studied in combination with July and August temperatures, accounted for 9 percent of the variability of corn yield in Kansas, and that variations in July and August temperatures, in similar combination, accounted, respectively, for 37 and 11 percent of corn yield variations. These figures add to 57 percent, the estimated total determination attributable to the three independent variables in combination.

It should be stated at once that the coefficients of separate determination give only approximations to what they purport to measure. The b in the numerator of each such coefficient is a true net measure, but the joint product p appearing in each numerator is not. We may say that in such a situation as that depicted above a portion of the total determination represents the joint influence of the several independent variables. This portion has been arbitrarily broken up, in the process of separation illustrated above, into portions assigned to the several separate variables. There can be no rigorous demonstration that this break-up represents the true situation. Hence the coefficients of separate determination must be employed as approximations, useful as rough indications of the relative importance of the several independent variables, but without standing as accurate measures.

Coefficients of incremental determination. A more satisfactory break-up of total determination is possible through the use of what may be called coefficients of incremental determination. These are, of course, subject to the same qualifications as to "determination" that have been expressed in speaking of the measure of total determination, but they are free of the arbitrary elements that are present in the coefficients of separate determination. Here we take the *successive* reductions in the "unexplained" variability of the dependent variable, and express each of these successive reductions as a fractional part of the original variability of the dependent variable, as measured by the variance. Thus we have[13]

$$d_{1.234} = \frac{s_1^2 - s_{1.2}^2}{s_1^2} + \frac{s_{1.2}^2 - s_{1.23}^2}{s_1^2} + \frac{s_{1.23}^2 - s_{1.234}^2}{s_1^2} \qquad (18.40)$$

The first term on the right hand side measures the reduction in the variability of X_1 that is "due to" the influence of X_2, this reduction being expressed as a part of the original variance of X_1. The second term measures the additional or *incremental* reduction in the variability of X_1 that is "due to" the influence of X_3, when X_3 is brought in after the influence of X_2 has been taken account of. This "in-

---

[13] The relations set forth in the formula (18.40) hold only when the several s's are derived by dividing the appropriate sums of squares by N. Thus these s's are to be regarded as *descriptive* measures, not as estimates of population values. If the s's are to be used as estimates, account must be taken of the number of degrees of freedom lost (say k) in the various instances. The divisors would then be of the form $N - k$. See Table 18-5 and accompanying discussion below.

cremental contribution" of X_3 is also expressed as a fractional part of the variance of X_1. The third term measures the "incremental contribution" of X_4 to an "explanation" of variability in X_1, when X_4 is brought in after X_2 and X_3 have been successively taken account of. Here, also, the added contribution of X_4 is expressed as a part of the original variance of X_1.[14]

In the corn yield example, as we have seen, the successive measures of residual or "unexplained" variability are

$$s_1^2 = 51.79$$

$$s_{1.2}^2 = 39.55$$

$$s_{1.23}^2 = 23.75$$

$$s_{1.234}^2 = 22.05$$

The influence of June temperature (X_2) on yield is measured by the reduction of the squared measure of variability in yield from 51.79 to 39.55, or by 12.24. The effect of variations in July temperature (X_3), when this variable is introduced after account has been taken of the influence of June temperature, is further to reduce the residual from 39.55 to 23.75, a drop of 15.80. When account is now taken of the effect of August temperature variations on yield, the residual is still further reduced from 23.75 to 22.05, or by 1.70. If each of these progressive reductions is expressed as a fractional part of the original variance, s_1^2, we have the desired measures of incremental determination.

Substituting these values in formula (18.40) we have

$$d_{1.234} = \frac{51.79 - 39.55}{51.79} + \frac{39.55 - 23.75}{51.79} + \frac{23.75 - 22.05}{51.79}$$

$$= 0.2363 + 0.3051 + 0.0328$$

$$= 0.5742$$

---

[14] Formula (18.40) reduces to the usual formula for the square of a coefficient of multiple correlation

$$d_{1.234} = \frac{s_1^2 - s_{1.234}^2}{s_1^2}$$

Representing each of these quantities by an appropriate symbol,[15] we may define the components of total determination thus:

$$d_{1.234} = d_{12} + {}_2d_{13} + {}_{23}d_{14} \qquad (18.41)$$

where

$$d_{12} = \frac{s_1^2 - s_{1.2}^2}{s_1^2} \qquad (18.42)$$

$${}_2d_{13} = \frac{s_{1.2}^2 - s_{1.23}^2}{s_1^2} \qquad (18.43)$$

and

$${}_{23}d_{14} = \frac{s_{1.23}^2 - s_{1.234}^2}{s_1^2} \qquad (18.44)$$

The first term ($d_{12} = 0.2363$) on the right-hand side of formula (18.41) is the coefficient of simple determination, with X_1 as a function of X_2. (This is of course equal to r_{12}^2.) This measure indicates that June temperature variations, when June is taken by itself, account for 24 percent of the variations in corn yield. (Any intercorrelation existing between X_2 and X_3 and between X_2 and X_4, or between X_2 and any other variable related to X_1, would be reflected in this coefficient.) The second term (${}_2d_{13} = 0.3051$) measures the contribution of X_3 to an "explanation" of the variability of X_1, when account has already been taken of the influence of X_2. The specific value here obtained indicates that under these conditions X_3 (July temperature) accounts for about 30 percent of the original variability of X_1. (Any intercorrelation between X_3 and X_4, or between X_3 and any other variable related to X_1, would be reflected in this coefficient.) The third term (${}_{23}d_{14} = 0.0328$) indicates that when X_4 (August temperature) is brought into the study, after account has been taken of the influence on X_1 of X_2 and X_3, the added variable X_4 accounts for an additional 3 percent of the original variability of X_1.

The process exemplified by formulas (18.40) and (18.41) is one of building up "determination" by successive increments, as account is taken, successively, of different independent variables. The "determination" attributed to the first independent variable includes any influence emanating from that variable, plus influences

---

[15] Ezekiel (Ref. 37) has used similar subscripts with r to represent coefficients of part correlation. The present d's are not derived from coefficients of part correlation.

that are merely channeled through the first independent variable because of intercorrelation with other variables correlated with X_1. This first measure of determination is the square of a simple, or zero order, coefficient of correlation. The "determination" attributed to the next added variable (say X_3 if the measure is $_2d_{13}$) includes a similar mixture of effects, except that any effect arising from correlation between X_2 and X_3 has already been taken account of in the first measure (d_{12}). So what we have in $_2d_{13}$ is not at all a measure of net effect; it is a measure of *incremental* effect, of the influence of X_3 when it is brought in after X_2. This may be thought of as a measure of the marginal contribution of a given variable. It will be clear that the marginal contribution, or incremental influence, of a given variable, say X_3, will depend on what other variables have been taken account of first, and on the correlation between X_3 and each of the previously included variables. Thus $_{24}d_{13}$ would measure the influence of X_3 if it were studied after both X_2 and X_4; this measure would differ from $_2d_{13}$, as it would from $_{245}d_{13}$. The incremental influence of each of a number of variables will depend on the order of their treatment. (The sum of their influences will, of course, be unaffected by order of introduction.)

This may be demonstrated by considering the incremental influence of each of the variables, June temperature (X_2), July temperature (X_3) and August temperature (X_4), on corn yield, as the order of treatment is varied. Each column below represents a different order (the figures are rounded to two places):

$$d_{12} = 0.24 \qquad d_{13} = 0.50 \qquad d_{14} = 0.27$$

$$_2d_{13} = 0.30 \qquad _3d_{12} = 0.04 \qquad _4d_{13} = 0.28$$

$$_{23}d_{14} = 0.03 \qquad _{23}d_{14} = 0.03 \qquad _{34}d_{12} = 0.02$$

June temperature appears to "determine" 24 percent of the variability in corn yield when June is treated by itself. This same variable appears to make an incremental contribution equal to 4 percent of the original variability of corn yield when it is brought in after account has been taken of the effects of July temperature variations, and an incremental contribution equal only to 2 percent of the original variability of X_1 when June temperature is treated after the effects of July and August temperatures have been studied. High intercorrelation between June temperature and July and August temperatures accounts, of course, for the sharp decline in the coefficients of incremental determination. July temperature, by itself, seems to account for 50 percent of the variations in corn yield. When July is brought in after account has been taken of June temperature, July temperature accounts for 30 percent of the variability of yield; when July is brought in after account has been taken of the influence of August temperature, its incremental contribution is equal to 28 percent of the variance of X_1. When July is brought in after account has been taken of the influence of both June and August temperatures, the incremental influence of July is measured by a coefficient of 0.1910 or 19 percent (this particular combination is not shown in the above table).

The reader should take note of a shift that takes place in the standard of reference when we pass from coefficients of net or partial correlation to coefficients of incremental determination. In each case we are, in effect, measuring the significance of successive additions to knowledge. The coefficient of partial correlation measures an accretion to knowledge with reference to an element of previous ignorance. Thus we get $r_{13.2}^2$ from $(s_{1.2}^2 - s_{1.23}^2)/s_{1.2}^2$. The reduction in unexplained variability defined by the numerator is measured with reference to $s_{1.2}^2$, the previously unexplained variability of X_1. But we derive $_2d_{13}$ from $(s_{1.2}^2 - s_{1.23}^2)/s_1^2$. The same numerator is now measured against s_1^2, the original variability of X_1.[16]

Coefficients of incremental determination are precise measures, free of the arbitrary elements that cloud the meaning of the coefficients of separate determination. They do not, to repeat, establish the existence of causal chains. Quotation marks should always be understood when the word "determination" is used in this connection, whether they are written out or not. But if there is reason to believe (as there is in the corn-yield example) that lines of true influence are present, these coefficients can be highly useful descriptive measures, in tracing inter-relations among the members of a group of variables.

---

[16] The coefficient of incremental determination may be readily derived, in the above example, by multiplying the squared coefficient of partial correlation by $s_{1.2}^2/s_1^2$. Thus

$$\frac{s_{1.2}^2 - s_{1.23}^2}{s_{1.2}^2} \times \frac{s_{1.2}^2}{s_1^2} = \frac{s_{1.2}^2 - s_{1.23}^2}{s_1^2}$$

The multiplier $s_{1.2}^2/s_1^2$ is, of course, equal to $1 - r_{12}^2$, the square of the coefficient of alienation. The multiplication shifts the base of reference from $s_{1.2}^2$ to s_1^2, the original variance of X_1, and permits the summation of the derived coefficients.

Note on the analysis of variance in a multiple correlation problem. The preceding pages have illustrated methods of breaking total "determination" into its components. The break-up of the total variation of a dependent variable may also be shown in terms of sums of squares, a procedure that lends itself to customary variance tests. In the corn-yield example the sum of the squares of the deviations of the 57 individual values of X_1 from their mean is 2,952.03. In Table 18-5 this total is broken up in three different ways.

TABLE 18-5

Elements of the Total Variation in Corn Yield as Defined by the Addition of Successive Independent Variables

(1) Element of total variation	(2) Sum of squares	(3) DF	(4) Variance
A: Influence of X_2	697.68	1	697.68
Residual	2254.35	55	40.99
Total	2952.03	56	
B: Influence of X_2	697.08	1	697.68
Added influence of X_3	900.60	1	900.60
Residual	1353.75	54	25.07
Total	2952.03	56	
C: Influence of X_2	697.68	1	697.68
Added influence of X_3	900.60	1	900.60
Added influence of X_4	96.83	1	96.83
Residual	1256.92	53	23.72
Total	2952.03	56	

In section A of Table 18-5 the total is divided into a portion representing the influence of X_2 (June temperature) on X_1, and a residual portion. The first, the "explained" portion (697.68) is the sum of the squares of the computed values of X_1 about their mean, when the relation is described by the function $X_1 = a + b_{12}X_2$. The residual, or "unexplained" portion (2254.35) is the sum of the squares of the deviations of the original observations from the computed values (i.e., the deviations from the line of regression). In section B of the table a second independent variable, X_3 (July temperature), has been added to the regression function. The "added influence" of X_3, as measured by the reduction in the residual variation, amounts to 900.60. We thus have in part B of the table three components of the total variability of X_1—a portion attributable to X_2, a portion attributable to X_3 when it is introduced after account has been taken of X_2, and a residual or "unexplained" portion. Finally, in section C of Table 18-5, account is taken of X_4, as a variable added after the influence of X_2 and X_3 has been defined. This "added influence" of X_4 is measured by the figure 96.83. Here the total variability of X_1 is broken into four parts, one of these being the residual variability, the portion remaining after account has been taken of the influence of temperature variations in each of three months.

We may note that the measures of incremental determination discussed in the preceding pages may be derived from the entries in column (2) of Table 18-5 that measure the influence of X_2 and the added influence of X_3 and X_4, respectively. Thus d_{12} is equal to $697.68/2952.03$; $_2d_{13}$ is equal to $900.60/2952.03$; $_{23}d_{14}$ is equal to $96.83/2952.03$.

The representation illustrated in Table 18-5 (a form due to L. H. C. Tippett, Ref. 160) permits tests of the significance of the contributions of successively added variables. Thus, just as we tested for significance the total contribution of the three independent variables (pp. 628-9 above), we may test the addition apparently made by X_4, coming after X_2 and X_3. This addition is measured by the quantity 96.83, as a sum of squares. We are to test the hypothesis that there is no relation between X_1 and X_4 additional to the relations previously established between X_1, X_2, and X_3. If there is in fact no such relation between X_1 and X_4 the increment of 96.83 to the "explained" variability of X_1 represents merely the play of chance. Chance would in this case be operating with the one degree of freedom given by the addition of the constant $b_{14.23}$ to the regression equation. Dividing 96.83 by this one degree of freedom, we obtain a measure of variance that may be taken, on the hypothesis stated, to reflect the play of chance. As in similar problems discussed in Chapter 16, the hypothesis is tested by setting this measure of variance against an estimate of the error variance independently derived. The residual variability, as given in section C of Table 18-5 amounts to 1256.92. Dividing the residual variability by the relevant degrees of freedom (53), we have 23.72 as the "error variance"—an estimate of the magnitude of fluctuations due to chance.[17]

Are 96.83 and 23.72 compatible, as independent estimates of the play of chance on corn yield? F, the ratio of these two variances, has a value of 4.08; n_1 is equal to 1, n_2 to 53. Using a 5-percent standard of significance, we should take this to be inconsistent with the null hypothesis—in other words, indicative of a real incremental influence of August temperature on corn yield. On a 1-percent standard, the difference is not significant. A conservative investigator would like more evidence before rejecting the null hypothesis.

Certain limitations. The measures we have described in dealing with problems of multiple and partial correlation are appropriate on the assumption that the relationships among the different variables are linear, or approximately so. (If the departures from linearity are moderate, the accuracy of estimates will be reduced somewhat but the estimates will not be invalidated.) Thus with four variables six different pairs may be obtained. The regression in each of these six cases should be linear if combined or net effects are to be studied by the methods outlined above. If the regression is nonlinear when natural numbers are dealt with, it may be possible to secure linear relationships by suitable transformations, as by correlating logarithms or reciprocals. Thus we might derive an estimating equation of the type

$$\text{Log } X_1 = a + b_{12.34}X_2 + b_{13.24}X_3 + b_{14.23}X_4$$

if the relations between X_1 in logarithmic form and each of the other variables in natural form, and between the independent variables in natural form, were all linear. The corresponding measures s and R, would then relate to ratios.[18]

---

[17] The reader may note that the total variance, and the several residual variances given in column (4) of Table 18.5, correspond to the squared s's cited in preceding pages (s_1, $s_{1.2}$, etc.). They differ, however, from the corresponding squared s's, because a common divisor N was used in deriving the squared s's, whereas the divisors in getting the variances in Table 18-5 were of the form $N - k$ (where k measures degrees of freedom lost in particular cases). We have regarded the s's as descriptive measures; the variances in Table 18-5 are regarded as estimates of population values.

[18] Considerable use has been made in agricultural economics of a method of measuring curvilinear multiple correlation developed by Mordecai Ezekiel, and of a simplified graphic procedure devised by Louis H. Bean. These procedures provide flexible instruments of analysis particularly well adapted to exploratory work in the study of relations among variable quantities. An illuminating discussion of various methods of correlation analysis is given by Ezekiel (Ref. 37).

One other limitation should be noted. Coefficients of multiple or of net correlation based upon a large number of variables have little significance unless the number of observations be large. Misleadingly high values will be secured when studies involving many variables are based upon small samples. (Application of the corrections referred to in the text will prevent misinterpretation, in such cases.) Within the limits set by these restrictions, the methods of multiple and partial correlation constitute powerful instruments of analysis.

REFERENCES

Cramér, H., *Mathematical Methods of Statistics*, Chap. 23.

Croxton, F. E., and Cowden, D. J., *Applied General Statistics*, Chap. 24.

Dean, J., "The Relation of Cost to Output for a Leather Belt Shop," *Technical Paper* 2, National Bureau of Economic Research, 1941.

Ezekiel, M., *Methods of Correlation Analysis*, 2nd ed., Chaps. 10, 12-15, 18.

Ferber, R., "A Study of Aggregate Consumption Functions," *Technical Paper* 8, National Bureau of Economic Research, 1953.

Frisch, R., *Statistical Confluence Analysis by Means of Complete Regression Systems*.

Goulden, C. H., *Methods of Statistical Analysis*, 2nd ed., Chap. 8.

Kelley, T. L., *Fundamentals of Statistics*, Chap. 12.

Kendall, M. G., *The Advanced Theory of Statistics*, 3rd ed., Vol. I, Chap. 15.

Lewis, E. E., *Methods of Statistical Analysis in Economics and Business*, Chap. 14.

Peters, C. C. and Van Voorhis, W. R., *Statistical Procedures and their Mathematical Bases*, Chap. 8.

Schultz, H., *Statistical Laws of Demand and Supply*.

Schultz, H., *The Theory and Measurement of Demand*.

Snedecor, G. W., *Statistical Methods*, 4th ed., Chap. 13.

Tippett, L. H. C., *The Methods of Statistics*, 4th ed., Chap. 10.

Walker, H. M. and Lev, J., *Statistical Inference*, Chap. 13.

Waugh, A. E., *Elements of Statistical Method*, 3rd ed., Chap. 16.

Yule, G. U. and Kendall, M. G., *An Introduction to the Theory of Statistics*, 14th ed., Chap. 12.

The publishers and the dates of publication of the books named in chapter reference lists are given in the bibliography at the end of this volume.

CHAPTER **19**

Sampling and Sample Surveys

The preceding pages have dealt with a variety of techniques that may be applied in the description and analysis of observations, and in generalizing from a set of observations. Our concern in the present chapter is with some of the problems that are faced in gathering statistical data. We have spoken of the great advances made in recent decades in the quantity and scope of the observations available to social scientists, businessmen, and public administrators. This expansion has given the social sciences a sounder empirical foundation, and has provided better bases for informed decisions in the making of business and public policies. But our concern with data is not alone with the number of social, economic, and business measurements published monthly or annually. The fruitfulness of the whole process of statistical analysis and inference rests upon the accuracy of the observations employed, and upon the suitability of these observations for the purposes they serve.

On Varieties of Statistical Data

In earlier discussions of the treatment of statistical observations we have emphasized that data should be obtained by methods of random sampling, if inferences with definable margins of error are to be made from them. Nonrandom observations have their place and value—and their value in research and decision-making may be great—but for purposes of statistical generalization and the testing of hypotheses, when conclusions are meant to hold with stated degrees of probability, random data are requisite.

In this respect great gains have been made in recent years. Truly random samples of social, economic, or business data were rarities a quarter of a century ago. The data gathered in these fields by public and private agencies were almost all obtained by what would today be regarded as unplanned procedures. What was readily available was picked up, sometimes without much reference to accuracy, often without adequate regard to its appropriateness for specific purposes. Such a method gives not a sample, but what Hauser and Deming have called a "chunk"—a convenient slice of population selected on grounds of ready availability. But the advances of recent years have strengthened statistics on this front. Techniques of data-gathering have been improved; casual collection of statistics is being replaced by well-designed procedures focused on specified objectives. The essential feature of all such designs is the emphasis on randomness.

This is not to say that random methods are today generally employed in the gathering of economic and social data. They are not, and in the nature of things cannot be. Many of the quantitative observations used by social scientists and administrators will remain nonrandom. But in major sectors of social and economic life carefully designed random samples are now currently drawn. Population surveys provide information on the size of the labor force and on its division between employed and unemployed; studies of consumer finances throw light on consumer behavior in spending and saving; samples of family budgets furnish weights for the consumer price index; the profits of corporations are currently reported on the basis of sample data; the distribution of income, by size, among income recipients is estimated from samples of income tax returns to federal and state authorities; market surveys are used by business research units in appraising markets and studying consumer attitudes. These, and many other sample surveys of limited as well as of wide scope, provide aids to rational judgment on current issues. Beyond this, they can be of great value in the development of all the social sciences.

In discussing the theory of sampling distributions and sampling errors the statistician lays down the conventional conditions that the probability of selection be definable for each element of the population sampled, and that the events (the draws) be independent. These conditions are usually illustrated by the drawing of cards from a pack or of balls from an urn. Since the requisite conditions are not hard to realize under the controlled circumstances of laboratory operation, teacher and student may give too little attention to the task of achieving these conditions, or an adequate approximation to them, in the complexities of actual field work. This task is far from simple. A sample haphazardly drawn is not a random sample. Close thought and careful design must precede the field work of drawing truly random samples, and scrupulous attention to detail is needed in the execution of the survey plan. Recent gains in the gathering of random data are not due, primarily, to the fact that sample surveys are more numerous and broader in scope. The significant advances have been gains in technique. It is not too much to say that a whole new art of survey design and field sampling has been developed within the last several decades. The art is not a finished one as yet, but its present contributions are great, and its potential contributions far greater.

The primary aim of this modern art is to obtain a *probability* sample. A probability sample is one for which the inclusion or exclusion of any individual element of the population depends on the application of probability methods, not on personal judgment, and which is so designed and drawn that the probability of inclusion of any individual element is known. Randomness in drawing is an essential feature of such a sample. Measures of precision, of sampling error, can be obtained for the results yielded by probability samples. As against probability samples we set a variety of other sample types, variously termed judgment samples, purposive samples, quota samples (in their usual form), etc. These differ widely in character, but they have one distinguishing feature: personal judgment rather than a random procedure determines the composition of what is to be taken as a representative sample. This judgment may affect the choice of individual elements; it may define specific attributes that are imposed purposively on the sample. All such samples are nonrandom, in one respect or more. This being so, no objective measure of precision may be attached to the results they yield.

Some Terms and Definitions. Sample surveys are concerned with the attributes of certain entities such as human beings, families, residential structures, business enterprises, or farms. The attributes that are the object of study are termed *characteristics*; the units possessing them are called *elementary units*. We may be concerned with *measurable* characteristics of such units (in which

case we work with one or more of a series of variates, designated
X, Y, etc.), or with the number or proportion of such units marked
by the presence or absence of some *qualitative* characteristic. Thus
if we are dealing with the incomes of individual income recipients
in the United States we are working, of course, with a measurable
characteristic; if with their status as married or unmarried, we are
studying a qualitative characteristic. The aggregate of elementary
units to which the conclusions of the study will apply is the
population. Field surveys deal with finite populations, in contrast
to the infinite populations usually assumed in formulations of
theories of statistical inference. (Some of the modifications called
for, when such theories are applied to finite populations, will be
noted.) The units that form the basis of the sampling process are
called *sampling units*. The sampling unit may be an elementary
unit, or it may be a group or cluster of such elementary units.
Thus the sampling unit might be a city block, although the
elementary units with which the investigator is ultimately concerned might be human individuals or residential structures. The
sample is the aggregate of sampling units actually chosen in
obtaining a representative subset from which inferences concerning the population may be drawn. From the sample we get objective
estimates of population means, totals, or proportions, and information needed in estimating the precision of such estimates. The
sampling plan is the blue print of steps to be taken in obtaining a
sample from a designated population. Finally, we note the need of
a basic survey instrument termed the *frame*—a list, or map, or
directory defining all the sampling units in the universe to be
covered by the survey. This frame may be constructed for the
purpose of the particular survey or, as is more usual, may consist
of previously available descriptions of the population in question.

Notation. The system of notation used in sample surveys is not
completely standardized, but substantial progress is being made in
that direction.[1] To accord with what is coming to be conventional
procedure, I shall in this chapter modify somewhat the notations
used in earlier chapters. A chief feature of sampling survey notation

---

[1] An approach to standard international practice in sampling survey terminology is
set forth in a United Nations document, "The Preparation of Sampling Survey
Reports," *Statistical Papers*, Series C, No. 1 (revised), Statistical Office of the United
Nations, February, 1950.

is the use of capital letters for the number of units, or the attributes of units, in the finite population being sampled, and of lower case letters for corresponding features of samples. Thus X is a general symbol for a variate defining a measurable characteristic of a unit of the population; X_i represents a particular value of that variate (i.e., a single observation). The symbols x and x_i have corresponding meanings for units of a sample. When population and sample are broken into classes, or strata, the subscript h is added, as in X_h, X_{hi}, x_h, x_{hi} to provide similar general symbols for the attributes of units falling in a class, or stratum. Some elements of the notation to be employed are outlined below.

Quantity or element	Symbol			
	Population		Sample	
	Total	A stratum	Total	A stratum
Number of units*	N	N_h	n	n_h
Mean value of a measured characteristic	$\overline{X}$	$\overline{X}_h$	$\overline{x}$	$\overline{x}_h$
Total value of a measured characteristic	X_t	X_{ht}	x_t	x_{ht}
Variance of a measured characteristic	S^2	S_h^2	s^2	s_h^2
Number of units possessing a given qualitative characteristic	U	U_h	u	u_h
Proportion of units possessing a given qualitative characteristic	$P\,(= U/N)$	P_h	$p\,(= u/n)$	p_h
Proportion of units not possessing the stated characteristic	$Q\,(= 1 - P)$	Q_h	$q\,(= 1 - p)$	q_h
Coefficient of variation of variate X	V		v	
Relative variance, or rel-variance, of variate X	V^2		v^2	

Specific strata will be designated by h_1, h_2, h_3 . . . , and symbols relating to such strata will bear corresponding subscripts (e.g., n_{h_1}, n_{h_2}, n_{h_3} . . .)

Symbol	Quantity or element represented
$\overline{X}'$:	an estimate of $\overline{X}$ (the sample value $\overline{x}$ is also used for such an estimate)
X_t':	an estimate of X_t
U':	an estimate of U

* Attention is drawn specifically to the only point of difference that might lead to uncertainty in this notation: the use of n in this chapter for the number of observations in a sample. Elsewhere in the book, and in the appended tables, n is used for degrees of freedom.

P': an estimate of P (the sample value p is also used for such an estimate)

$f\ (=n/N)$: sampling fraction; the proportion of the finite population included in the sample

$f_h\ (=\ n_h/N_h)$: sampling fraction of a stratum

$g\ (=\ 1/f\ =\ N/n)$: expansion factor; the factor by which a sample total is raised to give a population total

$g_h\ (=\ 1/f_h)$: the expansion factor for a stratum

$1-f\ \{=\ (N-n)/N\}$: the finite multiplier; the proportion of the population not included in the sample; a factor that affects the precision of sample estimates

$s_{X'_t}^2$: the variance of an estimate of a total

s_p^2: the variance of an estimate of a proportion

$v_{\bar{x}}^2$: the relative variance (square of the co-efficient of variation) of an estimate of a mean

$v_{X'_t}^2$: the relative variance of an estimate of a total

v_p^2: the relative variance of an estimate of a proportion

k: the multiplier of the coefficient of variation in specifying the precision to be sought in a sampling operation

$s_h^2\ \left\{\ =\ \dfrac{\Sigma(x_{hi}-\bar{x}_h)^2}{n_h-1}\right\}$: the variance of a stratum of a sample

$s_w^2\ \left\{\ =\ \dfrac{\Sigma(n_h s_h^2)}{n}\right\}$: an aggregated measure of variance within sample strata; a weighted average of stratum variances

D: a difference in relative terms between an estimated population mean and the true population mean

In interpreting and using formulas involving standard deviations or variances of original units, we shall assume throughout that these are derived with degrees of freedom equal to the number of units less 1 (equal, e.g., to $N-1$, or $n-1$).

Simple Random Sampling

Sample survey techniques employed today include a diversity of methods for obtaining representative samples. Of the methods that yield probability samples, *simple random sampling* is the simplest, and the one that is basic to all others. Modifications of this fundamental method are more frequently employed in actual field work, but all these modifications involve the principles represented in the basic procedure.

We have noted that, in simple sampling, a drawing from a population is random when the choice of an element is made in such a way that every element in the population has the same chance of being chosen. The same rule holds when a simple sample of stated size is to be randomly chosen. The drawing of a sample of n elements from a population is random when the sample is so selected that every possible set of n elements has the same chance of being drawn. With N of fairly large size, the number of such possible sets is of course very great. This number is given by the expression $\dfrac{N!}{n!\,(N-n)!}$. [Factorial N (i.e., $N!$) is the product of the integers from 1 to N.] Thus (to illustrate with unrealistically small numbers) for samples of 2 drawn from a population of 5, this becomes $\dfrac{5!}{2!\,(5-2)!}$, or 10. (Five individuals, a, b, c, d, e, can be combined in 10 different ways into samples of 2 each.) Of course, it is unnecessary in a specific case to compute the number of possible sets of stated size that might be drawn from a given population, but the process of sample selection should be such that the probability of selection is the same for every such set. When this condition is met, with equal probabilities for the selection of elements in a given set, we have a simple random sample.

The heart of any sampling process is in the means by which randomness is achieved in drawing the individual elements of a single sample, and in ensuring that all possible samples have the same chance of being selected. If we are to draw from a population containing N elementary units, the elementary unit being also the sampling unit in this case, it is necessary that each of the N units be individually numbered or otherwise distinctively designated. If the N numbers could be copied on individual cards, chips, or balls that are uniform in size and weight, if these cards, chips, or balls were then thoroughly mixed in an urn or bowl, and if n numbers were drawn at random from the vessel, the n units corresponding to these n numbers would be a simple random sample. (For true equality and independence of probabilities in the selection of a simple random sample, numbers drawn should be replaced before the next draw. This is not usually done, since it is seldom desirable to count one individual more than once. This minor departure from the strict requirements of simple sampling is of no consequence with N as large as it ordinarily is in field surveys.) There are some difficulties in this procedure. Mixing to obtain randomness in the urn is not as simple as it may appear to be. Cards may stick together, or may stick to the sides or bottom, so that the probability of being drawn is not the same for all the cards in the urn. Moreover, if N is large, the task becomes physically complicated. For any considerable undertaking, and even for small ones, better methods of ensuring randomness are available.

Use of a table of random numbers. If the N elements of a total population are numbered serially from 1 to N, a random sample may be most readily and most reliably drawn by using prepared tables of random numbers. Such tables enable an investigator to select n numbers at random from the full list of serial numbers from 1 to N. Table 19-1, which is an extract from a larger table constructed by the Interstate Commerce Commission, will exemplify such an arrangement and its uses. The digits in each column of Table 19-1 are in random order; so are the digits in each row. Since the arrangement is random in all directions, it makes no difference where one begins in his selection of random numbers from such a table. The column arrangement is usually found most convenient for reference, the number of columns used depending on the size of N.

Let us assume that an investigator wishes to select a random sample of 10 from a population of 900 units. The units in the population have been numbered from 1 to 900. Any convenient order of arrangement may be used in this numbering. The digits in three columns will be used, since N runs to 900. Any three columns may be employed, and the start may be made at any point in the table, but decisions on these matters should be made before turning to the table. (This is to avoid any possibility that the choice of a starting point might be nonrandom, as it could be if the decision on where to start were made after examination of

TABLE 19–1
Random Numbers*

Line	(1)	(2)	(3)	(4)	(5)	(6)	(7)	(8)
1	78994	36244	02673	25475	84953	61793	50243	63423
2	04909	58485	70686	93930	34880	73059	06823	80257
3	46582	73570	33004	51795	86477	46736	60460	70345
4	29242	89792	88634	60285	07190	07795	27011	85941
5	68104	81339	97090	20601	78940	20228	22803	96070
6	17156	02182	82504	19880	93747	80910	78260	25136
7	50711	94789	07171	02103	99057	98775	37997	18325
8	39449	52409	75095	77720	39729	03205	09313	43545
9	75629	82729	76916	72657	58992	32756	01154	84890
10	01020	55151	36132	51971	32155	60735	64867	35424
11	08337	89989	24260	08618	66708	25880	52860	57375
12	76829	47229	19706	30094	69430	92399	98749	22081
13	39708	30641	21267	56501	95182	72442	21445	17276
14	89836	55817	56747	75195	06818	83043	47403	58266
15	25903	61370	66081	54076	67442	52964	23823	02718
16	71345	03422	01015	68025	19703	77313	04555	83425
17	61454	92263	14617	08473	34124	10740	40839	05020
18	80376	08909	30470	40200	46558	61742	11643	92121
19	45144	54373	05505	90074	24783	86299	20900	15144
20	12191	88527	58852	51175	11534	87218	04876	85584
21	62936	59120	73957	35969	21598	47287	39394	08778
22	31588	96798	43668	12611	01714	77266	55079	24690
23	20787	96048	84726	17512	39450	43618	30629	24356
24	45003	00745	84635	43079	52724	14262	05750	89373
25	31606	64782	34027	56734	09365	20008	93559	78384
26	10452	33074	76718	99556	16026	00013	78411	95107
27	37016	64633	67301	50949	91298	74968	73631	57397
28	66725	97865	25409	37498	00816	99262	14471	10232
29	07380	74438	82120	17890	40963	55757	13492	68294
30	71621	57688	58256	47702	74724	89419	08025	68519
31	03466	13263	23917	20417	11315	52805	33072	07723
32	12692	32931	97387	34822	53775	91674	76549	37635
33	52192	30941	44998	17833	94563	23062	95725	38463
34	56691	72529	66063	73570	86860	68125	40436	31303
35	74952	43041	58869	15677	78598	43520	97521	83248
36	18752	43693	32867	53017	22661	39610	03796	02622
37	61691	04944	43111	28325	82319	65589	66048	98498
38	49197	63948	38947	60207	70667	39843	60607	15328
39	19436	87291	71684	74859	76501	93456	95714	92518
40	39143	64893	14606	13543	09621	68301	69817	52140
41	82244	67549	76491	09761	74494	91307	64222	66592
42	55847	56155	42878	23708	97999	40131	52360	90390
43	94095	95970	07826	25991	37584	56966	68623	83454
44	11751	60460	25521	44097	07511	88076	30122	67542
45	69902	08995	27821	11758	64989	61902	32121	28165
46	21850	25352	25556	92161	23592	43294	10479	37879
47	75850	46992	25165	55906	62339	88958	91717	15756
48	29648	22086	42581	85677	20251	39641	65786	80689
49	82740	28443	42734	25518	82827	35825	90288	32911
50	36842	42092	52075	83926	42875	71500	69216	01350

* A portion of page 5 of *Table of 105,000 Random Decimal Digits* constructed by H. Burke Horton and R. Tynes Smith III, for the Bureau of Transport Economics and Statistics, Interstate Commerce Commission. These numbers are reproduced here with the permission of W. H. S. Stevens, Director of that Bureau.

the table to be used.) In the present instance the investigator decides to use the last three columns of the set of five columns making up group (3), as numbered on the horizontal axis of Table 19-1, and to start at the seventh line. The entry on the seventh line in these three columns is made up of three digits 1 7 1. The element numbered 171 is included in the sample. Next in order are the digits 0 9 5; unit number 95 is included. The next entry is 916; since this is larger than N, this number is ignored; there is no element of the population so numbered. Continuing in this fashion the investigator selects the following 10 numbers, in all:

171   95   132   260   706   267   747   81   15   647

The population units corresponding to these numbers are the desired random sample.

The procedure here outlined will ensure the necessary conditions for a simple random sample. The table from which the 10 numbers were obtained is completely random, in the order of arrangements of digits. All individual elements of the parent population have equal and independent probabilities of being included in a given sample. The probability of being chosen is known for each such element. (The ratio n/N gives the probability that any individual element will be selected in a simple random sample of n elements drawn from a population containing N elements. In the present case this is 10/900.) Moreover, all possible combinations of 10 elements among the 900 in the population have the same probability of being drawn, when a given sample of 10 is being selected. This probability need not, in fact, be worked out, but it should be capable of determination.

Estimates from a Simple Random Sample. Logically, we are concerned here, first, with the determination of a sample statistic that is to provide an estimate of a population parameter, secondly, with the form of the estimate by which we pass from sample statistics to population parameters and, thirdly, with the determination of the sampling error of such an estimate. These steps, for simple random samples, have been discussed in a somewhat different context in Chapters 6, 7, and 8. Since certain new terms and procedures enter into field sampling, however, we shall briefly cover these steps, in order.

Sample statistics and the estimation of population values. The required sample statistics are determined by familiar methods. For the variate X we may derive the following from a simple random sample:

$x_t = \Sigma x$ (e.g., total income reported by a sample of income recipients)

$\bar{x} = \Sigma x/n$ (e.g., arithmetic average of the incomes reported by a sample of income recipients)

$p = u/n$ (e.g., proportion of unemployed persons in a sample of members of the labor force)

When we pass to estimates of population values, certain of the sample values must be modified since the sample covers only a fraction of a given finite population. We use $f \, (= n/N)$, the *sampling fraction*, to denote the portion of the population included in the sample. The expansion factor, $g \, (= 1/f)$, is used to raise sample totals to estimates of population totals. N is of course equal to gn. Thus, for estimates of population values corresponding to the specified sample values, we have

$$X'_t = gx_t \qquad\qquad (19.1)$$

$$\bar{X}' = \bar{x} \qquad\qquad (19.2)$$

$$U' = gu \qquad\qquad (19.3)$$

$$P' = U'/N \qquad\qquad (19.4)$$

(The sample $p \, (= u/n)$ will be equal to the estimate P' given above. In subsequent discussions of sampling errors I shall use p to designate this estimate, as I shall use x as the estimate of the population mean. The capital letters X'_t and U' will be used for estimates of population totals, since they differ in absolute value from the corresponding sample totals.)

Estimates of sampling errors. In defining the errors involved in applying to *finite* populations results obtained from samples, we must modify procedures intended for use with infinite populations. This modification is made through the application of a *finite multiplier*, which is also termed a *finite population correction*. It entails the multiplication of the variances of the sample statistics by a quantity equal to the proportion that the uncovered portion of the population is of the whole population. This multiplier is of the form $(N - n)/N$. Or, since the symbol f has been used for n/N, the sampling fraction, the expression for the uncovered proportion may be written $1 - f$. The effect of the correction is to reduce the variance of a given statistic by the proportion f. For an f of 0.25 the finite multiplier will be 0.75; its use will reduce the variance of the specified statistic by 25 percent. If f is very small the correction is negligible. In taking a sample of 10,000 from a population of 150,000,000 we are, for practical purposes, sampling from an infinite population. In such a case the finite multiplier is virtually unity and may be ignored. (Cochran suggests that this correction may be neglected whenever the sampling fraction is 5 percent or less.)

The estimates to be made from the sample statistics (or the hypotheses to be tested with reference to these statistics) relate, in many surveys, to the mean value of some characteristic of the individual elements being studied—to mean family income, to average weekly earnings of factory workers, to average bond yields. The variance of such a mean (the square of its standard error), for a sample of n units drawn from an infinite population of X's, is given by $s_{\bar{x}}^2$ or s^2/n, where the sample variance s^2 has been derived with $n - 1$ degrees of freedom. For a sample drawn from a finite population including N elements, the expression for the variance of the mean becomes

$$s_{\bar{x}}^2 = \frac{s^2}{n}\left(\frac{N - n}{N}\right) = \frac{s^2}{n}(1 - f) \qquad (19.5)$$

The square root of this quantity is the standard error of the estimate of the population mean. Having this measure of sampling error, the investigator proceeds with the setting of confidence limits or the testing of hypotheses, in the manner discussed in Chapters 7 and 8.

From the results of a given field survey we may wish to estimate population values of statistics other than the mean. For most such statistics—medians, standard deviations, etc.—the procedures developed in Chapters 7 and 8 for infinite populations are applicable to simple random samples from finite populations, with the corrections given by the use of the finite multiplier. These require no special discussion here. Of greater practical importance are procedures for estimating two other simple measures—the *total value* of some specified characteristic for all elements of the population, and the *proportion* of the total number of elements in the population possessing a stated qualitative characteristic. No new principles are involved in dealing with such measures, but their sampling errors call for brief comment.

The estimation of totals is a frequent objective of sample surveys. What is the total income of farmers? What is the aggregate value of the savings bonds held by householders in a given community? What is the total number of children of school age in a stated region? Let us say that in a given sample including n individual elements the sum of the values of a specified characteristic is x_t. As we have seen, an estimate, X'_t, of the aggregate value of this characteristic for all elements of the population is given by gx_t, where g is the expansion factor, N/n. The variance of X'_t (the square of its standard error) may be estimated from[2]

$$s^2_{X'_t} = \frac{ns^2}{f^2}(1 - f) \qquad (19.6)$$

In this expression s^2 is the sample variance used as an approximation to the population variance.

A simple example will illustrate this procedure. Assume that we are sampling households in a small town for the purpose of estimating the total holdings of U. S. saving bonds. We shall say that there are 10,000 households (technically, the elementary and sampling unit will be a *spending unit*, as defined in Chapter 15). A simple random sample of 1,000 households shows total holdings of $900,000. The standard deviation is $300. The sampling fraction is 0.10 and g is 10. For the estimate of the total holdings of savings bonds in the population we have (using formula 19.1 above)

$$X'_t = 10 \times \$900,000 = \$9,000,000$$

From formula (19.6) we have, for the estimated standard error of the estimated population total,

$$s_{X'_t} = \sqrt{\frac{1,000 \times 90,000}{0.01}(1 - 0.10)} = \sqrt{8,100,000,000}$$

$$= \$90,000.$$

Confidence limits at the 0.95 level are given by $9,000,000 \pm$

---

[2] The variance of an estimate of a total is equal to N^2 times the variance of the estimate of the corresponding mean. The right-hand member of (19.6) is equivalent to N^2 times the right-hand member of (19.5), i.e., to $\dfrac{N^2s^2}{n}(1 - f)$.

(1.96 × \$90,000). Thus we may state with the indicated degree of confidence that the total holdings of U. S. savings bonds in the community in question lies between \$8,823,600 and \$9,176,400.

The problem of estimating *proportions* arises when interest attaches to the portion of a given population possessing some definable qualitative characteristic, which is either present or not present in each unit. What proportion of residential structures were unoccupied at a given time? What proportion of spending units saved money in a given year? What percentage of families in a stated community own TV sets? In such problems, with simple random sampling, an unbiased estimate of the desired population proportion is given by the proportion p found in the sample.

The variance of p, as derived from a sample drawn from a finite population, is given by a slight modification of the familiar formula for the standard deviation of a distribution of relative frequencies, $\sqrt{pq/n}$. Not knowing the true population proportions, P and Q, we use the sample values, p and q, and have as our estimate of the variance of p

$$s_p^2 = \frac{pq}{n-1}(1-f) \qquad (19.7)$$

Let us say that in a community containing 25,000 members of the labor force, an unemployment survey covering 5,000 members shows 8 percent unemployed at a given time. We wish to set confidence limits at a 0.95 level, for an estimate of the proportion of the population of 25,000 who were unemployed at that date. The sampling fraction is 0.20, and the finite multiplier is 0.80; p is 0.08, q is 0.92, and n is 5,000. For the standard error of p, using the relationship shown in (19.7), we have

$$s_p = \sqrt{\frac{0.08 \times 0.92}{5,000 - 1}(1 - 0.20)}$$

$$= \sqrt{\frac{0.0736}{4,999}(0.80)}$$

$$= 0.00343$$

The desired confidence interval is given by $p \pm 1.96s_p$, or 0.08 ± 0.0067. Our conclusion, therefore, in which we have a confidence measured by a coefficient of 0.95, is that the proportion of unemployed in the population of 25,000 falls between 0.0733 and 0.0867.

Precision and Sample Size. When we speak of the *precision* of an estimate based on a sample we are referring to the variability to be expected in sampling results. Thus it is only errors of sampling to which standard errors of sample results relate. Errors that arise out of the method of measurement employed in a given case, out of bias on the part of interviewers, out of the use of ambiguous or slanted questions, are not sampling errors, in this sense. Such nonsampling errors affect the *accuracy* of the final results, meaning by accuracy closeness of approach to the true values sought, and are of course of high concern to the investigator. But these are apart from the errors of sampling to which the standard deviations of sampling distributions, or the standard errors of estimates from samples, relate. The term precision is by convention restricted to errors of sampling.

If the method of simple random sampling is employed in a survey of a given population, the precision of the results depends only on the size of the sample. Precision may therefore be controlled. In deciding on the level of precision desired, and thus on the size of the sample to be drawn, the investigator will weigh the possible consequences of erroneous conclusions, setting these risks against the costs of achieving various degrees of precision. The decision may be a fairly easy one to make if the objectives of a planned study are few (and if cost factors are definable). On the other hand, if a single survey is designed to serve several purposes, the different objectives may give rise to conflicting needs as to sample size. Here a practicable working balance will have to be struck. In the present discussion we consider only the problem involved in selecting an appropriate size for a simple random sample, after a decision has been made as to the degree of precision desired.

The measures of sampling error dealt with in earlier sections have all defined absolute errors, i.e., errors expressed in the original units of measurement. Thus in estimating a population mean for family savings, absolute confidence limits are set in terms of dollars; in estimating mean wheat yield for a population of wheat farms, absolute confidence limits are set in bushels. In planning a sample survey it is usually more convenient to work with reference to *relative precision*. When this is the case, relative rather than absolute errors are of interest. We define in relative terms the tolerable margin of error—the tolerable relative difference between an estimate of a population parameter and the actual parameter value—and plan a sample size that will enable us to state with a given degree of probability that the error lies within this tolerable margin.

Measures of relative sampling errors.[3] In Chapter 5 we discussed the concept of relative variation. As a coefficient of relative variation we used the ratio of the standard deviation of a distribution to the arithmetic mean of that distribution. That is $v = s/\bar{x}$. (In the earlier presentation the symbol V was used, and the quantity was multiplied by 100 to put it in percentage terms. Here we shall treat it as a ratio, and shall use a lower case v for all such ratios derived from sample data.) The concept of relative variation may be extended, to apply to sampling distributions (that is, to distributions of means, proportions, coefficients of correlation, etc.) as well as to distributions of original observations. The symbol v, with a subscript to indicate the variable in question, may be used for all such measures of relative variation. When the measures relate to sampling distributions, v is the ratio of a standard error to the value being estimated. Thus $v_{\bar{x}} = s_{\bar{x}}/\bar{x}$ (where $\bar{x}$ is a sample mean, regarded as an estimate of a population mean), and $v_p = s_p/p$ (where p is a sample proportion regarded as an estimate of a population proportion).

It is convenient to work in terms of the squared coefficient of variation, a quantity that Hansen, Hurwitz, and Madow call the *relative variance* or, for short, the rel-variance. Estimates of the relative variances of certain of the quantities with which sample surveys commonly deal are given below. (The finite multiplier entering into the estimates is ordinarily used when the sampling fraction is 5 percent or more; when the sampling fraction is less than 5 percent it is usually disregarded.)

$$v^2 = \frac{s^2}{\bar{x}^2} \tag{19.8}$$

---

[3] In this discussion of relative sampling errors and of procedures employed in defining appropriate sample sizes I have followed the development of these topics by Hansen, Hurwitz, and Madow, and have employed certain terms and symbols introduced by them. For proofs and illustrations see Vol. I, Chap. 4 and Vol. II, Chap. 4 of their comprehensive work on sample surveys (Ref. 67).

(When v^2 is used without subscript it is a symbol for the relative variance of the original observations.)

$$v_{\bar{x}}^2 = \frac{v^2}{n}(1 - f) \tag{19.9}$$

$$v_{\hat{X}_t}^2 = \frac{v^2}{n}(1 - f) \tag{19.10}$$

$$v_p^2 = \frac{q}{(n-1)p}(1 - f) \tag{19.11}$$

Each of these relative variances is the ratio of a squared standard error to the square of the value being estimated. Thus for estimates relating to an infinite population

$$v_{\bar{x}}^2 = \frac{s_{\bar{x}}^2}{\bar{x}^2} = \frac{s^2/n}{\bar{x}^2} = \frac{s^2}{\bar{x}^2 n}$$

$$= \frac{v^2}{n}$$

Applying the finite multiplier $(1 - f)$ we have formula (19.9) as given above. Formulas 19.10 and 19.11 may be derived in similar fashion from the expressions defining in absolute terms the standard errors of the measures to which they relate.

The use of these formulas may be illustrated with reference to measures derived from a simple random sample:

$N = 1000 \quad n = 100 \quad f = 0.10 \qquad\qquad 1 - f = 0.90$

$\bar{x} = \$200 \quad s = \$40 \quad v = 40/200 = 0.20 \qquad v^2 = 0.04$

$v_{\bar{x}}^2 = \dfrac{v^2}{n}(1 - f) = \dfrac{0.04}{100} \times 0.90 = 0.00036$

$v_{\bar{x}} = \sqrt{0.00036} = 0.019$

The coefficient of variation of the estimate of the mean is 0.019, or 1.9 percent. In using this measure of relative error in setting confidence limits we follow the same general procedure as in using measures of absolute error. Thus with confidence measured by a probability of 0.68 we may say: the mean of the population from which this sample comes falls between \$196.20 and \$203.80 [where $196.20 = 200 - (0.019 \times 200)$ and $203.80 = 200 + (0.019 \times 200)$]. Or, if we wish to be practically certain that the limits we set will include the population value, we may use a range of $3v$'s on each side of the mean; for this the confidence coefficient is 0.9973.

The variance s^2 which enters into formula (19.8), and thus into formulas (19.9) and (19.10), is the variance of the sample, used as an approximation to the population σ^2. The accuracy of the estimates of $v_{\bar{x}}^2$ and $v_{X_t'}^2$ will depend, obviously, on the closeness with which s^2 approximates σ^2. There will, in any case, be sampling fluctuations in s^2, but the range of these fluctuations will be less the larger the sample. The same is true of p, a sample proportion used as an approximation to a population proportion.

Estimates of sample size. The relations set forth in formulas (19.9), (19.10), and (19.11) may be used for the very practical purpose of estimating the size of sample needed to achieve a specified degree of precision in sample results. Here, again, the investigator must usually be content with approximations. He cannot, with accuracy, determine the sample size needed for a given degree of precision unless he knows something about the kind of population being sampled (e.g., normal, skewed, flat-topped) and can approximate one or more of the basic parameters (e.g., the population variance or relative variance, or a population proportion). Not infrequently he will have such information from other studies covering the same or a related population. If not, he may have to conduct a limited pilot study before a general survey is launched. If the standard deviation of a population can be estimated with a relative error no greater than 10-12 percent an investigator can determine with acceptable accuracy the size of sample needed for estimating, with a stated degree of precision, a population mean or a population total.

We let D equal the difference, in relative terms, between an estimate of a population mean, made from sample results, and the true population mean. We may set D at any relative level we choose —5 percent, 10 percent, 15 percent—and then decide on the risks we are willing to run that the error will be greater than this. If the consequences of a large error would be very serious, we may set D very low, and then state that the chance of exceeding this error must be no greater than 3 out of 1,000. For this probability we should set D equal to $3v_{\bar{x}}$, and then determine the size of sample that would be expected to yield results meeting these conditions.

If we know that the sampling fraction will be 5 percent or less we may proceed as though we were to sample an infinite population.

That is, we do not apply the finite multiplier. In such a situation the general formula (19.9) for the relative variance of a sample mean becomes

$$v_{\bar{x}}^2 = \frac{v^2}{n} \qquad (19.12)$$

We shall assume, for purposes of illustration, that in a particular case the finite multiplier is not to be applied, that we set D at 0.06, and that we wish to work with a confidence coefficient of 0.997. That is, we wish to take a very small chance indeed that the relative difference between the estimated and the true population means will exceed 6 percent. Thus $D = 3v_{\bar{x}}$, or $v_{\bar{x}} = D/3$. We shall use $v^2 = 0.16$ as an estimate of the population V^2 (this estimate being derived from prior studies or a pilot investigation). For $v_{\bar{x}}^2$ in formula (19.12) we substitute what is, for present purposes, its equivalent, $(D/3)^2$. Thus

$$\frac{D^2}{9} = \frac{v^2}{n} \qquad (19.13)$$

From which

$$n = \frac{9v^2}{D^2} \qquad (19.14)$$

Substituting the given values of v^2 and of D,

$$n = \frac{9 \times 0.16}{0.0036} = 400$$

The size of the sample needed to achieve the precision suggested is thus estimated to be 400.

If the sampling fraction is expected to be greater than 5 percent, the finite multiplier would be applied, and the equation corresponding to (19.13) would be

$$\frac{D^2}{9} = \frac{v^2}{n}(1 - f) \qquad (19.15)$$

Substituting for the finite multiplier its equivalent $\dfrac{N - n}{N}$ (where N is the population total) we have

$$\frac{D^2}{9} = \frac{v^2}{n} \cdot \frac{N - n}{N} \qquad (19.16)$$

which reduces to

$$n = \frac{9Nv^2}{ND^2 + 9v^2} \tag{19.17}$$

Let us assume that we are drawing a sample from a small population of 2,000 units, D and v^2 having the same values as in the preceding example. Then

$$n = \frac{9 \times 2,000 \times 0.16}{(2,000 \times 0.0036) + (9 \times 0.16)} = \frac{2880}{8.64}$$
$$= 333$$

The relations expressed in formulas (19.14) and (19.17) apply to the special case in which D, the relative difference between an estimated population mean and the true mean, is set equal to $3v_{\bar{x}}$. This range is designed to give virtual assurance that the error will not be greater than D. If a smaller range will serve, with a greater risk that the actual error in a given case will exceed D, a smaller sample will serve. Thus if in the first example cited above (where the finite multiplier was not applied) the investigator had been willing to accept a chance of 45.5 out of 1,000 that D would be greater than 0.06, D would be set equal to $2v_{\bar{x}}$. (It will be recalled that 0.0455 of the area under a normal curve falls outside ordinates erected two standard deviations above and below the mean. The distribution of relative deviations will be similar, in this respect, to the distribution of absolute deviations.) We therefore substitute $(D/2)^2$ for $v_{\bar{x}}^2$ in formula (19.12), and formula (19.14) becomes

$$n = \frac{4v^2}{D^2} \tag{19.18}$$

For the desired size, $n = 177$.

We may use k as a general symbol for the multiplier of the coefficient of variation, in specifying the precision to be sought in a given sampling operation. In working with a confidence coefficient of 0.997, $k = 3$; with a confidence coefficient of 0.9545, $k = 2$. These are values of normal deviates corresponding to the stated probabilities. We have as a general expression for the estimation of n, when the use of a finite multiplier is not necessary,

$$n = \frac{k^2 v^2}{D^2} \tag{19.19}$$

When the sampling fraction is expected to exceed 5 percent, and a finite multiplier is necessary, the formula for estimating sample size is

$$n = \frac{k^2 N v^2}{N D^2 + k^2 v^2}$$ (19.20)

D and k together fix the precision sought in a given sampling operation. D specifies a given relative error, plus or minus; in terms of the coefficient k we define the probability that the error involved in generalizing the sample result will not be greater than D. Under conditions of simple random sampling these general formulas apply to estimates of population means, totals, or proportions.

In general, if contemplated samples are to include several hundred cases or more, estimates of the sample size required for a given degree of precision are not dependent on assumptions concerning the character of the parent population. This is so because of the tendency toward normality in sampling distributions, as n increases. Extreme skewness in the population being sampled may give rise to trouble, however, when the variance of the parent population has to be estimated from the sample variance. For pronounced skewness in the population can mean great instability in the variances of samples. A few extreme items in a given sample may distort the estimate of the population variance. If, in sampling for a mean, extreme skewness is suspected, special pilot studies may be required to provide exact information about the form of the parent population. One precaution to be taken is to plan on samples larger than those indicated by the formulas cited in preceding pages. When it is known that the parent population is sharply skewed, the methods of stratification discussed below may be employed to reduce the variability of estimates.[4]

When a population *proportion* is being estimated (i.e., the proportion of units in a population possessing a specified qualitative characteristic that is either present or absent in each unit), this particular danger may be avoided. For if methods of simple sampling are used in such a study, and if the elementary unit is also the sampling unit, estimates of population proportions are not affected by the type of population sampled.

---

[4] See Cochran, Ref. 17, 20-28 for a discussion of problems growing out of skewness in the parent universe.

Stratified Random Sampling

The Meaning and Purposes of Stratified Sampling. In simple random sampling the population to be sampled is treated as an undifferentiated whole; the individual elements of the sample are drawn at random from the whole universe. However, it is often possible and desirable to break the parent population into distinctive classes, or *strata*, and then to obtain a sample by drawing, at random, specified numbers of sampling units from each of the classes thus set up. This may be desirable because of interest in the separate sectors of the universe, as well as in the universe as a whole. In a study of farms we may wish to learn about the separate attributes of wheat farms and cattle ranches, as well as about farms as a whole; in a study of consumer budgets we may wish to study spending and saving patterns among urban and rural families separately, as well as among the aggregate of all families. Such subdivisions for which specific information is desired are termed *domains of study*. But the existence of sectors of special interest is not the only reason nor usually, indeed, the main reason for breaking a population into classes in a sample survey. Most populations are heterogeneous, in the sense that the application to them of rational principles of classification will break the whole into classes having distinctive attributes. This means that the classes, taken separately, will be more homogeneous than the total population. For example, we should expect among wheat farms less variation, in respect of a stated operating characteristic, than among all farms. Industrial workers will vary less in their consumption patterns than will all income recipients. When it is possible thus to distinguish subgroups the members of which are more alike than are the members of the whole population being studied, the efficiency of sampling may be materially improved by stratification. Estimates of a required degree of precision may be obtained from a smaller sample (and this usually means at a lower cost); or, with a sample of stated size, more precise estimates may be made from a stratified than from a nonstratified sample.

In stratified random sampling, which is the term employed for this process, the population is subdivided into strata before the sample is drawn. These strata should not overlap. A sample of specified size is then drawn by random methods from the sampling units that make up each stratum. If a given stratum is of interest in its own right the corresponding subsample will provide the basis for estimates concerning the attributes of the population stratum, or subuniverse, from which it is drawn. The total of the subsamples will constitute the full sample on which estimates of attributes of the full population will be based. When a single stratum is itself a domain of study, estimating procedures for that stratum are essentially those discussed above in dealing with simple random sampling. The new problems that arise relate to the making of estimates and the determination of sampling errors when results obtained from a stratified sample are to be applied to the whole population.

Stratification is an effective sampling device to the degree that it sets off classes that are more homogeneous than the total. When this can be done, we distinguish classes that differ among themselves in respect of a stated characteristic. Unless we mark off classes that differ among themselves, stratification is futile. So what is sought in stratification, we may say, is homogeneity *within* classes, heterogeneity *between* classes.

The symbols used to designate stratum measures are the same as those used for population and sample values, with appropriate subscripts. These symbols have been given in the section on notation, above.

Allocation in Stratified Sampling. A central field problem in stratified sampling is the determination of the sizes of the subsamples to be drawn from the several strata. The procedure employed in determining subsample sizes is termed *allocation*. One simple principle would be to have all the subsamples of the same size; that is, we might have $n_{h_1} = n_{h_2} = n_{h_3} = \ldots$. But we should lose many of the advantages of stratification with such a procedure. Three more suitable methods of allocation will be briefly described.

Allocation proportional to sizes of strata. We have defined a sampling fraction f as the ratio of the sample size to the total population. For a simple random sample $f = n/N$. On the same principle the sampling fraction for a single stratum h_1 is $f_{h_1} = n_{h_1}/N_{h_1}$; for stratum h_2 it is $f_{h_2} = n_{h_2}/N_{h_2}$. In making sample sizes proportional to sizes of strata a *uniform sampling fraction* is used. That is, we determine sample sizes for the several strata in such a way that $f_{h_1} = f_{h_2} = f_{h_3} = \ldots$. The logic of this is clear. In seeking a sample representative of a given universe, it is reasonable to select for the sample twice as many sampling units from stratum h_1

than from stratum h_2 if, in the universe, there are twice as many sampling units in stratum h_1 than in stratum h_2. In making estimates for population characteristics we would wish to give more weight to information on stratum h_1 than to information on stratum h_2; the method of proportional allocation does this. It is a self-weighting procedure; although no weights are consciously introduced in subsequent operations, we are in fact using weights proportional to the N's in the population strata.

The term "proportional allocation," used without qualification or further explanation, means allocation on the basis of a uniform sampling fraction.

Allocation proportional to standard deviations of strata. In discussing sampling distributions in earlier chapters we have noted that the degree of dispersion found in such distributions is related to the degree of dispersion in the populations sampled. Thus for the standard error of the mean we have $\sigma_m = \sigma/\sqrt{N}$. Here the variation in the sampling distribution is directly proportional to the variation in the universe. This suggests that in determining sample sizes for the several classes of a stratified sample it is reasonable to relate the sizes of the samples drawn from the several strata to the degrees of dispersion characterizing these strata. To achieve a given degree of accuracy in estimates based on samples from several such strata, larger samples will be needed from strata marked by wide dispersion than from those with slight dispersion. A single observation, indeed, gives a perfect representation of a universe in which there is no variation. The principle of allocation to which these considerations lead is one that would make the sample n's from the various strata directly proportional to the standard deviations of these strata. That is,

$$\frac{n_{h_1}}{\sigma_{h_1}} = \frac{n_{h_2}}{\sigma_{h_2}} = \frac{n_{h_3}}{\sigma_{h_3}} = \ldots$$

If these three σ's were, respectively, 10, 20, and 30, this condition would be satisfied by having the n's equal, respectively, to 100, 200, and 300.

This procedure calls, obviously, for knowledge of the standard deviations of the different strata into which the population is to be divided. Census counts, or other sources, may provide such information. If not, small-scale trial samplings preceding the main survey may be necessary. The requirements of the main survey may be served adequately by rather rough approximations to the standard deviations of the separate strata; such approximations may be come by at fairly low cost, with well-designed trial borings.

The principle of allocation proportional to stratum standard deviations will be satisfactory, by itself, if the N's of the various strata (N_{h1}, N_{h2}, N_{h3} ...) are equal, or approximately so. If the N's are not equal, and they seldom are, we still face the problems raised by such inequalities. We need a method of allocation that will take account of differences among both the N's and the σ's of the various strata.

Optimum allocation. The method of optimum allocation represents a combination of the two principles described above. Instead of using a uniform sampling fraction, we vary the fraction, making differences among the fractions proportional to differences among the standard deviations of the strata. That is, we set

$$\frac{f_{h1}}{\sigma_{h1}} = \frac{f_{h2}}{\sigma_{h2}} = \frac{f_{h3}}{\sigma_{h3}} = \ldots$$

This mode of allocation, which makes the sample sizes in the various classes proportional to *products* of corresponding class sizes and class standard deviations in the universe being sampled, leads to theoretically optimum sampling fractions.[5]

We should note that exact proportionality of such products may in fact be difficult to realize for any of several reasons. Precise information on universe values may be lacking. When the individual strata are of interest in their own right as domains of study, the investigator may wish to obtain larger samples from certain strata than would be given by strict proportionality. If a single survey is serving several purposes, so that the population values of more than one characteristic are to be estimated from sample results, it is unlikely that any single set of class sample sizes would be proportional to the class standard deviations of these several characteristics. In practice, allocation proportional to stratum sizes, alone, is most commonly employed. Subsequent computations and estimates are much simpler with a uniform sampling fraction than with sampling fractions that vary from stratum to stratum. If the stratum standard deviations are known to differ widely, and if the stratum standard deviations may be determined

The original memoir on this subject is a classic paper by Jerzy Neyman, "On the two different aspects of the representative method." See Neyman, Ref. 120.

with some precision in advance of the full field survey, optimum allocation may be desirable and feasible. But these conditions are not frequently encountered.

In the selection of sampling fractions the concern of the investigator is not solely with maximum precision. Precision and cost, whether dealt with on a unit or aggregate basis, have to be weighed together, and a working solution reached. A special problem is introduced when unit costs of sampling operations vary from class to class—a circumstance that may necessitate a departure from optimum or proportional allocation. Recent works on sampling survey theory introduce such unit costs into the functions used to estimate desirable sample sizes. Thus Cochran (Ref. 17 p. 75) gives a working formula designed to yield optimum allocation with varying unit costs. The allocation to which this theorem leads would give (as between two strata) a larger stratum n_h to the stratum that is larger, to the stratum marked by the greater internal variation, and to the stratum for which sampling is cheaper.

Estimates from a Stratified Random Sample. In this section we consider the determination of sample values and the estimation of population values—means, totals, proportions—from sample results; we then deal with measures of the precision of such estimates.

Sample statistics and the estimation of population values.[6] We first note the case for which the sampling fraction is uniform for all strata. Under these conditions sample statistics for a total, a mean, and a proportion are derived just as they are for a simple random sample (see pp. 666 ff.). Thus $\bar{x} = \dfrac{\Sigma(\Sigma x_{hi})}{n}$, where x_{hi} is a general symbol for a value of the variate x in a stratum h. The numerator of this expression is equivalent to Σx, over the whole range of sample data. So, also, estimates of population values based on a stratified sample with uniform sampling fraction may be made from the relations specified for simple random samples. (It is here understood that the actual numbers N_h, in the several population strata, are known and have been used in defining the sampling fractions.) As we have noted above, allocation with a uniform sampling fraction is a self-weighting procedure; there is no occasion to apply

---

[6] We shall here use the same symbols ($\bar{x}$, $\bar{X}'$, p, P', etc.) that were used for means, proportions, etc., in unstratified samples. The context will indicate whether the measures are for simple random samples or for stratified samples.

weights to the measures for the different strata. For the observations in the several sample strata, being proportional to the N_h's in the corresponding population strata, combine to give a total that is automatically weighted according to stratum sizes.

When the sampling fraction is not uniform, the making of estimates is based on sample values that are built up from stratum values. Requisite sample statistics of the types we have been discussing may be obtained from the following relations:

A sample total $= x_t = \Sigma(\Sigma x_{hi}) = \Sigma x$

A sample mean $= \bar{x} = x_t/N$

A sample number of units possessing
a stated attribute $= u = \Sigma u_h$

A sample proportion $= p = u/N$

(The subscript h indicates variates, totals, and numbers relating to strata, h being here a generic symbol for any stratum.) Using capital letters with prime marks for estimates of population values, and f_h as a general symbol for a series of sampling fractions (unequal) for different strata, we have for these estimates:

A population total $= X'_t = \Sigma(x_{ht}g_h)$ (19.21)

(The total x_{ht} for each sample stratum is raised by the expansion factor g_h to give an estimated total for that stratum in the population; these stratum population estimates are summed to give an estimated total X'_t for the whole population.)

A population mean $= \bar{X}' = X'_t/N$ (19.22)

(Alternatively, a population mean may be estimated from $\bar{X}' = (\Sigma N_h \bar{x}_h)/N$. This is a weighted average of the stratum means, each stratum mean being weighted by the corresponding stratum N_h. With these weights we obtain an unbiased estimate of the population mean.)

A population number of units possessing a stated
attribute $= U' = \Sigma(u_h g_h)$ (19.23)

(This parallels formula (19.21). Here, for each stratum, the number of units possessing a stated characteristic is raised by the expansion factor for that stratum to give an estimated total for that stratum in the population; the sum of these stratum estimates is the estimated population total, U'.)

A population proportion $= P' = U'/N$ (19.24)

(Alternatively, a population proportion may be estimated from $P' = \dfrac{\Sigma(N_h p_h)}{N}$. This is a weighted average of the stratum proportions, each stratum proportion being weighted by the corresponding stratum N_h.)

Having these estimates of population values, derived from a stratified sample, we must estimate the sampling errors to which they are subject.

Estimates of sampling errors. The great advantage of stratification, in improving estimates of population values, may be simply stated. The total variability of the observations in a stratified sample may be thought of as having two components; the variability *within* the several strata, and the variability *between* the several strata. The variability within strata is measured by the variance about the respective stratum means; the variability between strata is measured by the variance of the stratum means about the mean of the whole sample. By stratification we take account of the variability between strata, so that it does not contribute to the sampling error, in the generalization of sample results. Thus, so far as the variability of observations is concerned, the sampling error of the mean of a stratified sample is affected only by the variability within strata. (This stands in contrast, of course, to the case of a simple random sample. Estimates of sampling errors from such a sample are affected by the variability of the observations in the sample as a whole.) If the variability within strata is substantially less than the variability of the observations in the full sample, stratification results in a distinct reduction of the sampling error of sample statistics, and thus in a gain in the precision of estimates. For this reason, the investigator who is planning a stratification design seeks to set off strata that differ materially among themselves (i.e., that are marked by wide variance among the strata means), and that are internally as homogeneous as possible.

We may bring out this point in the simplest way by considering the standard error of the mean of a stratified sample in a case for which the sampling fraction is uniform, and so small for each stratum (say less than 5 percent) that the finite multipliers may be neglected. Here, as in the cases cited later, all n's and n_h's are taken to be large, or moderately large. We shall assume that the variance within population strata is the same for all strata, an assumption consistent with the use of proportional allocation (a uniform sampling fraction), rather than optimum allocation. To obtain an estimate of this common stratum variance, we average the variances within the several sample strata, weighting each by the corresponding n_h. We shall let s_h^2 serve as a general symbol for the variance within a sample stratum, that is,

$$s_h^2 = \frac{\Sigma(x_{hi} - \bar{x}_h)^2}{n_h - 1} \tag{19.25}$$

The weighted average of all such stratum variances for a given sample, which is the desired estimate of the common stratum variance, is given by

$$s_w^2 = \frac{\Sigma(n_h s_h^2)}{n} \tag{19.26}$$

As an estimate of the variance of the mean of a stratified sample, with a uniform sampling fraction, we then have

$$s_{\bar{x}}^2 = \frac{s_w^2}{n} \tag{19.27}$$

This will be recognized as the familiar expression for the square of the standard error of an arithmetic mean, with the variance within strata replacing the variance of the sample as a whole.

When the sampling fraction is large enough to call for the application of the finite multiplier, the sampling fraction being uniform, formula (19.27) becomes

$$s_{\bar{x}}^2 = \frac{s_w^2}{n}(1 - f) \tag{19.28}$$

With a variable sampling fraction, all sampling fractions being small enough so that the finite multiplier may be neglected, the variance of the mean of a stratified sample may be estimated from

$$s_{\bar{x}}^2 = \frac{1}{N^2}\Sigma\left(\frac{N_h^2 s_h^2}{n_h}\right) \tag{19.29}$$

Finally, we have the case in which the finite multiplier is to be applied and in which the sampling fraction is variable. The variance of the mean of any single stratum h is given by the general formula

$$s_{\bar{x}_h}^2 = \frac{s_h^2}{n_h}(1 - f_h) \tag{19.30}$$

where f_h is the sampling fraction for the stratum in question. When the conditions of randomness within strata and independence of sampling operations in the several strata are realized, as they are in the kind of stratified random sampling here discussed, the variance of the mean of a stratified sample may be derived from the following weighted combination of the variances of the means of the separate strata:

$$s_{\bar{x}}^2 = \frac{\Sigma(N_h^2 s_{\bar{x}_h}^2)}{N^2} \tag{19.31}$$

where N_h is the number of cases (sampling units) in a population stratum and N is the number of cases in the population as a whole. Here, as in the simpler case represented by formula (19.27), the sampling variance of the mean of the stratified sample depends on the degree of variation within the individual strata. The reader will note that the only measure of variance in the right-hand member of expression (19.31) is $s_{\bar{x}_h}^2$; the value of each $s_{\bar{x}_h}^2$ will depend on the degree of variation *within* a stratum [see formulas (19.25) and (19.30)].

We shall give, without discussion, expressions defining the sampling errors of other commonly employed sample statistics when obtained from stratified random samples.[6] These will be given in their squared form, as variances. In these summary statements, as in the expressions given above for sampling errors of arithmetic means, we use the sample variances and sample p's as estimates of the required population values, a procedure that is justified for the measures here cited. We assume, in all cases, that the n's and n_h's are at least moderately large.

Uniform sampling fraction, finite multiplier neglected

Variance of the estimate of a total:

$$s_{X_t'}^2 = \frac{N^2 s_w^2}{n} \tag{19.32}$$

where s_w^2 is defined as in formula (19.26). (As we have noted above, the variance of an estimate of a total is N^2 times the variance of the estimate of the corresponding mean.)

---

[6] For proofs and illustrations the works of Cochran (Ref. 17), Deming (Ref. 29), Hansen, Hurwitz, and Madow (Ref. 67), and Yates (Ref. 197) may be consulted.

Variance of the estimate of a proportion:

$$s_p^2 = \frac{\Sigma(N_h p_h q_h)}{Nn} \tag{19.33}$$

Uniform sampling fraction, finite multiplier applied
Variance of the estimate of a total:

$$s_{X_t'}^2 = \frac{N^2 s_w^2}{n}(1 - f) \tag{19.34}$$

Variance of the estimate of a proportion:

$$s_p^2 = \frac{\Sigma(N_h p_h q_h)}{Nn}(1 - f) \tag{19.35}$$

Variable sampling fraction, finite multiplier neglected
Variance of the estimate of a total:

$$s_{X_t'}^2 = \Sigma\left(\frac{N_h^2 s_h^2}{n_h}\right) \tag{19.36}$$

where s_h^2 is defined as in formula (19.25)
Variance of the estimate of a proportion:

$$s_p^2 = \frac{1}{N^2}\Sigma\left\{\frac{N_h^3}{(N_h - 1)} \cdot \frac{p_h q_h}{n_h}\right\} \tag{19.37}$$

Variable sampling fraction, finite multiplier applied
Variance of the estimate of a total:

$$s_{X_t'}^2 = \Sigma\left\{\frac{N_h^2 s_h^2}{n_h}(1 - f_h)\right\} \tag{19.38}$$

This is equivalent to

$$s_{X_t'}^2 = \Sigma(N_h^2 s_{\bar{x}_h}^2) \tag{19.39}$$

where $s_{\bar{x}_h}^2$ is defined as in formula (19.30)
Variance of the estimate of a proportion:

$$s_p^2 = \frac{1}{N^2}\Sigma\left\{\frac{N_h^2(N_h - n_h)}{(N_h - 1)} \cdot \frac{p_h q_h}{n_h}\right\} \tag{19.40}$$

Since $1/N_h$ will in general be a negligible quantity, we may use for the variance of a proportion the somewhat simpler expression given by Cochran

$$s_p^2 = \frac{1}{N^2}\Sigma\left\{N_h(N_h - n_h)\frac{p_h q_h}{n_h}\right\} \tag{19.41}$$

On earlier pages we have discussed methods by which, with simple random sampling, one may estimate the sample size needed to yield sample results having a desired degree of precision. We there dealt with precision and sample size alone, with no regard to cost factors, but we noted that costs, aggregate and per unit, necessarily enter into the determination of sample size. With stratified sampling the determination of sample size takes on new dimensions. The form of stratification, the method of allocation (proportional or optimal), the nature of the sampling unit—these, as well as the tolerable margin of error and the confidence level with which the investigator chooses to work, enter into decisions on sample size. And all these factors must be considered with reference to the aggregate and unit costs that will be faced in the field work, and to the available budget. The modern art of survey planning and sample design is largely concerned with procedures for dealing with these inter-related problems. On these issues, the reader must be referred to the excellent basic treatises now available on the theory and procedures of field sampling.[7]

Some Other Sampling Designs

The sampling forms described above are the fundamental types. In practice these are often modified in various ways, in adapting survey designs to the characteristics of given populations and to the cost and precision requirements of particular studies. The most important of these modifications are termed *multi-stage sampling* and *multi-phase* sampling, although more frequently than not the "multi" reduces to "two."

Multi-stage Sampling. The essential feature of this sampling form is suggested by the term *cluster sampling*, which is often used for it. We have spoken above of *elementary units*, the individual entities whose attributes are the objects of study. These units may

---

[7] Until recently the chief reference sources on the rapidly developing theory and practice of sampling surveys have been articles in scientific and professional journals. Within the last several years, however, a number of systematic treatises have appeared. Two major contributions were made in 1953, in the works of Cochran (Ref. 17) and of Hanson, Hurwitz, and Madow (Ref. 67). These, with the earlier books of Deming (Ref. 29) and Yates (Ref. 197) provide the student and field worker with comprehensive treatments of the problems faced in planning and executing sample surveys. Reference should be made, in addition, to the discussion of sampling human populations in Chapter III of the Second Edition (1952) of Neyman's *Lectures and Conferences on Mathematical Statistics and Probability* (Ref. 119), and to P. V. Sukhatme's *Sampling Theory of Surveys* (Ref. 155), which draws examples from agricultural surveys.

be farms, families, individuals, corporations, townships—any of the things that for purposes of ultimate analysis are treated as undivided wholes. The unit of the sampling process, at a first or even at a later stage, may be a *cluster* of such elementary units, the cluster being later broken down into the units whose characteristics are being investigated. Any sampling procedure that involves the use of such clusters as sampling units is termed cluster sampling.

Thus the *primary sampling unit* (which is usually shortened to psu) may be an elementary unit or a cluster of units. If it is a cluster, the process may obviously be repeated; i.e., there may be a *subsampling* of the primary units, such a subsample from a particular primary unit being either a sample of new clusters (smaller than the first) or a sample of elementary units. If the sampling unit at this second stage is a cluster, a second subsampling process is possible—a process that may entail the selection of samples made up of still other clusters or of elementary units. For example, to cite an illustration of multi-stage sampling suggested in the United Nations report on sampling surveys, a given investigation might be concerned with the characteristics of farms, these being the elementary units. For the purposes of the survey, the country might be divided into districts, a number of districts being selected as first-stage or primary sampling units; the districts could be divided into villages, a number of villages being selected as second-stage sampling units; the villages could be divided into farms, a sample of farms being then selected from each village. In this case the third-stage sampling units—the farms—are the elementary units that are the objects of study.

If the sampling process stops at the first stage, that is, if all the elementary units included in the clusters making up the primary sampling units make up the sample of elementary units that is to be analyzed in detail, the process is termed *single-stage cluster sampling*. We should have this form of sampling if all the farms included in the sample of districts mentioned above constituted the sample of farms whose characteristics were studied in detail. We should have *double-stage sampling* if all the elementary units in the clusters selected as second-stage sampling units make up the sample of elementary units that is to be studied in detail. This would be the case if all farms in the sample of villages mentioned above made up the final sample of farms. The farm example cited is actually a case of *triple-stage sampling*; the process goes into its third stage when the sample of villages is subsampled to give the final sample of farms.

The sampling process at each stage may be either random or stratified. We have *simple cluster sampling,* of one or more stages, if the sampling units chosen at each stage are selected by the method of simple random sampling. We have *stratified cluster sampling,* of one or more stages, if stratification is employed wherever sampling units are to be selected.

The constitution of the sampling unit at each stage is of course a matter of high concern in all forms of cluster sampling. Great attention is given to the scope of such units, to their internal structure, and to all their relevant quantitative and qualitative characteristics. The ultimate considerations here are the precision of the final estimates to be based on sample results, and costs; these in turn must be weighed with reference to a variety of factors, including the structure of the population to be sampled, the information at hand concerning it (the frame), the geographical extent of the survey, stratification possibilities, the degree of subsampling contemplated, etc. Methods used in the evaluation of these different factors, and in combining them to reach operating decisions, are treated in the standard works on sample surveys. We should note here, however, that these are not matters of operational interest only. For those who use the results of sample surveys, information on the scope and character of the sampling units employed is necessary to intelligent appraisal of the estimates based on such surveys.

Area sampling. A form of cluster sampling that is widely used is one that associates the elementary units of a population with a geographical area. The populations under study need not be human —they could be populations of animals, of trees, or houses—but in most applications of this method, which is termed *area sampling,* the units under study are human beings. Each of these units must be associated with a single definable area. For a human being this is usually the area in which he resides. The investigator works, in a first stage, with a list of such areas, rather than with a list of the units of the whole population. By random methods a sample of areas is selected. If need be subsamples of the chosen sample areas may then be selected by random methods. At an appropriate stage the elementary units residing in the selected sample areas may be individually enumerated. These enumerated elements may constitute the final sample for interview or detailed study, or the final sample may be obtained by a further sampling operation among the enumerated elements. If these procesess are carried through by random methods the conditions of probability sampling will have been met, and estimates based on sample results may be made in probability terms.

An important feature of this procedure is that no list of elements in the full population is required to ensure conditions of probability sampling. The essential condition that all members of the parent population have a definable probability of inclusion in the final sample is ensured by the random sampling of *areas*. The enumeration of elements is then necessary only in the limited number of selected areas. This type of cluster sampling may be used, therefore, where simple random sampling would not be possible, because no list of population elements exists. Even when a list exists, area sampling may be much less costly. Procedures used in area sampling will be more fully discussed in a later section of this chapter.

Multi-phase Sampling. The successive sampling operations in multi-stage sampling entail the selection of sampling units of different types at different stages. The term *multi-phase* sampling is used when sampling units of the same type are the objects of different *phases* of observation. Typically, in one of these phases all the units in a sample are studied with respect to certain characteristics, while in a later phase some of the units, a subsample of the full sample, are studied with respect to certain additional characteristics. Thus we should have two-phase or *double sampling* if information concerning family income alone were gathered for all the members of a sample of 10,000 families, while additional information concerning the sources of income and the uses of income were gathered for a subsample of 1,000 families. The additional information for members of the smaller group might be gathered at the same time the information was collected for the full sample, or might be gathered at a later time. Not infrequently the two (or more) phases relate to samples gathered at different times. A comprehensive first survey might be made, at low cost per unit because only limited facts are collected; the results of the first phase could then be used in planning an intensive second phase covering the same kind of units. (The second sample need not be a subsample of the first, though it often is.) Sometimes the first phase of such a study is designed to obtain information about a variable related to the variable that is the direct object of study. The information obtained from this preliminary sample can then be used for purposes of effective stratification, in the second or main phase of the inquiry.

Systematic Sampling. Another sampling form, simple in design and execution, may be employed when the members of the population to be sampled are arranged in order, the order corresponding to consecutive numbers. The arrangement of names in a telephone directory, or blocks in a city, of income tax returns in the Treasury's files, are examples of such ordering. If a sample of suitable size may be obtained by taking every tenth unit of the population, one of the first ten units in this ordered arrangement is chosen at random. The sample is completed by selecting every tenth unit from the rest of the list. If the first unit selected should be the fourth, the investigator would include in his sample the fourteenth, the twenty-fourth, the thirty-fourth, etc. In general terms, if the requirements of the survey call for the inclusion in the sample of one unit out of every k units in the population, a unit is chosen at random from the first k units; thereafter, every kth unit in the population, as arranged in order, is included in the sample. This mode of selection is called *systematic sampling*.

The type of sample obtained by this method depends on the structure of the population being sampled. Systematic sampling gives a stratified sample containing one unit from each stratum. If the arrangement of population elements in the order employed in the systematic sampling process is in fact random, these strata will all be alike in constitution, except for purely random differences. A systematic sample is then, in effect, a simple random sample; the standard errors of measures obtained from the systematic sample will be, on the average, the same as those obtained from simple random samples. But if the ordered arrangement of population elements is nonrandom, the systematic sample will not be a purely random one. The "strata" will differ among themselves. Under these conditions a sample containing one unit from each stratum will be preferable to a simple random sample.

It is helpful, in obtaining an understanding of systematic sampling, to regard it, as Cochran puts it, as a form of cluster sampling. The systematic sample is itself a cluster—one of many that might have been drawn from the population by selecting at random one unit from each stratum. Since the single selected cluster given by systematic sampling constitutes the whole sample, it should reflect, in its composition, all the elements of diversity that are present in the population.

Whether systematic selection will be efficient, in providing sample measures with low sampling errors, or otherwise, depends largely on the make-up of the population from which a sample is to be drawn, and on the order underlying the mode of selection. If there should be periodicity in the elements of a population, as arranged for purposes of systematic selection, this method could give a highly unrepresentative sample. Thus if one were picking every twelfth unit, and if the arrangement were such that the units so selected were alike in some distinctive respect, the sample would be a poor one. (This danger would be a serious one if the elements of the population were observations arranged chronologically. Sales of department stores, sampled systematically so that only observations for Decembers of successive years were included, are a case in point.) On the other hand, the internal diversity that makes a systematic sample preferable to a simple random sample will be realized if units k numbers apart on the ordered list of population elements differ more from one another than do adjacent units. Thus if adjoining houses tend to resemble one another, a sampling procedure that selects only every twentieth house will be better than one that permits adjoining houses to be included in a sample. The general principle here is that systematic sampling is preferable to simple random sampling if there is high serial correlation among the units of a population, as ordered for the purposes of a sample survey.

The Current Population Survey

We shall complete this chapter on sampling theory and procedures by a concrete example. The Current Population Survey, conducted by the Bureau of the Census, provides the basis of the Monthly Report on the Labor Force—now one of the most revealing of our current social records and one of the most closely watched of our economic indicators. A brief discussion of the major features of this Survey, which is an excellent example of modern sampling methods, will illustrate the practical application of some of the techniques developed on earlier pages.[8] Although we shall not deal in any detail with the administrative aspects of this Survey, the discussion will suggest the nature of the administrative problems that are faced in planning and executing a sample survey.

Background and Objectives of the Population Survey. During the depression of the 1930's, public administrators and social scientists became acutely aware of the gaps in our knowledge of current economic processes and of our human resources. Particularly disturbing was our ignorance of the number of unemployed. At a time when unemployment was our most serious social problem, estimates of this critical magnitude differed by many millions, and there was no basis for a sound choice among differing guesses. Under the auspices of the Works Progress Administration a good beginning was made in the design of an objective sampling procedure for determining the volume of unemployment, and a monthly report on the labor force was begun by this agency in 1940. In 1942 the task was taken over by the Bureau of the Census, which has administered the survey since then. The original design has been modified from time to time by the Census Bureau, most recently in 1954. The latest design will be briefly described here.

In the early stages of this enterprise the chief objective was the estimation of unemployment, on a monthly basis. This remains a major purpose, but as changes have occurred in the social and economic conditions of American life, the Survey has come to serve other ends as well. Basically, the objective of the Survey is to provide estimates of the employment status of those members of the population of the United States who are 14 years of age and over. Such members fall into two groups—those who are members of the labor force and those who are outside the labor force. The *labor force* comprises persons in the armed forces and civilians who are classed as employed or unemployed. The Survey seeks to cover the civilian groups only.

---

[8] I have drawn on Census Bureau sources in this account, and am particularly indebted to Joseph Steinberg, of the Population and Housing Division of the Bureau of the Census. A preliminary report on the concepts and methods used in the current survey is given in *Current Population Reports*, July 30, 1954, Series P–23, No. 2.

Results of the Population Survey are published monthly in *Current Population Reports*, Labor Force, Series P–57. A report that summarizes employment and unemployment statistics collected by both the Department of Commerce and the Department of Labor, appears monthly as a "Combined Employment and Unemployment Release" of the two Departments.

Each of the terms used above calls for the most precise definition, for ambiguities can lead to substantial margins of uncertainty in the final estimates. The main elements of the definitions of the two major groups in the labor force are these:

> *Employed persons* comprise (1) all those who during the survey week (a calendar week specified as the survey time period) did any work at all as paid employees or in their own businesses or professions, or on their own farms, or who worked 15 hours or more as unpaid workers on farms or in businesses operated by members of their families, and (2) all those who were not working or looking for work but who had jobs or businesses from which they were temporarily absent for any of a number of specified reasons, including illness and labor-management disputes.

> *Unemployed persons* include all persons who did no work (as defined above) in the survey week, and who were looking for work. All those who made efforts to find jobs during the preceding 60-day period are considered to be looking for work.

The final estimates and the reports supplementary to these estimates provide information on the distribution by age and sex of those outside the labor force and, for the labor force, details concerning the structure of employment, the degree and nature of part-time employment, the duration of unemployment for those seeking work, the annual incomes of persons and families, etc. This survey is becoming thus an instrument for the regular recording, on a comprehensive scale, of current information on the activities and welfare of the population of the United States. As such, it represents a major development in our system of social and economic reporting.

The Survey Design. The final sample sought by the Census Bureau each month is designed to include about 25,000 designated dwelling units. These are obtained by random sampling within each of 230 primary sampling units, each of which is a geographical area. These primary sampling units (psu's) have come, in their turn, from 230 different strata. The two major sampling steps in this process are the selection of sample areas and the selection of households.

Stratification, and the selection of a sample of primary sampling units. A first step in the sampling process was the division of the total area of the United States into 2,000 primary sampling units.

For this purpose, use was made of certain pre-existing political divisions—divisions into counties, of which there are about 3,000 in the country, and into the geographical units that are termed standard metropolitan areas. The 1950 Census recognized 168 such areas. Each of the standard metropolitan areas constituted a primary sampling unit. Each of the other 1,832 psu's in the country consisted of a separate county or of a grouping of adjoining counties. In the grouping of several counties to form a single psu diversity of social and economic conditions was sought, so that there might be as much heterogeneity as possible within the psu. (We may here suggest the reason for this heterogeneity. Since a selected psu will in the final sample represent the whole stratum from which that psu was drawn, as much as possible of the diversity existing in the stratum should be present in each psu in that stratum.) Thus a typical psu would include urban and rural residents, low income groups and high income groups, and varied industrial and occupational groups.

The process of stratification entailed the combination of the 2,000 psu's into 230 strata, each of which was to be as homogeneous as possible. (The reader will recall that in stratification one seeks heterogeneity *between* strata, homogeneity *within* strata. The size of sampling errors of estimates based on stratified samples depends upon the variance *within* strata.) Among the criteria used in the allocation of psu's to strata were population density, types of industrial concentration, predominant types of farming (for rural areas), rate of growth in the preceding decade, and geographical location. Attempts were made to combine in a single stratum sample areas (that is, selected psu's) that were alike in all or some of these respects. Certain of the primary sampling units—the 44 largest standard metropolitan areas and a limited number of other metropolitan areas—were large enough to constitute strata by themselves. But the bulk of the 230 strata consisted of combinations of psu's. All strata thus built up were made approximately equal in terms of their 1950 population.

The sample of areas, comprising 230 primary sampling units, was obtained in this fashion:

> 60 primary sampling units large enough to constitute strata
> by themselves were automatically included in the sample

170 primary sampling units were randomly selected from the remaining 170 strata. Probabilities of selection, for the psu's in a given stratum, were made proportional to their 1950 population.

Sampling within selected sample areas: the selection of sample households. Each primary sampling unit is, of course, a cluster of the units ultimately sought. Since these clusters are too large for the inclusion in the final sample of all the units they contain, a further sampling process *within* psu's was necessary. This was done by area sampling methods. In this work use was made of certain administrative units, called *enumeration districts*, that were employed in the 1950 Census, and of subdivisions of these districts into small land areas termed *segments*. Each segment comprised about six dwelling units. In drawing a sample of enumeration districts from a primary sampling unit, chances of selection were made proportionate to 1950 population. In drawing segments from enumeration districts, chances of selection were made proportional to the estimated number of dwelling units in the various segments. All the households in the selected segments constituted the final sample of households. (In certain exceptional cases, where segments were unavoidably large, subsampling within segments was necessary.)

In planning the current survey the final sample of households was set, in advance, at about 25,000. This meant (as of 1954) that about 1 out of every 2,250 households in the population was to be selected. This over-all sampling fraction, which applied in each stratum, was adjusted within strata to the relative sizes of selected primary sampling units. For example, if a selected psu included one ninth of the population of the stratum from which it came, the proper proportion (1/2250) within the stratum would be attained by drawing 1 out of every 250 households within the psu (1/2250 ÷ 1/9 = 1/250). If the psu included less than one ninth of the stratum population, the sampling fraction for the psu would be higher; if the psu were relatively larger, the sampling fraction would be lower. This sampling fraction for a given psu is constant from month to month, which means that the absolute size of the sample of households from that psu will vary, if the population of the psu varies.

I have used the past tense in describing most of these operations since the basic sample design is fixed for a term of years. However, there is variation in the make-up of the sample of households. Use is made by the Census Bureau of a system of rotation, the effect of which is to keep a given household in the sample for a period of eight months, divided into two equal periods of four months each. These two four-month periods are designed to fall in the same calendar months of successive years. This rotation is effected by groups of households, so that 75 percent of the sample segments are common from month to month, while 50 percent are common from year to year.

Survey techniques. Not the least important part of the sample survey is the actual interviewing of representatives of selected households by field agents. Biased or tactless interviewers, badly phrased or slanted questions, inaccurate reporting, or substantial nonresponse[9] may defeat the purposes of a survey, no matter how good the design. A striking incident, illustrating the importance of the form of questions put to householders, is recorded in the early history of the labor force survey. In March 1942 two supplementary questions were put to those who were classed as neither employed nor unemployed (i.e., to civilians who were counted as not in the labor force). Each of these persons was asked whether he would take a full-time job if one were available within 30 days, and when he had last worked on a full-time job. The answers served to increase the estimate of the civilian labor force by almost a million. Responses to the standard questions had failed to reveal the willingness of many who were classed as housewives or students to take jobs if they were offered. Such persons belong in the labor force, as defined. As a result of this and of many similar experiences, far more attention is now given in sample survey work to questionnaire preparation and interviewing procedures. But these arts, important as they are, are beyond the scope of the present discussion.

The actual field work on the Population Survey is done by a staff of some 350 part-time interviewers, under the supervision of

---

[9] The problem of nonresponse is particularly troublesome in sample surveys. If there is considerable nonresponse the actual sample may be a biased one, because those responding may differ in significant ways from those not responding. Thus a question on family income may bring relatively more responses from those with medium or high incomes than from those with low incomes. When a particular sampling unit has been selected for inclusion in a sample, great efforts are usually made to ensure response from that unit, even at high cost. In the Population Survey an adjustment is made for sample households that cannot be interviewed, for one reason or another. This proportion is usually from 3 to 5 percent of the households in a sample.

full-time supervisors. Representatives of sample households are interviewed each month during the calendar week containing the fifteenth day. Activities of household members during the *survey week* (the week containing the eighth day of the month) determine their classification as employed, unemployed, or not in the labor force. Answers to questions covering these and various supplementary points are recorded by the interviewer in such a way that transfer of data to punch cards and all subsequent operations can be done by machine. An electric digital computer is used in this subsequent work. Release of national estimates is thus possible about three weeks after the collection of the data.

Estimates and Sampling Errors. The making of national estimates from the sample results for any given month involves some steps that need not concern us here in detail. We may note, however, that the final estimate on any characteristic is a composite of two estimates. The first of these, which is called a ratio estimate, entails the customary inflation of sample results, with adjustments to bring the sample population into agreement with the known distribution of the entire population with respect to certain basic attributes, such as age, sex, color, farm-nonfarm residence, etc. The second component of the final estimate is obtained by projecting the composite estimate of a given characteristic (e.g., employment) for the preceding month on the basis of the recorded change in that characteristic for that portion of the sample that is common to the two months. (As was noted above, this common portion will be 75 percent of the sample for a given month.) An average of these two components, with equal weights, gives the composite national estimate for the current month. This process of averaging gives a final estimate with a sampling error lower than that attaching to the ratio estimate alone.

The chief objective of the new survey design that was adopted by the Bureau of the Census in January, 1954, was to reduce the sampling errors attaching to estimates of the labor force and its components. The relative sampling errors of summary estimates of the major magnitudes (civilian labor force, total employment, nonagricultural employment) are now given as approximately 0.6 percent. This is a coefficient of variation multiplied by 100 to put it in percentage terms. The absolute measure used in deriving it is a standard error, or standard deviation, hence the customary probabilities for a normal deviate apply to limits defined as multiples of this quantity. Thus if the total civilian labor force for a given month were estimated at 65 million, confidence limits corresponding to a probability of 0.68 would be set at 64.61 and 65.39 [i.e., at 65 − (65 × .006) and at 65 + (65 × .006)]. Confidence limits corresponding to a probability of 0.95 would be set at 65 ± 1.176 percent, or at 64.24 and 65.76 millions. (For purposes of explanation these limits are given to more decimal places than are warranted by the character of the estimates.) For estimates of the smaller magnitudes, unemployment and agricultural employment, the relative sampling error is higher, being now given as roughly 4 percent. If for a given month unemployment were estimated at 3 millions, 0.95 confidence limits would be given by 3 ± 7.84 percent. Thus with a confidence of 0.95 we could state that the number of unemployed in the population at large was between 2.76 millions and 3.24 millions.

In the decade and a half that have passed since the Labor Force Survey was begun, the effectiveness of this instrument has been materially increased. Underlying concepts and techniques have been sharpened and improved. Conditions essential to a probability sample have been established, the scope of the Survey has been expanded, and the accuracy of estimates increased. However, it is not to be expected that the most recent revision will be the last. Both the makers and the users of these estimates recognize possibilities of further improvement. These possibilities have to do with the more accurate performance of the present job, and with expansions and extensions of this job.

For both purposes, additional area coverage and a larger sample of households have been recommended. These changes would, among other things, make for more accurate estimates of the number of unemployed—one of the controversial elements in labor force estimation. In view of the crucial role of accurate and unbiased interviewing, emphasis is placed also on the need for careful training of all field workers and for close checks on interviewing procedures. The reduction of nonresponse, which now runs to 3 to 5 percent of the sample, and of response bias, would be furthered by such training and controls.

Problems of a different sort relate to definitions and classifications. Years of debate have failed to bring full agreement on the meaning of such terms as "employed" and "unemployed." Should a person temporarily laid off, but with a job to which he expects to return, be classed as "employed"? Where should the dividing line be drawn between a part-time worker who is employed and a part-time worker who is unemployed? Should there be a separate category of the "partially unemployed"? The persistence of such issues suggests that there are bound to be fringe groups in the labor force, classifiable in different ways for different purposes. If the major groups are clearly defined such fringe elements can be separately recorded, and classified by users of the estimates in such ways as their specific needs may dictate. This is the direction in which the Current Population Survey is now moving.

We have noted that the original labor force survey was intended primarily to provide reliable information on the volume of unemployment in the country at large. Other and more varied purposes are now served, and we may expect this extension of purposes to continue. Administrative and analytical needs would be better served by detailed estimates for local areas, for diverse individual components of the employed labor force, for different elements of the unemployed. More details are wanted, and greater accuracy in estimates relating to elements of the total. Good design and efficient execution may do something toward serving these expanding purposes, but most of them require heavier expenditures. A balance has to be reached between administrative and scientific needs on the one hand, and the interests of the taxpayer on the other. Where this balance is to be found is not altogether a statistical question.[10]

REFERENCES

Cochran, W. G., *Sampling Techniques*, Chaps. 1-5.
Deming, W. E., *Some Theory of Sampling*, Chaps. 1, 2, 4, 9, 10.
Federal Reserve System, Board of Governors, "1954 Survey of Consumer Finances," *Federal Reserve Bulletin*, March, June, July 1954.
Festinger, L. and Katz, D., ed., *Research Methods in the Behavioral Sciences*.

[10] Among other sample surveys of interest to students of the social sciences and of business, special mention should be made of the annual surveys of Consumer Finances, sponsored by the Board of Governors of the Federal Reserve System and conducted by the Survey Research Center of the Institute for Social Research, of the University of Michigan. Reports on these surveys appear currently in the *Federal Reserve Bulletin*. An account of methods used is given in that *Bulletin* for July, 1950. For more general discussions of methods used in these and other surveys see Katona and Mueller, Ref. 75, and Festinger and Katz, Ref. 45.

Hansen, M. H., Hurwitz, W. N. and Madow, W. G., *Sample Survey Methods and Theories*, Vol. I, Chaps. 1-5, 12; Vol. II, Chaps. 1-5.

Katona, G. and Mueller, E., *Consumer Attitudes and Demand.*

Klein, L. R., *Contributions of Survey Methods to Economics.*

Mosteller, F. and others, "The Pre-Election Polls of 1948," Social Science Research Council, *Bulletin* 60, 1949.

Neyman, J., *Lectures and Conferences on Mathematical Statistics and Probability*, 2nd ed., Chap. 3, part 1.

Neyman, J., "On the Two Different Aspects of the Representative Method," *Journal of the Royal Statistical Society*, Vol. 97, 1934.

Parten, M. B., *Surveys, Polls, and Samples*, Chaps. 2, 3, 7, 9.

Sukhatme, P. V., *Sampling Theory of Surveys*, Chaps. 1-3.

United Nations Statistical Office, "The Preparation of Sampling Survey Reports," *Statistical Papers Series C*, No. 1 (revised), Feb. 1950.

U. S. Bureau of the Census, "Concepts and Methods Used in the Current Labor Force Statistics Prepared by the Bureau of the Census," *Current Population Reports*, Series P-23, No. 2, July 30, 1954.

Yates, F., *Sampling Methods for Censuses and Surveys*, 2nd ed., Chaps. 1-3, 6, 7.

Yule, G. U. and Kendall, M. G., *An Introduction to the Theory of Statistics*, 14th ed., Chaps. 16, 23.

The publishers and the dates of publication of the books named in chapter reference lists are given in the bibliography at the end of this volume.

:
:
•

Statistical Data: the Raw
Materials of Analysis

In all but the last of the preceding chapters we have discussed statistics as a method of combining and analyzing data of observation, and of generalizing from such data. We have assumed in these earlier chapters that the data to be employed were in hand; we have broken into the process of inquiry after observations had been made. The final chapter (19) was given to an exposition of sample design and the planning of field surveys. This Appendix is intended to serve as a briefer and more general discussion of the raw materials that are employed in statistical inquiries. As a reference to be consulted at an early stage of a course of instruction it may help to orient students of the social sciences and business administration, and to encourage discrimination in the use of statistical data. The examination, appraisal, and full understanding of the basic data of observation are obvious but sometimes neglected prerequisites to the meaningful use of data in subsequent analysis.[1]

The observations with which a statistician deals are obtained in diverse ways. A full discussion of these ways would include the arts of designing experiments, conducting interviews, framing and circulating questionnaires, planning samples and administering field survey forces; it would deal with the extensive collections of data compiled by governmental bodies — federal, state, and local — and by international agencies; it would comprehend the practices of business enterprises and the varied records of business

[1] For an effective statement on this point see Mahalanobis, P. C., "Professional Training in Statistics," *Bulletin* of the International Statistical Institute, Vol. 33, Part V.

operations provided by books of account; it would give attention to the growing bodies of data assembled by private agencies of research and investigation. The sources of statistical data are, indeed, coextensive with the activities of man. A treatment of such scope is, of course, out of the question. Our immediate purpose will be served by distinguishing problems that are faced in obtaining observations at first hand from the problems involved in using data compiled by others. In doing this, certain related matters of general concern to the practicing statistician will be brought out.

Direct Observation Versus Use of Existing Records. A research scientist, or an administrator weighing a decision that entails objective reference, may utilize the results of direct observation, planned with reference to the specific problems faced. The physical scientist may design a laboratory experiment; the social scientist may plan a field study; the business administrator may conduct a market survey of consumer demand. Alternatively, in any of the cases cited, use may be made of records made by others, for other purposes. The physicist may find that recorded results of other experiments bear upon his problem; the social scientist may use vital statistics or wage payments recorded by governmental agencies; the business administrator may find that income records by states and previous studies of consumer finances and inclinations provide all that is needed for the decision he must make. There are wide differences, among fields of research and among decision-making procedures, in the degree of emphasis placed on direct observation on the one hand and on resort to existing records on the other. With some reservations we may say that in deriving his data the physical scientist places heavy weight on planned experiment[2]; that the social scientist looks in the main to existing public and private records, but is making increasing use of sharply focused surveys, yielding original observations; that the business administrator uses business records, relevant published statistics, and, to a growing extent, observations derived from specific investigations of customer preference.

The common characteristic of social science and administration (both public and private) is their use of a mixture of observations

[2] The qualifications to this statement are not unimportant. The physical scientist has always made extensive use of the observations of his predecessors and contemporaries; progress, indeed, has depended upon the accumulation of a large body of verified observations. Yet frontier studies demand ever new observations, directly relevant to particular problems. The design of appropriate experiments is a major aspect of physical research.

derived from special studies and of data provided by existing records. For investigations of wide scope, dealing with the vital processes of the whole society or with the operations of the whole economy, or of major sectors of the economy, there is a necessary dependence upon government. To a degree never true of the physical sciences, the sciences of society must draw their data from public agencies. Yet such data fall far short of meeting the diverse needs of curious investigators, seeking to understand social and economic processes. Among the most promising of recent developments in the social sciences has been the use of sampling techniques designed to yield data pertinent to specific questions. This has been notably true of sociology and social psychology. The economist remains, and must remain, a heavy user of data gathered by public agencies, but here, too, studies entailing the use of original observations are growing in number and in fruitfulness. The business administrator, also, in seeking to gauge market needs and potentials, has resorted increasingly in recent years to direct examination of representative sample groups.

Those to whom this book is addressed will have occasion to employ data of the two types distinguished above — those derived from original observations and those drawn from public or private records. Methods of obtaining the original data that constitute random samples, and that provide, thus, proper bases for statistical generalizations have been discussed in Chapter 19. The opening section of that chapter may suitably be read at this point, if not already covered by the student. But we said little there about the arts employed in observing the behavior of individuals and of groups, in measuring attributes and reactions, in obtaining directly from individuals data bearing on their experience, their attitudes and opinions, their planned actions. Recent advances in these arts have been impressive, and full of promise for the future. They are replacing casual contacts and highly personal judgments in the appraisal of people in their economic and social relations by objective procedures for the making of observations on behavior, attitudes, and expectations.

I should render no service to the reader if I were to attempt to reduce these procedures to a few apparently simple rules for interviewing and preparing questionnaires. These are not simple arts. Most pertinent are the remarks of Goode and Hatt, on the design of such approaches as these: "The good schedule grows from good hypotheses. . . . It is unlikely that an excellent set of questions can be developed without serious library research, much discussion of the problems with colleagues, and considerable experience with the subject matter." One who is planning any serious endeavor to gather original data by such methods should study some of the technical publications now available on these topics.[3]

The Use of Existing Records. The sources to which the social scientist and the business administrator may turn for data are diverse, and of varying reliability. They include the accounts and other records of business enterprises and trade associations, the compilations of administrative and regulating agencies of government (e.g., the Interstate Commerce Commission, the Bureau of Internal Revenue); federal and state registration data such as vital statistics, educational statistics, and records of automobiles in use; the publications of public-purpose collection agencies (such as the Bureau of the Census and the Bureau of Labor Statistics); the series on national economic accounts, on production, on banking and credit, etc., prepared by public agencies of analysis and research (e.g., the Office of Business Economics of the Department of Commerce, the Division of Research and Statistics of the Board of Governors of the Federal Reserve System) [4]; the statistical compilations of the United Nations and other international agencies; the publications and files of private research agencies such as the National Bureau of Economic Research, The Brookings Institution, the National Industrial Conference Board, the Twentieth Century Fund, etc.; and the documents of varied origin that may provide data relevant to particular problems.

[3] See, among others,
Blankenship, A. B., ed., *How To Conduct Consumer and Opinion Research* (New York, Harpers, 1946); Festinger, L. and Katz, D., ed., *Research Methods in the Behavioral Sciences* (New York, Dryden Press, 1953), esp. Chapter 8 and accompanying bibliography; Goode, W. J. and Hatt, P. K., *Methods in Social Research* (New York, McGraw-Hill, 1952), Chapters 11–13; Jahoda, M., Deutsch, M., and Cook, S. W., *Research Methods in Social Relations* (New York, Dryden Press, 1951); Katona, G. and Mueller, E., *Consumer Attitudes and Demand* (Survey Research Center, University of Michigan, 1953); Likert, R., "The Sample Interview Survey," in Dennis, W., ed., *Readings in General Psychology* (New York, Prentice-Hall, 1949); Parten, M. B., *Surveys, Polls and Samples* (New York, Harpers, 1950).

[4] The statistical work of agencies of the central government is discussed and appraised in Hauser, P. M. and Leonard, W. R., *Government Statistics for Business Use* (New York, Wiley, 1946) and in Mills, F. C. and Long, C., *The Statistical Agencies of the Federal Government* (New York, National Bureau of Economic Research, 1949). The chief elements of the statistical intelligence system of the federal government are given in Mills and Long, pp. 9–15.

Although nothing like an exhaustive list of sources can be given in brief compass, it may be helpful to name some of the more comprehensive and most readily available published sources of social, economic, and business data. In the main, this list is limited to official publications. It should be understood that many of these are secondary sources, a term that is explained in the following section. They are, however, reliable sources.

United States
Decennial, Quinquennial, Annual, or Occasional

Agricultural Statistics, U.S. Bureau of Agricultural Economics (Annual)
Annual Report, U.S. Comptroller of the Currency
Annual Report, U.S. Treasury Department
Annual Survey of Manufactures, U.S. Bureau of the Census
Census of Agriculture, U.S. Bureau of the Census (Quinquennial)
Census of Business, U.S. Bureau of the Census (Quinquennial)
Census of Manufactures, U.S. Bureau of the Census (Quinquennial)
Census of Population, U.S. Bureau of the Census (Decennial)
Economic Almanac, National Industrial Conference Board, New York, Crowell (Annual)
Economic Report of the President, U.S. Council of Economic Advisers (Annual)
Foreign Commerce and Navigation of the United States, U.S. Bureau of the Census (Annual)
Handbook of Labor Statistics, U.S. Bureau of Labor Statistics
Historical Statistics of the United States, 1789–1945, U.S. Bureau of the Census, Washington, Government Printing Office, 1949
Minerals Yearbook, U.S. Bureau of Mines
National Income, 1954 edition, U.S. Office of Business Economics (Supplement to the *Survey of Current Business*)
Statistical Abstract of the United States, U.S. Bureau of the Census (Annual)
Statistics of Income, U.S. Bureau of Internal Revenue (Annual)
Vital Statistics of the United States, National Office of Vital Statistics (Annual)

United States
Quarterly or Monthly

Abstract of Reports of Condition of National Banks, U.S. Comptroller of the Currency (Quarterly)
Construction Review, U.S. Departments of Labor and Commerce (Monthly)
Current Population Reports, U.S. Bureau of the Census (Monthly)
Economic Indicators, U.S. Council of Economic Advisers (Monthly; *Historical and Descriptive Supplement*, prepared by the Staff of the

Joint Committee on the Economic Report and the U.S. Office of Statistical Standards, 1953)

Federal Reserve Bulletin, Board of Governors, Federal Reserve System (Monthly)

Monthly Labor Review, U.S. Bureau of Labor Statistics (Monthly)

Monthly Vital Statistics Report, National Office of Vital Statistics

Survey of Current Business, U.S. Office of Business Economics (Monthly; biennial supplement)

International

Commodity Trade Statistics, United Nations Statistical Office (Quarterly)

Demographic Yearbook, United Nations Statistical Office

Monthly Bulletin of Statistics, United Nations Statistical Office

Statistical Yearbook, United Nations Statistical Office

Woytinsky, W. S. and Woytinsky, E.S., *World Population and Production*, New York, The Twentieth Century Fund, 1953

Yearbook of Food and Agricultural Statistics, United Nations Food and Agricultural Organization

Yearbook of International Trade Statistics, United Nations Statistical Office

Primary and secondary sources. An essential distinction is to be made between *primary* and *secondary* sources of materials taken from existing records. A primary source is one that publishes (or otherwise makes available) data for which it is itself responsible as the agency of original collection and compilation. A secondary source is one that reprints data from a primary source; in this case the publishing agency is not the agency responsible for the original collection of the data. Many of the publications of the Bureau of the Census are primary sources; the *Statistical Abstract*, the *Economic Almanac* of the National Industrial Conference Board, the *Statistical Yearbook* of the United Nations are examples of secondary sources. Obviously, more reliability attaches to the data derived directly from a primary source, for not only are errors in copying avoided, but the precise meaning of the figures, the conditions under which they were gathered, and the limitations to be borne in mind in interpreting them will be clearly understood by the editors, and are more likely to be explained to the readers. Not only is it important to understand whether the source from which data are secured is primary or secondary, but the general reliability of the agency which gathered the data should be determined. Data may be unreliable because of loose methods of gathering or assembling, or because of conscious or unconscious bias in the responsible agency. The fact of such unreliability should be established, if it exists.

On the meaning of published figures. A first responsibility of the user of data derived from existing records is to determine their precise meaning. For this purpose the user should know what unit has been used, and how reliable are the data recorded.

a. Definition of the unit. The elementary process of *counting* is basic in quantitative work, but to understand the results of a counting operation one must be sure of what has been counted. This calls for a precise definition of the unit employed.

One of the most serviceable classifications of statistical units, that given by G. P. Watkins, divides all such units into the following classes and subclasses:

Classification of statistical units

(1) Individual things

    (*a*) Natural kinds

        Examples: man, hog, hen

        Such natural kinds are much more easily distinguished than artificial units, the meaning of which depends often upon convention. Hence the counting of natural things, such as the number of animals on farms, is likely to be more accurate than a counting of artificial units.

    (*b*) Produced kinds; manufactured commodities and instruments

        Examples: shoe, door, chair

(2) Units of measurement

    (*a*) Units of physical measurement

        Examples: ton, gallon, kilowatt hour

        Such units are employed as a result of convention. Frequently the same term is employed with varying meanings, a practice that leads to ambiguity and uncertainty in interpreting the results.

    (*b*) Pecuniary units

        Units of commercial value, such as the dollar, pound, and franc, are the least satisfactory of the units with which the statistician must deal, yet these are the most important in ordinary business analysis and in much economic research. The chief defect of this class of unit arises from the changes to which it is subject, as a measure of value, because of changes in the general price level. Index numbers of prices represent an attempt to correct for some of the deficiencies of the pecuniary unit, but such devices fail to remove all the defects of units of this type.

In using published data care must be taken that the unit is interpreted precisely as it was by the original investigators. Thus, if one is using Census figures of the number of manufacturing establishments in the United States at a certain date, the precise meaning given to the term "manufacturing establishment" must be understood. Where any ambiguity is likely to exist, the definition given to the enumerators should be published with the data.

b. Determination of degree of error in the data. No compilation can be accurate in an absolute sense. Errors may arise from faulty collection or recording, ambiguities or bias in questions propounded, errors in tabulation or computation. Data bearing every indication of accuracy to four or five places may in fact represent rough estimates. If the user of published data is unaware of the errors that may be present he may make serious mistakes in generalizing from them, or in using them to test hypotheses or to guide decisions. There should be a statement in the primary source of a given body of data indicating the degree of reliability attaching to them and this information should be repeated in secondary sources. If feasible, reliability should be defined in quantitative terms, but this is possible only for data derived from probability samples. If the margin of error may not be measured, the degree of confidence to be had in the data may be indicated in qualitative terms.[5]

In this day of extensive statistical records and of heavy reliance on them, the need of information on the reliability of published statistics is great. The urge to "quantify" — to count, to measure, to record in quantitative terms — is strong today. Governmental agencies and private research workers alike have responded to this urge. In part, the response appears in reliable and well-documented statistics; in part, it takes the form of estimates of highly uncertain reliability. The utility of the present extensive collections of quantitative data, collections so pleasing to the statistically minded investigator, will be materially augmented when all published statistics are accompanied by information that enables the user accurately to appraise their reliability.

There are, of course, other types of information one should have if one is to use published figures with accuracy. Such simple matters

[5] For some bodies of statistics numerical measures of reliability, if essayed, would be misleading. Thus Earl R. Rolph writes, with reference to statistics of income and wealth, "Milton Gilbert maintains, persuasively in my judgment, that the reliability of a national income component can be learned only by reviewing the sources of the data and the methods of estimation employed." The same thing is true, of course, of many published statistical series. In such cases the user has a right to expect a full disclosure of sources and methods.

On this subject students of economics and business may with profit consult Professor Oskar Morgenstern's book, *On the Accuracy of Economic Observations* (Princeton University Press, 1950).

as the bases of percentages are often undefined. The time period to which the observations on a historical variable relate — a calendar year or a fiscal year, a selected day in a given month or all days, averaged — may not be stated. The kind of marketing transaction that gave rise to a given price quotation may be unspecified. Standards of presentation and explanation are improving in public practice. There is no better way to insure further improvement than for a body of critical and demanding users to maintain pressure on the responsible agencies.

APPENDIX **B**

:

Note on Statistical Calculations[1]

Statistical work involves, of necessity, a considerable amount of calculation. If this work is to be done with expedition and accuracy, in a given case, the enterprise must be planned and details organized. This calls for the proper lay-out of the work, in advance of analysis, the preparation of suitable work sheets, and the reduction of all the operations to a smooth, consistent procedure, with the different stages properly interrelated, and with provision made for suitable checks. A slovenly arrangement is fatal to both speed and accuracy. Careful preliminary arrangement will pay for itself many times over in increased accuracy and in saving of time.

The Lay-out of Work; the Work Sheet. The first step in calculation is the lay-out of the data, with reference to subsequent calculations. Before observations are recorded, or transferred from the primary tables, a general scheme should have been prepared, a framework into which the various steps in the later calculations will fit. This scheme, of course, will vary with the data and with the objects of the study, but no matter what the data or the ultimate objects such a scheme is necessary. With the lay-out prepared in advance, the original observations may often be recorded in tabular form immediately adapted to the first stages of the calculation process, thus avoiding the necessity of recopying.

The preparation of suitable work sheets is essential to the organization and carrying through of extensive calculations. The degree of care that may be given to the preparation of such sheets

---

[1] This note is based in part upon material formerly included in *A Manual of Problems and Tables in Statistics*, by F. C. Mills and D. H. Davenport. This *Manual* is now out of print.

will depend upon the magnitude of the problem and, more particularly, upon whether a series of similar problems is to be attacked. In this latter case, when there will be a fairly constant demand within the organization for the same sort of work sheets, it may be advisable to construct a special model and to have special plates made. If this is not expedient, work sheet forms prepared for the market may be found to meet all the requirements of the problem or may be adapted to the purpose in mind. Supplies of those forms which are most generally employed or which have the widest utility should be kept in stock in the statistical laboratory. A third method of securing the needed forms is the simple and convenient one of ruling standard sheets to conform to the desired model.

In organizing a work sheet attention should be given to the proper spacing of columns and lines and to the clear and unambiguous heading of all columns, so that there shall be no uncertainty as to the derivation and meaning of the data or calculations recorded therein. All columns should be numbered to permit of ready reference. It is often possible to insert work sheets directly into an adding machine, thus having the printed record on the sheet. This may greatly facilitate checking and later calculations. The size, form, and spacing of the work sheet should be adapted to this purpose, if the adding machine record is to be utilized. Forms appropriate to the computation of the primary statistical measures are exemplified in the body of the preceding text.

Methods and Accuracy of Calculation. Calculation procedure will have been decided upon in planning the lay-out of work and work sheets. The general method, in practically all cases involving the handling of a considerable mass of data, will call for the tabular arrangement of original data and of all subsequent calculations. A tabular arrangement is far better adapted to a consistent procedure than is any less formal method, and in handling masses of material such a procedure is necessary.[2] Once such a scheme has been prepared, the carrying out of the calculations is a fairly simple matter. In the original lay-out of such a scheme available methods for reducing labor should be employed. It is not here possible to

---

[2] Chapter 3 contains a brief discussion of certain principles of tabulation, relating chiefly to frequency distributions. For treatment of the general process of tabulation and discussion of effective methods of tabular presentation see Mudgett, Bruce D., *Statistical Tables and Graphs* (Boston, Houghton Mifflin, 1930) and the *Manual of Tabular Presentation*, prepared for the Bureau of the Census by B. L. Jenkinson (Washington, Government Printing Office, 1950).

discuss in detail all such labor-saving methods, but certain general aids to calculation may be listed.

1. *Aids to calculation.*

The standard tables that may be employed to facilitate numerical calculations are familiar to all students, but often not sufficiently familiar so that they are used readily and accurately. *Tables of logarithms* are, of course, indispensable. With mechanical calculators generally available, logarithms are not widely employed for the operations of multiplication and division, but they still offer the simplest method of raising to powers and extracting roots, except where prepared tables of powers and roots are available. Logarithms will generally be employed in the calculation of the geometric mean of a frequency series (see Chap. 4 for example). In fitting curves in the equations to which the x or y variable appears in logarithmic form such tables are necessary (see Chap. 10 for example). For graphic presentation the use of logarithmic paper will often render unnecessary the use of logarithms. A table of five-place logarithms is given in Appendix Table XII.

Tables of squares, square roots, and reciprocals are of equally wide utility. The most complete set of tables of this type is that bearing the name of Barlow (Barlow's *Tables of Squares, Square Roots, Cubes, Cube Roots and Reciprocals*), covering numbers up to 10,000. The uses of such tables in statistical work are many, and need no detailed description. Attention may be called to one use of the tables of reciprocals. When a problem calls for dividing a series of numbers by a constant base (as in computing percentages), the reciprocal of the constant base may be employed, and the operation of division supplanted by that of multiplication (i.e., $6 \div 3$ is equivalent to $6 \times \frac{1}{3}$). By placing this reciprocal as the multiplier on any of the mechanical calculators now on the market, the required percentages may be run off in short order. Squares, square roots, and reciprocals of the numbers 1 to 1,000 are given in Appendix Table X.

Many tables defining the attributes of particular distributions or used in applying particular tests have been referred to in the text. The publications that contain these tables also contain tables that facilitate various statistical calculations. For convenience of reference I here note selected collections of tables that have many applications in statistical work.

Fisher, Sir Ronald (R. A.) and Yates, F., *Statistical Tables for Biological, Agricultural, and Medical Research*, 3rd ed., New York, Hafner, 1948.

Glover, J. W., *Tables of Applied Mathematics*, Ann Arbor, Michigan, George Wahr, 1923.

Kelley, T. L., *The Kelley Statistical Tables*, rev., ed., Harvard University Press, 1948.

Miner, J. R., *Tables of $\sqrt{1 - r^2}$ and $1 - r^2$ for Use in Partial Correlation and in Trigonometry*, Baltimore, The Johns Hopkins Press.

Pearson, E. S. and Hartley, H. O., *Biometrika Tables for Statisticians*, Vol. I, Cambridge University Press, 1954.

(This volume and others that will follow carry forward the earlier work, in this field, of the Biometric Laboratory, under Karl Pearson. Many of the tables published in Karl Pearson's earlier compilations will be included either in their original or in modified form, in these volumes. However, the two volumes next listed contain a number of tables of current value, not yet available elsewhere.)

Pearson, Karl, *Tables for Statisticians and Biometricians*, Part I (1914, 1930), Part II (1931), Cambridge University Press.

Of the greatest value in statistical work today are the various calculating machines now on the market at prices that make them generally available. By the use of electric or hand machines, the labor of calculation that accompanies all quantitative work has been immeasurably reduced. Statistical methods are being adapted to these machines, and more will be done in this direction. For more extensive operations, punched card equipment and mechanical sorters and tabulators may be used. Added to these, the introduction of electronic computers has opened new vistas to the statistician. Thus, as we have noted in the text, the Bureau of the Census is employing such a computer (UNIVAC) in making seasonal corrections to time series. For a ten-year monthly series, all calculations involved in an adaptation of the ratio-to-moving average method are completed in about one minute.

Elementary principles of interpolation. All tables are of necessity limited to a certain restricted number of values of the functions recorded. Thus, reading from the table of logarithms appended (Table XII), we have

Argument	Function
Natural number	Logarithm
22.82	1.35832
22.83	1.35851
22.84	1.35870
22.85	1.35889
22.86	1.35908

If it is desired to secure the logarithm of a number between those given above, it is necessary to *interpolate* between the intervals of the argument. That is, one must find that value of the function corresponding to the particular value of the argument and consistent with the tabled values of function and argument. This problem arises in using many tables, and in many other statistical tasks. A full treatment of the theory of interpolation would carry us beyond the limits of the present discussion. We here confine ourselves to simple proportional interpolation.[3]

This method involves the assumption of a linear relationship between function and argument. We may use the figures set down above as an example. Required: the logarithm of 22.834

$$\text{Log } 22.840 = 1.35870$$
$$\text{Log } 22.830 = 1.35851$$
$$\text{Difference } = \overline{.00019}$$

A difference of .010 in the argument corresponds to a difference of .00019 in the function. The number given, 22.834, exceeds by .004 the smaller of the two numbers tabled in the argument, and we may write

19

1	1.9
2	3.8
3	5.7
4	7.6
5	9.5
6	11.4
7	13.3
8	15.2
9	17.1

$$\text{Log } 22.834 = 1.35851 + (\tfrac{4}{10} \times .00019)$$
$$= 1.35851 + .000076$$
$$= 1.35859 \text{ (rounded off to the fifth}$$
$$\text{decimal place)}$$

This operation is facilitated by the use of tables of proportional parts that are given in the margins of many tables of logarithms. Thus, in performing the above interpolation, we should use the marginal table headed 19 (the difference, in a five place table of logarithms, between successive logarithmic values at this point). Of the two columns below the figure 19, that at the left gives the fifth figure of the natural number, the logarithm of which is desired, while that at the right gives the amount to be added to the logarithm lying just below the desired number. In the present case the fifth figure of the natural number in question (22.834) is 4, hence we add .000076 to the logarithm 1.35851.

[3] For detailed expositions of various interpolation procedures see Scarborough, J. B., *Numerical Mathematical Analysis*, 2nd ed., Baltimore, the Johns Hopkins Press, 1950; and Whittaker, E. T. and Robinson, G., *The Calculus of Observations*, London, Blackie and Son, 1924.

The problem of interpolation frequently arises in the handling of simple statistical series, of which the following is an example:

Steam Railways in the United States
Miles of Road Owned, 1870–1950 *

1870	52,922
1880	93,267
1890	163,597
1900	193,346
1910	240,439
1920	252,845
1930	249,052
1940	233,670
1950	223,779

* Source: Interstate Commerce Commission, *Statistics of Railways in the United States.* Figures relate to June 30 up to 1920, to December 31 for 1920 and thereafter.

We desire the approximate mileage in 1877, a year that falls in a decade of rapid growth. Assuming that the increase from year to year during the decade 1870–1880 was by equal absolute increments, we interpolate here by proportional parts.

$$\text{Mileage } 1877 = 52,922 + (\tfrac{7}{10} \times 40,345)$$
$$= 52,922 + 28,241.5$$
$$= 81,163.5, \text{ or } 81,163$$

This method of interpolation makes use only of the pair of observations above and below the value to be estimated. Such interpolation by proportional parts or first differences is equivalent to the fitting of a straight line to the two observations on which interpolation is based. For nonlinear series, particularly when the difference between successive observations is considerable, it is preferable to interpolate on the basis of a polynomial of the second degree, fitted to three points, or even of curves of higher degree. This may be done, without actually fitting the curves, by the employment of interpolation formulas that make use of second, third, or higher differences. The use of such formulas is explained in Whittaker and Robinson (Ref. 190).

2. *The checking of numerical calculations.*

In the organization of statistical work full provision must be made for the checking and cross-checking of all calculations. The work of no mortal person is free from error; the inevitable mistakes in any extensive series of calculations may be corrected, or reduced to a minimum, only by the careful checking of all operations.

By recognizing in advance the necessity of such checking, methods may be adopted that will enable checks to be most effectively applied.

Two types of checks are available to the quantitative worker. Calculations may be checked, first, by a repetition of the operations. If this is done, it is advisable that the second operation be performed by a person other than the original calculator; if that is not possible, the sequence of operations may be altered when the check is made, or a slightly different method of securing the same result may be employed. Thus a column may be added in the opposite direction from that first followed, or multiplier and multiplicand may be reversed. The second type of check is that which provides a numerical test of the accuracy of given calculations. That is, certain values useful merely for checking purposes may be computed, in addition to those actually required in the given problem. The Charlier check upon the operation of computing the standard deviation (see Chap. 5) is an example of this type. A more elaborate example, in which a whole series of checks is provided for testing the accuracy of the work at various stages, is afforded by the Doolittle method of solving simultaneous equations (see Appendix C). Checks of this latter type should be employed whenever available.

Perhaps more important than all such checks is the habit, on the part of the operator, of mentally verifying the major results of his calculations as he proceeds. If two figures are to be multiplied the operator should determine, by inspection, the approximate value of the product and the number of decimal places it will contain. In any arithmetic operation the same rough check should be employed, for by this means the most serious errors, such as arise from the misplacing of decimal points, may be prevented. Many checks of the same sort are possible in connection with statistical calculations. Thus the standard deviation may be compared with the range (the latter will not, in general, be more than six times the standard deviation), and geometric, harmonic, and arithmetic measures may be checked against each other, if all have been computed in a given instance. Inconsistencies in the results usually reveal the most serious errors, and careful watch should be kept for such discrepancies.

By plotting the results of calculations errors may often be detected. If a serious mistake has been made in fitting a line to certain data, it will be immediately evident when data and line are plotted. If the ordinates of a fitted curve have not been correctly determined, breaks in the smoothness of the curve will usually reveal the errors when the curve is plotted.

In seeking to avoid mistakes no one precept is more important than this: *Keep a neat, careful, and complete record of all calculations.* This is not only necessary as an aid to subsequent checking but it is essential to accurate calculation. When a series of computations is laid out in proper form and performed in a systematic fashion, the probability of error is very much less than when the computations are performed in a slipshod, unsystematic fashion.

3. *The accuracy of measurements and calculations.*

In planning calculations the investigator must determine the degree of refinement desired in calculations and the degree of accuracy sought in results. Failure to take account of this problem usually leads to a waste of time in carrying out the calculations to an unnecessary degree, and to the securing of results that have a fictitious appearance of accuracy. The first consideration, in approaching this problem, relates to the accuracy of the original observations.

The operation of measurement involves in all cases a comparison of magnitudes. Thus a given magnitude, the height of John Smith, is compared with certain standard units of linear measurement, the foot and the inch. In setting up such a comparison absolute accuracy is never possible. We may say that John Smith is 5 feet 8 inches tall, which means that his height lies between 5 feet 7.5 inches, and 5 feet 8.5 inches. The *absolute error* (the difference between the observed and the true values) may in this case be as great as 0.5 inches. Or, employing more accurate instruments, we may report that John Smith's height is 5 feet 8.3 inches. This means that his height is between 5 feet 8.25 inches and 5 feet 8.35 inches. The absolute error in this case may be as great as 0.05 inches.

In interpreting recorded measurements, therefore, due attention must be paid to the number of *significant figures*, that is, figures that are known to be correct. There are certain standard rules that should be followed in recording and interpreting measurements with respect to the significant figures. Only the number of correct figures should be recorded, with zeros added, of course, to indicate the absolute magnitude of the measurement. Thus if a distance is recorded as being 4300 feet, it means that the true distance that was measured lies between 4250 and 4350 feet. There are only two significant figures in this example. If wheat production in the United States in 1952 is given as 1,291,000,000 bushels the amount is recorded to four significant figures. (If the production has been given as 1,290,000,000 bushels, this number to be taken as significant to four digits, a dot or a bar could be placed above the last significant figure, thus: 1,290,000,000. Without such an indication the reader would assume that there were only three significant figures.) Similarly, if a magnitude is given as 0.0472, there are but three significant figures, the zeros being added, as in the above examples, to indicate the absolute magnitude of the measure. A zero added to the right of the last recorded figure, however, if to the right of the decimal point, is significant, in indicating the degree of accuracy. Thus the value 12.50 has four significant figures, the last zero being added to show that the true value of the recorded magnitude is between 12.495 and 12.505. If it had been given as 12.5, this would be interpreted to mean that the true value lies between 12.45 and 12.55.

Determining the accuracy of computations. When observations are combined, it is important to be able to define the degree of accuracy of the resultant figures. This may be determined approximately if the accuracy of the original observations is known. The problem may be considered with respect to the four chief arithmetical operations.

Addition. In the addition of measurements, no attempt should be made to give the total an appearance of greater accuracy than the constituent items. If these items differ in accuracy, *the total is no more accurate than the least accurate measurement.* Thus, in the addition of the following four figures:

$$25.23$$
$$1610.1$$
$$17.375$$
$$2.$$
$$\overline{1654.705}$$

the total should be rounded off to 1655. It would give a quite spurious impression of accuracy to present the sum as 1654.705.

The actual limits within which the true sum falls may be readily determined by computing the maximum sum and the minimum sum that could be secured from the observations in question. Thus, substituting for each of the above values the maximum value that the quantity in question might have, we secure

$$25.235$$
$$1610.15$$
$$17.3755$$
$$\underline{2.5}$$
$$1655.2605$$

Substituting the minimum values, we have

$$25.225$$
$$1610.05$$
$$17.3745$$
$$\underline{1.5}$$
$$1654.1495$$

To have presented the original total as accurate to the third decimal place would have been clearly faulty. Nor would it have been accurate to have rounded off the individual items before adding, until their accuracy was equal to that of the least accurate item. The rounding off should be done after the total is secured, as the fullest possible use is thus made of the knowledge we have.

If the limits of error of the individual items (i.e., the differences between the maximum and minimum possible values) be added, it will be found to total 1.111, equal to the difference between the maximum and minimum possible values of the sum of the items. *The error of a sum may be determined by adding the errors of the constituent items.* (The range between the maximum and minimum possible values is obviously twice the maximum *absolute error*, as defined above.)

Subtraction. By precisely analogous reasoning it may be shown that the limits of error of the differences between measurements may also be determined by adding the limits of error of the individual items. Here, as in addition, the result is no more accurate than the less accurate of the two measurements entering into the calculation. The point of significance in this less accurate number (e.g., the column of hundreds, tens, units, tenths, or hundredths) sets the level of significance for the difference.

Multiplication. If it is desired to know precisely the accuracy of the product secured by multiplying one quantity by another, it is possible to employ the process illustrated above, namely, to determine the maximum possible value and the minimum possible value. Thus as the maximum possible value of the product of 11.30 and 2.3 we have 11.305×2.35, or 26.56675. As the minimum possible value of the product we have 11.295×2.25, or 25.41375. The product of the numbers as given, 11.30×2.3 is 25.990. Comparing this with the two limits as computed above, we have 26 as the product expressed in terms of significant figures only. A general rule to follow in multiplication is this: If n is the number of significant figures in the factor having the smaller number of significant figures, the product should be considered to have only n significant figures. In the example just cited, this is two.

Division. The rule for significant figures in a quotient is similar to that for a product. Let n be the number of significant figures in that quantity — dividend or divisor — that has the smaller number of significant figures. The quotient should be considered to have n significant figures.

In the physical sciences and in engineering fairly standard practices have been established in the matter of recording results, so that the user of published figures may know what the reliability of a given measure is. In the physical sciences it is customary to present numerical values with one more figure than those known to be significant. The next to the last figure, that is, may be taken to be correct. In recording engineering calculations, on the other hand, only the significant figures are given. The last figure may be taken to be correct, within half a unit, as in the examples given above. No standard practice has been established in statistics, but it would seem expedient in general to follow the engineering practice, recording only those figures that are known to be significant, the last one not being in error by more than half a unit. In the actual calculations, however, two additional figures may be retained, these being dropped when the final result is recorded.

When a statistical measure such as the mean, the standard deviation or the coefficient of correlation has been derived, the useful working rule suggested by T. L. Kelley (and mentioned in the text of Chap. 7) may be followed. The rule is to *keep to the place indicated by the first figure of one third the standard error.* Thus if the arithmetic mean of a given distribution is calculated to be 36.5321, with a standard error of 0.963, the recorded value of the mean should be 36.5. For one third the standard error is 0.321, the first figure being in the column of tenths. With this standard error it is useless to carry the value of the mean beyond the first decimal place. In all calculations the value of the mean would be carried to two additional places, but these would be dropped in recording.

4. *Tables and formulas to employ in the analysis of time series.*

In fitting lines of trend to time series it is necessary to secure the powers of certain numbers, and the sums of these powers. Barlow's *Tables* are available for securing the squares and the cubes of natural numbers. Table XXVII of Pearson's *Tables for Statisticians and Biometricians* (Part I) gives the second to the seventh powers of the natural numbers from 1 to 100. Table XXVIII of Pearson's *Tables* (Part I) gives the sums of the powers from one to seven of the first hundred natural numbers. This table is particularly useful in securing the sums of the powers of x when x represents time in connection with the fitting of a line of trend. Appendix Table VIII of the present volume gives the second to the sixth powers and Appendix Table IX gives the sums of the first six powers of the first fifty natural numbers.

It is possible to secure the sums of the various powers by formulas when tables are not readily available.[4] We may denote by t the total number of terms in the series 1, 2, 3, 4, 5, 6 . . ., and by $S_1, S_2, S_3, S_4, S_5,$ and S_6 the sums of the first, second, third, fourth, fifth, and sixth powers of these numbers. The required formulas are

$$S_1 = \frac{t(t+1)}{2}$$

$$S_2 = \frac{2t^3 + 3t^2 + t}{6} = S_1\left(\frac{2t+1}{3}\right)$$

$$S_3 = \frac{t^4 + 2t^3 + t^2}{4} = (S_1)^2$$

$$S_4 = \frac{6t^5 + 15t^4 + 10t^3 - t}{30} = S_2\left(\frac{3t^2 + 3t - 1}{5}\right)$$

$$S_5 = \frac{2t^6 + 6t^5 + 5t^4 - t^2}{12} = (S_1)^2\left(\frac{2t^2 + 2t - 1}{3}\right)$$

$$S_6 = \frac{6t^7 + 21t^6 + 21t^5 - 7t^3 + t}{42} = S_2\left(\frac{3t^4 + 6t^3 - 3t + 1}{7}\right)$$

---

[4] See Frank A. Ross, "Formulae for Facilitating Computations in Time Series Analysis," *Journal of the American Statistical Association*, March, 1925. The formulas in the present and immediately succeeding sections are taken from this summary.

If a line of trend is to be fitted to a time series, with n observations, n being odd, and if the origin be taken mid-way in the series, then t, of the above formulas, is equal to $\dfrac{n-1}{2}$. (Thus if there are data for eleven years, the origin will fall at the sixth year and there will be five observations on each side of the origin. In this case n will equal 11 and t will equal 5.) Professor Ross has adapted the above formulas to this case, so that the value of n may be inserted directly. The revised formulas for the sums of the powers of x (deviations from the origin being represented by x) are

$$\Sigma x = 0$$

$$\Sigma x^2 = \frac{n^3 - n}{12}$$

$$\Sigma x^3 = 0$$

$$\Sigma x^4 = (\Sigma x^2)\left(\frac{3n^2 - 7}{20}\right)$$

$$\Sigma x^5 = 0$$

$$\Sigma x^6 = (\Sigma x^2)\left(\frac{3n^4 - 18n^2 + 31}{112}\right)$$

where x is one time unit.

In working with time series it is often convenient to employ a time unit of one-half year and so to place the origin that the x-values will be 1, 3, 5, 7, 9, ... The sums of the powers of the elements of such a series are given by the formulas that follow. In these formulas t denotes the number of terms in the series 1, 3, 5, 7, . . ., while $_0S_1$, $_0S_2$, $_0S_3$, $_0S_4$, $_0S_5$, $_0S_6$ represent the sums of the first, second, third, fourth, fifth, and sixth powers of these numbers.

$$_0S_1 = t^2$$

$$_0S_2 = \frac{4t^3 - t}{3}$$

$$_0S_3 = 2t^4 - t^2 = {}_0S_1(2t^2 - 1)$$

$$_0S_4 = \frac{48t^5 - 40t^3 + 7t}{15} = {}_0S_2\left(\frac{12t^2 - 7}{5}\right)$$

$$_0S_5 = \frac{16t^6 - 20t^4 + 7t^2}{3} = {}_0S_1\left(\frac{16t^4 - 20t^2 + 7}{3}\right)$$

$$_0S_6 = \frac{192t^7 - 336t^5 + 196t^3 - 31t}{21} = {}_0S_2\left(\frac{48t^4 - 72t^2 + 31}{7}\right)$$

When the number of observations, n, in a time series is even, and the origin is taken mid-way in the time series, $t = \dfrac{n}{2}$. Representing by x deviations from the origin, the x unit being one half the time unit, we have

$$\Sigma x = 0$$

$$\Sigma x^2 = n\left(\frac{(n+1)(n-1)}{3}\right)$$

$$\Sigma x^3 = 0$$

$$\Sigma x^4 = (\Sigma x^2)\left(\frac{3n^2 - 7}{5}\right)$$

$$\Sigma x^5 = 0$$

$$\Sigma x^6 = (\Sigma x^4)\left(\frac{3n^4 - 18n^2 + 31}{7}\right)$$

In fitting certain types of curves it is necessary to compute the sums of the logarithms of x, and the sums of the squares of the logarithms of x. Appendix V of Pearl's *Introduction to Medical Biometry and Statistics* (Philadelphia, Saunders, 1930) contains a useful table that gives the sums of the first and second powers of log x for the natural numbers from 1 to 100.

A curve of the ordinary exponential type, $y = ab^x$, may be fitted by reducing the equation to logarithmic form. If the fitting be by least squares, this means the securing of a curve from which the sum of the squares of the logarithmic deviations is a minimum. As we have noted in the text, Professor James W. Glover has employed another method of fitting a curve of this type, and has prepared a table that greatly simplifies the task of determining the constants in the equation to the curve of best fit. This table is found on pages 468–481 of Glover's *Tables of Applied Mathematics*, Ann Arbor, Michigan, George Wahr, 1923.

For fitting higher degree polynomials, methods are available that lessen the labor involved, particularly if curves of different degree are to be fitted to the same data. These methods, which reduce the fitting process to a series of simple adding machine operations, are appropriate to extended research projects. Their use is not advisable, however, unless work involving a considerable number of routine operations is contemplated. It is desirable that the student master the basic least squares procedures, utilizing other methods only in case extended computing tasks are undertaken.

For accounts of systematic methods suited to extensive calculations, see Fisher (Ref. 50) and Sasuly (Ref. 134). The application of the method of orthogonal polynomials developed by Fisher is facilitated by the use of prepared tables. See Fisher and Yates (Ref. 51), Table XXIII.

:
:
:

The Method of Least Squares as Applied to Certain Statistical Problems

In the case of a single unknown quantity the method of least squares is merely a procedure for obtaining the most probable value of that quantity from a number of separate observations. The most probable value is that for which the sum of the squares of the deviations (or residuals) is a minimum. This is the arithmetic mean of the observations.

Where the measurements or observations do not relate directly to a single unknown quantity, but to *functions* of a number of unknown quantities, the problem is somewhat different. In the first case mentioned each observation is in the form of a single magnitude. In the present case each observation is in the form of an *observation equation* in which the observed values of the variables, as found in combination, are entered. The unknown quantities are the constants that define the functional relationship between the variables in question. Our problem is that of finding the most probable values of these constants, the true values being unknown.

As in the simpler case the most probable values are those for which the sum of the squares of the residuals is a minimum. In this case, however, the residuals are deviations, not from a single magnitude, as in the case of the arithmetic mean, but from the curve that describes the most probable functional relationship. The residuals are the differences between the computed and the actual values of the dependent variable.

The Normal Equations. Representing by Y an observed value of the dependent variable, by Y_c the corresponding computed value, by v the residual, or difference between Y and Y_c, and by W_1, W_2, W_3, and W_4 different independent variables (or different functions of a single independent variable), we may write

$$Y_c = f(W_1, W_2, W_3, W_4)$$
$$v = Y_c - Y$$
$$= f(W_1, W_2, W_3, W_4) - Y$$
$$\Sigma(v^2) = \Sigma[f(W_1, W_2, W_3, W_4) - Y]^2$$

If the function in a particular case is of the type

$$Y_c = aW_1 + bW_2 + cW_3 + dW_4$$

we have

$$\Sigma(v^2) = \Sigma[(aW_1 + bW_2 + cW_3 + dW_4) - Y]^2$$

Our problem is that of determining the most probable values of the constants that define the function. These constants are represented, in the present case, by a, b, c, and d. (The W's, it should be noted, refer to quantities that are known, once the observation equations are given. In the usual case the W's are different functions of a single variable, but this is not essential.) On the assumption that the errors of observation are distributed in accordance with the normal law of error, it may be demonstrated that the most probable values of a, b, c, and d, in the above equation, are those that render $\Sigma(v^2)$ a minimum; i.e.,

$$\Sigma[(aW_1 + bW_2 + cW_3 + dW_4) - Y]^2 = \text{a minimum} \qquad (\text{A})$$

The normal equations necessary for the solution may be obtained by equating to zero the partial derivatives of the above expression with respect to the unknowns, a, b, c, and d. That is, we first differentiate the above function with respect to a, holding b, c, and d constant, then with respect to b, holding a, c, and d constant, then with respect to c, holding a, b, and d constant, then with respect to d, holding a, b, and c constant. Carrying through this operation with respect to a, we have

$$\frac{\partial}{\partial a} \Sigma[(aW_1 + bW_2 + cW_3 + dW_4) - Y]^2 = 0$$

or

$$\text{I} \quad \Sigma W_1[(aW_1 + bW_2 + cW_3 + dW_4) - Y] = 0$$

Differentiating equation (A) now with respect to b, we have

$$\frac{\partial}{\partial b} \Sigma[(aW_1 + bW_2 + cW_3 + dW_4) - Y]^2 = 0$$

or

$$\text{II} \quad \Sigma W_2[(aW_1 + bW_2 + cW_3 + dW_4) - Y] = 0$$

Differentiating equation (A) with respect to c,

$$\frac{\partial}{\partial c} \Sigma[(aW_1 + bW_2 + cW_3 + dW_4) - Y]^2 = 0$$

or

$$\text{III} \quad \Sigma W_3[(aW_1 + bW_2 + cW_3 + dW_4) - Y] = 0$$

Differentiating equation (A) with respect to d,

$$\frac{\partial}{\partial d} \Sigma[(aW_1 + bW_2 + cW_3 + dW_4) - Y]^2 = 0$$

or

$$\text{IV} \quad \Sigma W_4[(aW_1 + bW_2 + cW_3 + dW_4) - Y] = 0$$

The most probable values of the quantities a, b, c, and d are secured by solving simultaneously the four normal equations thus obtained (numbered above I, II, III, IV).

Formation of the normal equations. When the observation equations are all of the first degree (i.e., of the first degree with respect to the unknown quantities, a, b, c, etc.) the normal equations may be secured by the following process:

1. Write the equation that describes the assumed relationship. The observation equations are derived by substituting in this equation the observed values of the variables, as found in combination.

2. Multiply each observation equation by the coefficient of the first unknown in that equation; the sum of the resulting equations constitutes the first normal equation.

3. Multiply each observation equation by the coefficient of the second unknown in that equation; the sum of the resulting equations constitutes the second normal equation.

Continue this process until normal equations equal in number to the unknown quantities are obtained.

The actual process of forming the normal equations in curve fitting may be simplified, and the writing out of the separate observation equations avoided, as was demonstrated in earlier sections. The following may be laid down as general rules for the formation of the desired normal equations:

1. Write the equation of the curve to be fitted. For the purpose of this explanation we may employ the general form

$$Y = aW_1 + bW_2 + cW_3 + dW_4 + \cdots \tag{1}$$

where Y represents the dependent variable, a, b, c, d,...represent the constants in the equation (the unknown quantities in the present instance) and W_1, W_2, W_3, W_4,...represent the coefficients of these unknowns. Call this equation (1).

2. Multiply each term in equation (1) by the coefficient of the first unknown in (1) (i.e., by W_1) and place the summation sign, Σ, before each variable. This is the first normal equation (I).

3. Multiply each term in equation (1) by the coefficient of the second unknown (i.e., by W_2) and place the summation sign before each variable. This is the second normal equation (II).

4. Multiply each term in equation (1) by the coefficient of the third unknown (i.e., by W_3) and place the summation sign before each variable. This is the third normal equation (III).

5. Multiply each term in equation (1) by the coefficient of the fourth unknown (i.e., by W_4) and place the summation sign before each variable. This is the fourth normal equation (IV).

The process may be continued until normal equations equal in number to the unknown quantities are obtained.[1]

A standard set of normal equations. As a set of generalized normal equations secured by the above process and applying to any equation that can be put in the form

$$Y = aW_1 + bW_2 + cW_3 + dW_4 + \cdots$$

we have

I $\Sigma(W_1 Y)$
$$= a\Sigma(W_1^2) + b\Sigma(W_1 W_2) + c\Sigma(W_1 W_3) + d\Sigma(W_1 W_4) + \cdots$$

II $\Sigma(W_2 Y)$
$$= a\Sigma(W_1 W_2) + b\Sigma(W_2^2) + c\Sigma(W_2 W_3) + d\Sigma(W_2 W_4) + \cdots$$

III $\Sigma(W_3 Y)$
$$= a\Sigma(W_1 W_3) + b\Sigma(W_2 W_3) + c\Sigma(W_3^2) + d\Sigma(W_3 W_4) + \cdots$$

IV $\Sigma(W_4 Y)$
$$= a\Sigma(W_1 W_4) + b\Sigma(W_2 W_4) + c\Sigma(W_3 W_4) + d\Sigma(W_4^2) + \cdots$$

By substituting for W_1, W_2, W_3, W_4, etc., the particular functions

---

[1] These rules represent an adaptation of a similar series formulated by Raymond Pearl in *Medical Biometry and Statistics*, 341.

employed in a given case, these equations may be readily adapted to any type of curve in the fitting of which the method of least squares is applicable. Thus in fitting a curve represented by the equation

$$Y = a + bX + cX^2 + dX^3$$

substitutions in the standard normal equations given above are based upon the following relations:

$$W_1 = 1$$
$$W_2 = X$$
$$W_3 = X^2$$
$$W_4 = X^3$$

The changes to be made in the normal equations are obvious. $\Sigma(W_1 Y)$ becomes $\Sigma(Y)$; $\Sigma(W_1^2)$ is equivalent to $\Sigma(1^2)$, which is equal to N, the total number of observations. The first normal equation becomes

$$\Sigma(Y) = Na + b\Sigma(X) + c\Sigma(X^2) + d\Sigma(X^3)$$

The other normal equations are modified correspondingly.

In the example just given, three of the coefficients are different functions of a single independent variable, X. It is not, of course, essential to the method of least squares that this be so. The coefficients, W_1, W_2, W_3, etc., may represent a number of independent variables, as in the case of multiple correlation.

The limitations to the method of least squares must be borne in mind in making use of it. In its direct application this method is limited to cases in which the equation to the curve to be fitted is linear in the constants, i.e., the observation equations must all be linear as regards the unknown values, a, b, c, etc. (This does not mean, of course, that the equation to the fitted curve must be linear.) As an example of this limitation, we may cite a curve having as equation $y = ab^{c^x}$, which cannot be fitted directly by the method of least squares. If the observation equations are nonlinear they may be reduced to the linear form in many instances by the use of logarithms, and the method of least squares then employed.

Derivation of the Formula for the Standard Error of Estimate. It has been pointed out in the body of the text that the standard error of estimate may be derived as a by-product of the method of least squares. A more complete demonstration of this process may be given at this point.

When the partial derivative with respect to a, of the expression

$$\Sigma[(aW_1 + bW_2 + cW_3 + dW_4) - Y]^2$$

is equated to zero, we have

$$\Sigma W_1[(aW_1 + bW_2 + cW_3 + dW_4) - Y] = 0$$

Since

$$aW_1 + bW_2 + cW_3 + dW_4 - Y = v$$

we have as a necessary condition of fitting

$$\Sigma(vW_1) = 0$$

When the partial derivative of the same expression with respect to b is equated to zero, we have

$$\Sigma W_2[(aW_1 + bW_2 + cW_3 + dW_4) - Y] = 0$$

or, making the same substitution as in the preceding case,

$$\Sigma(vW_2) = 0$$

Repeating the operation with respect to c and d, we may show that

$$\Sigma(vW_3) = 0$$

and

$$\Sigma(vW_4) = 0$$

In summary: When the method of least squares is employed in determining the most probable values of certain unknown quantities, having as known coefficients the quantities W_1, W_2, W_3, W_4, the following relations hold as a necessary condition of the least squares method:

$$\Sigma(vW_1) = 0$$
$$\Sigma(vW_2) = 0$$
$$\Sigma(vW_3) = 0$$
$$\Sigma(vW_4) = 0$$

A knowledge of these relationships gives us a method of securing readily the value $\Sigma(v^2)$ and the standard error of estimate. Assume that, by the method of least squares, we have determined the constants in an equation of the type

$$Y_c = aW_1 + bW_2 + cW_3 + dW_4$$

For each residual we have the relation

$$v = aW_1 + bW_2 + cW_3 + dW_4 - Y \qquad (1)$$

Multiplying throughout by v, and summing, we have

$$\Sigma(v^2) = a\Sigma(vW_1) + b\Sigma(vW_2) + c\Sigma(vW_3) + d\Sigma(vW_4) - \Sigma(Yv). \quad (2)$$

But

$$\Sigma(vW_1) = 0$$
$$\Sigma(vW_2) = 0$$
$$\Sigma(vW_3) = 0$$
$$\Sigma(vW_4) = 0$$

therefore,

$$\Sigma(v^2) = -\Sigma(Yv) \quad (3)$$

Multiplying each equation (1) throughout by Y, and adding, we have

$$\Sigma(Yv) = a\Sigma(W_1Y) + b\Sigma(W_2Y) + c\Sigma(W_3Y) + d\Sigma(W_4Y)$$
$$- \Sigma(Y^2) \quad (4)$$

Substituting in (3) the equivalent of $\Sigma(Yv)$, we have

$$\Sigma(v^2) = \Sigma(Y^2) - a\Sigma(W_1Y) - b\Sigma(W_2Y) - c\Sigma(W_3Y)$$
$$- d\Sigma(W_4Y) \quad (5)$$

This gives us a method of obtaining the value $\Sigma(v^2)$ without computing the separate residuals, a method that is applicable whenever the equation of the curve to be fitted is of the form, or may be reduced by the use of logarithms, reciprocals, or other manipulation to the form,

$$Y = aW_1 + bW_2 + cW_3 + dW_4$$

In applying this to a particular case it is necessary only to replace W_1, W_2, W_3, W_4, etc., by the functions that actually appear as coefficients of the unknown quantities in the original equation. Thus in fitting a curve the equation to which is

$$Y = a + bX + cX^2 + dX^3$$

we find, as noted above, that

$$W_1 = 1$$
$$W_2 = X$$
$$W_3 = X^2$$
$$W_4 = X^3$$

Making these substitutions in equation (5) above, we have

$$\Sigma(v^2) = \Sigma(Y^2) - a\Sigma(Y) - b\Sigma(XY) - c\Sigma(X^2Y) - d\Sigma(X^3Y) \quad (6)$$

The standard error, $s_{y \cdot x}$, is derived from the equation

$$s_{y \cdot x}^2 = \frac{\Sigma(d^2)^*}{N}$$

where d is used to represent a deviation from a fitted curve. The deviation d, then, is but another term for the residual v. Accordingly, as a general expression for the standard error of Y, with W_1, W_2, W_3, and W_4 as independent variables, we have

$$s_{y \cdot x}^2 = \frac{\Sigma Y^2 - a\Sigma(W_1 Y) - b\Sigma(W_2 Y) - c\Sigma(W_3 Y) - d\Sigma(W_4 Y)}{N} \tag{7}$$

As in the previous case, this may be applied to a particular problem by replacing W_1, W_2, W_3, W_4, etc., by the actual coefficients of the unknown quantities.

Checks on the Formation of the Normal Equations. There are so many possibilities of arithmetical error in the formation and solution of a set of normal equations that checks should be employed wherever possible. A convenient check on the calculations leading to the normal equations is afforded by the introduction in each observation equation of an additional term, s, equal to the sum of all the known quantities in that equation. Thus, in the following system of observation equations, formed in fitting a line to the points 1, 3; 2, 4; 3, 6; 4, 5; 5, 10; 6, 9; 7, 10; 8, 12; 9, 11, the values of s are as indicated:

$$
\begin{array}{rcl}
 & & s \\
3 &= a + 1b & 5 \\
4 &= a + 2b & 7 \\
6 &= a + 3b & 10 \\
5 &= a + 4b & 10 \\
10 &= a + 5b & 16 \\
9 &= a + 6b & 16 \\
10 &= a + 7b & 18 \\
12 &= a + 8b & 21 \\
11 &= a + 9b & 21 \\
\end{array}
$$

(The coefficient of a in each case is 1, and this is added to the other known quantities.)

---

* Since our object is to measure the actual "scatter" about the fitted curve, the formula $\dfrac{\Sigma(d^2)}{N}$ is used, rather than the formula $\dfrac{\Sigma(d^2)}{N - N_c}$ (where N represents the number of observations and N_c the number of constants in the equation to the fitted curve).

In fitting a curve described by the type equation

$$Y = aW_1 + bW_2 + cW_3 + dW_4$$

the following relations prevail between s and the other quantities computed. For each observation equation,

$$Y + W_1 + W_2 + W_3 + W_4 = s$$

For the normal equations,

$$\Sigma(W_1Y) + \Sigma(W_1^2) + \Sigma(W_1W_2) + \Sigma(W_1W_3) + \Sigma(W_1W_4) = \Sigma(W_1s)$$
$$\Sigma(W_2Y) + \Sigma(W_1W_2) + \Sigma(W_2^2) + \Sigma(W_2W_3) + \Sigma(W_2W_4) = \Sigma(W_2s)$$
$$\Sigma(W_3Y) + \Sigma(W_1W_3) + \Sigma(W_2W_3) + \Sigma(W_3^2) + \Sigma(W_3W_4) = \Sigma(W_3s)$$
$$\Sigma(W_4Y) + \Sigma(W_1W_4) + \Sigma(W_2W_4) + \Sigma(W_3W_4) + \Sigma(W_4^2) = \Sigma(W_4s)$$

This form is capable of application to any specific problem. In each case the s-equations are formed in precisely the same way as the corresponding normal equations.

In applying these checks several additional columns are needed in the working tables, but the extra trouble is more than compensated by the opportunity to check the work at each stage. The application is illustrated in the following working table, showing the calculations involved in fitting a second degree curve of the form

$$Y = a + bX + cX^2$$

to the nine points 1, 2; 2, 6; 3, 7; 4, 8; 5, 10; 6, 11; 7, 11; 8, 10; 9, 9.

TABLE A

Illustrating the Use of Checks on the Formation of Normal Equations

Y	X	X^2	XY	X^2Y	s	Xs	X^2s
2	1	1	2	2	5	5	5
6	2	4	12	24	13	26	52
7	3	9	21	63	20	60	180
8	4	16	32	128	29	116	464
10	5	25	50	250	41	205	1,025
11	6	36	66	396	54	324	1,944
11	7	49	77	539	68	476	3,332
10	8	64	80	640	83	664	5,312
9	9	81	81	729	100	900	8,100
74	45	285	421	2,771	413	2,776	20,414

(Columns for X^3 and X^4 are omitted, as the values $\Sigma(X^3)$ and $\Sigma(X^4)$ may be derived from prepared tables.)

Each of the values in the column headed s is secured from the corresponding observation equation. Thus, from the first observation equation

$$2 = 1a + 1b + 1c$$

we have 5 as the value of s (2, plus the coefficients of the three constants). These values of s are secured readily from the table by adding the figures in the columns headed Y, X, and X^2, plus 1, the coefficient of the constant term a.

Adding the various columns, the arithmetic work is verified by the following checks:

$$\Sigma(Y) + N + \Sigma(X) + \Sigma(X^2) = \Sigma(s)$$
$$74 + 9 + 45 + 285 = 413$$
$$\Sigma(XY) + \Sigma(X) + \Sigma(X^2) + \Sigma(X^3) = \Sigma(Xs)$$
$$421 + 45 + 285 + 2{,}025 = 2{,}776$$
$$\Sigma(X^2Y) + \Sigma(X^2) + \Sigma(X^3) + \Sigma(X^4) = \Sigma(X^2s)$$
$$2{,}771 + 285 + 2{,}025 + 15{,}333 = 20{,}414$$

Further uses of a check of this kind are explained below, in discussing the solution of the normal equations.

Other tests. The possibility of checking the calculations in other ways has been suggested in the preceding sections. Thus, where the coefficients of the constants in the equation to the fitted curve are represented by W_1, W_2, W_3, W_4, we know that

$$\Sigma(vW_1) = 0$$
$$\Sigma(vW_2) = 0$$
$$\Sigma(vW_3) = 0$$
$$\Sigma(vW_4) = 0$$

If a curve of the type

$$Y = a + bX + cX^2 + dX^3$$

has been fitted, this means that

$$\Sigma(v) = 0$$
$$\Sigma(vX) = 0$$
$$\Sigma(vX^2) = 0$$
$$\Sigma(vX^3) = 0$$

The accuracy of the work may be tested by checking these relations.

Finally, we may test the accuracy of the work by computing the standard error of estimate in two different ways. We may compute the separate residuals by taking the difference between computed and actual values of the dependent variable, and from these values determine S. This may be compared with the results secured by applying the general formula for the standard error, as derived above. In the fitting of the second degree curve, the data of which were used to illustrate the method of checking the normal equations, the equation derived was

$$Y = -0.92860 + 3.52316X - 0.267316X^2$$

From the residuals separately computed, we have

$$s_{y \cdot x} = .4941$$

From the formula

$$s_{y \cdot x}^2 = \frac{\Sigma(Y^2) - a\Sigma(Y) - b\Sigma(XY) - c\Sigma(X^2Y)}{N}$$

we have

$$s_{y \cdot x} = 0.4947$$

This constitutes a final check upon the accuracy of the calculations.

Simplification of Normal Equations in a Multiple Correlation Problem.[2] In the discussion of multiple correlation procedure in Chapter 18 the normal equations as first derived in the form

I $\quad \Sigma(X_1) = Na + b_{12.34}\Sigma(X_2) + b_{13.24}\Sigma(X_3) + b_{14.23}\Sigma(X_4)$

II $\quad \Sigma(X_1X_2) = a\Sigma(X_2) + b_{12.34}\Sigma(X_2^2) + b_{13.24}\Sigma(X_2X_3)$
$\qquad\qquad + b_{14.23}\Sigma(X_2X_4)$

III $\quad \Sigma(X_1X_3) = a\Sigma(X_3) + b_{12.34}\Sigma(X_2X_3) + b_{13.24}\Sigma(X_3^2)$
$\qquad\qquad + b_{14.23}\Sigma(X_3X_4)$

IV $\quad \Sigma(X_1X_4) = a\Sigma(X_4) + b_{12.34}\Sigma(X_2X_4) + b_{13.24}\Sigma(X_3X_4)$
$\qquad\qquad + b_{14.23}\Sigma(X_4^2)$

were reduced in number and modified to facilitate their solution. Details of the method are here given.

Letting A_1, A_2, A_3, and A_4 represent the arithmetic means of the several variables, and x_1, x_2, x_3, and x_4 represent deviations from the means, we may replace the variables X_1, X_2, X_3, and X_4

[2] Adapted from H. R. Tolley and M. J. B. Ezekiel, "A Method of Handling Multiple Correlation Problems," *Journal of the American Statistical Association*, Vol. 18, 993–1003.

by their equivalents $x_1 + A_1$, $x_2 + A_2$, $x_3 + A_3$, $x_4 + A_4$. The normal equations now become:

I $\quad \Sigma(x_1 + A_1) = Na + \Sigma(x_2 + A_2) \cdot b_{12.34} + \Sigma(x_3 + A_3) \cdot b_{13.24}$
$\qquad + \Sigma(x_4 + A_4) \cdot b_{14.23}$

II $\quad \Sigma[(x_1 + A_1)(x_2 + A_2)] = \Sigma[(x_2 + A_2) \cdot a + \Sigma(x_2 + A_2)^2] \cdot b_{12.34}$
$\qquad + \Sigma[(x_2 + A_2)(x_3 + A_3)] \cdot b_{13.24}$
$\qquad + \Sigma(x_2 + A_2)(x_4 + A_4) \cdot b_{14.23}$

III $\quad \Sigma[(x_1 + A_1)(x_3 + A_3)] = \Sigma(x_3 + A_3) \cdot a$
$\qquad + \Sigma[(x_3 + A_3)(x_2 + A_2)] \cdot b_{12.34} + \Sigma(x_3 + A_3)^2 \cdot b_{13.24}$
$\qquad + \Sigma[(x_3 + A_3)(x_4 + A_4)] \cdot b_{14.23}$

IV $\quad \Sigma[(x_1 + A_1)(x_4 + A_4)] = \Sigma(x_4 + A_4) \cdot a$
$\qquad + \Sigma[(x_4 + A_4)(x_2 + A_2)] \cdot b_{12.34}$
$\qquad + \Sigma[(x_4 + A_4)(x_3 + A_3)] \cdot b_{13.24} + \Sigma(x_4 + A_4)^2 \cdot b_{14.23}$

Since $\Sigma(x_1 + A_1) = \Sigma x_1 + NA_1$, and since $\Sigma x_1 = 0$, $\Sigma(x_1 + A_1)$ and all similar expressions may be replaced by NA_1, NA_2, etc.

If we expand $\Sigma(x_2 + A_2)^2$ to $\Sigma(x_2^2 + 2A_2x_2 + A_2^2)$, the middle term drops out, because $\Sigma x_2 = 0$, and the expression may be written $\Sigma x_2^2 + NA_2^2$. The sums of all similar squares may be put in similar form.

The product sum $\Sigma(x_1 + A_1)(x_2 + A_2) = \Sigma(x_1x_2 + A_1x_2 + A_2x_1 + A_1A_2) = \Sigma x_1x_2 + NA_1A_2$ since $\Sigma x_1 = 0$ and $\Sigma x_2 = 0$. Product sums of the same type may be similarly modified. The normal equations now take the form:

I $\quad NA_1 = Na + NA_2b_{12.34} + NA_3b_{13.24} + NA_4b_{14.23}$

II $\quad \Sigma(x_1x_2) + NA_1A_2 = NA_2a + [\Sigma(x_2)^2 + NA_2^2]b_{12.34}$
$\qquad + [\Sigma(x_2x_3) + NA_2A_3]b_{13.24} + [\Sigma(x_2x_4) + NA_2A_4]b_{14.23}$

III $\quad \Sigma(x_1x_3) + NA_1A_3 = NA_3a + [\Sigma(x_2x_3) + NA_2A_3]b_{12.34}$
$\qquad + [\Sigma(x_3)^2 + NA_3^2]b_{13.24} + [\Sigma(x_3x_4) + NA_3A_4]b_{14.23}$

IV $\quad \Sigma(x_1x_4) + NA_1A_4 = NA_4a + [\Sigma(x_2x_4) + NA_2A_4]b_{12.34}$
$\qquad + [\Sigma(x_3x_4) + NA_3A_4]b_{13.24} + [\Sigma(x_4)^2 + NA_4^2]b_{14.23}$

If we now divide through by N, and substitute p_{12} for $\dfrac{\Sigma x_1x_2}{N}$, s_2^2 for $\dfrac{\Sigma(x_2^2)}{N}$, and similar symbols for other mean products and mean squares, the normal equations become

I $\quad A_1 = a + A_2b_{12.34} + A_3b_{13.24} + A_4b_{14.23}$

II $\quad p_{12} + A_1A_2 = A_2a + (s_2^2 + A_2^2)b_{12.34} + (p_{23} + A_2A_3)b_{13.24}$
$\qquad + (p_{24} + A_2A_4)b_{14.23}$

III $\quad p_{13} + A_1A_3 = A_3a + (p_{23} + A_2A_3)b_{12.34} + (s_3^2 + A_3^2)b_{13.24}$
$\qquad + (p_{34} + A_3A_4)b_{14.23}$

IV $\quad p_{14} + A_1A_4 = A_4a + (p_{24} + A_2A_4)b_{12.34} + (p_{34} + A_3A_4)b_{13.24}$
$\qquad + (s_4^2 + A_4^2)b_{14.23}$

These four simultaneous equations may now be reduced to three. We multiply equation I, throughout, by A_2, and subtract the result from equation II; we then multiply equation I by A_3, and subtract the result from equation III; we then multiply equation I by A_4, and subtract the result from equation IV. All the terms containing A's are thus eliminated and we obtain the three normal equations

$$p_{12} = s_2^2 b_{12.34} + p_{23}b_{13.24} + p_{24}b_{14.23}$$
$$p_{13} = p_{23}b_{12.34} + s_3^2 b_{13.24} + p_{34}b_{14.23}$$
$$p_{14} = p_{24}b_{12.34} + p_{34}b_{13.24} + s_4^2 b_{14.23}$$

Inserting the observed values of the p's and the s's, these are solved for the coefficients b. The value a may then be obtained by inserting the values of the A's and the b's in the equation

$$A_1 = a + A_2b_{12.34} + A_3b_{13.24} + A_4b_{14.23}$$

Solution of the Normal Equations: The Doolittle Method. The task of solving the normal equations is not a difficult one in most of the cases presented to the economic statistician. If there are only two or three unknowns the corresponding number of normal equations may be solved by simple algebraic methods. Even with three equations, however, it is advisable to employ a systematic procedure, and with more than three equations this is imperative. Several systematic methods of solving simultaneous equations have been developed. The Doolittle method, which is convenient for general usage, is demonstrated below.

The coefficients of the unknowns in the normal equations are always symmetrical with respect to the principal diagonal. Thus in securing the most probable values of the constants in the equation

$$Y = aW_1 + bW_2 + cW_3 + dW_4$$

we have the four normal equations

$$a\Sigma(W_1^2) + b\Sigma(W_1W_2) + c\Sigma(W_1W_3) + d\Sigma(W_1W_4) - \Sigma(W_1Y) = 0$$
$$a\Sigma(W_1W_2) + b\Sigma(W_2^2) + c\Sigma(W_2W_3) + d\Sigma(W_2W_4) - \Sigma(W_2Y) = 0$$
$$a\Sigma(W_1W_3) + b\Sigma(W_2W_3) + c\Sigma(W_3^2) + d\Sigma(W_3W_4) - \Sigma(W_3Y) = 0$$
$$a\Sigma(W_1W_4) + b\Sigma(W_2W_4) + c\Sigma(W_3W_4) + d\Sigma(W_4^2) - \Sigma(W_4Y) = 0$$

The symmetrical arrangement about the diagonal, when Y-terms are neglected, is obvious. Starting with any term on the principal diagonal, we have the same coefficients directly above as to the left. Thus, above the diagonal term in which the coefficient $\Sigma(W_3^2)$ appears, we have the coefficients $\Sigma(W_2W_3)$ and $\Sigma(W_1W_3)$. The same coefficients are found to the left of the given diagonal term, and on the same line. For the purposes of solution, therefore, the terms to the left of each diagonal entry may be omitted, and we may put the remaining terms of the normal equations in the form

$$a\Sigma(W_1^2) + b\Sigma(W_1W_2) + c\Sigma(W_1W_3) + d\Sigma(W_1W_4) - \Sigma(W_1Y)$$
$$+ b\Sigma(W_2^2) + c\Sigma(W_2W_3) + d\Sigma(W_2W_4) - \Sigma(W_2Y)$$
$$+ c\Sigma(W_3^2) + d\Sigma(W_3W_4) - \Sigma(W_3Y)$$
$$+ d\Sigma(W_4^2) - \Sigma(W_4Y)$$

The Doolittle method may be illustrated with reference to the following normal equations:

$$8.3564a + 2.790b + 2.932c + 47.967 = 0$$
$$2.790a + 6.6645b + 2.063c + 62.039 = 0$$
$$2.932a + 2.063b + 7.7893c + 47.519 = 0$$

Putting these, for the purposes of the solution, in the abbreviated form given above, we have

$$8.3564a + 2.790b \quad + 2.932c \quad + 47.967$$
$$+ 6.6645b + 2.063c \quad + 62.039$$
$$+ 7.7893c + 47.519$$

We wish to solve these for the constants a, b, and c. All the work of computation, with the necessary checks, is shown in the table on page 741.

Explanation. The coefficients of the unknown quantities, a, b, and c, are listed in the designated columns. The known term in each normal equation is listed in column (5). (The sign of this known term, it should be noted, is that which it would have when the entire expression, of which it is one term, is equated to zero.) Column s is employed as a check. The value in column s, in each of the lines I, II, and III, is the algebraic sum of the known values in the given normal equation. In securing this sum the coefficients to the left of the diagonal, which have been omitted from the table as it stands, must be included.

TABLE B

Solution of Normal Equations by the Doolittle Method

Line	(1) Reciprocals	(2) a	(3) b	(4) c	(5)	(6) s
I		8.3564	2.790	2.932	47.967	62.0454
II		6.6645	2.063	62.039	73.5565
III			7.7893	47.519	60.3033
1		8.35640	2.790	2.932	47.967	62.0454
2	− 0.11966876	− 1.00000	− 0.333876	− 0.350869	− 5.740151	− 7.424896 check
3			6.6645	2.063	62.039	73.5565
4			− 0.931514	− 0.978924	− 16.015030	− 20.715470
5			5.732986	1.084076	46.023970	52.841030 check
6	− 0.17442917		− 1.000000	− 0.189094	− 8.027923	− 9.217017 check
7				7.7893	47.519	60.3033
8				− 1.028748	− 16.830133	− 21.769807
9				0.204992	− 8.702857	− 9.991922
10				6.555560	21.986010	28.541571 check
11	− 0.15254227			− 1.000000	− 3.353796	− 4.353796 check

Back Solution

c	b	a
− 3.353796	− 8.027923	− 5.740151
− 3.353796	+ 0.634183	+ 2.468592
	− 7.393740	+ 1.176743
		− 2.094816

$$a = -2.094816$$
$$b = -7.393740$$
$$c = -3.353796$$

Check:
Equation I:

$$8.3564a + 2.790b + 2.932c = -47.967$$

Substituting the given values,

$$8.3564(-2.094816) + 2.790(-7.393740)$$
$$+ 2.932(-3.353796) = -47.966985$$

The following is a summary of the procedure in solving the normal equations:

1. In line (1) write normal equation I.
2. In line (2), column (1), write the reciprocal of the value in line (1), column (2), *with sign changed*. (This is the reciprocal of the coefficient of *a*.) Multiply each item in line (1) by this reciprocal, entering the products in

the corresponding columns in line (2). [The algebraic sum of the items in columns (2), (3), (4), and (5) of line (2) should equal the value in column (6).] This operation has eliminated the unknown a, by expressing it in terms of b and c. [The -1 in line (2), column (2), has been included only to facilitate the checking process. The same is true in lines (6) and (11).] A heavy line may be drawn across the table below line (2).

3. Write normal equation II in line (3).

4. Multiply by the coefficient of b in line (2) (i.e., -0.333876) the items in columns (3), (4), (5), and (6) in line (1). Enter the products in the corresponding columns of line (4).

5. Add lines (3) and (4), entering the sums in line (5). [The algebraic sum of the items in columns (3), (4), and (5) of line (5) should equal the value in column (6).]

6. In column (1), line (6), enter the reciprocal of the value in column (3), line (5), *reversing the sign*. Multiply each term in line (5) by this reciprocal, entering the products in line (6). [The sum of the items in columns (3), (4), and (5) of line (6) should equal the value in column (6).] This operation has eliminated the unknown b, by expressing it in terms of c. A heavy line may be drawn across the table below line (6).

7. Write normal equation III in line (7).

8. Multiply by the coefficient of c in line (2) (i.e., -0.350869) the items in columns (4), (5), and (6) of line (1). Enter the products in the corresponding columns of line (8).

9. Multiply by the coefficient of c in line (6) (i.e., -0.189094) the items in columns (4), (5), and (6) of line (5). Enter the products in the corresponding columns of line (9).

10. Add lines (7), (8), and (9), entering the sums in line (10). [The algebraic sum of the items in columns (4) and (5) of line (10) should equal the value in column (6).]

11. In column (1), line (11), enter the reciprocal of the value in column (4) of line (10), *reversing the sign*. Multiply each term in line (10) by this reciprocal, entering the products in line (11). [The algebraic sum of the items in columns (4) and (5) of line (11) should equal the value in column (6).] This operation gives the value of c, which is found in column (5) of line (11). A heavy line may be drawn across the table below line (11).

Were there additional unknowns, as d and e, this last operation would have given c as a function of d and e and it would be necessary to carry the process still further, repeating the steps taken above. The next operation would be to bring down the fourth normal equation, entering it in line (12). Then the coefficients of d in lines (2), (6), and (11) would be used to multiply the necessary items in lines (1), (5), and (10), the products being entered in lines (13), (14), and (15). The sum of the items in lines (12), (13), (14), and (15) would be entered in line (16) and checked by the item in the *s* column. Multiplying through by the reciprocal of the coefficient of *d* in line (16), with sign reversed, the value of *d* would be obtained in terms of *e*. The value of *e* would be derived in a similar fashion.

The checks on these various operations have been indicated in the table. The testing of the results at each step reduces the possibility of error to a minimum.

The back solution presents no difficulties. We have, from line (11),

$$c = -3.353796$$

from line (6)

$$b = -0.189094c - 8.027923$$

from line (2)

$$a = -0.333876b - 0.350869c - 5.740151$$

[The items in column (6) are inserted merely as checks. The items − 1.000000 which appear in lines (2), (6), and (11) are inserted to assist in the checking.]

The computations involved in the back solution appear in the table.

A final check is afforded by inserting the values secured by this process in one of the normal equations. This check, as carried out for equation I, is shown below the table.

REFERENCES

Brown, J. A. C., Houthakker, H. S., and Prais, S. J., "Electronic Computation in Economic Statistics," *Journal of American Statistical Association*, Sept., 1953.

Hartree, D. R., *Numerical Analysis*, Oxford University Press, 1952.

Scarborough, J. B., *Numerical Mathematical Analysis*, 2nd ed., Baltimore, The Johns Hopkins Press, 1950.

Tolley, H. R. and Ezekiel, M. J. B., "A Method of Handling Multiple Correlation Problems," *Journal of the American Statistical Association*. Dec., 1923.

Whittaker, E. T. and Robinson, G., *The Calculus of Observations*, London, Blackie and Son, 1924.

Derivation of Formulas for Mean and Standard Deviation of the Binomial Distribution [1]

For convenience we put the binomial in the form $(q + p)^n$, where q = probability of a failure, p = probability of a success, and $q + p = 1$. Expanding the binomial, we have

$$(q + p)^n = q^n + nq^{n-1}p^1 + \frac{n(n-1)}{1 \cdot 2} q^{n-2}p^2$$
$$+ \frac{n(n-1)(n-2)}{1 \cdot 2 \cdot 3} q^{n-3}p^3 + \cdots + p^n$$

The terms of this expansion indicate, in order, the probable frequencies of no successes, 1 success, 2 successes, 3 successes, and so on, to n successes. A frequency table of the familiar type may be constructed from these materials.

The items in column (2) of Table C constitute the terms of the binomial expansion. Their sum is thus equal to $(q + p)^n$, which is, by definition, equal to 1. The items in column (3), added in order, give

$$nq^{(n-1)}p^1 + n(n-1)q^{n-2}p^2 + \frac{n(n-1)(n-2)}{1 \cdot 2} q^{n-3}p^3$$
$$+ \frac{n(n-1)(n-2)(n-3)}{1 \cdot 2 \cdot 3} q^{n-4}p^4 + \cdots + np^n$$

---

[1] These derivations are adapted from the proof given by D. C. Jones in *A First Course in Statistics*, London, Bell & Sons, 1921, 143–145.

TABLE C

Derivation of Mean and Standard Deviation of the Binomial Distribution

(1) Number of successes m	(2) Frequency f	(3) fm	(4) fm^2
0	q^n	0	0
1	$nq^{n-1}p^1$	$nq^{n-1}p^1$	$nq^{n-1}p^1$
2	$\dfrac{n(n-1)}{1\cdot 2}\,q^{n-2}p^2$	$n(n-1)q^{n-2}p^2$	$2n(n-1)q^{n-2}p^2$
3	$\dfrac{n(n-1)(n-2)}{1\cdot 2\cdot 3}\,q^{n-3}p^3$	$\dfrac{n(n-1)(n-2)}{1\cdot 2}\,q^{n-3}p^3$	$\dfrac{3n(n-1)(n-2)}{1\cdot 2}\,q^{n-3}p^3$
4	$\dfrac{n(n-1)(n-2)(n-3)}{1\cdot 2\cdot 3\cdot 4}\,q^{n-4}p^4$	$\dfrac{n(n-1)(n-2)(n-3)}{1\cdot 2\cdot 3}\,q^{n-4}p^4$	$\dfrac{4n(n-1)(n-2)(n-3)}{1\cdot 2\cdot 3}\,q^{n-4}p^4$
⋮	⋮	⋮	⋮
n	p^n	np^n	n^2p^n
Total	1	np	$np[1+p(n-1)]$

Since the factors n and p appear in each of these terms, this reduces to

$$np\bigg[q^{n-1} + (n-1)(q^{n-2}p^1) + \frac{(n-1)(n-2)}{1\cdot 2}q^{n-3}p^2$$
$$+ \frac{(n-1)(n-2)(n-3)}{1\cdot 2\cdot 3}q^{n-4}p^3 + \cdots p^{n-1}\bigg]$$

But the terms within brackets, following np, represent the expansion of the binomial $(q+p)^{n-1}$. Since $q+p = 1$, the sum of these terms is 1. Accordingly the sum of the items in column (3) reduces to

$$np(q+p)^{n-1} = np$$

For the mean of this distribution we have

$$M = \frac{\Sigma(fm)}{\Sigma(f)} = \frac{np}{1} = np$$

Adding the items in column (4) in order, we have

$$nq^{n-1}p^1 + 2n(n-1)q^{n-2}p^2 + \frac{3n(n-1)(n-2)}{1\cdot 2}q^{n-3}p^3$$
$$+ \frac{4n(n-1)(n-2)(n-3)}{1\cdot 2\cdot 3}q^{n-4}p^4 + \cdots + n^2p^n$$
$$= np\bigg[q^{n-1} + 2(n-1)q^{n-2}p^1 + \frac{3(n-1)(n-2)}{1\cdot 2}q^{n-3}p^2$$
$$+ \frac{4(n-1)(n-2)(n-3)}{1\cdot 2\cdot 3}q^{n-4}p^3 + \cdots + np^{n-1}\bigg]$$

The terms within brackets may be broken into two groups, giving

$$np\bigg[\bigg\{q^{n-1} + (n-1)q^{n-2}p^1 + \frac{(n-1)(n-2)}{1\cdot 2}q^{n-3}p^2$$
$$+ \frac{(n-1)(n-2)(n-3)}{1\cdot 2\cdot 3}q^{n-4}p^3 + \cdots + p^{n-1}\bigg\}$$
$$+ \bigg\{(n-1)q^{n-2}p^1 + \frac{2(n-1)(n-2)}{1\cdot 2}q^{n-3}p^2$$
$$+ \frac{3(n-1)(n-2)(n-3)}{1\cdot 2\cdot 3}q^{n-4}p^3 + \cdots + (n-1)p^{n-1}\bigg\}\bigg]$$

The terms within the first of these two groups constitute the expansion of the binomial $(q+p)^{n-1}$. These terms may be replaced by that binomial; the second group of terms may be simplified, since they contain the common factors $n - 1$ and p. These operations give us

$$np\left[(q + p)^{n-1} + (n - 1)p\left\{q^{n-2} + (n - 2)q^{n-3}p^1\right.\right.$$
$$\left.\left.+ \frac{(n - 2)(n - 3)}{1 \cdot 2}q^{n-4}p^2 + \cdots + p^{n-2}\right\}\right]$$

The second group of terms, thus simplified, is seen to be $(n - 1)p$ multiplied by the expansion of the binomial $(q + p)^{n-2}$. Thus we have, as the sum of the items in column (4) of the preceding table,

$$np[(q + p)^{n-1} + (n - 1)p(q + p)^{n-2}]$$

But since $q + p = 1$, $(q + p)^{n-1} = 1$ and $(q + p)^{n-2} = 1$. Accordingly, the total of column (4) becomes

$$np[1 + p(n - 1)]$$

As a general formula for the standard deviation, in squared form, we have

$$\sigma^2 = \frac{\Sigma f m^2}{N} - c^2$$

where c is the difference between the mean of the distribution and the arbitrary origin. In the present instance, the origin is at 0, or "no successes," and c is equal to the mean, or np. N is equal to $\Sigma(f)$, or 1, in this case. Thus the standard deviation of the binomial distribution is given by

$$\begin{aligned}
\sigma^2 &= np[1 + p(n - 1)] - n^2p^2 \\
&= np[np + (1 - p)] - n^2p^2 \\
&= n^2p^2 + np(1 - p) - n^2p^2 \\
&= np(1 - p) \\
&= npq \\
\sigma &= \sqrt{npq}
\end{aligned}$$

Derivation of the Standard Error of the Arithmetic Mean

We have made n random, hence independent, observations on a given variable. The respective observations may be represented by X_1, X_2, X_3, ... X_n. Representing the sum of the n observations by W, we have

$$W = X_1 + X_2 + X_3 + \cdots + X_n \qquad (1)$$

Additional samples are now taken until we have N values of X_1, N values of X_2, etc., and hence N values of the sum W. We have N samples, therefore, of n observations each. The mean values, which we may represent by barred letters, stand in the same relationship of equality:

$$\overline{W} = \overline{X}_1 + \overline{X}_2 + \overline{X}_3 + \cdots + \overline{X}_n \qquad (2)$$

Using small letters (w, x_1, x_2, etc.) to define deviations of the actual observations from these mean values, we may write, for any given sample, or series of observations,

$$w = x_1 + x_2 + x_3 + \cdots + x_n \qquad (3)$$

Squaring the two sides of this equation, we have

$$\begin{aligned} w^2 = x_1^2 + x_2^2 + x_3^2 + \cdots + x_n^2 + 2x_1x_2 + 2x_1x_3 + \cdots \\ + 2x_1x_n + 2x_2x_3 + \cdots + 2x_2x_n + \cdots \\ + 2x_3x_n + \cdots \end{aligned} \qquad (4)$$

Each term on the right-hand side of (3) will appear in squared form in (4), and there will also appear product terms of the form

$2x_1x_2$ corresponding to all possible pairings of the terms on the right-hand side.

The next step involves the summation of the equations of type (4), derived from the N samples, and division throughout by N. Each product term, when thus summed and divided by N, will be of the form

$$\frac{2\Sigma x_1 x_2}{N}$$

This, with the modification introduced by the factor 2, resembles the familiar mean product, $\dfrac{\Sigma xy}{N}$, encountered in correlation procedure. This mean product, we have seen, has a value of zero when the variables x and y are uncorrelated. But, by hypothesis, the observations that have given us x_1, x_2, x_3, etc., are independent of one another, and hence these variables are uncorrelated. Accordingly, each of the product terms, derived when N equations corresponding to (4) above are summed and divided by N, is equal to zero. The process of summation and division gives us, therefore,

$$\frac{\Sigma w^2}{N} = \frac{\Sigma x_1^2}{N} + \frac{\Sigma x_2^2}{N} + \frac{\Sigma x_3^2}{N} + \cdots + \frac{\Sigma x_n^2}{N} \tag{5}$$

or

$$\sigma_w^2 = \sigma_1^2 + \sigma_2^2 + \sigma_3^2 + \cdots + \sigma_n^2 \tag{6}$$

If all the observations relate to the same universe (i.e., if the samples are all drawn from the same parent population), which is true, by hypothesis, the standard deviations appearing in the right-hand member of equation (6) are equal to one another and to the standard deviation of the population. Accordingly, using σ to represent that standard deviation, we have

$$\sigma_w^2 = n\sigma^2 \tag{7}$$

The next argument, that leads directly to the desired measurement, follows precisely these steps, which have been given in the above form to indicate the reasoning involved. It starts, however, with a variant form of equation (3). Dividing that equation throughout by n, we have

$$\frac{w}{n} = \frac{x_1}{n} + \frac{x_2}{n} + \frac{x_3}{n} + \cdots + \frac{x_n}{n} \tag{8}$$

Working with the variables $\frac{w}{n}, \frac{x_1}{n}, \frac{x_2}{n}$, etc., just as we have done with w, x_1, x_2, etc., we may go through the operations represented by equations (4), (5), and (6), above. The product terms disappear, as in passing from (4) to (5). In the process of squaring, the term $\frac{w}{n}$ is treated as an entity; the sum of the squared values is thus $\Sigma\left(\frac{w}{n}\right)^2$. Numerator and denominator of each of the terms of type $\frac{x_1}{n}$ are squared separately, however, and the sum is of the form $\frac{\Sigma x^2}{n^2}$. Division throughout by N then gives the quantities appearing in equation (9), which corresponds to equation (6).

$$\sigma_{\frac{w}{n}}^2 = \frac{\sigma_1^2}{n^2} + \frac{\sigma_2^2}{n^2} + \frac{\sigma_3^2}{n^2} + \cdots + \frac{\sigma_n^2}{n^2} \tag{9}$$

Since all observations relate to the same universe, this reduces to

$$\sigma_{\frac{w}{n}}^2 = \frac{n\sigma^2}{n^2}. \tag{10}$$

From this

$$\sigma_{\frac{w}{n}} = \frac{\sigma}{\sqrt{n}}. \tag{11}$$

But w is the sum of n quantities drawn from a universe having a standard deviation of σ, and $\frac{w}{n}$ is the mean of these observations. Hence, $\sigma_{\frac{w}{n}}$ is the standard deviation of a distribution of arithmetic means, corresponding to the familiar symbol σ_M. This is the desired expression for the standard error of the arithmetic mean, appropriate for use when the σ of the population is known.

:
.

Illustrating the Measurement of Trend by a Modified Exponential Curve, a Gompertz Curve, and a Logistic Curve

The discussion in Chapter 10 of mathematical functions suitable for use in measuring the secular trends of time series dealt with types required in ordinary practice. We here discuss briefly three other types suited to the measurement of long-term movements in economic and business series.

The Modified Exponential Curve

An exponential curve, which plots as a straight line on ratio paper, is a suitable measure of trend for a series that is increasing or decreasing at a constant rate. The figures defining the successive trend values of a series of this type constitute a geometric progression. The trends of certain economic series that depart from constancy of relative growth may be accurately defined by a simple modification of the exponential curve. This is the case when the observed values may be transformed, by the addition (or subtraction) of a constant magnitude, to a series closely approximating such a geometric progression.

If we represent by K the constant magnitude that is to be added (algebraically) to each observed value in effecting the desired transformation, the task of fitting the trend line involves the following steps:

Determination of K.

Correction of observed values by K, to obtain the modified series.

Fitting an exponential curve to the modified series, and computation of trend values of the modified series.

Correction of trend values of the modified series by K to obtain trend values of original series.

If y represents the ordinates of trend of the original series and x represents time, the equation to the desired line of trend may be put in the form

$$y = ab^x - K$$

where K is the correction factor noted above and a and b are constants to be determined by fitting an exponential curve to the modified series. The procedure may be illustrated with reference

TABLE D

Illustrating the Fitting of a Modified Exponential Curve
Manufacturers' Shipments of Room Air Conditioners *
1946–1954
(Number shipped, in thousands)

(1)	(2) Original series	(3) Group mean	(4) Modified series (2) + K	(5) Trend values modified series	(6) Trend values original series (5) − K
1946	30		8.7	11.7	33.0
1947	43	$M_1 = 49$	21.7	21.4	42.7
1948	74		52.7	39.2	60.5
1949	89		67.7	71.7	93.0
1950	201	$M_2 = 176$	179.7	131.4	152.7
1951	238		216.7	240.5	261.8
1952	380		358.7	440.4	461.7
1953	1,045	$M_3 = 885$	1,023.7	806.5	827.8
1954	1,230		1,208.7	1,476.9	1,498.2

* Source: *Electrical Merchandising*

to the data on shipments of room air conditioners, shown in Table D. A short series is used to simplify the presentation. In employing this method we approximate K empirically by breaking the observed series into three parts, representing equal periods of time, and determining the mean of the observations for each period. We may designate these means, in chronological order, by M_1, M_2, and M_3. The desired value, K, is given by

$$K = [M_2^2 - (M_1 \times M_3)] \div [(M_1 + M_3) - 2M_2]$$

If the observed series constitute a geometric progression the value of K will be zero; if the *addition* of a constant magnitude to the members of the original series will yield a series approximating a geometric progression, K will be positive; if the *subtraction* of a constant amount from the observed values will yield a series approximating a geometric progression, K will be negative. (In practice, K is given the sign obtained by the employment of the method described above, and then added algebraically to the observed series.)

In the present case we have

$$K = [(176)^2 - (49 \times 885)] \div [(49 + 885) - (2 \times 176)] = -21.3$$

Adding this amount to each of the values recorded in column (2) of Table D, we obtain the modified series in column (4). In fitting an exponential curve to the modified series, it is desirable to use logarithms, that is, to solve the constants in an equation of the type $\log y = \log a + (\log b)x$. This procedure was explained in Chapter 10. For $\log a$ of this curve we obtain 2.11845, and for $\log b$, 0.26272. (The origin is at 1950.) The antilogarithms of the series of trend values thus obtained are given in column (5). These define the trend of the modified series. Subtracting K (algebraically) from these values we obtain the trend values of the original series, which appear in column (6). (In practice, the figures in column (6) would be rounded to the nearest digit, to accord with the original series. The first decimal is kept in this example, so that the procedure may be clear.)

The original series measuring shipments of room air conditioners and the modified exponential curve fitted to this series are shown graphically in Fig. A. The equation to the curve there plotted is

$$y = 131.4(1.8311^x) - (-21.3)$$

with reference to an origin at 1950. The fit is not bad. However, it will be understood that the time period covered is too short to warrant acceptance of the given function as a reliable measure of long-term trend.

It is essential that the three M's used in the determination of K relate to equal numbers of observations and that the midpoints, in time, of the three periods be equidistant. In the above example the number of years included in the period is a multiple of three, and no difficulty arises. If the number of years included is not a multiple of three, intervals that overlap slightly may be employed.

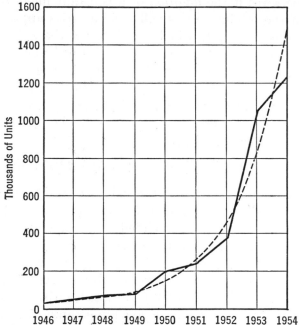

FIG. A. Manufacturers' Shipments of Room Air Conditioners in the United States, 1946–1954, with Modified Exponential Curve.

For example, if our series had run from 1942 to 1954, the three averages might have been derived from the five-year periods 1942–1946, 1946–1950, 1950–1954. These would center, respectively, at 1944, 1948, and 1952, and would thus be equidistant in time from one another. Alternatively, if monthly data are available, division of the total period into three equal parts may be facilitated by using a time-unit of 4 or 8 months, rather than 12 months.

The Gompertz Curve

The Gompertz curve, which has important uses in actuarial science, has had some application in the study of economic and social trends. The term "growth curve" is applicable to it, since it portrays a process of cumulative expansion to a maximum value. This expansion proceeds by decreasing relative amounts from the beginning stages, but continues to the end without retrogression. It may not be assumed that this form of growth is typical of all industrial development, but the curve has value as an empirical representation of certain trend movements.

For the purpose of fitting, the equation to the curve is transformed from the natural form

$$y = ab^{c^x}$$

to the logarithmic form

$$\log y = \log a + (\log b)c^x$$

When fitted to an appropriate set of observations, measuring the expansion of an industry or the growth of an economic element, $\log a$ is the logarithm of the maximum value — the *ceiling* that the curve approaches. The second term measures the amount by which the trend value at a given time falls short of this maximum, an amount that diminishes, of course, with the passage of time. (The series for which this curve is an appropriate measure of trend will be expanding by decreasing relative amounts in the later stages of its life history, and c, derived in the manner indicated below, will have a value between zero and unity.) The origin on the x-scale (time) is taken at the year to which the first entry relates.

The method employed in fitting this curve is an approximative one, since the least squares procedure in customary form is not applicable. Here, as in the preceding example, the series is broken into three equal portions. The sum of the logarithms of the observations in each of these segments is obtained; from these sums, and the differences between them, the necessary constants may be computed. The method is illustrated with reference to the domestic shipments of rayon filament yarns for the years 1922–1954, which appear in Table E.

We may use n to define the number of terms entering into each of the three subtotals (in the present example $n = 11$); the subtotals are represented, in chronological order, by S_1, S_2, and S_3; the first differences [1] between the subtotals are represented by d_1

---

[1] The condition, previously noted, that the series to which the curve is to be fitted be one that is expanding by decreasing logarithmic increments in the later stages of the period covered, is met when d_2 is less than d_1.

TABLE E

Computation of Quantities Required in the Fitting of a Gompertz
Curve to Domestic Shipments by Producers of Rayon
Filament Yarn, 1922–1954
(Annual totals, in millions of pounds)

(1) Year	(2) Shipments of rayon yarn y	(3) Log y	(4) Subtotals	(5) First differences
1922	22.6	1.35411		
1923	29.5	1.46982		
1924	40.3	1.60531		
1925	52.8	1.72263		
1926	51.3	1.71012		
1927	85.0	1.92942	$S_1 = 20.22250$	
1928	88.0	1.94448		
1929	116.4	2.06595		
1930	111.6	2.04766		
1931	155.5	2.19173		
1932	151.8	2.18127		
				$d_1 = S_2 - S_1$
1933	210.9	2.32408		$= 7.29523$
1934	194.7	2.28937		
1935	252.7	2.40261		
1936	297.3	2.47319		
1937	266.2	2.42521		
1938	273.8	2.43743	$S_2 = 27.51773$	
1939	359.6	2.55582		
1940	388.7	2.58961		
1941	452.4	2.65552		
1942	468.8	2.67099		
1943	494.2	2.69390		
				$d_2 = S_3 - S_2$
1944	539.1	2.73167		$= 4.12837$
1945	602.4	2.77988		
1946	666.4	2.82373		
1947	729.0	2.86273		
1948	836.5	2.92247		
1949	782.4	2.89343	$S_3 = 31.64610$	
1950	949.1	2.97731		
1951	860.3	2.93465		
1952	844.8	2.92675		
1953	864.7	2.93687		
1954	718.8	2.85661		

and d_2. We use these quantities in solving for the three constants
c, log b, and log a. The general relations from which these values
are determined are the following:

$$c^n = \frac{d_2}{d_1}$$

$$\log b = \frac{d_1(c - 1)}{(c^n - 1)^2}$$

$$\log a = \frac{1}{n}\left(S_1 - \frac{d_1}{c^n - 1}\right)$$

Inserting the proper quantities, we have

$$c^n = c^{11} = \frac{4.12837}{7.29523} = 0.565900$$

$$c = \sqrt[11]{0.565900} = 0.94956$$

$$\log b = \frac{7.29523(-0.05044)}{(-0.4341)^2} = -1.95270$$

$$\log a = \frac{1}{11}\left(20.22250 - \frac{7.29523}{-0.43410}\right) = 3.36617$$

The required equation is, therefore,

$$\log y = 3.36617 - 1.95270(0.94956^x)$$

in which x relates to deviations from an origin at the position of the first term.

Substituting in this trend equation the values of x given in Table F, logarithms of the trend values are obtained. The corresponding natural numbers define the course of the line of trend. The method of calculation is indicated in Table F. The original data and the Gompertz curve fitted to them are shown graphically in Fig. B.

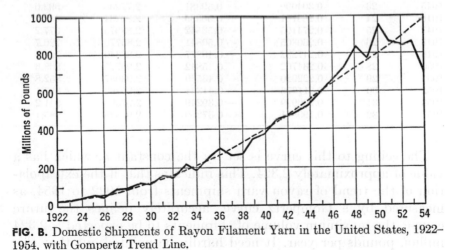

FIG. B. Domestic Shipments of Rayon Filament Yarn in the United States, 1922–1954, with Gompertz Trend Line.

Illustrating the Computation of Ordinates of Trend of a Gompertz
Curve Fitted to Shipments of Rayon Filament Yarn, 1922–1954

(1)	(2)	(3)	(4)	(5)	(6)
					y
Year	x	c^x	$(\log b)c^x$	$\log y$ $(4) + \log a$	Anti-log of (5) (in millions of pounds)
1922	0	1.00000	-1.95270	1.41347	25.9
1923	1	0.94956	-1.85421	1.51196	32.5
1924	2	0.901664	-1.76067	1.60550	40.3
1925	3	0.856184	-1.67187	1.69430	49.5
1926	4	0.812998	-1.58754	1.77863	60.1
1927	5	0.771991	-1.50747	1.85870	72.2
1928	6	0.733051	-1.43143	1.93474	86.0
1929	7	0.696076	-1.35923	2.00694	101.6
1930	8	0.660966	-1.29067	2.07550	119.0
1931	9	0.627627	-1.22557	2.14060	138.2
1932	10	0.595970	-1.16375	2.20242	159.4
1933	11	0.565909	-1.10505	2.26112	182.4
1934	12	0.537364	-1.04931	2.31686	207.4
1935	13	0.510260	-0.99638	2.36979	234.3
1936	14	0.484522	-0.94613	2.42004	263.0
1937	15	0.460083	-0.89840	2.46777	293.6
1938	16	0.436876	-0.85309	2.51308	325.9
1939	17	0.414840	-0.81006	2.55611	359.8
1940	18	0.393916	-0.76920	2.59697	395.3
1941	19	0.374047	-0.73040	2.63577	432.3
1942	20	0.355180	-0.69356	2.67261	470.6
1943	21	0.337265	-0.65858	2.70759	510.0
1944	22	0.320253	-0.62536	2.74081	550.6
1945	23	0.304099	-0.59381	2.77236	592.0
1946	24	0.288761	-0.56386	2.80231	634.3
1947	25	0.274195	-0.53542	2.83075	677.2
1948	26	0.260365	-0.50841	2.85776	720.7
1949	27	0.247232	-0.48277	2.88340	764.5
1950	28	0.234762	-0.45842	2.90775	808.6
1951	29	0.222920	-0.43530	2.93087	852.8
1952	30	0.211676	-0.41334	2.95283	897.1
1953	31	0.200999	-0.39249	2.97368	941.2
1954	32	0.190861	-0.37269	2.99348	985.1

The ceiling to this curve is set by the constant a, which has a
value of approximately 2,324. This indicates that if the extrapolation of the trend of rayon yarn shipments from 1922 to 1954, as
measured by a Gompertz curve, accurately defines the future
course, the maximum volume of shipments to be expected is 2,324
million pounds per year. It need hardly be pointed out that this

extrapolation involves some doubtful assumptions, and that no mystic significance is to be attached to it. In particular, the asymptote a may be expected to change, as conditions affecting the industry and the demand for its products vary in the future. As we shall see, a different growth function may yield a quite different asymptote.

The Logistic Curve

The logistic curve, sometimes termed the Pearl-Reed growth curve because of the extensive use made of it in population studies by Raymond Pearl and L. J. Reed, resembles somewhat the Gompertz curve discussed above. It represents a modified geometric progression, the growth of a series that tends to decrease as it approaches some specified limit. Like the Gompertz curve it may be used as an empirical approximation to the trends of certain economic series. Extrapolations are subject, of course, to the same uncertainties that attach to projections of other empirically derived trend lines.

A form of this curve adapted to use as a measure of trend is defined by the equation

$$\frac{1}{y} = a + bc^x$$

This, it will be noted, is the equation to a modified exponential curve, except that the dependent variable is $\frac{1}{y}$, rather than y. (The symbols here used for the constants differ somewhat from those employed in treating the modified exponential curve.) A method of fitting somewhat similar to those employed in the preceding examples may be employed, with necessary modifications required by the use of reciprocals of y. The method may be discussed with reference to the series used in the preceding example — domestic shipments of rayon filament yarn. Initial stages in the fitting process are illustrated in Table G. Computations are facilitated by multiplying the reciprocals of y by a suitable power of 10, as is done in column (3) of this table.

As in the two preceding illustrations, the observations are divided, chronologically, into three equal groups. Group subtotals

TABLE G

Computation of Quantities Required in the Fitting of a Logistic
Curve to Domestic Shipments by Producers of
Rayon Filament Yarn, 1922–1954 *
(Annual totals, in millions of pounds)

(1) Year	(2) Shipments of rayon yarn y	(3) $\dfrac{100,000}{y}$	(4) Subtotals	(5) First differences
1922	22.6	4,425		
1923	29.5	3,390		
1924	40.3	2,481		
1925	52.8	1,894		
1926	51.3	1,949	$S_1 = 19,507$	
1927	85.0	1,176		
1928	88.0	1,136		
1929	116.4	859		
1930	111.6	896		
1931	155.5	643		
1932	151.8	658		
				$d_1 = S_2 - S_1$
1933	210.9	474		$= -15,875$
1934	194.7	514		
1935	252.7	396		
1936	297.3	336		
1937	266.2	376	$S_2 = 3,632$	
1938	273.8	365		
1939	359.6	278		
1940	388.7	257		
1941	452.4	221		
1942	468.8	213		
1943	494.2	202		
				$d_2 = S_3 - S_2$
1944	539.1	185		$= -2,152$
1945	602.4	166		
1946	666.4	150		
1947	729.0	137		
1948	836.5	120	$S_3 = 1,480$	
1949	782.4	128		
1950	949.1	105		
1951	860.3	116		
1952	844.8	118		
1953	864.7	116		
1954	718.8	139		

* Source: *Textile Organon*, Textile Economics Bureau

and the first differences between these subtotals are computed.
The symbol n is used for the number of terms in each of these subgroups. The origin of the x-scale (time) is set at the date of the first
observation.

The constants in the desired equation may be derived from the following relations.

$$c^n = \frac{d_2}{d_1}$$

$$b = \frac{d_1(c - 1)}{(c^n - 1)^2}$$

$$a = \frac{1}{n}\left(S_1 - \frac{d_1}{c^n - 1}\right)$$

Substituting the given values, we have

$$c^n = c^{11} = \frac{-2{,}152}{-15{,}875} = +0.135559$$

$$c = \sqrt[11]{+0.135559} = 0.83388$$

$$b = \frac{-15{,}875(-0.16612)}{(0.135559 - 1)^2} = +3{,}529.11$$

$$a = \frac{1}{11}\left(19{,}507 - \frac{-15.875}{(.0135559 - 1)}\right) = +103.87$$

These results relate to initial observations that have been modified by the multiplication of $\frac{1}{y}$ by 100,000. The desired equation is, therefore,

$$\frac{100{,}000}{y} = 103.87 + 3{,}529.11(0.83388^x)$$

where x measures deviations in years from an origin at 1922.

Succeeding calculations are shown in Table H. The process of calculation is a straightforward one. The reciprocals of the entries in column (5), multiplied by 100,000, yield the desired trend values given in column (6). These values, with the original series, are shown graphically in Fig. C.

As in the case of the Gompertz curve, the logistic is suitable for measuring the trend of a series marked by decelerating expansion, without actual retrogression. The curve resembles an elongated S rising from a lower asymptote of zero to an upper limit indicated by the constant a. Since a in this case refers to an equation in which the dependent variable is $\frac{100{,}000}{y}$, the actual asymptote is $\frac{100{,}000}{a}$.

TABLE H

Computation of Ordinates of Trend of Logistic Curve Fitted to Domestic Shipments of Rayon Filament Yarn

(1) Year	(2) x	(3) c^x	(4) bc^x	(5) $\dfrac{100,000}{y}$ $(a + bc^x)$	(6) $\left(100,000 \times \dfrac{1}{(\text{col. 5})}\right)$ y
1922	0	1.00000	3,529.1	3,633.0	27.5
1923	1	0.83388	2,942.9	3,046.8	32.8
1924	2	0.69536	2,454.0	2,557.9	39.1
1925	3	0.57984	2,046.3	2,150.2	46.5
1926	4	0.48352	1,706.4	1,810.3	55.2
1927	5	0.40320	1,422.9	1,526.8	65.5
1928	6	0.33622	1,186.6	1,290.5	77.5
1929	7	0.28037	989.5	1,093.4	91.5
1930	8	0.23379	825.1	929.0	107.6
1931	9	0.19495	688.0	791.9	126.3
1932	10	0.16257	573.7	677.6	147.6
1933	11	0.13556	478.4	582.3	171.7
1934	12	0.11304	398.9	502.8	198.9
1935	13	0.09426	332.6	436.5	229.1
1936	14	0.07860	277.3	381.2	262.3
1937	15	0.06555	231.3	335.2	298.3
1938	16	0.05466	192.9	296.8	336.9
1939	17	0.04558	160.9	264.8	377.6
1940	18	0.03801	134.1	238.0	420.2
1941	19	0.03169	111.8	215.7	463.6
1942	20	0.02643	93.3	197.2	507.1
1943	21	0.02204	77.8	181.7	550.4
1944	22	0.01838	64.9	168.8	592.4
1945	23	0.01532	54.1	158.0	632.9
1946	24	0.01278	45.1	149.0	671.1
1947	25	0.01066	37.6	141.5	706.7
1948	26	0.00889	31.4	135.3	739.1
1949	27	0.00741	26.2	130.1	768.6
1950	28	0.00618	21.8	125.7	795.5
1951	29	0.00515	18.2	122.1	819.0
1952	30	0.00430	15.2	119.1	839.6
1953	31	0.00358	12.6	116.5	858.8
1954	32	0.00299	10.6	114.5	873.4

From the given value of a, 103.87, we derive 963 (in millions of pounds) as the upper limit of the trend line here derived. (The reader will note the wide difference between this asymptote and the ceiling of 2,324 million pounds given by the Gompertz curve.) The limit given by the logistic was closely approached in 1950, at the peak of the postwar surge. Whether this limit may be accepted as a reasonable long-term expectation depends on the nature of the forces behind the declines of recent years. In any rational extrapolation, appraisal of these forces must supplement the descriptive information given by the trend limit. Within the limits of the observations the present logistic curve gives a fairly good representation of the stages of slow initial growth, acceleration, and retardation in the life history of this industry.

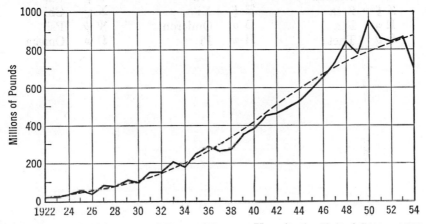

FIG. C. Domestic Shipments of Rayon Filament Yarn in the United States, 1922–1954, with Logistic Trend.

GREEK ALPHABET

Letters	Names	Letters	Names	Letters	Names
A α	Alpha	I ι	Iota	P ρ	Rho
B β	Beta	K κ	Kappa	Σ σ	Sigma
Γ γ	Gamma	Λ λ	Lambda	T τ	Tau
Δ δ	Delta	M μ	Mu	Υ υ	Upsilon
E ϵ	Epsilon	N ν	Nu	Φ ϕ	Phi
Z ζ	Zeta	Ξ ξ	Xi	X χ	Chi
H η	Eta	O o	Omicron	Ψ ψ	Psi
Θ θ	Theta	Π π	Pi	Ω ω	Omega

Areas and Ordinates of the Normal Curve
of Error in Terms of the Abscissa

x/σ	Area between maximum ordinate and ordinate at x/σ	Ordinate at x/σ	x/σ	Area between maximum ordinate and ordinate at x/σ	Ordinate at x/σ
.00	.00000	.39894	.50	.19146	.35207
.01	.00399	.39892	.51	.19497	.35029
.02	.00798	.39886	.52	.19847·	.34849
.03	.01197	.39876	.53	.20194	.34667
.04	.01595	.39862	.54	.20540	.34482
.05	.01994	.39844	.55	.20884	.34294
.06	.02392	.39822	.56	.21226	.34105
.07	.02790	.39797	.57	.21566	.33912
.08	.03188	.39767	.58	.21904	.33718
.09	.03586	.39733	.59	.22240	.33521
.10	.03983	.39695	.60	.22575	.33322
.11	.04380	.39654	.61	.22907	.33121
.12	.04776	.39608	.62	.23237	.32918
.13	.05172	.39559	.63	.23565	.32713
.14	.05567	.39505	.64	.23891	.32506
.15	.05962	.39448	.65	.24215	.32297
.16	.06356	.39387	.66	.24537	.32086
.17	.06749	.39322	.67	.24857	.31874
.18	.07142	.39253	.68	.25175	.31659
.19	.07535	.39181	.69	.25490	.31443
.20	.07926	.39104	.70	.25804	.31225
.21	.08317	.39024	.71	.26115	.31006
.22	.08706	.38940	.72	.26424	.30785
.23	.09095	.38853	.73	.26730	.30563
.24	.09483	.38762	.74	.27035	.30339
.25	.09871	.38667	.75	.27337	.30114
.26	.10257	.38568	.76	.27637	.29887
.27	.10642	.38466	.77	.27935	.29659
.28	.11026	.38361	.78	.28230	.29431
.29	.11409	.38251	.79	.28524	.29200
.30	.11791	.38139	.80	.28814	.28969
.31	.12172	.38023	.81	.29103	.28737
.32	.12552	.37903	.82	.29389	.28504
.33	.12930	.37780	.83	.29673	.28269
.34	.13307	.37654	.84	.29955	.28034
.35	.13683	.37524	.85	.30234	.27798
.36	.14058	.37391	.86	.30511	.27562
.37	.14431	.37255	.87	.30785	.27324
.38	.14803	.37115	.88	.31057	.27086
.39	.15173	.36973	.89	.31327	.26848
.40	.15542	.36827	.90	.31594	.26609
.41	.15910	.36678	.91	.31859	.26369
.42	.16276	.36526	.92	.32121	.26129
.43	.16640	.36371	.93	.32381	.25888
.44	.17003	.36213	.94	.32639	.25647
.45	.17364	.36053	.95	.32894	.25406
.46	.17724	.35889	.96	.33147	.25164
.47	.18082	.35723	.97	.33398	.24923
.48	.18439	.35553	.98	.33646	.24681
.49	.18793	.35381	.99	.33891	.24439

Areas and Ordinates of the Normal Curve of Error in Terms of the Abscissa

x/σ	Area between maximum ordinate and ordinate at x/σ	Ordinate at x/σ	x/σ	Area between maximum ordinate and ordinate at x/σ	Ordinate at x/σ
1.00	.34134	.24197	1.50	.43319	.12952
1.01	.34375	.23955	1.51	.43448	.12758
1.02	.34614	.23713	1.52	.43574	.12566
1.03	.34850	.23471	1.53	.43699	.12376
1.04	.35083	.23230	1.54	.43822	.12188
1.05	.35314	.22988	1.55	.43943	.12001
1.06	.35543	.22747	1.56	.44062	.11816
1.07	.35769	.22506	1.57	.44179	.11632
1.08	.35993	.22265	1.58	.44295	.11450
1.09	.36214	.22025	1.59	.44408	.11270
1.10	.36433	.21785	1.60	.44520	.11092
1.11	.36650	.21546	1.61	.44630	.10915
1.12	.36864	.21307	1.62	.44738	.10741
1.13	.37076	.21069	1.63	.44845	.10567
1.14	.37286	.20831	1.64	.44950	.10396
1.15	.37493	.20594	1.65	.45053	.10226
1.16	.37698	.20357	1.66	.45154	.10059
1.17	.37900	.20121	1.67	.45254	.09893
1.18	.38100	.19886	1.68	.45352	.09728
1.19	.38298	.19652	1.69	.45449	.09566
1.20	.38493	.19419	1.70	.45543	.09405
1.21	.38686	.19186	1.71	.45637	.09246
1.22	.38877	.18954	1.72	.45728	.09089
1.23	.39065	.18724	1.73	.45818	.08933
1.24	.39251	.18494	1.74	.45907	.08780
1.25	.39435	.18265	1.75	.45994	.08628
1.26	.39617	.18037	1.76	.46080	.08478
1.27	.39796	.17810	1.77	.46164	.08329
1.28	.39973	.17585	1.78	.46246	.08183
1.29	.40147	.17360	1.79	.46327	.08038
1.30	.40320	.17137	1.80	.46407	.07895
1.31	.40490	.16915	1.81	.46485	.07754
1.32	.40658	.16694	1.82	.46562	.07614
1.33	.40824	.16474	1.83	.46638	.07477
1.34	.40988	.16256	1.84	.46712	.07341
1.35	.41149	.16038	1.85	.46784	.07206
1.36	.41309	.15822	1.86	.46856	.07074
1.37	.41466	.15608	1.87	.46926	.06943
1.38	.41621	.15395	1.88	.46995	.06814
1.39	.41774	.15183	1.89	.47062	.06687
1.40	.41924	.14973	1.90	.47128	.06562
1.41	.42073	.14764	1.91	.47193	.06438
1.42	.42220	.14556	1.92	.47257	.06316
1.43	.42364	.14350	1.93	.47320	.06195
1.44	.42507	.14146	1.94	.47381	.06077
1.45	.42647	.13943	1.95	.47441	.05959
1.46	.42786	.13742	1.96	.47500	.05844
1.47	.42922	.13542	1.97	.47558	.05730
1.48	.43056	.13344	1.98	.47615	.05618
1.49	.43189	.13147	1.99	.47670	.05508

Areas and Ordinates of the Normal Curve of Error in Terms of the Abscissa

x/σ	Area between maximum ordinate and ordinate at x/σ	Ordinate at x/σ	x/σ	Area between maximum ordinate and ordinate at x/σ	Ordinate at x/σ
2.00	.47725	.05399	2.50	.49379	.01753
2.01	.47778	.05292	2.51	.49396	.01709
2.02	.47831	.05186	2.52	.49413	.01667
2.03	.47882	.05082	2.53	.49430	.01625
2.04	.47932	.04980	2.54	.49446	.01585
2.05	.47982	.04879	2.55	.49461	.01545
2.06	.48030	.04780	2.56	.49477	.01506
2.07	.48077	.04682	2.57	.49492	.01468
2.08	.48124	.04586	2.58	.49506	.01431
2.09	.48169	.04491	2.59	.49520	.01394
2.10	.48214	.04398	2.60	.49534	.01358
2.11	.48257	.04307	2.61	.49547	.01323
2.12	.48300	.04217	2.62	.49560	.01289
2.13	.48341	.04128	2.63	.49573	.01256
2.14	.48382	.04041	2.64	.49585	.01223
2.15	.48422	.03955	2.65	.49598	.01191
2.16	.48461	.03871	2.66	.49609	.01160
2.17	.48500	.03788	2.67	.49621	.01130
2.18	.48537	.03706	2.68	.49632	.01100
2.19	.48574	.03626	2.69	.49643	.01071
2.20	.48610	.03547	2.70	.49653	.01042
2.21	.48645	.03470	2.71	.49664	.01014
2.22	.48679	.03394	2.72	.49674	.00987
2.23	.48713	.03319	2.73	.49683	.00961
2.24	.48745	.03246	2.74	.49693	.00935
2.25	.48778	.03174	2.75	.49702	.00909
2.26	.48809	.03103	2.76	.49711	.00885
2.27	.48840	.03034	2.77	.49720	.00861
2.28	.48870	.02965	2.78	.49728	.00837
2.29	.48899	.02898	2.79	.49736	.00814
2.30	.48928	.02833	2.80	.49744	.00792
2.31	.48956	.02768	2.81	.49752	.00770
2.32	.48983	.02705	2.82	.49760	.00748
2.33	.49010	.02643	2.83	.49767	.00727
2.34	.49036	.02582	2.84	.49774	.00707
2.35	.49061	.02522	2.85	.49781	.00687
2.36	.49086	.02463	2.86	.49788	.00668
2.37	.49111	.02406	2.87	.49795	.00649
2.38	.49134	.02349	2.88	.49801	.00631
2.39	.49158	.02294	2.89	.49807	.00613
2.40	.49180	.02239	2.90	.49813	.00595
2.41	.49202	.02186	2.91	.49819	.00578
2.42	.49224	.02134	2.92	.49825	.00562
2.43	.49245	.02083	2.93	.49831	.00545
2.44	.49266	.02033	2.94	.49836	.00530
2.45	.49286	.01984	2.95	.49841	.00514
2.46	.49305	.01936	2.96	.49846	.00499
2.47	.49324	.01889	2.97	.49851	.00485
2.48	.49343	.01842	2.98	.49856	.00471
2.49	.49361	.01797	2.99	.49861	.00457

Areas and Ordinates of the Normal Curve of Error in Terms of the Abscissa

x/σ	Area between maximum ordinate and ordinate at x/σ	Ordinate at x/σ	x/σ	Area between maximum ordinate and ordinate at x/σ	Ordinate at x/σ
3.00	.49865	.00443	3.50	.49977	.00087
3.01	.49869	.00430	3.51	.49978	.00084
3.02	.49874	.00417	3.52	.49978	.00081
3.03	.49878	.00405	3.53	.49979	.00079
3.04	.49882	.00393	3.54	.49980	.00076
3.05	.49886	.00381	3.55	.49981	.00073
3.06	.49889	.00370	3.56	.49981	.00071
3.07	.49893	.00358	3.57	.49982	.00068
3.08	.49897	.00348	3.58	.49983	.00066
3.09	.49900	.00337	3.59	.49983	.00063
3.10	.49903	.00327	3.60	.49984	.00061
3.11	.49906	.00317	3.61	.49985	.00059
3.12	.49910	.00307	3.62	.49985	.00057
3.13	.49913	.00298	3.63	.49986	.00055
3.14	.49916	.00288	3.64	.49986	.00053
3.15	.49918	.00279	3.65	.49987	.00051
3.16	.49921	.00271	3.66	.49987	.00049
3.17	.49924	.00262	3.67	.49988	.00047
3.18	.49926	.00254	3.68	.49988	.00046
3.19	.49929	.00246	3.69	.49989	.00044
3.20	.49931	.00238	3.70	.49989	.00042
3.21	.49934	.00231	3.71	.49990	.00041
3.22	.49936	.00224	3.72	.49990	.00039
3.23	.49938	.00216	3.73	.49990	.00038
3.24	.49940	.00210	3.74	.49991	.00037
3.25	.49942	.00203	3.75	.49991	.00035
3.26	.49944	.00196	3.76	.49992	.00034
3.27	.49946	.00190	3.77	.49992	.00033
3.28	.49948	.00184	3.78	.49992	.00031
3.29	.49950	.00178	3.79	.49992	.00030
3.30	.49952	.00172	3.80	.49993	.00029
3.31	.49953	.00167	3.81	.49993	.00028
3.32	.49955	.00161	3.82	.49993	.00027
3.33	.49957	.00156	3.83	.49994	.00026
3.34	.49958	.00151	3.84	.49994	.00025
3.35	.49960	.00146	3.85	.49994	.00024
3.36	.49961	.00141	3.86	.49994	.00023
3.37	.49962	.00136	3.87	.49995	.00022
3.38	.49964	.00132	3.88	.49995	.00021
3.39	.49965	.00127	3.89	.49995	.00021
3.40	.49966	.00123	3.90	.49995	.00020
3.41	.49968	.00119	3.91	.49995	.00019
3.42	.49969	.00115	3.92	.49996	.00018
3.43	.49970	.00111	3.93	.49996	.00018
3.44	.49971	.00107	3.94	.49996	.00017
3.45	.49972	.00104	3.95	.49996	.00016
3.46	.49973	.00100	3.96	.49996	.00016
3.47	.49974	.00097	3.97	.49996	.00015
3.48	.49975	.00094	3.98	.49997	.00014
3.49	.49976	.00090	3.99	.49997	.00014

APPENDIX TABLE II

Percentile Values of the Normal Distribution *

Area to the left of T †	T †	Area to the left of T †	T †
.001	− 3.090	.600	+ .253
.002	− 2.878	.700	+ .524
.003	− 2.748	.800	+ .842
.004	− 2.652	.900	+ 1.282
.005	− 2.576	.910	+ 1.341
.006	− 2.512	.920	+ 1.405
.007	− 2.457	.930	+ 1.476
.008	− 2.409	.940	+ 1.555
.009	− 2.366	.950	+ 1.645
.010	− 2.326	.960	+ 1.751
.020	− 2.054	.970	+ 1.881
.030	− 1.881	.980	+ 2.054
.040	− 1.751	.990	+ 2.326
.050	− 1.645	.991	+ 2.366
.060	− 1.555	.992	+ 2.409
.070	− 1.476	.993	+ 2.457
.080	− 1.405	.994	+ 2.512
.090	− 1.341	.995	+ 2.576
.100	− 1.282	.996	+ 2.652
.200	− .842	.997	+ 2.748
.300	− .524	.998	+ 2.878
.400	− .253	.999	+ 3.090
.500	.000		

* This table contains selected values from Table I of Truman L. Kelley's *The Kelley Statistical Tables* (Harvard University Press, 1948). I am indebted to Professor Kelley and the Harvard University Press for permission to publish these excerpts.

† T is here used as a symbol for a normal deviate: i.e., a deviation from the mean of a normal distribution expressed in units of the standard deviation. Areas are expressed as proportionate parts of the total area under a normal curve.

APPENDIX TABLE III *

Table of t

n	$P = .05$	.02	.01
1	12.706	31.821	63.657
2	4.303	6.965	9.925
3	3.182	4.541	5.841
4	2.776	3.747	4.604
5	2.571	3.365	4.032
6	2.447	3.143	3.707
7	2.365	2.998	3.499
8	2.306	2.896	3.355
9	2.262	2.821	3.250
10	2.228	2.764	3.169
11	2.201	2.718	3.106
12	2.179	2.681	3.055
13	2.160	2.650	3.012
14	2.145	2.624	2.977
15	2.131	2.602	2.947
16	2.120	2.583	2.921
17	2.110	2.567	2.898
18	2.101	2.552	2.878
19	2.093	2.539	2.861
20	2.086	2.528	2.845
21	2.080	2.518	2.831
22	2.074	2.508	2.819
23	2.069	2.500	2.807
24	2.064	2.492	2.797
25	2.060	2.485	2.787
26	2.056	2.479	2.779
27	2.052	2.473	2.771
28	2.048	2.467	2.763
29	2.045	2.462	2.756
30	2.042	2.457	2.750
∞	1.95996	2.32634	2.57582

* Appendix Table III is abridged from Table IV of R. A. Fisher, *Statistical Methods for Research Workers*, published by Oliver and Boyd, Ltd., of Edinburgh. The abridgment is published here by permission of the author and publishers.

APPENDIX TABLE IV *

Values of the Correlation Coefficient for Different Levels of Significance

n	$P = .05$	.02	.01
1	.996917	.9995066	.9998766
2	.95000	.98000	.990000
3	.8783	.93433	.95873
4	.8114	.8822	.91720
5	.7545	.8329	.8745
6	.7067	.7887	.8343
7	.6664	.7498	.7977
8	.6319	.7155	.7646
9	.6021	.6851	.7348
10	.5760	.6581	.7079
11	.5529	.6339	.6835
12	.5324	.6120	.6614
13	.5139	.5923	.6411
14	.4973	.5742	.6226
15	.4821	.5577	.6055
16	.4683	.5425	.5897
17	.4555	.5285	.5751
18	.4438	.5155	.5614
19	.4329	.5034	.5487
20	.4227	.4921	.5368
25	.3809	.4451	.4809
30	.3494	.4093	.4487
35	.3246	.3810	.4182
40	.3044	.3578	.3932
45	.2875	.3384	.3721
50	.2732	.3218	.3541
60	.2500	.2948	.3248
70	.2319	.2737	.3017
80	.2172	.2565	.2830
90	.2050	.2422	.2673
100	.1946	.2301	.2540

For a total correlation, n is 2 less than the number of pairs in the sample; for a partial correlation, the number of eliminated variates also should be subtracted.

* Appendix Table IV is abridged from Table V-A of R. A. Fisher, *Statistical Methods for Research Workers*, published by Oliver and Boyd, Ltd., of Edinburgh. The abridgment is published here by permission of the author and publishers.

APPENDIX TABLE V

Showing the Relations between r and z' for Values of z' from 0 to 5 *

z'	.00	.01	.02	.03	.04	.05	.06	.07	.08	.09
.0	.0000	.0100	.0200	.0300	.0400	.0500	.0599	.0699	.0798	.0898
.1	.0997	.1096	.1194	.1293	.1391	.1489	.1587	.1684	.1781	.1878
.2	.1974	.2070	.2165	.2260	.2355	.2449	.2543	.2636	.2729	.2821
.3	.2913	.3004	.3095	.3185	.3275	.3364	.3452	.3540	.3627	.3714
.4	.3800	.3885	.3969	.4053	.4136	.4219	.4301	.4382	.4462	.4542
.5	.4621	.4700	.4777	.4854	.4930	.5005	.5080	.5154	.5227	.5299
.6	.5370	.5441	.5511	.5581	.5649	.5717	.5784	.5850	.5915	.5980
.7	.6044	.6107	.6169	.6231	.6291	.6352	.6411	.6469	.6527	.6584
.8	.6640	.6696	.6751	.6805	.6858	.6911	.6963	.7014	.7064	.7114
.9	.7163	.7211	.7259	.7306	.7352	.7398	.7443	.7487	.7531	.7574
1.0	.7616	.7658	.7699	.7739	.7779	.7818	.7857	.7895	.7932	.7969
1.1	.8005	.8041	.8076	.8110	.8144	.8178	.8210	.8243	.8275	.8306
1.2	.8337	.8367	.8397	.8426	.8455	.8483	.8511	.8538	.8565	.8591
1.3	.8617	.8643	.8668	.8693	.8717	.8741	.8764	.8787	.8810	.8832
1.4	.8854	.8875	.8896	.8917	.8937	.8957	.8977	.8996	.9015	.9033
1.5	.9052	.9069	.9087	.9104	.9121	.9138	.9154	.9170	.9186	.9202
1.6	.9217	.9232	.9246	.9261	.9275	.9289	.9302	.9316	.9329	.9342
1.7	.9354	.9367	.9379	.9391	.9402	.9414	.9425	.9436	.9447	.9458
1.8	.9468	.9478	.9498	.9488	.9508	.9518	.9527	.9536	.9545	.9554
1.9	.9562	.9571	.9579	.9587	.9595	.9603	.9611	.9619	.9626	.9633
2.0	.9640	.9647	.9654	.9661	.9668	.9674	.9680	.9687	.9693	.9699
2.1	.9705	.9710	.9716	.9722	.9727	.9732	.9738	.9743	.9748	.9753
2.2	.9757	.9762	.9767	.9771	.9776	.9780	.9785	.9789	.9793	.9797
2.3	.9801	.9805	.9809	.9812	.9816	.9820	.9823	.9827	.9830	.9834
2.4	.9837	.9840	.9843	.9846	.9849	.9852	.9855	.9858	.9861	.9863
2.5	.9866	.9869	.9871	.9874	.9876	.9879	.9881	.9884	.9886	.9888
2.6	.9890	.9892	.9895	.9897	.9899	.9901	.9903	.9905	.9906	.9908
2.7	.9910	.9912	.9914	.9915	.9917	.9919	.9920	.9922	.9923	.9925
2.8	.9926	.9928	.9929	.9931	.9932	.9933	.9935	.9936	.9937	.9938
2.9	.9940	.9941	.9942	.9943	.9944	.9945	.9946	.9947	.9949	.9950
3.0	.9951									
4.0	.9993									
5.0	.9999									

* The figures in the body of the table are values of r corresponding to z'-values read from the scales on the left and top of the table.

APPENDIX TABLE VI *

Selected Percentile Values of the χ^2 Distribution *

n	$\chi^2_{.01}$	$\chi^2_{.05}$	$\chi^2_{.50}$	$\chi^2_{.90}$	$\chi^2_{.95}$	$\chi^2_{.99}$
1	.000157	.00393	.455	2.706	3.841	6.635
2	.0201	.103	1.386	4.605	5.991	9.210
3	.115	.352	2.366	6.251	7.815	11.341
4	.297	.711	3.357	7.779	9.488	13.277
5	.554	1.145	4.351	9.236	11.070	15.086
6	.872	1.635	5.348	10.645	12.592	16.812
7	1.239	2.167	6.346	12.017	14.067	18.475
8	1.646	2.733	7.344	13.362	15.507	20.090
9	2.088	3.325	8.343	14.684	16.919	21.666
10	2.558	3.940	9.342	15.987	18.307	23.209
11	3.053	4.575	10.341	17.275	19.675	24.725
12	3.571	5.226	11.340	18.549	21.026	26.217
13	4.107	5.892	12.340	19.812	22.362	27.688
14	4.660	6.571	13.339	21.064	23.685	29.141
15	5.229	7.261	14.339	22.307	24.996	30.578
16	5.812	7.962	15.338	23.542	26.296	32.000
17	6.408	8.672	16.338	24.769	27.587	33.409
18	7.015	9.390	17.338	25.989	28.809	34.805
19	7.633	10.117	18.338	27.204	30.144	36.191
20	8.260	10.851	19.337	28.412	31.410	37.566
21	8.897	11.591	20.337	29.615	32.671	38.932
22	9.542	12.338	21.337	30.813	33.924	40.289
23	10.196	13.091	22.337	32.007	35.172	41.638
24	10.856	13.848	23.337	33.196	36.415	42.980
25	11.524	14.611	24.337	34.382	37.652	44.314
26	12.198	15.379	25.336	35.563	38.885	45.642
27	12.879	16.151	26.336	36.741	40.113	46.963
28	13.565	16.928	27.336	37.916	41.337	48.278
29	14.256	17.708	28.336	39.087	42.557	49.588
30	14.953	18.493	29.336	40.256	43.773	50.892

For larger values of n, the expression $\sqrt{2\chi^2} - \sqrt{2n-1}$ may be used as a normal deviate with unit standard error. A deviate thus determined is to be interpreted as in a one-tailed test.

* Appendix Table VI is abridged from Table III of R. A. Fisher, *Statistical Methods for Research Workers*, published by Oliver and Boyd, Ltd., of Edinburgh. The abridgment is published here by permission of the authors and publishers.

n_2 = degrees of freedom for denominator

n_2	1	2	3	4	5	6	7	8	9	10	11	12
1	161 / **4,052**	200 / **4,999**	216 / **5,403**	225 / **5,625**	230 / **5,764**	234 / **5,859**	237 / **5,928**	239 / **5,981**	241 / **6,022**	242 / **6,056**	243 / **6,082**	244 / **6,106**
2	18.51 / **98.49**	19.00 / **99.01**	19.16 / **99.17**	19.25 / **99.25**	19.30 / **99.30**	19.33 / **99.33**	19.36 / **99.34**	19.37 / **99.36**	19.38 / **99.38**	19.39 / **99.40**	19.40 / **99.41**	19.41 / **99.42**
3	10.13 / **34.12**	9.55 / **30.81**	9.28 / **29.46**	9.12 / **28.71**	9.01 / **28.24**	8.94 / **27.91**	8.88 / **27.67**	8.84 / **27.49**	8.81 / **27.34**	8.78 / **27.23**	8.76 / **27.13**	8.74 / **27.05**
4	7.71 / **21.20**	6.94 / **18.00**	6.59 / **16.69**	6.39 / **15.98**	6.26 / **15.52**	6.16 / **15.21**	6.09 / **14.98**	6.04 / **14.80**	6.00 / **14.66**	5.96 / **14.54**	5.93 / **14.45**	5.91 / **14.37**
5	6.61 / **16.26**	5.79 / **13.27**	5.41 / **12.06**	5.19 / **11.39**	5.05 / **10.97**	4.95 / **10.67**	4.88 / **10.45**	4.82 / **10.27**	4.78 / **10.15**	4.74 / **10.05**	4.70 / **9.96**	4.68 / **9.89**
6	5.99 / **13.74**	5.14 / **10.92**	4.76 / **9.78**	4.53 / **9.15**	4.39 / **8.75**	4.28 / **8.47**	4.21 / **8.26**	4.15 / **8.10**	4.10 / **7.98**	4.06 / **7.87**	4.03 / **7.79**	4.00 / **7.72**
7	5.59 / **12.25**	4.74 / **9.55**	4.35 / **8.45**	4.12 / **7.85**	3.97 / **7.46**	3.87 / **7.19**	3.79 / **7.00**	3.73 / **6.84**	3.68 / **6.71**	3.63 / **6.62**	3.60 / **6.54**	3.57 / **6.47**
8	5.32 / **11.26**	4.46 / **8.65**	4.07 / **7.59**	3.84 / **7.01**	3.69 / **6.63**	3.58 / **6.37**	3.50 / **6.19**	3.44 / **6.03**	3.39 / **5.91**	3.34 / **5.82**	3.31 / **5.74**	3.28 / **5.67**
9	5.12 / **10.56**	4.26 / **8.02**	3.86 / **6.99**	3.63 / **6.42**	3.48 / **6.06**	3.37 / **5.80**	3.29 / **5.62**	3.23 / **5.47**	3.18 / **5.35**	3.13 / **5.26**	3.10 / **5.18**	3.07 / **5.11**
10	4.96 / **10.04**	4.10 / **7.56**	3.71 / **6.55**	3.48 / **5.99**	3.33 / **5.64**	3.22 / **5.39**	3.14 / **5.21**	3.07 / **5.06**	3.02 / **4.95**	2.97 / **4.85**	2.94 / **4.78**	2.91 / **4.71**
11	4.84 / **9.65**	3.98 / **7.20**	3.59 / **6.22**	3.36 / **5.67**	3.20 / **5.32**	3.09 / **5.07**	3.01 / **4.88**	2.95 / **4.74**	2.90 / **4.63**	2.86 / **4.54**	2.82 / **4.46**	2.79 / **4.40**
12	4.75 / **9.33**	3.88 / **6.93**	3.49 / **5.95**	3.26 / **5.41**	3.11 / **5.06**	3.00 / **4.82**	2.92 / **4.65**	2.85 / **4.50**	2.80 / **4.39**	2.76 / **4.30**	2.72 / **4.22**	2.69 / **4.16**
13	4.67 / **9.07**	3.80 / **6.70**	3.41 / **5.74**	3.18 / **5.20**	3.02 / **4.86**	2.92 / **4.62**	2.84 / **4.44**	2.77 / **4.30**	2.72 / **4.19**	2.67 / **4.10**	2.63 / **4.02**	2.60 / **3.96**
14	4.60 / **8.86**	3.74 / **6.51**	3.34 / **5.56**	3.11 / **5.03**	2.96 / **4.69**	2.85 / **4.46**	2.77 / **4.28**	2.70 / **4.14**	2.65 / **4.03**	2.60 / **3.94**	2.56 / **3.86**	2.53 / **3.80**
15	4.54 / **8.68**	3.68 / **6.36**	3.29 / **5.42**	3.06 / **4.89**	2.90 / **4.56**	2.79 / **4.32**	2.70 / **4.14**	2.64 / **4.00**	2.59 / **3.89**	2.55 / **3.80**	2.51 / **3.73**	2.48 / **3.67**
16	4.49 / **8.53**	3.63 / **6.23**	3.24 / **5.29**	3.01 / **4.77**	2.85 / **4.44**	2.74 / **4.20**	2.66 / **4.03**	2.59 / **3.89**	2.54 / **3.78**	2.49 / **3.69**	2.45 / **3.61**	2.42 / **3.55**
17	4.45 / **8.40**	3.59 / **6.11**	3.20 / **5.18**	2.96 / **4.67**	2.81 / **4.34**	2.70 / **4.10**	2.62 / **3.93**	2.55 / **3.79**	2.50 / **3.68**	2.45 / **3.59**	2.41 / **3.52**	2.38 / **3.45**
18	4.41 / **8.28**	3.55 / **6.01**	3.16 / **5.09**	2.93 / **4.58**	2.77 / **4.25**	2.66 / **4.01**	2.58 / **3.85**	2.51 / **3.71**	2.46 / **3.60**	2.41 / **3.51**	2.37 / **3.44**	2.34 / **3.37**
19	4.38 / **8.18**	3.52 / **5.93**	3.13 / **5.01**	2.90 / **4.50**	2.74 / **4.17**	2.63 / **3.94**	2.55 / **3.77**	2.48 / **3.63**	2.43 / **3.52**	2.38 / **3.43**	2.34 / **3.36**	2.31 / **3.30**
20	4.35 / **8.10**	3.49 / **5.85**	3.10 / **4.94**	2.87 / **4.43**	2.71 / **4.10**	2.60 / **3.87**	2.52 / **3.71**	2.45 / **3.56**	2.40 / **3.45**	2.35 / **3.37**	2.31 / **3.30**	2.28 / **3.23**
21	4.32 / **8.02**	3.47 / **5.78**	3.07 / **4.87**	2.84 / **4.37**	2.68 / **4.04**	2.57 / **3.81**	2.49 / **3.65**	2.42 / **3.51**	2.37 / **3.40**	2.32 / **3.31**	2.28 / **3.24**	2.25 / **3.17**
22	4.30 / **7.94**	3.44 / **5.72**	3.05 / **4.82**	2.82 / **4.31**	2.66 / **3.99**	2.55 / **3.76**	2.47 / **3.59**	2.40 / **3.45**	2.35 / **3.35**	2.30 / **3.26**	2.26 / **3.18**	2.23 / **3.12**
23	4.28 / **7.88**	3.42 / **5.66**	3.03 / **4.76**	2.80 / **4.26**	2.64 / **3.94**	2.53 / **3.71**	2.45 / **3.54**	2.38 / **3.41**	2.32 / **3.30**	2.28 / **3.21**	2.24 / **3.14**	2.20 / **3.07**
24	4.26 / **7.82**	3.40 / **5.61**	3.01 / **4.72**	2.78 / **4.22**	2.62 / **3.90**	2.51 / **3.67**	2.43 / **3.50**	2.36 / **3.36**	2.30 / **3.25**	2.26 / **3.17**	2.22 / **3.09**	2.18 / **3.03**
25	4.24 / **7.77**	3.38 / **5.57**	2.99 / **4.68**	2.76 / **4.18**	2.60 / **3.86**	2.49 / **3.63**	2.41 / **3.46**	2.34 / **3.32**	2.28 / **3.21**	2.24 / **3.13**	2.20 / **3.05**	2.16 / **2.99**
26	4.22 / **7.72**	3.37 / **5.53**	2.98 / **4.64**	2.74 / **4.14**	2.59 / **3.82**	2.47 / **3.59**	2.39 / **3.42**	2.32 / **3.29**	2.27 / **3.17**	2.22 / **3.09**	2.18 / **3.02**	2.15 / **2.96**

TABLE VII

Values of the F Distribution *

99th Percentile in Bold-Face Type

for numerator

14	16	20	24	30	40	50	75	100	200	500	∞	n_2
245	246	248	249	250	251	252	253	253	254	254	254	1
6,142	**6,169**	**6,208**	**6,234**	**6,258**	**6,286**	**6,302**	**6,323**	**6,334**	**6,352**	**6,361**	**6,366**	
19.42	19.43	19.44	19.45	19.46	19.47	19.47	19.48	19.49	19.49	19.50	19.50	2
99.43	**99.44**	**99.45**	**99.46**	**99.47**	**99.48**	**99.48**	**99.49**	**99.49**	**99.49**	**99.50**	**99.50**	
8.71	8.69	8.66	8.64	8.62	8.60	8.58	8.57	8.56	8.54	8.54	8.53	3
26.92	**26.83**	**26.69**	**26.60**	**26.50**	**26.41**	**26.35**	**26.27**	**26.23**	**26.18**	**26.14**	**26.12**	
5.87	5.84	5.80	5.77	5.74	5.71	5.70	5.68	5.66	5.65	5.64	5.63	4
14.24	**14.15**	**14.02**	**13.93**	**13.83**	**13.74**	**13.69**	**13.61**	**13.57**	**13.52**	**13.48**	**13.46**	
4.64	4.60	4.56	4.53	4.50	4.46	4.44	4.42	4.40	4.38	4.37	4.36	5
9.77	**9.68**	**9.55**	**9.47**	**9.38**	**9.29**	**9.24**	**9.17**	**9.13**	**9.07**	**9.04**	**9.02**	
3.96	3.92	3.87	3.84	3.81	3.77	3.75	3.72	3.71	3.69	3.68	3.67	6
7.60	**7.52**	**7.39**	**7.31**	**7.23**	**7.14**	**7.09**	**7.02**	**6.99**	**6.94**	**6.90**	**6.88**	
3.52	3.49	3.44	3.41	3.38	3.34	3.32	3.29	3.28	3.25	3.24	3.23	7
6.35	**6.27**	**6.15**	**6.07**	**5.98**	**5.90**	**5.85**	**5.78**	**5.75**	**5.70**	**5.67**	**5.65**	
3.23	3.20	3.15	3.12	3.08	3.05	3.03	3.00	2.98	2.96	2.94	2.93	8
5.56	**5.48**	**5.36**	**5.28**	**5.20**	**5.11**	**5.06**	**5.00**	**4.96**	**4.91**	**4.88**	**4.86**	
3.02	2.98	2.93	2.90	2.86	2.82	2.80	2.77	2.76	2.73	2.72	2.71	9
5.00	**4.92**	**4.80**	**4.73**	**4.64**	**4.56**	**4.51**	**4.45**	**4.41**	**4.36**	**4.33**	**4.31**	
2.80	2.82	2.77	2.74	2.70	2.67	2.64	2.61	2.59	2.56	2.55	2.54	10
4.60	**4.52**	**4.41**	**4.33**	**4.25**	**4.17**	**4.12**	**4.05**	**4.01**	**3.96**	**3.93**	**3.91**	
2.74	2.70	2.65	2.61	2.57	2.53	2.50	2.47	2.45	2.42	2.41	2.40	11
4.29	**4.21**	**4.10**	**4.02**	**3.94**	**3.86**	**3.80**	**3.74**	**3.70**	**3.66**	**3.62**	**3.60**	
2.64	2.60	2.54	2.50	2.46	2.42	2.40	2.36	2.35	2.32	2.31	2.30	12
4.05	**3.98**	**3.86**	**3.78**	**3.70**	**3.61**	**3.56**	**3.49**	**3.46**	**3.41**	**3.38**	**3.36**	
2.55	2.51	2.46	2.42	2.38	2.34	2.32	2.28	2.26	2.24	2.22	2.21	13
3.85	**3.78**	**3.67**	**3.59**	**3.51**	**3.42**	**3.37**	**3.30**	**3.27**	**3.21**	**3.18**	**3.16**	
2.48	2.44	2.39	2.35	2.31	2.27	2.24	2.21	2.19	2.16	2.14	2.13	14
3.70	**3.62**	**3.51**	**3.43**	**3.34**	**3.26**	**3.21**	**3.14**	**3.11**	**3.06**	**3.02**	**3.00**	
2.43	2.39	2.33	2.29	2.25	2.21	2.18	2.15	2.12	2.10	2.08	2.07	15
3.56	**3.48**	**3.36**	**3.29**	**3.20**	**3.12**	**3.07**	**3.00**	**2.97**	**2.92**	**2.89**	**2.87**	
2.37	2.33	2.28	2.24	2.20	2.16	2.13	2.09	2.07	2.04	2.02	2.01	16
3.45	**3.37**	**3.25**	**3.18**	**3.10**	**3.01**	**2.96**	**2.89**	**2.86**	**2.80**	**2.77**	**2.75**	
2.33	2.29	2.23	2.19	2.15	2.11	2.08	2.04	2.02	1.99	1.97	1.96	17
3.35	**3.27**	**3.16**	**3.08**	**3.00**	**2.92**	**2.86**	**2.79**	**2.76**	**2.70**	**2.67**	**2.65**	
2.29	2.25	2.19	2.15	2.11	2.07	2.04	2.00	1.98	1.95	1.93	1.92	18
3.27	**3.19**	**3.07**	**3.00**	**2.91**	**2.83**	**2.78**	**2.71**	**2.68**	**2.62**	**2.59**	**2.57**	
2.26	2.21	2.15	2.11	2.07	2.02	2.00	1.96	1.94	1.91	1.90	1.88	19
3.19	**3.12**	**3.00**	**2.92**	**2.84**	**2.76**	**2.70**	**2.63**	**2.60**	**2.54**	**2.51**	**2.49**	
2.23	2.18	2.12	2.08	2.04	1.99	1.96	1.92	1.90	1.87	1.85	1.84	20
3.13	**3.05**	**2.94**	**2.86**	**2.77**	**2.69**	**2.63**	**2.56**	**2.53**	**2.47**	**2.44**	**2.42**	
2.20	2.15	2.09	2.05	2.00	1.96	1.93	1.89	1.87	1.84	1.82	1.81	21
3.07	**2.99**	**2.88**	**2.80**	**2.72**	**2.63**	**2.58**	**2.51**	**2.47**	**2.42**	**2.38**	**2.36**	
2.18	2.13	2.07	2.03	1.98	1.93	1.91	1.87	1.84	1.81	1.80	1.78	22
3.02	**2.94**	**2.83**	**2.75**	**2.67**	**2.58**	**2.53**	**2.46**	**2.42**	**2.37**	**2.33**	**2.31**	
2.14	2.10	2.04	2.00	1.96	1.91	1.88	1.84	1.82	1.79	1.77	1.76	23
2.97	**2.89**	**2.78**	**2.70**	**2.62**	**2.53**	**2.48**	**2.41**	**2.37**	**2.32**	**2.28**	**2.26**	
2.13	2.09	2.02	1.98	1.94	1.89	1.86	1.82	1.80	1.76	1.74	1.73	24
2.93	**2.85**	**2.74**	**2.66**	**2.58**	**2.49**	**2.44**	**2.36**	**2.33**	**2.27**	**2.23**	**2.21**	
2.11	2.06	2.00	1.96	1.92	1.87	1.84	1.80	1.77	1.74	1.72	1.71	25
2.89	**2.81**	**2.70**	**2.62**	**2.54**	**2.45**	**2.40**	**2.32**	**2.29**	**2.23**	**2.19**	**2.17**	
2.10	2.05	1.99	1.95	1.90	1.85	1.82	1.78	1.76	1.72	1.70	1.69	26
2.86	**2.77**	**2.66**	**2.58**	**2.50**	**2.41**	**2.36**	**2.28**	**2.25**	**2.19**	**2.15**	**2.13**	

n_2 = degrees of freedom for denominator

* Reproduced, with the permission of author and publisher, from *Statistical Methods*, 4th ed., by George W. Snedecor, Iowa State College Press, 1946.

95th and 99th Percentile

95th Percentile in Light-Face Type,

n_1 = degrees of freedom

n_2 = degrees of freedom for denominator

n_2	1	2	3	4	5	6	7	8	9	10	11	12
27	4.21 **7.68**	3.35 **5.49**	2.96 **4.60**	2.73 **4.11**	2.57 **3.79**	2.46 **3.56**	2.37 **3.39**	2.30 **3.26**	2.25 **3.14**	2.20 **3.06**	2.16 **2.98**	2.13 **2.93**
28	4.20 **7.64**	3.34 **5.45**	2.95 **4.57**	2.71 **4.07**	2.56 **3.76**	2.44 **3.53**	2.36 **3.36**	2.29 **3.23**	2.24 **3.11**	2.19 **3.03**	2.15 **2.95**	2.12 **2.90**
29	4.18 **7.60**	3.33 **5.42**	2.93 **4.54**	2.70 **4.04**	2.54 **3.73**	2.43 **3.50**	2.35 **3.33**	2.28 **3.20**	2.22 **3.08**	2.18 **3.00**	2.14 **2.92**	2.10 **2.87**
30	4.17 **7.56**	3.32 **5.39**	2.92 **4.51**	2.69 **4.02**	2.53 **3.70**	2.42 **3.47**	2.34 **3.30**	2.27 **3.17**	2.21 **3.06**	2.16 **2.98**	2.12 **2.90**	2.09 **2.84**
32	4.15 **7.50**	3.30 **5.34**	2.90 **4.46**	2.67 **3.97**	2.51 **3.66**	2.40 **3.42**	2.32 **3.25**	2.25 **3.12**	2.19 **3.01**	2.14 **2.94**	2.10 **2.86**	2.07 **2.80**
34	4.13 **7.44**	3.28 **5.29**	2.88 **4.42**	2.65 **3.93**	2.49 **3.61**	2.38 **3.38**	2.30 **3.21**	2.23 **3.08**	2.17 **2.97**	2.12 **2.89**	2.08 **2.82**	2.05 **2.76**
36	4.11 **7.39**	3.26 **5.25**	2.86 **4.38**	2.63 **3.89**	2.48 **3.58**	2.36 **3.35**	2.28 **3.18**	2.21 **3.04**	2.15 **2.94**	2.10 **2.86**	2.06 **2.78**	2.03 **2.72**
38	4.10 **7.35**	3.25 **5.21**	2.85 **4.34**	2.62 **3.86**	2.46 **3.54**	2.35 **3.32**	2.26 **3.15**	2.19 **3.02**	2.14 **2.91**	2.09 **2.82**	2.05 **2.75**	2.02 **2.69**
40	4.08 **7.31**	3.23 **5.18**	2.84 **4.31**	2.61 **3.83**	2.45 **3.51**	2.34 **3.29**	2.25 **3.12**	2.18 **2.99**	2.12 **2.88**	2.07 **2.80**	2.04 **2.73**	2.00 **2.66**
42	4.07 **7.27**	3.22 **5.15**	2.83 **4.29**	2.59 **3.80**	2.44 **3.49**	2.32 **3.26**	2.24 **3.10**	2.17 **2.96**	2.11 **2.86**	2.06 **2.77**	2.02 **2.70**	1.99 **2.64**
44	4.06 **7.24**	3.21 **5.12**	2.82 **4.26**	2.58 **3.78**	2.43 **3.46**	2.31 **3.24**	2.23 **3.07**	2.16 **2.94**	2.10 **2.84**	2.05 **2.75**	2.01 **2.68**	1.98 **2.62**
46	4.05 **7.21**	3.20 **5.10**	2.81 **4.24**	2.57 **3.76**	2.42 **3.44**	2.30 **3.22**	2.22 **3.05**	2.14 **2.92**	2.09 **2.82**	2.04 **2.73**	2.00 **2.66**	1.97 **2.60**
48	4.04 **7.19**	3.19 **5.08**	2.80 **4.22**	2.56 **3.74**	2.41 **3.42**	2.30 **3.20**	2.21 **3.04**	2.14 **2.90**	2.08 **2.80**	2.03 **2.71**	1.99 **2.64**	1.96 **2.58**
50	4.03 **7.17**	3.18 **5.06**	2.79 **4.20**	2.56 **3.72**	2.40 **3.41**	2.29 **3.18**	2.20 **3.02**	2.13 **2.88**	2.07 **2.78**	2.02 **2.70**	1.98 **2.62**	1.95 **2.56**
55	4.02 **7.12**	3.17 **5.01**	2.78 **4.16**	2.54 **3.68**	2.38 **3.37**	2.27 **3.15**	2.18 **2.98**	2.11 **2.85**	2.05 **2.75**	2.00 **2.66**	1.97 **2.59**	1.93 **2.53**
60	4.00 **7.08**	3.15 **4.98**	2.76 **4.13**	2.52 **3.65**	2.37 **3.34**	2.25 **3.12**	2.17 **2.95**	2.10 **2.82**	2.04 **2.72**	1.99 **2.63**	1.95 **2.56**	1.92 **2.50**
65	3.99 **7.04**	3.14 **4.95**	2.75 **4.10**	2.51 **3.62**	2.36 **3.31**	2.24 **3.09**	2.15 **2.93**	2.08 **2.79**	2.02 **2.70**	1.98 **2.61**	1.94 **2.54**	1.90 **2.47**
70	3.98 **7.01**	3.13 **4.92**	2.74 **4.08**	2.50 **3.60**	2.35 **3.29**	2.23 **3.07**	2.14 **2.91**	2.07 **2.77**	2.01 **2.67**	1.97 **2.59**	1.93 **2.51**	1.89 **2.45**
80	3.96 **6.96**	3.11 **4.88**	2.72 **4.04**	2.48 **3.56**	2.33 **3.25**	2.21 **3.04**	2.12 **2.87**	2.05 **2.74**	1.99 **2.64**	1.95 **2.55**	1.91 **2.48**	1.88 **2.41**
100	3.94 **6.90**	3.09 **4.82**	2.70 **3.98**	2.46 **3.51**	2.30 **3.20**	2.19 **2.99**	2.10 **2.82**	2.03 **2.69**	1.97 **2.59**	1.92 **2.51**	1.88 **2.43**	1.85 **2.36**
125	3.92 **6.84**	3.07 **4.78**	2.68 **3.94**	2.44 **3.47**	2.29 **3.17**	2.17 **2.95**	2.08 **2.79**	2.01 **2.65**	1.95 **2.56**	1.90 **2.47**	1.86 **2.40**	1.83 **2.33**
150	3.91 **6.81**	3.06 **4.75**	2.67 **3.91**	2.43 **3.44**	2.27 **3.14**	2.16 **2.92**	2.07 **2.76**	2.00 **2.62**	1.94 **2.53**	1.89 **2.44**	1.85 **2.37**	1.82 **2.30**
200	3.89 **6.76**	3.04 **4.71**	2.65 **3.88**	2.41 **3.41**	2.26 **3.11**	2.14 **2.90**	2.05 **2.73**	1.98 **2.60**	1.92 **2.50**	1.87 **2.41**	1.83 **2.34**	1.80 **2.28**
400	3.86 **6.70**	3.02 **4.66**	2.62 **3.83**	2.39 **3.36**	2.23 **3.06**	2.12 **2.85**	2.03 **2.69**	1.96 **2.55**	1.90 **2.46**	1.85 **2.37**	1.81 **2.29**	1.78 **2.23**
1,000	3.85 **6.66**	3.00 **4.62**	2.61 **3.80**	2.38 **3.34**	2.22 **3.04**	2.10 **2.82**	2.02 **2.66**	1.95 **2.53**	1.89 **2.43**	1.84 **2.34**	1.80 **2.26**	1.76 **2.20**
∞	3.84 **6.64**	2.99 **4.60**	2.60 **3.78**	2.37 **3.32**	2.21 **3.02**	2.09 **2.80**	2.01 **2.64**	1.94 **2.51**	1.88 **2.41**	1.83 **2.32**	1.79 **2.24**	1.75 **2.18**

TABLE VII — *Continued*

Values of the *F* Distribution (*Continued*)

99th Percentile in Bold-Face Type

for numerator

14	16	20	24	30	40	50	75	100	200	500	∞	n_1
2.08	2.03	1.97	1.93	1.88	1.84	1.80	1.76	1.74	1.71	1.68	1.67	27
2.83	**2.74**	**2.63**	**2.55**	**2.47**	**2.38**	**2.33**	**2.25**	**2.21**	**2.16**	**2.12**	**2.10**	
2.06	2.02	1.96	1.91	1.87	1.81	1.78	1.75	1.72	1.69	1.67	1.65	28
2.80	**2.71**	**2.60**	**2.52**	**2.44**	**2.35**	**2.30**	**2.22**	**2.18**	**2.13**	**2.09**	**2.06**	
2.05	2.00	1.94	1.90	1.85	1.80	1.77	1.73	1.71	1.68	1.65	1.64	29
2.77	**2.68**	**2.57**	**2.49**	**2.41**	**2.32**	**2.27**	**2.19**	**2.15**	**2.10**	**2.06**	**2.03**	
2.04	1.99	1.93	1.89	1.84	1.79	1.76	1.72	1.69	1.66	1.64	1.62	30
2.74	**2.66**	**2.55**	**2.47**	**2.38**	**2.29**	**2.24**	**2.16**	**2.13**	**2.07**	**2.03**	**2.01**	
2.02	1.97	1.91	1.86	1.82	1.76	1.74	1.69	1.67	1.64	1.61	1.59	32
2.70	**2.62**	**2.51**	**2.42**	**2.34**	**2.25**	**2.20**	**2.12**	**2.08**	**2.02**	**1.98**	**1.96**	
2.00	1.95	1.89	1.84	1.80	1.74	1.71	1.67	1.64	1.61	1.59	1.57	34
2.66	**2.58**	**2.47**	**2.38**	**2.30**	**2.21**	**2.15**	**2.08**	**2.04**	**1.98**	**1.94**	**1.91**	
1.98	1.93	1.87	1.82	1.78	1.72	1.69	1.65	1.62	1.59	1.56	1.55	36
2.62	**2.54**	**2.43**	**2.35**	**2.26**	**2.17**	**2.12**	**2.04**	**2.00**	**1.94**	**1.90**	**1.87**	
1.90	1.92	1.85	1.80	1.76	1.71	1.67	1.63	1.60	1.57	1.54	1.53	38
2.59	**2.51**	**2.40**	**2.32**	**2.22**	**2.14**	**2.08**	**2.00**	**1.97**	**1.90**	**1.86**	**1.84**	
1.95	1.90	1.84	1.79	1.74	1.69	1.66	1.61	1.59	1.55	1.53	1.51	40
2.56	**2.49**	**2.37**	**2.29**	**2.20**	**2.11**	**2.05**	**1.97**	**1.94**	**1.88**	**1.84**	**1.81**	
1.94	1.89	1.82	1.78	1.73	1.68	1.64	1.60	1.57	1.54	1.51	1.49	42
2.54	**2.46**	**2.35**	**2.26**	**2.17**	**2.08**	**2.02**	**1.94**	**1.91**	**1.85**	**1.80**	**1.78**	
1.92	1.88	1.81	1.76	1.72	1.66	1.63	1.58	1.56	1.52	1.50	1.48	44
2.52	**2.44**	**2.32**	**2.24**	**2.15**	**2.06**	**2.00**	**1.92**	**1.88**	**1.82**	**1.78**	**1.75**	
1.91	1.87	1.80	1.75	1.71	1.65	1.62	1.57	1.54	1.51	1.48	1.46	46
2.50	**2.42**	**2.30**	**2.22**	**2.13**	**2.04**	**1.98**	**1.90**	**1.86**	**1.80**	**1.76**	**1.72**	
1.90	1.86	1.79	1.74	1.70	1.64	1.61	1.56	1.53	1.50	1.47	1.45	48
2.48	**2.40**	**2.28**	**2.20**	**2.11**	**2.02**	**1.96**	**1.88**	**1.84**	**1.78**	**1.73**	**1.70**	
1.90	1.85	1.78	1.74	1.69	1.63	1.60	1.55	1.52	1.48	1.46	1.44	50
2.46	**2.39**	**2.26**	**2.18**	**2.10**	**2.00**	**1.94**	**1.86**	**1.82**	**1.76**	**1.71**	**1.68**	
1.88	1.83	1.76	1.72	1.67	1.61	1.58	1.52	1.50	1.46	1.43	1.41	55
2.43	**2.35**	**2.23**	**2.15**	**2.06**	**1.96**	**1.90**	**1.82**	**1.78**	**1.71**	**1.66**	**1.64**	
1.86	1.81	1.75	1.70	1.65	1.59	1.56	1.50	1.48	1.44	1.41	1.39	60
2.40	**2.32**	**2.20**	**2.12**	**2.03**	**1.93**	**1.87**	**1.79**	**1.74**	**1.68**	**1.63**	**1.60**	
1.85	1.80	1.73	1.68	1.63	1.57	1.54	1.49	1.46	1.42	1.39	1.37	65
2.37	**2.30**	**2.18**	**2.09**	**2.00**	**1.90**	**1.84**	**1.76**	**1.71**	**1.64**	**1.60**	**1.56**	
1.84	1.79	1.72	1.67	1.62	1.56	1.53	1.47	1.45	1.40	1.37	1.35	70
2.35	**2.28**	**2.15**	**2.07**	**1.98**	**1.88**	**1.82**	**1.74**	**1.69**	**1.62**	**1.56**	**1.53**	
1.82	1.77	1.70	1.65	1.60	1.54	1.51	1.45	1.42	1.38	1.35	1.32	80
2.32	**2.24**	**2.11**	**2.03**	**1.94**	**1.84**	**1.78**	**1.70**	**1.65**	**1.57**	**1.52**	**1.49**	
1.79	1.75	1.68	1.63	1.57	1.51	1.48	1.42	1.39	1.34	1.30	1.28	100
2.26	**2.19**	**2.06**	**1.98**	**1.89**	**1.79**	**1.73**	**1.64**	**1.59**	**1.51**	**1.46**	**1.43**	
1.77	1.72	1.65	1.60	1.55	1.49	1.45	1.39	1.36	1.31	1.27	1.25	125
2.23	**2.15**	**2.03**	**1.94**	**1.85**	**1.75**	**1.68**	**1.59**	**1.54**	**1.46**	**1.40**	**1.37**	
1.76	1.71	1.64	1.59	1.54	1.47	1.44	1.37	1.34	1.29	1.25	1.22	150
2.20	**2.12**	**2.00**	**1.91**	**1.83**	**1.72**	**1.66**	**1.56**	**1.51**	**1.43**	**1.37**	**1.33**	
1.74	1.60	1.62	1.57	1.52	1.45	1.42	1.35	1.32	1.26	1.22	1.19	200
2.17	**2.09**	**1.97**	**1.88**	**1.79**	**1.69**	**1.62**	**1.53**	**1.48**	**1.39**	**1.33**	**1.28**	
1.72	1.67	1.60	1.54	1.49	1.42	1.38	1.32	1.28	1.22	1.16	1.13	400
2.12	**2.04**	**1.92**	**1.84**	**1.74**	**1.64**	**1.57**	**1.47**	**1.42**	**1.32**	**1.24**	**1.19**	
1.70	1.65	1.58	1.53	1.47	1.41	1.36	1.30	1.26	1.19	1.13	1.08	1,000
2.09	**2.01**	**1.89**	**1.81**	**1.71**	**1.61**	**1.54**	**1.44**	**1.38**	**1.28**	**1.19**	**1.11**	
1.69	1.64	1.57	1.52	1.46	1.40	1.35	1.28	1.24	1.17	1.11	1.00	∞
2.07	**1.99**	**1.87**	**1.79**	**1.69**	**1.59**	**1.52**	**1.41**	**1.36**	**1.25**	**1.15**	**1.00**	

n_2 = degrees of freedom for denominator

APPENDIX TABLE VIII

First Six Powers of the Natural Numbers from 1 to 50

n	n^2	n^3	n^4	n^5	n^6	n
1	1	1	1	1	1	1
2	4	8	16	32	64	2
3	9	27	81	243	729	3
4	16	64	256	1 024	4 096	4
5	25	125	625	3 125	15 625	5
6	36	216	1 296	7 776	46 656	6
7	49	343	2 401	16 807	117 649	7
8	64	512	4 096	32 768	262 144	8
9	81	729	6 561	59 049	531 441	9
10	100	1 000	10 000	100 000	1 000 000	10
11	121	1 331	14 641	161 051	1 771 561	11
12	144	1 728	20 736	248 832	2 985 984	12
13	169	2 197	28 561	371 293	4 826 809	13
14	196	2 744	38 416	537 824	7 529 536	14
15	225	3 375	50 625	759 375	11 390 625	15
16	256	4 096	65 536	1 048 576	16 777 216	16
17	289	4 913	83 521	1 419 857	24 137 569	17
18	324	5 832	104 976	1 889 568	34 012 224	18
19	361	6 859	130 321	2 476 099	47 045 881	19
20	400	8 000	160 000	3 200 000	64 000 000	20
21	441	9 261	194 481	4 084 101	85 766 121	21
22	484	10 648	234 256	5 153 632	113 379 904	22
23	529	12 167	279 841	6 436 343	148 035 889	23
24	576	13 824	331 776	7 962 624	191 102 976	24
25	625	15 625	390 625	9 765 625	244 140 625	25
26	676	17 576	456 976	11 881 376	308 915 776	26
27	729	19 683	531 441	14 348 907	387 420 489	27
28	784	21 952	614 656	17 210 368	481 890 304	28
29	841	24 389	707 281	20 511 149	594 823 321	29
30	900	27 000	810 000	24 300 000	729 000 000	30
31	961	29 791	923 521	28 629 151	887 503 681	31
32	1 024	32 768	1 048 576	33 554 432	1 073 741 824	32
33	1 089	35 937	1 185 921	39 135 393	1 291 467 969	33
34	1 156	39 304	1 336 336	45 435 424	1 544 804 416	34
35	1 225	42 875	1 500 625	52 521 875	1 838 265 625	35
36	1 296	46 656	1 679 616	60 466 176	2 176 782 336	36
37	1 369	50 653	1 874 161	69 343 957	2 565 726 409	37
38	1 444	54 872	2 085 136	79 235 168	3 010 936 384	38
39	1 521	59 319	2 313 441	90 224 199	3 518 743 761	39
40	1 600	64 000	2 560 000	102 400 000	4 096 000 000	40
41	1 681	68 921	2 825 761	115 856 201	4 750 104 241	41
42	1 764	74 088	3 111 696	130 691 232	5 489 031 744	42
43	1 849	79 507	3 418 801	147 008 443	6 321 363 049	43
44	1 936	85 184	3 748 096	164 916 224	7 256 313 856	44
45	2 025	91 125	4 100 625	184 528 125	8 303 765 625	45
46	2 116	97 336	4 477 456	205 962 976	9 474 296 896	46
47	2 209	103 823	4 879 681	229 345 007	10 779 215 329	47
48	2 304	110 592	5 308 416	254 803 968	12 230 590 464	48
49	2 401	117 649	5 764 801	282 475 249	13 841 287 201	49
50	2 500	125 000	6 250 000	312 500 000	15 625 000 000	50

Sums of the First Six Powers of the Natural Numbers from 1 to 50

n	$\Sigma(n)$	$\Sigma(n^2)$	$\Sigma(n^3)$	$\Sigma(n^4)$	$\Sigma(n^5)$	$\Sigma(n^6)$
1	1	1	1	1	1	1
2	3	5	9	17	33	65
3	6	14	36	98	276	794
4	10	30	100	354	1 300	4 890
5	15	55	225	979	4 425	20 515
6	21	91	441	2 275	12 201	67 171
7	28	140	784	4 676	29 008	184 820
8	36	204	1 296	8 772	61 776	446 964
9	45	285	2 025	15 333	120 825	978 405
10	55	385	3 025	25 333	220 825	1 978 405
11	66	506	4 356	39 974	381 876	3 749 966
12	78	650	6 084	60 710	630 708	6 735 950
13	91	819	8 281	89 271	1 002 001	11 562 759
14	105	1 015	11 025	127 687	1 539 825	19 092 295
15	120	1 240	14 400	178 312	2 299 200	30 482 920
16	136	1 496	18 496	234 848	3 347 776	47 260 136
17	153	1 785	20 409	327 369	4 767 633	71 397 705
18	171	2 109	29 241	432 345	6 657 201	105 409 929
19	190	2 470	36 100	562 666	9 133 300	152 455 810
20	210	2 870	44 100	722 666	12 333 300	216 455 810
21	231	3 311	53 361	917 147	16 417 401	302 221 931
22	253	3 795	64 009	1 151 403	21 571 033	415 601 835
23	276	4 324	76 176	1 431 244	28 007 376	563 637 724
24	300	4 900	90 000	1 763 020	35 970 000	754 740 700
25	325	5 525	105 625	2 153 645	45 735 625	998 881 325
26	351	6 201	123 201	2 610 621	57 617 001	1 307 797 101
27	378	6 930	142 884	3 142 062	71 965 908	1 695 217 590
28	406	7 714	164 036	3 756 718	89 176 276	2 177 107 894
29	435	8 555	189 225	4 463 999	109 687 425	2 771 931 215
30	465	9 455	216 225	5 273 999	133 987 425	3 500 931 215
31	496	10 416	246 016	6 197 520	162 616 576	4 388 434 896
32	528	11 440	278 784	7 246 096	196 171 008	5 462 176 720
33	561	12 529	314 721	8 432 017	235 306 401	6 753 644 689
34	595	13 685	354 025	9 768 353	280 741 825	8 298 449 105
35	630	14 910	396 900	11 268 978	333 263 700	10 136 714 730
36	666	16 206	443 556	12 948 594	393 729 876	12 313 497 066
37	703	17 575	494 209	14 822 755	463 073 833	14 879 223 475
38	741	19 019	549 081	16 907 891	542 309 001	17 890 159 859
39	780	20 540	608 400	19 221 332	632 533 200	21 408 903 620
40	820	22 140	672 400	21 781 332	734 933 200	25 504 903 620
41	861	23 821	741 321	24 607 093	850 789 401	30 255 007 861
42	903	25 585	815 409	27 718 789	981 480 633	35 744 039 605
43	946	27 434	894 916	31 137 590	1 128 489 076	42 065 402 654
44	990	29 370	980 100	34 885 686	1 293 405 300	49 321 716 510
45	1 035	31 395	1 071 225	38 986 311	1 477 933 425	57 625 482 135
46	1 081	33 511	1 168 561	43 463 767	1 683 896 401	67 099 779 031
47	1 128	35 720	1 272 384	48 343 448	1 913 241 408	77 878 994 360
48	1 176	38 024	1 382 976	53 651 864	2 168 045 376	90 109 584 824
49	1 225	40 425	1 500 625	59 416 665	2 450 520 625	103 950 872 025
50	1 275	42 925	1 625 625	65 666 665	2 763 020 625	119 575 872 025

Squares, Square Roots, and Reciprocals of the
Natural Numbers from 1 to 1,000

n	n^2	$n^{1/2}$	$1/n$
1	1	1.000 0000	1.000 000 000
2	4	1.414 2136	0.500 000 000
3	9	1.732 0508	.333 333 333
4	16	2.000 0000	.250 000 000
5	25	2.236 0680	.200 000 000
6	36	2.449 4897	.166 666 667
7	49	2.645 7513	.142 857 143
8	64	2.828 4271	.125 000 000
9	81	3.000 0000	.111 111 111
10	1 00	3.162 2777	.100 000 000
11	1 21	3.316 6248	.090 909 091
12	1 44	3.464 1016	.083 333 333
13	1 69	3.605 5513	.076 923 077
14	1 96	3.741 6574	.071 428 571
15	2 25	3.872 9833	.066 666 667
16	2 56	4.000 0000	.062 500 000
17	2 89	4.123 1056	.058 823 529
18	3 24	4.242 6407	.055 555 556
19	3 61	4.358 8989	.052 631 579
20	4 00	4.472 1360	.050 000 000
21	4 41	4.582 5757	.047 619 048
22	4 84	4.690 4158	.045 454 545
23	5 29	4.795 8315	.043 478 261
24	5 76	4.898 9795	.041 666 667
25	6 25	5.000 0000	.040 000 000
26	6 76	5.099 0195	.038 461 538
27	7 29	5.196 1524	.037 037 037
28	7 84	5.291 5026	.035 714 286
29	8 41	5.385 1648	.034 482 759
30	9 00	5.477 2256	.033 333 333
31	9 61	5.567 7644	.032 258 065
32	10 24	5.656 8542	.031 250 000
33	10 89	5.744 5626	.030 303 030
34	11 56	5.830 9519	.029 411 765
35	12 25	5.916 0798	.028 571 429
36	12 96	6.000 0000	.027 777 778
37	13 69	6.082 7625	.027 027 027
38	14 44	6.164 4140	.026 315 789
39	15 21	6.244 9980	.025 641 026
40	16 00	6.324 5553	.025 000 000
41	16 81	6.403 1242	.024 390 244
42	17 64	6.480 7407	.023 809 524
43	18 49	6.557 4385	.023 255 814
44	19 36	6.633 2496	.022 727 273
45	20 25	6.708 2039	.022 222 222
46	21 16	6.782 3300	.021 739 130
47	22 09	6.855 6546	.021 276 596
48	23 04	6.928 2032	.020 833 333
49	24 01	7.000 0000	.020 408 163
50	25 00	7.071 0678	.020 000 000

Squares, Square Roots, and Reciprocals of the
Natural Numbers from 1 to 1,000

n	n^2	$n^{1/2}$	$1/n$
51	26 01	7.141 4284	.019 607 843
52	27 04	7.211 1026	.019 230 769
53	28 09	7.280 1099	.018 867 925
54	29 16	7.348 4692	.018 518 519
55	30 25	7.416 1985	.018 181 818
56	31 36	7.483 3148	.017 857 143
57	32 49	7.549 8344	.017 543 860
58	33 64	7.615 7731	.017 241 379
59	34 81	7.681 1457	.016 949 153
60	36 00	7.745 9667	.016 666 667
61	37 21	7.810 2497	.016 393 443
62	38 44	7.874 0079	.016 129 032
63	39 69	7.937 2539	.015 873 016
64	40 96	8.000 0000	.015 625 000
65	42 25	8.062 2577	.015 384 615
66	43 56	8.124 0384	.015 151 515
67	44 89	8.185 3528	.014 925 373
68	46 24	8.246 2113	.014 705 882
69	47 61	8.306 6239	.014 492 754
70	49 00	8.366 6003	.014 285 714
71	50 41	8.426 1498	.014 084 507
72	51 84	8.485 2814	.013 888 889
73	53 29	8.544 0037	.013 698 630
74	54 76	8.602 3253	.013 513 514
75	56 25	8.660 2540	.013 333 333
76	57 76	8.717 7979	.013 157 895
77	59 29	8.774 9644	.012 987 013
78	60 84	8.831 7609	.012 820 513
79	62 41	8.888 1944	.012 658 228
80	64 00	8.944 2719	.012 500 000
81	65 61	9.000 0000	.012 345 679
82	67 24	9.055 3851	.012 195 122
83	68 89	9.110 4336	.012 048 193
84	70 56	9.165 1514	.011 904 762
85	72 25	9.219 5445	.011 764 706
86	73 96	9.273 6185	.011 627 907
87	75 69	9.327 3791	.011 494 253
88	77 44	9.380 8315	.011 363 636
89	79 21	9.433 9811	.011 235 955
90	81 00	9.486 8330	.011 111 111
91	82 81	9.539 3920	.010 989 011
92	84 64	9.591 6630	.010 869 565
93	86 49	9.643 6508	.010 752 688
94	88 36	9.695 3597	.010 638 298
95	90 25	9.746 7943	.010 526 316
96	92 16	9.797 9590	.010 416 667
97	94 09	9.848 8578	.010 309 278
98	96 04	9.899 4949	.010 204 082
99	98 01	9.949 8744	.010 101 010
100	1 00 00	10.000 0000	.010 000 000

Squares, Square Roots, and Reciprocals of the
Natural Numbers from 1 to 1,000

n	n^2	$n^{1/2}$	$1/n$
101	1 02 01	10.049 8756	.009 900 990
102	1 04 04	10.099 5049	.009 803 922
103	1 06 09	10.148 8916	.009 708 738
104	1 08 16	10.198 0390	.009 615 385
105	1 10 25	10.246 9508	.009 523 810
106	1 12 36	10.295 6301	.009 433 962
107	1 14 49	10.344 0804	.009 345 794
108	1 16 64	10.392 3048	.009 259 259
109	1 18 81	10.440 3065	.009 174 312
110	1 21 00	10.488 0885	.009 090 909
111	1 23 21	10.535 6538	.009 009 009
112	1 25 44	10.583 0052	.008 928 571
113	1 27 69	10.630 1458	.008 849 558
114	1 29 96	10.677 0783	.008 771 930
115	1 32 25	10.723 8053	.008 695 652
116	1 34 56	10.770 3296	.008 620 690
117	1 36 89	10.816 6538	.008 547 009
118	1 39 24	10.862 7805	.008 474 576
119	1 41 61	10.908 7121	.008 403 361
120	1 44 00	10.954 4512	.008 333 333
121	1 46 41	11.000 0000	.008 264 463
122	1 48 84	11.045 3610	.008 196 721
123	1 51 29	11.090 5365	.008 130 081
124	1 53 76	11.135 5287	.008 064 516
125	1 56 25	11.180 3399	.008 000 000
126	1 58 76	11.224 9722	.007 936 508
127	1 61 29	11.269 4277	.007 874 016
128	1 63 84	11.313 7085	.007 812 500
129	1 66 41	11.357 8167	.007 751 938
130	1 69 00	11.401 7543	.007 692 308
131	1 71 61	11.445 5231	.007 633 588
132	1 74 24	11.489 1253	.007 575 758
133	1 76 89	11.532 5626	.007 518 797
134	1 79 56	11.575 8369	.007 462 687
135	1 82 25	11.618 9500	.007 407 407
136	1 84 96	11.661 9038	.007 352 941
137	1 87 69	11.704 6999	.007 299 270
138	1 90 44	11.747 3401	.007 246 377
139	1 93 21	11.789 8261	.007 194 245
140	1 96 00	11.832 1596	.007 142 857
141	1 98 81	11.874 3422	.007 092 199
142	2 01 64	11.916 3753	.007 042 254
143	2 04 49	11.958 2607	.006 993 007
144	2 07 36	12.000 0000	.006 944 444
145	2 10 25	12.041 5946	.006 896 552
146	2 13 16	12.083 0460	.006 849 315
147	2 16 09	12.124 3557	.006 802 721
148	2 19 04	12.165 5251	.006 756 757
149	2 22 01	12.206 5556	.006 711 409
150	2 25 00	12.247 4487	.006 666 667

Squares, Square Roots, and Reciprocals of the
Natural Numbers from 1 to 1,000

n	n^2	$n^{1/2}$	$1/n$
151	2 28 01	12.288 2057	.006 622 517
152	2 31 04	12.328 8280	.006 578 947
153	2 34 09	12.369 3169	.006 535 948
154	2 37 16	12.409 6736	.006 493 506
155	2 40 25	12.449 8996	.006 451 613
156	2 43 36	12.489 9960	.006 410 256
157	2 46 49	12.529 9641	.006 369 427
158	2 49 64	12.569 8051	.006 329 114
159	2 52 81	12.609 5202	.006 289 308
160	2 56 00	12.649 1106	.006 250 000
161	2 59 21	12.688 5775	.006 211 180
162	2 62 44	12.727 9221	.006 172 840
163	2 65 69	12.767 1453	.006 134 969
164	2 68 96	12.806 2485	.006 097 561
165	2 72 25	12.845 2326	.006 060 606
166	2 75 56	12.884 0987	.006 024 096
167	2 78 89	12.922 8480	.005 988 024
168	2 82 24	12.961 4814	.005 952 381
169	2 85 61	13.000 0000	.005 917 160
170	2 89 00	13.038 4048	.005 882 353
171	2 92 41	13.076 6968	.005 847 953
172	2 95 84	13.114 8770	.005 813 953
173	2 99 29	13.152 9464	.005 780 347
174	3 02 76	13.190 9060	.005 747 126
175	3 06 25	13.228 7566	.005 714 286
176	3 09 76	13.266 4992	.005 681 818
177	3 13 29	13.304 1347	.005 649 718
178	3 16 84	13.341 6641	.005 617 978
179	3 20 41	13.379 0882	.005 586 592
180	3 24 00	13.416 4079	.005 555 556
181	3 27 61	13.453 6240	.005 524 862
182	3 31 24	13.490 7376	.005 494 505
183	3 34 89	13.527 7493	.005 464 481
184	3 38 56	13.564 6600	.005 434 783
185	3 42 25	13.601 4705	.005 405 405
186	3 45 96	13.638 1817	.005 376 344
187	3 49 69	13.674 7943	.005 347 594
188	3 53 44	13.711 3092	.005 319 149
189	3 57 21	13.747 7271	.005 291 005
190	3 61 00	13.784 0488	.005 263 158
191	3 64 81	13.820 2750	.005 235 602
192	3 68 64	13.856 4065	.005 208 333
193	3 72 49	13.892 4440	.005 181 347
194	3 76 36	13.928 3883	.005 154 639
195	3 80 25	13.964 2400	.005 128 205
196	3 84 16	14.000 0000	.005 102 041
197	3 88 09	14.035 6688	.005 076 142
198	3 92 04	14.071 2473	.005 050 505
199	3 96 01	14.106 7360	.005 025 126
200	4 00 00	14.142 1356	.005 000 000

Squares, Square Roots, and Reciprocals of the
Natural Numbers from 1 to 1,000

n	n^2	$n^{1/2}$	$1/n$
201	4 04 01	14.177 4469	.004 975 124
202	4 08 04	14.212 6704	.004 950 495
203	4 12 09	14.247 8068	.004 926 108
204	4 16 16	14.282 8569	.004 901 961
205	4 20 25	14.317 8211	.004 878 049
206	4 24 36	14.352 7001	.004 854 369
207	4 28 49	14.387 4946	.004 830 918
208	4 32 64	14.422 2051	.004 807 692
209	4 36 81	14.456 8323	.004 784 689
210	4 41 00	14.491 3767	.004 761 905
211	4 45 21	14.525 8390	.004 739 336
212	4 49 44	14.560 2198	.004 716 981
213	4 53 69	14.594 5195	.004 694 836
214	4 57 96	14.628 7388	.004 672 897
215	4 62 25	14.662 8783	.004 651 163
216	4 66 56	14.696 9385	.004 629 630
217	4 70 89	14.730 9199	.004 608 295
218	4 75 24	14.764 8231	.004 587 156
219	4 79 61	14.798 6486	004 566 210
220	4 84 00	14.832 3970	.004 545 455
221	4 88 41	14.866 0687	.004 524 887
222	4 92 84	14.899 6644	.004 504 505
223	4 97 29	14.933 1845	.004 484 305
224	5 01 76	14.966 6295	.004 464 286
225	5 06 25	15.000 0000	.004 444 444
226	5 10 76	15.033 2964	.004 424 779
227	5 15 29	15.066 5192	.004 405 286
228	5 19 84	15.099 6689	.004 385 965
229	5 24 41	15.132 7460	.004 366 812
230	5 29 00	15.165 7509	.004 347 826
231	5 33 61	15.198 6842	.004 329 004
232	5 38 24	15.231 5462	.004 310 345
233	5 42 89	15.264 3375	.004 291 845
234	5 47 56	15.297 0585	.004 273 504
235	5 52 25	15.329 7097	.004 255 319
236	5 56 96	15.362 2915	.004 237 288
237	5 61 69	15.394 8043	.004 219 409
238	5 66 44	15.427 2486	.004 201 681
239	5 71 21	15.459 6248	.004 184 100
240	5 76 00	15.491 9334	.004 166 667
241	5 80 81	15.524 1747	.004 149 378
242	5 85 64	15.556 3492	.004 132 231
243	5 90 49	15.588 4573	.004 115 226
244	5 95 36	15.620 4994	.004 098 361
245	6 00 25	15.652 4758	.004 081 633
246	6 05 16	15.684 3871	.004 065 041
247	6 10 09	15.716 2336	.004 048 583
248	6 15 04	15.748 0157	.004 032 258
249	6 20 01	15.779 7338	.004 016 064
250	6 25 00	15.811 3883	.004 000 000

Squares, Square Roots, and Reciprocals of the
Natural Numbers from 1 to 1,000

n	n^2	$n^{1/2}$	$1/n$
251	6 30 01	15.842 9795	.003 984 064
252	6 35 04	15.874 5079	.003 968 254
253	6 40 09	15.905 9737	.003 952 569
254	6 45 16	15.937 3775	.003 937 008
255	6 50 25	15.968 7194	.003 921 569
256	6 55 36	16.000 0000	.003 906 250
257	6 60 49	16.031 2195	.003 891 051
258	6 65 64	16.062 3784	.003 875 969
259	6 70 81	16.093 4769	.003 861 004
260	6 76 00	16.124 5155	.003 846 154
261	6 81 21	16.155 4944	.003 831 418
262	6 86 44	16.186 4141	.003 816 794
263	6 91 69	16.217 2747	.003 802 281
264	6 96 96	16.248 0768	.003 787 879
265	7 02 25	16.278 8206	.003 773 585
266	7 07 56	16.309 5064	.003 759 398
267	7 12 89	16.340 1346	.003 745 318
268	7 18 24	16.370 7055	.003 731 343
269	7 23 61	16.401 2195	.003 717 472
270	7 29 00	16.431 6767	.003 703 704
271	7 34 41	16.462 0776	.003 690 037
272	7 39 84	16.492 4225	.003 676 471
273	7 45 29	16.522 7116	.003 663 004
274	7 50 76	16.552 9454	.003 649 635
275	7 56 25	16.583 1240	.003 636 364
276	7 61 76	16.613 2477	.003 623 188
277	7 67 29	16.643 3170	.003 610 108
278	7 72 84	16.673 3320	.003 597 122
279	7 78 41	16.703 2931	.003 584 229
280	7 84 00	16.733 2005	.003 571 429
281	7 89 61	16.763 0546	.003 558 719
282	7 95 24	16.792 8556	.003 546 099
283	8 00 89	16.822 6038	.003 533 569
284	8 06 56	16.852 2995	.003 521 127
285	8 12 25	16.881 9430	.003 508 772
286	8 17 96	16.911 5345	.003 496 503
287	8 23 69	16.941 0743	.003 484 321
288	8 29 44	16.970 5627	.003 472 222
289	8 35 21	17.000 0000	.003 460 208
290	8 41 00	17.029 3864	.003 448 276
291	8 46 81	17.058 7221	.003 436 426
292	8 52 64	17.088 0075	.003 424 658
293	8 58 49	17.117 2428	.003 412 969
294	8 64 36	17.146 4282	.003 401 361
295	8 70 25	17.175 5640	.003 389 831
296	8 76 16	17.204 6505	.003 378 378
297	8 82 09	17.233 6879	.003 367 003
298	8 88 04	17.262 6765	.003 355 705
299	8 94 01	17.291 6165	.003 344 482
300	9 00 00	17.320 5081	.003 333 333

Squares, Square Roots, and Reciprocals of the
Natural Numbers from 1 to 1,000

n	n^2	$n^{1/2}$	$1/n$
301	9 06 01	17.349 3516	.003 322 259
302	9 12 04	17.378 1472	.003 311 258
303	9 18 09	17.406 8952	.003 300 330
304	9 24 16	17.435 5958	.003 289 474
305	9 30 25	17.464 2492	.003 278 689
306	9 36 36	17.492 8557	.003 267 974
307	9 42 49	17.521 4155	.003 257 329
308	9 48 64	17.549 9288	.003 246 753
309	9 54 81	17.578 3958	.003 236 246
310	9 61 00	17.606 8169	.003 225 806
311	9 67 21	17.635 1921	.003 215 434
312	9 73 44	17.663 5217	.003 205 128
313	9 79 69	17.691 8060	.003 194 888
314	9 85 96	17.720 0451	.003 184 713
315	9 92 25	17.748 2393	.003 174 603
316	9 98 56	17.776 3888	.003 164 557
317	10 04 89	17.804 4938	.003 154 574
318	10 11 24	17.832 5545	.003 144 654
319	10 17 61	17.860 5711	.003 134 796
320	10 24 00	17.888 5438	.003 125 000
321	10 30 41	17.916 4729	.003 115 265
322	10 36 84	17.944 3584	.003 105 590
323	10 43 29	17.972 2008	.003 095 975
324	10 49 76	18.000 0000	.003 086 420
325	10 56 25	18.027 7564	.003 076 923
326	10 62 76	18.055 4701	.003 067 485
327	10 69 29	18.083 1413	.003 058 104
328	10 75 84	18.110 7703	.003 048 780
329	10 82 41	18.138 3571	.003 039 514
330	10 89 00	18.165 9021	.003 030 303
331	10 95 61	18.193 4054	.003 021 148
332	11 02 24	18.220 8672	.003 012 048
333	11 08 89	18.248 2876	.003 003 003
334	11 15 56	18.275 6669	.002 994 012
335	11 22 25	18.303 0052	.002 985 075
336	11 28 96	18.330 3028	.002 976 190
337	11 35 69	18.357 5598	.002 967 359
338	11 42 44	18.384 7763	.002 958 580
339	11 49 21	18.411 9526	.002 949 853
340	11 56 00	18.439 0889	.002 941 176
341	11 62 81	18.466 1853	.002 932 551
342	11 69 64	18.493 2420	.002 923 977
343	11 76 49	18.520 2592	.002 915 452
344	11 83 36	18.547 2370	.002 906 977
345	11 90 25	18.574 1756	.002 898 551
346	11 97 16	18.601 0752	.002 890 173
347	12 04 09	18.627 9360	.002 881 844
348	12 11 04	18.654 7581	.002 873 563
349	12 18 01	18.681 5417	.002 865 330
350	12 25 00	18.708 2869	.002 857 143

Squares, Square Roots, and Reciprocals of the Natural Numbers from 1 to 1,000

n	n^2	$n^{1/2}$	$1/n$
351	12 32 01	18.734 9940	.002 849 003
352	12 39 04	18.761 6630	.002 840 909
353	12 46 09	18.788 2942	.002 832 861
354	12 53 16	18.814 8877	.002 824 859
355	12 60 25	18.841 4437	.002 816 901
356	12 67 36	18.867 9623	.002 808 989
357	12 74 49	18.894 4436	.002 801 120
358	12 81 64	18.920 8879	.002 793 296
359	12 88 81	18.947 2953	.002 785 515
360	12 96 00	18.973 6660	.002 777 778
361	13 03 21	19.000 0000	.002 770 083
362	13 10 44	19.026 2976	.002 762 431
363	13 17 69	19.052 5589	.002 754 821
364	13 24 96	19.078 7840	.002 747 253
365	13 32 25	19.104 9732	.002 739 726
366	13 39 56	19.131 1265	.002 732 240
367	13 46 89	19.157 2441	.002 724 796
368	13 54 24	19.183 3261	.002 717 391
369	13 61 61	19.209 3727	.002 710 027
370	13 69 00	19.235 3841	.002 702 703
371	13 76 41	19.261 3603	.002 695 418
372	13 83 84	19.287 3015	.002 688 172
373	13 91 29	19.313 2079	.002 680 965
374	13 98 76	19.339 0796	.002 673 797
375	14 06 25	19.364 9167	.002 666 667
376	14 13 76	19.390 7194	.002 659 574
377	14 21 29	19.416 4878	.002 652 520
378	14 28 84	19.442 2221	.002 645 503
379	14 36 41	19.467 9223	.002 638 522
380	14 44 00	19.493 5887	.002 631 579
381	14 51 61	19.519 2213	.002 624 672
382	14 59 24	19.544 8203	.002 617 801
383	14 66 89	19.570 3858	.002 610 966
384	14 74 56	19.595 9179	.002 604 167
385	14 82 25	19.621 4169	.002 597 403
386	14 89 96	19.646 8827	.002 590 674
387	14 97 69	19.672 3156	.002 583 979
388	15 05 44	19.697 7156	.002 577 320
389	15 13 21	19.723 0829	.002 570 694
390	15 21 00	19.748 4177	.002 564 103
391	15 28 81	19.773 7199	.002 557 545
392	15 36 64	19.798 9899	.002 551 020
393	15 44 49	19.824 2276	.002 544 529
394	15 52 36	19.849 4332	.002 538 071
395	15 60 25	19.874 6069	.002 531 646
396	15 68 16	19.899 7487	.002 525 253
397	15 76 09	19.924 8588	.002 518 892
398	15 84 04	19.949 9373	.002 512 563
399	15 92 01	19.974 9844	.002 506 266
400	16 00 00	20.000 0000	.002 500 000

Squares, Square Roots, and Reciprocals of the
Natural Numbers from 1 to 1,000

n	n^2	$n^{1/2}$	$1/n$
401	16 08 01	20.024 9844	.002 493 766
402	16 16 04	20.049 9377	.002 487 562
403	16 24 09	20.074 8599	.002 481 390
404	16 32 16	20.099 7512	.002 475 248
405	16 40 25	20.124 6118	.002 469 136
406	16 48 36	20.149 4417	.002 463 054
407	16 56 49	20.174 2410	.002 457 002
408	16 64 64	20.199 0099	.002 450 980
409	16 72 81	20.223 7484	.002 444 988
410	16 81 00	20.248 4567	.002 439 024
411	16 89 21	20.273 1349	.002 433 090
412	16 97 44	20.297 7831	.002 427 184
413	17 05 69	20.322 4014	.002 421 308
414	17 13 96	20.346 9899	.002 415 459
415	17 22 25	20.371 5488	.002 409 639
416	17 30 56	20.396 0781	.002 403 846
417	17 38 89	20.420 5779	.002 398 082
418	17 47 24	20.445 0483	.002 392 344
419	17 55 61	20.469 4895	.002 386 635
420	17 64 00	20.493 9015	.002 380 952
421	17 72 41	20.518 2845	.002 375 297
422	17 80 84	20.542 6386	.002 369 668
423	17 89 29	20.566 9638	.002 364 066
424	17 97 76	20.591 2603	.002 358 491
425	18 06 25	20.615 5281	.002 352 941
426	18 14 76	20.639 7674	.002 347 418
427	18 23 29	20.663 9783	.002 341 920
428	18 31 84	20.688 1609	.002 336 449
429	18 40 41	20.712 3152	.002 331 002
430	18 49 00	20.736 4414	.002 325 581
431	18 57 61	20.760 5395	.002 320 186
432	18 66 24	20.784 6097	.002 314 815
433	18 74 89	20.808 6520	.002 309 469
434	18 83 56	20.832 6667	.002 304 147
435	18 92 25	20.856 6536	.002 298 851
436	19 00 96	20.880 6130	.002 293 578
437	19 09 69	20.904 5450	.002 288 330
438	19 18 44	20.928 4495	.002 283 105
439	19 27 21	20.952 3268	.002 277 904
440	19 36 00	20.976 1770	.002 272 727
441	19 44 81	21.000 0000	.002 267 574
442	19 53 64	21.023 7960	.002 262 443
443	19 62 49	21.047 5652	.002 257 336
444	19 71 36	21.071 3075	.002 252 252
445	19 80 25	21.095 0231	.002 247 191
446	19 89 16	21.118 7121	.002 242 152
447	19 98 09	21.142 3745	.002 237 136
448	20 07 04	21.166 0105	.002 232 143
449	20 16 01	21.189 6201	.002 227 171
450	20 25 00	21.213 2034	.002 222 222

Squares, Square Roots, and Reciprocals of the
Natural Numbers from 1 to 1,000

n	n^2	$n^{1/2}$	$1/n$
451	20 34 01	21.236 7606	.002 217 295
452	20 43 04	21.260 2916	.002 212 389
453	20 52 09	21.283 7967	.002 207 506
454	20 61 16	21.307 2758	.002 202 643
455	20 70 25	21.330 7290	.002 197 802
456	20 79 36	21.354 1565	.002 192 982
457	20 88 49	21.377 5583	.002 188 184
458	20 97 64	21.400 9346	.002 183 406
459	21 06 81	21.424 2853	.002 178 649
460	21 16 00	21.447 6106	.002 173 913
461	21 25 21	21.470 9106	.002 169 197
462	21 34 44	21.494 1853	.002 164 502
463	21 43 69	21.517 4348	.002 159 827
464	21 52 96	21.540 6592	.002 155 172
465	21 62 25	21.563 8587	.002 150 538
466	21 71 56	21.587 0331	.002 145 923
467	21 80 89	21.610 1828	.002 141 328
468	21 90 24	21.633 3077	.002 136 752
469	21 99 61	21.656 4078	.002 132 196
470	22 09 00	21.679 4834	.002 127 660
471	22 18 41	21.702 5344	.002 123 142
472	22 27 84	21.725 5610	.002 118 644
473	22 37 29	21.748 5632	.002 114 165
474	22 46 76	21.771 5411	.002 109 705
475	22 56 25	21.794 4947	.002 105 263
476	22 65 76	21.817 4242	.002 100 840
477	22 75 29	21.840 3297	.002 096 436
478	22 84 84	21.863 2111	.002 092 050
479	22 94 41	21.886 0686	.002 087 683
480	23 04 00	21.908 9023	.002 083 333
481	23 13 61	21.931 7122	.002 079 002
482	23 23 24	21.954 4984	.002 074 689
483	23 32 89	21.977 2610	.002 070 393
484	23 42 56	22.000 0000	.002 066 116
485	23 52 25	22.022 7155	.002 061 856
486	23 61 96	22.045 4077	.002 057 613
487	23 71 69	22.068 0765	.002 053 388
488	23 81 44	22.090 7220	.002 049 180
489	23 91 21	22.113 3444	.002 044 990
490	24 01 00	22.135 9436	.002 040 816
491	24 10 81	22.158 5198	.002 036 660
492	24 20 64	22.181 0730	.002 032 520
493	24 30 49	22.203 6033	.002 028 398
494	24 40 36	22.226 1108	.002 024 291
495	24 50 25	22.248 5955	.002 020 202
496	24 60 16	22.271 0575	.002 016 129
497	24 70 09	22.293 4968	.002 012 072
498	24 80 04	22.315 9136	.002 008 032
499	24 90 01	22.338 3079	.002 004 008
500	25 00 00	22.360 6798	.002 000 000

Squares, Square Roots, and Reciprocals of the
Natural Numbers from 1 to 1,000

n	n^2	$n^{1/2}$	$1/n$
501	25 10 01	22.383 0293	.001 996 008
502	25 20 04	22.405 3565	.001 992 032
503	25 30 09	22.427 6615	.001 988 072
504	25 40 16	22.449 9443	.001 984 127
505	25 50 25	22.472 2051	.001 980 198
506	25 60 36	22.494 4438	.001 976 285
507	25 70 49	22.516 6605	.001 972 387
508	25 80 64	22.538 8553	.001 968 504
509	25 90 81	22.561 0283	.001 964 637
510	26 01 00	22.583 1796	.001 960 784
511	26 11 21	22.605 3091	.001 956 947
512	26 21 44	22.627 4170	.001 953 125
513	26 31 69	22.649 5033	.001 949 318
514	26 41 96	22.671 5681	.001 945 525
515	26 52 25	22.693 6114	.001 941 748
516	26 62 56	22.715 6334	.001 937 984
517	26 72 89	22.737 6340	.001 934 236
518	26 83 24	22.759 6134	.001 930 502
519	26 93 61	22.781 5715	.001 926 782
520	27 04 00	22.803 5085	.001 923 077
521	27 14 41	22.825 4244	.001 919 386
522	27 24 84	22.847 3193	.001 915 709
523	27 35 29	22.869 1933	.001 912 046
524	27 45 76	22.891 0463	.001 908 397
525	27 56 25	22.912 8785	.001 904 762
526	27 66 76	22.934 6899	.001 901 141
527	27 77 29	22.956 4806	.001 897 533
528	27 87 84	22.978 2506	.001 893 939
529	27 98 41	23.000 0000	.001 890 359
530	28 09 00	23.021 7289	.001 886 792
531	28 19 61	23.043 4372	.001 883 239
532	28 30 24	23.065 1252	.001 879 699
533	28 40 89	23.086 7928	.001 876 173
534	28 51 56	23.108 4400	.001 872 659
535	28 62 25	23.130 0670	.001 869 159
536	28 72 96	23.151 6738	.001 865 672
537	28 83 69	23.173 2605	.001 862 197
538	28 94 44	23.194 8270	.001 858 736
539	29 05 21	23.216 3735	.001 855 288
540	29 16 00	23.237 9001	.001 851 852
541	29 26 81	23.259 4067	.001 848 429
542	29 37 64	23.280 8935	.001 845 018
543	29 48 49	23.302 3604	.001 841 621
544	29 59 36	23.323 8076	.001 838 235
545	29 70 25	23.345 2351	.001 834 862
546	29 81 16	23.366 6429	.001 831 502
547	29 92 09	23.388 0311	.001 828 154
548	30 03 04	23.409 3998	.001 824 818
549	30 14 01	23.430 7490	.001 821 494
550	30 25 00	23.452 0788	.001 818 182

Squares, Square Roots, and Reciprocals of the
Natural Numbers from 1 to 1,000

n	n^2	$n^{1/2}$	$1/n$
551	30 36 01	23.473 3892	.001 814 882
552	30 47 04	23.494 6802	.001 811 594
553	30 58 09	23.515 9520	.001 808 318
554	30 69 16	23.537 2046	.001 805 054
555	30 80 25	23.558 4380	.001 801 802
556	30 91 36	23.579 6522	.001 798 561
557	31 02 49	23.600 8474	.001 795 332
558	31 13 64	23.622 0236	.001 792 115
559	31 24 81	23.643 1808	.001 788 909
560	31 36 00	23.664 3191	.001 785 714
561	31 47 21	23.685 4386	.001 782 531
562	31 58 44	23.706 5392	.001 779 359
563	31 69 69	23.727 6210	.001 776 199
564	31 80 96	23.748 6842	.001 773 050
565	31 92 25	23.769 7286	.001 769 912
566	32 03 56	23.790 7545	.001 766 784
567	32 14 89	23.811 7618	.001 763 668
568	32 26 24	23.832 7506	.001 760 563
569	32 37 61	23.853 7209	.001 757 469
570	32 49 00	23.874 6728	.001 754 386
571	32 60 41	23.895 6063	.001 751 313
572	32 71 84	23.916 0304	.001 748 252
573	32 83 29	23.937 4184	.001 745 201
574	32 94 76	23.958 2971	.001 742 160
575	33 06 25	23.979 1576	.001 739 130
576	33 17 76	24.000 0000	.001 736 111
577	33 29 29	24.020 8243	.001 733 102
578	33 40 84	24.041 6306	.001 730 104
579	33 52 41	24.062 4188	.001 727 116
580	33 64 00	24.083 1891	.001 724 138
581	33 75 61	24.103 0416	.001 721 170
582	33 87 24	24.124 6762	.001 718 213
583	33 98 89	24.145 3929	.001 715 266
584	34 10 56	24.166 0919	.001 712 329
585	34 22 25	24.186 7732	.001 709 402
586	34 33 96	24.207 4369	.001 706 485
587	34 45 69	24.228 0829	.001 703 578
588	34 57 44	24.248 7113	.001 700 680
589	34 69 21	24.269 3222	.001 697 793
590	34 81 00	24.289 9156	.001 694 915
591	34 92 81	24.310 4916	.001 692 047
592	35 04 64	24.331 0501	.001 689 189
593	35 16 49	24.351 5913	.001 686 341
594	35 28 36	24.372 1152	.001 683 502
595	35 40 25	24.392 6218	.001 680 672
596	35 52 16	24.413 1112	.001 677 852
597	35 64 09	24.433 5834	.001 675 042
598	35 76 04	24.454 0385	.001 672 241
599	35 88 01	24.474 4765	.001 669 449
600	36 00 00	24.494 8974	.001 666 667

Squares, Square Roots, and Reciprocals of the
Natural Numbers from 1 to 1,000

n	n^2	$n^{1/2}$	$1/n$
601	36 12 01	24.515 3013	.001 663 894
602	36 24 04	24.535 6883	.001 661 130
603	36 36 09	24.556 0583	.001 658 375
604	36 48 16	24.576 4115	.001 655 629
605	36 60 25	24.596 7478	.001 652 893
606	36 72 36	24.617 0673	.001 650 165
607	36 84 49	24.637 3700	.001 647 446
608	36 96 64	24.657 6560	.001 644 737
609	37 08 81	24.677 9254	.001 642 036
610	37 21 00	24.698 1781	.001 639 344
611	37 33 21	24.718 4142	.001 636 661
612	37 45 44	24.738 6338	.001 633 987
613	37 57 69	24.758 8368	.001 631 321
614	37 69 96	24.779 0234	.001 628 664
615	37 82 25	24.799 1935	.001 626 016
616	37 94 56	24.819 3473	.001 623 377
617	38 06 89	24.839 4847	.001 620 746
618	38 19 24	24.859 6058	.001 618 123
619	38 31 61	24.879 7106	.001 615 509
620	38 44 00	24.899 7992	.001 612 903
621	38 56 41	24.919 8716	.001 610 306
622	38 68 84	24.939 9278	.001 607 717
623	38 81 29	24.959 9679	.001 605 136
624	38 93 76	24.979 9920	.001 602 564
625	39 06 25	25.000 0000	.001 600 000
626	39 18 76	25.019 9920	.001 597 444
627	39 31 29	25.039 9681	.001 594 896
628	39 43 84	25.059 9282	.001 592 357
629	39 56 41	25.079 8724	.001 589 825
630	39 69 00	25.099 8008	.001 587 302
631	39 81 61	25.119 7134	.001 584 786
632	39 94 24	25.139 6102	.001 582 278
633	40 06 89	25.159 4913	.001 579 779
634	40 19 56	25.179 3566	.001 577 287
635	40 32 25	25.199 2063	.001 574 803
636	40 44 96	25.219 0404	.001 572 327
637	40 57 69	25.238 8589	.001 569 859
638	40 70 44	25.258 6619	.001 567 398
639	40 83 21	25.278 4493	.001 564 945
640	40 96 00	25.298 2213	.001 562 500
641	41 08 81	25.317 9778	.001 560 062
642	41 21 64	25.337 7189	.001 557 632
643	41 34 49	25.357 4447	.001 555 210
644	41 47 36	25.377 1551	.001 552 795
645	41 60 25	25.396 8502	.001 550 388
646	41 73 16	25.416 5301	.001 547 988
647	41 86 09	25.436 1947	.001 545 595
648	41 99 04	25.455 8441	.001 543 210
649	42 12 01	25.475 4784	.001 540 832
650	42 25 00	25.495 0976	.001 538 462

Squares, Square Roots, and Reciprocals of the
Natural Numbers from 1 to 1,000

n	n^2	$n^{1/2}$	$1/n$
651	42 38 01	25.514 7016	.001 536 098
652	42 51 04	25.534 2907	.001 533 742
653	42 64 09	25.553 8647	.001 531 394
654	42 77 16	25.573 4237	.001 529 052
655	42 90 25	25.592 9678	.001 526 718
656	43 03 36	25.612 4969	.001 524 390
657	43 16 49	25.632 0112	.001 522 070
658	43 29 64	25.651 5107	.001 519 757
659	43 42 81	25.670 9953	.001 517 451
660	43 56 00	25.690 4652	.001 515 152
661	43 69 21	25.709 9203	.001 512 859
662	43 82 44	25.729 3607	.001 510 574
663	43 95 69	25.748 7864	.001 508 296
664	44 08 96	25.768 1975	.001 506 024
665	44 22 25	25.787 5939	.001 503 759
666	44 35 56	25.806 9758	.001 501 502
667	44 48 89	25.826 3431	.001 499 250
668	44 62 24	25.845 6960	.001 497 006
669	44 75 61	25.865 0343	.001 494 768
670	44 89 00	25.884 3582	.001 492 537
671	45 02 41	25.903 6677	.001 490 313
672	45 15 84	25.922 9628	.001 488 095
673	45 29 29	25.942 2435	.001 485 884
674	45 42 76	25.961 5100	.001 483 680
675	45 56 25	25.980 7621	.001 481 481
676	45 69 76	26.000 0000	.001 479 290
677	45 83 29	26.019 2237	.001 477 105
678	45 96 84	26.038 4331	.001 474 926
679	46 10 41	26.057 6284	.001 472 754
680	46 24 00	26.076 8096	.001 470 588
681	46 37 61	26.095 9767	.001 468 429
682	46 51 24	26.115 1297	.001 466 276
683	46 64 89	26.134 2687	.001 464 129
684	46 78 56	26.153 3937	.001 461 988
685	46 92 25	26.172 5047	.001 459 854
686	47 05 96	26.191 6017	.001 457 726
687	47 19 69	26.210 6848	.001 455 604
688	47 33 44	26.229 7541	.001 453 488
689	47 47 21	26.248 8095	.001 451 379
690	47 61 00	26.267 8511	.001 449 275
691	47 74 81	26.286 8789	.001 447 178
692	47 88 64	26.305 8929	.001 445 087
693	48 02 49	26.324 8932	.001 443 001
694	48 16 36	26.343 8797	.001 440 922
695	48 30 25	26.362 8527	.001 438 849
696	48 44 16	26.381 8119	.001 436 782
697	48 58 09	26.400 7576	.001 434 720
698	48 72 04	26.419 6896	.001 432 665
699	48 86 01	26.438 6081	.001 430 615
700	49 00 00	26.457 5131	.001 428 571

Squares, Square Roots, and Reciprocals of the
Natural Numbers from 1 to 1,000

n	n^2	$n^{1/2}$	$1/n$
701	49 14 01	26.476 4046	.001 426 534
702	49 28 04	26.495 2826	.001 424 501
703	49 42 09	26.514 1472	.001 422 475
704	49 56 16	26.532 9983	.001 420 455
705	49 70 25	26.551 8361	.001 418 440
706	49 84 36	26.570 6605	.001 416 431
707	49 98 49	26.589 4716	.001 414 427
708	50 12 64	26.608 2694	.001 412 429
709	50 26 81	26.627 0539	.001 410 437
710	50 41 00	26.645 8252	.001 408 451
711	50 55 21	26.664 5833	.001 406 470
712	50 69 44	26.683 3281	.001 404 494
713	50 83 69	26.702 0598	.001 402 525
714	50 97 96	26.720 7784	.001 400 560
715	51 12 25	26.739 4839	.001 398 601
716	51 26 56	26.758 1763	.001 396 648
717	51 40 89	26.776 8557	.001 394 700
718	51 55 24	26.795 5220	.001 392 758
719	51 69 61	26.814 1754	.001 390 821
720	51 84 00	26.832 8157	.001 388 889
721	51 98 41	26.851 4432	.001 386 963
722	52 12 84	26.870 0577	.001 385 042
723	52 27 29	26.888 6593	.001 383 126
724	52 41 76	26.907 2481	.001 381 215
725	52 56 25	26.925 8240	.001 379 310
726	52 70 76	26.944 3872	.001 377 410
727	52 85 29	26.962 9375	.001 375 516
728	52 99 84	26.981 4751	.001 373 626
729	53 14 41	27.000 0000	.001 371 742
730	53 29 00	27.018 5122	.001 369 863
731	53 43 61	27.037 0117	.001 367 989
732	53 58 24	27.055 4985	.001 366 120
733	53 72 89	27.073 9727	.001 364 256
734	53 87 56	27.092 4344	.001 362 398
735	54 02 25	27.110 8834	.001 360 544
736	54 16 96	27.129 3199	.001 358 696
737	54 31 69	27.147 7439	.001 356 852
738	54 46 44	27.166 1554	.001 355 014
739	54 61 21	27.184 5544	.001 353 180
740	54 76 00	27.202 9410	.001 351 351
741	54 90 81	27.221 3152	.001 349 528
742	55 05 64	27.239 6769	.001 347 709
743	55 20 49	27.258 0263	.001 345 895
744	55 35 36	27.276 3634	.001 344 086
745	55 50 25	27.294 6881	.001 342 282
746	55 65 16	27.313 0006	.001 340 483
747	55 80 09	27.331 3007	.001 338 688
748	55 95 04	27.349 5887	.001 336 898
749	56 10 01	27.367 8644	.001 335 113
750	56 25 00	27.386 1279	.001 333 333

Squares, Square Roots, and Reciprocals of the
Natural Numbers from 1 to 1,000

n	n^2	$n^{1/2}$	$1/n$
751	56 40 01	27.404 3792	.001 331 558
752	56 55 04	27.422 6184	.001 329 787
753	56 70 09	27.440 8455	.001 328 021
754	56 85 16	27.459 0604	.001 326 260
755	57 00 25	27.477 2633	.001 324 503
756	57 15 36	27.495 4542	.001 322 751
757	57 30 49	27.513 6330	.001 321 004
758	57 45 64	27.531 7998	.001 319 261
759	57 60 81	27.549 9546	.001 317 523
760	57 76 00	27.568 0975	.001 315 789
761	57 91 21	27.586 2284	.001 314 060
762	58 06 44	27.604 3475	.001 312 336
763	58 21 69	27.622 4546	.001 310 616
764	58 36 96	27.640 5499	.001 308 901
765	58 52 25	27.658 6334	.001 307 190
766	58 67 56	27.676 7050	.001 305 483
767	58 82 89	27.694 7648	.001 303 781
768	58 98 24	27.712 8129	.001 302 083
769	59 13 61	27.730 8492	.001 300 390
770	59 29 00	27.748 8739	.001 298 701
771	59 44 41	27.766 8868	.001 297 017
772	59 59 84	27.784 8880	.001 295 337
773	59 75 29	27.802 8775	.001 293 661
774	59 90 76	27.820 8555	.001 291 990
775	60 06 25	27.838 8218	.001 290 323
776	60 21 76	27.856 7766	.001 288 660
777	60 37 29	27.874 7197	.001 287 001
778	60 52 84	27.892 6514	.001 285 347
779	60 68 41	27.910 5715	.001 283 697
780	60 84 00	27.928 4801	.001 282 051
781	60 99 61	27.946 3772	.001 280 410
782	61 15 24	27.964 2629	.001 278 772
783	61 30 89	27.982 1372	.001 277 139
784	61 46 56	28.000 0000	.001 275 510
785	61 62 25	28.017 8515	.001 273 885
786	61 77 96	28.035 6915	.001 272 265
787	61 93 69	28.053 5203	.001 270 648
788	62 09 44	28.071 3377	.001 269 036
789	62 25 21	28.089 1438	.001 267 427
790	62 41 00	28.106 9386	.001 265 823
791	62 56 81	28.124 7222	.001 264 223
792	62 72 64	28.142 4946	.001 262 626
793	62 88 49	28.160 2557	.001 261 034
794	63 04 36	28.178 0056	.001 259 446
795	63 20 25	28.195 7444	.001 257 862
796	63 36 16	28.213 4720	.001 256 281
797	63 52 09	28.231 1884	.001 254 705
798	63 68 04	28.248 8938	.001 253 133
799	63 84 01	28.266 5881	.001 251 564
800	64 00 00	28.284 2712	.001 250 000

Squares, Square Roots, and Reciprocals of the Natural Numbers from 1 to 1,000

n	n^2	$n^{1/2}$	$1/n$
801	64 16 01	28.301 9434	.001 248 439
802	64 32 04	28.319 6045	.001 246 883
803	64 48 09	28.337 2546	.001 245 330
804	64 64 16	28.354 8938	.001 243 781
805	64 80 25	28.372 5219	.001 242 236
806	64 96 36	28.390 1391	.001 240 695
807	65 12 49	28.407 7454	.001 239 157
808	65 28 64	28.425 3408	.001 237 624
809	65 44 81	28.442 9253	.001 236 094
810	65 61 00	28.460 4989	.001 234 568
811	65 77 21	28.478 0617	.001 233 046
812	65 93 44	28.495 6137	.001 231 527
813	66 09 69	28.513 1549	.001 230 012
814	66 25 96	28.530 6852	.001 228 501
815	66 42 25	28.548 2048	.001 226 994
816	66 58 56	28.565 7137	.001 225 490
817	66 74 89	28.583 2119	.001 223 990
818	66 91 24	28.600 6993	.001 222 494
819	67 07 61	28.618 1760	.001 221 001
820	67 24 00	28.635 6421	.001 219 512
821	67 40 41	28.653 0976	.001 218 027
822	67 56 84	28.670 5424	.001 216 545
823	67 73 29	28.687 9766	.001 215 067
824	67 89 76	28.705 4002	.001 213 592
825	68 06 25	28.722 8132	.001 212 121
826	68 22 76	28.740 2157	.001 210 654
827	68 39 29	28.757 6077	.001 209 190
828	68 55 84	28.774 9891	.001 207 729
829	68 72 41	28.792 3601	.001 206 273
830	68 89 00	28.809 7206	.001 204 819
831	69 05 61	28.827 0706	.001 203 369
832	69 22 24	28.844 4102	.001 201 923
833	69 38 89	28.861 7394	.001 200 480
834	69 55 56	28.879 0582	.001 199 041
835	69 72 25	28.896 3666	.001 197 605
836	69 88 96	28.913 6646	.001 196 172
837	70 05 69	28.930 9523	.001 194 743
838	70 22 44	28.948 2297	.001 193 317
839	70 39 21	28.965 4967	.001 191 895
840	70 56 00	28.982 7535	.001 190 476
841	70 72 81	29.000 0000	.001 189 061
842	70 89 64	29.017 2363	.001 187 648
843	71 06 49	29.034 4623	.001 186 240
844	71 23 36	29.051 6781	.001 184 834
845	71 40 25	29.068 8837	.001 183 432
846	71 57 16	29.086 0791	.001 182 033
847	71 74 09	29.103 2644	.001 180 638
848	71 91 04	29.120 4396	.001 179 245
849	72 08 01	29.137 6046	.001 177 856
850	72 25 00	29.154 7595	.001 176 471

Squares, Square Roots, and Reciprocals of the Natural Numbers from 1 to 1,000

n	n^2	$n^{1/2}$	$1/n$
851	72 42 01	29.171 9043	.001 175 088
852	72 59 04	29.189 0390	.001 173 709
853	72 76 09	29.206 1637	.001 172 333
854	72 93 16	29.223 2784	.001 170 960
855	73 10 25	29.240 3830	.001 169 591
856	73 27 36	29.257 4777	.001 168 224
857	73 44 49	29.274 5623	.001 166 861
858	73 61 64	29.291 6370	.001 165 501
859	73 78 81	29.308 7018	.001 164 144
860	73 96 00	29.325 7566	.001 162 791
861	74 13 21	29.342 8015	.001 161 440
862	74 30 44	29.359 8365	.001 160 093
863	74 47 69	29.376 8616	.001 158 749
864	74 64 96	29.393 8769	.001 157 407
865	74 82 25	29.410 8823	.001 156 069
866	74 99 56	29.427 8779	.001 154 734
867	75 16 89	29.444 8637	.001 153 403
868	75 34 24	29.461 8397	.001 152 074
869	75 51 61	29.478 8059	.001 150 748
870	75 69 00	29.495 7624	.001 149 425
871	75 86 41	29.512 7091	.001 148 106
872	76 03 84	29.529 6461	.001 146 789
873	76 21 29	29.546 5734	.001 145 475
874	76 38 76	29.563 4910	.001 144 165
875	76 56 25	29.580 3989	.001 142 857
876	76 73 76	29.597 2972	.001 141 553
877	76 91 29	29.614 1858	.001 140 251
878	77 08 84	29.631 0648	.001 138 952
879	77 26 41	29.647 9342	.001 137 656
880	77 44 00	29.664 7939	.001 136 364
881	77 61 61	29.681 6442	.001 135 074
882	77 79 24	29.698 4848	.001 133 787
883	77 96 89	29.715 3159	.001 132 503
884	78 14 56	29.732 1375	.001 131 222
885	78 32 25	29.748 9496	.001 129 944
886	78 49 96	29.765 7521	.001 128 668
887	78 67 69	29.782 5452	.001 127 396
888	78 85 44	29.799 3289	.001 126 126
889	79 03 21	29.816 1030	.001 124 859
890	79 21 00	29.832 8678	.001 123 596
891	79 38 81	29.849 6231	.001 122 334
892	79 56 64	29.866 3690	.001 121 076
893	79 74 49	29.883 1056	.001 119 821
894	79 92 36	29.899 8328	.001 118 568
895	80 10 25	29.916 5506	.001 117 318
896	80 28 16	29.932 2591	.001 116 071
897	80 46 09	29.949 9583	.001 114 827
898	80 64 04	29.966 6481	.001 113 586
899	80 82 01	29.983 3287	.001 112 347
900	81 00 00	30.000 0000	.001 111 111

Squares, Square Roots, and Reciprocals of the
Natural Numbers from 1 to 1,000

n	n^2	$n^{1/2}$	$1/n$
901	81 18 01	30.016 6620	.001 109 878
902	81 36 04	30.033 3148	.001 108 647
903	81 54 09	30.049 9584	.001 107 420
904	81 72 16	30.066 5928	.001 106 195
905	81 90 25	30.083 2179	.001 104 972
906	82 08 36	30.099 8339	.001 103 753
907	82 26 49	30.116 4407	.001 102 536
908	82 44 64	30.133 0383	.001 101 322
909	82 62 81	30.149 6269	.001 100 110
910	82 81 00	30.166 2063	.001 098 901
911	82 99 21	30.182 7765	.001 097 695
912	83 17 44	30.199 3377	.001 096 491
913	83 35 69	30.215 8899	.001 095 290
914	83 53 96	30.232 4329	.001 094 092
915	83 72 25	30.248 9669	.001 092 896
916	83 90 56	30.265 4919	.001 091 703
917	84 08 89	30.282 0079	.001 090 513
918	84 27 24	30.298 5148	.001 089 325
919	84 45 61	30.315 0128	.001 088 139
920	84 64 00	30.331 5018	.001 086 957
921	84 82 41	30.347 9818	.001 085 776
922	85 00 84	30.364 4529	.001 084 599
923	85 19 29	30.380 9151	.001 083 424
924	85 37 76	30.397 3683	.001 082 251
925	85 56 25	30.413 8127	.001 081 081
926	85 74 76	30.430 2481	.001 079 914
927	85 93 29	30.446 6747	.001 078 749
928	86 11 84	30.463 0924	.001 077 586
929	86 30 41	30.479 5013	.001 076 426
930	86 49 00	30.495 9014	.001 075 269
931	86 67 61	30.512 2926	.001 074 114
932	86 86 24	30.528 6750	.001 072 961
933	87 04 89	30.545 0487	.001 071 811
934	87 23 56	30.561 4136	.001 070 664
935	87 42 25	30.577 7697	.001 069 519
936	87 60 96	30.594 1171	.001 068 376
937	87 79 69	30.610 4557	.001 067 236
938	87 98 44	30.626 7857	.001 066 098
939	88 17 21	30.643 1069	.001 064 963
940	88 36 00	30.659 4194	.001 063 830
941	88 54 81	30.675 7233	.001 062 699
942	88 73 64	30.692 0185	.001 061 571
943	88 92 49	30.708 3051	.001 060 445
944	89 11 36	30.724 5830	.001 059 322
945	89 30 25	30.740 8523	.001 058 201
946	89 49 16	30.757 1130	.001 057 082
947	89 68 09	30.773 3651	.001 055 966
948	89 87 04	30.789 6086	.001 054 852
949	90 06 01	30.805 8436	.001 053 741
950	90 25 00	30.822 0700	.001 052 632

Squares, Square Roots, and Reciprocals of the Natural Numbers from 1 to 1,000

n	n^2	$n^{1/2}$	$1/n$
951	90 44 01	30.838 2879	.001 051 525
952	90 63 04	30.854 4972	.001 050 420
953	90 82 09	30.870 6981	.001 049 318
954	91 01 16	30.886 8904	.001 048 218
955	91 20 25	30.903 0743	.001 047 120
956	91 39 36	30.919 2497	.001 046 025
957	91 58 49	30.935 4166	.001 044 932
958	91 77 64	30.951 5751	.001 043 841
959	91 96 81	30.967 7251	.001 042 753
960	92 16 00	30.983 8668	.001 041 667
961	92 35 21	31.000 0000	.001 040 583
962	92 54 44	31.016 1248	.001 039 501
963	92 73 69	31.032 2413	.001 038 422
964	92 92 96	31.048 3494	.001 037 344
965	93 12 25	31.064 4491	.001 036 269
966	93 31 56	31.080 5405	.001 035 197
967	93 50 89	31.096 6236	.001 034 126
968	93 70 24	31.112 6984	.001 033 058
969	93 89 61	31.128 7648	.001 031 992
970	94 09 00	31.144 8230	.001 030 928
971	94 28 41	31.160 8729	.001 029 866
972	94 47 84	31.176 9145	.001 028 807
973	94 67 29	31.192 9479	.001 027 749
974	94 86 76	31.208 9731	.001 026 694
975	95 06 25	31.224 9900	.001 025 641
976	95 25 76	31.240 9987	.001 024 590
977	95 45 29	31.256 9992	.001 023 541
978	95 64 84	31.272 9915	.001 022 495
979	95 84 41	31.288 9757	.001 021 450
980	96 04 00	31.304 9517	.001 020 408
981	96 23 61	31.320 9195	.001 019 368
982	96 43 24	31.336 8792	.001 018 330
983	96 62 89	31.352 8308	.001 017 294
984	96 82 56	31.368 7743	.001 016 260
985	97 02 25	31.384 7097	.001 015 228
986	97 21 96	31.400 6369	.001 014 199
987	97 41 69	31.416 5561	.001 013 171
988	97 61 44	31.432 4673	.001 012 146
989	97 81 21	31.448 3704	.001 011 122
990	98 01 00	31.464 2654	.001 010 101
991	98 20 81	31.480 1525	.001 009 082
992	98 40 64	31.496 0315	.001 008 065
993	98 60 49	31.511 9025	.001 007 049
994	98 80 36	31.527 7655	.001 006 036
995	99 00 25	31.543 6206	.001 005 025
996	99 20 16	31.559 4677	.001 004 016
997	99 40 09	31.575 3068	.001 003 009
998	99 60 04	31.591 1380	.001 002 004
999	99 80 01	31.606 9613	.001 001 001
1000	1 00 00 00	31.622 7766	.001 000 000

APPENDIX TABLE XI *
Random Numbers

Line	(1)	(2)	(3)	(4)	(5)	(6)	(7)	(8)
1	78994	36244	02673	25475	84953	61793	50243	63423
2	04909	58485	70686	93930	34880	73059	06823	80257
3	46582	73570	33004	51795	86477	46736	60460	70345
4	29242	89792	88634	60285	07190	07795	27011	85941
5	68104	81339	97090	20601	78940	20228	22803	96070
6	17156	02182	82504	19880	93747	80910	78260	25136
7	50711	94789	07171	02103	99057	98775	37997	18325
8	39449	52409	75095	77720	39729	03205	09313	43545
9	75629	82729	76916	72657	58992	32756	01154	84890
10	01020	55151	36132	51971	32155	60735	64867	35424
11	08337	89989	24260	08618	66798	25889	52860	57375
12	76829	47229	19706	30094	69430	92399	98749	22081
13	39708	30641	21267	56501	95182	72442	21445	17276
14	89836	55817	56747	75195	06818	83043	47403	58266
15	25903	61370	66081	54076	67442	52964	23823	02718
16	71345	03422	01015	68025	19703	77313	04555	83425
17	61454	92263	14647	08473	34124	10740	40839	05620
18	80376	08909	30470	40200	46558	61742	11643	92121
19	45144	54373	05505	90074	24783	86299	20900	15144
20	12191	88527	58852	51175	11534	87218	04876	85584
21	62936	59120	73957	35969	21598	47287	39394	08778
22	31588	96798	43668	12611	01714	77266	55079	24690
23	20787	96048	84726	17512	39450	43618	30629	24356
24	45603	00745	84635	43079	52724	14262	05750	89373
25	31606	64782	34027	56734	09365	20008	93559	78384
26	10452	33074	76718	99556	16026	00013	78411	95107
27	37016	64633	67301	50949	91298	74968	73631	57397
28	66725	97865	25409	37498	00816	99262	14471	10232
29	07380	74438	82120	17890	40963	55757	13492	68294
30	71621	57688	58256	47702	74724	89419	08025	68519
31	03466	13263	23917	20417	11315	52805	33072	07723
32	12692	32931	97387	34822	53775	91674	76549	37635
33	52192	30941	44998	17833	94563	23062	95725	38463
34	56691	72529	66063	73570	86860	68125	40436	31303
35	74952	43041	58869	15677	78598	43520	97521	83248
36	18752	43693	32867	53017	22661	39610	03796	02622
37	61691	04944	43111	28325	82319	65589	66048	98498
38	49197	63948	38947	60207	70667	39843	60607	15328
39	19436	87291	71684	74859	76501	93456	95714	92518
40	39143	64893	14606	13543	09621	68301	69817	52140
41	82244	67549	76491	09761	74494	91307	64222	66592
42	55847	56155	42878	23708	97999	40131	52360	90390
43	94095	95970	07826	25991	37584	56966	68623	83454
44	11751	69469	25521	44097	07511	88976	30122	67542
45	69902	08995	27821	11758	64989	61902	32121	28165
46	21850	25352	25556	92161	23592	43294	10479	37879
47	75850	46992	25165	55906	62339	88958	91717	15756
48	29648	22086	42581	85677	20251	39641	65786	80689
49	82740	28443	42734	25518	82827	35825	90288	32911
50	36842	42092	52075	83926	42875	71500	69216	01350

* A portion of page 5 of *Table of 105,000 Random Decimal Digits* constructed by H. Burke Horton and R. Tynes Smith III, for the Bureau of Transport Economics and Statistics, Interstate Commerce Commission. Reproduced here with the permission of W. H. S. Stevens, Director of that Bureau.

APPENDIX TABLE XII

Common Logarithms (Five-Place) of the Natural Numbers 1 to 10,000

N	Log	N	Log	N	Log	N	Log	N	Log
0	—	20	1.30 103	40	1.60 206	60	1.77 815	80	1.90 309
1	0.00 000	21	1.32 222	41	1.61 278	61	1.78 533	81	1.90 849
2	0.30 103	22	1.34 242	42	1.62 325	62	1.79 239	82	1.91 381
3	0.47 712	23	1.36 173	43	1.63 347	63	1.79 934	83	1.91 908
4	0.60 206	24	1.38 021	44	1.64 345	64	1.80 618	84	1.92 428
5	0.69 897	25	1.39 794	45	1.65 321	65	1.81 291	85	1.92 942
6	0.77 815	26	1.41 497	46	1.66 276	66	1.81 954	86	1.93 450
7	0.84 510	27	1.43 136	47	1.67 210	67	1.82 607	87	1.93 952
8	0.90 309	28	1.44 716	48	1.68 124	68	1.83 251	88	1.94 448
9	0.95 424	29	1.46 240	49	1.69 020	69	1.83 885	89	1.94 939
10	1.00 000	30	1.47 712	50	1.69 897	70	1.84 510	90	1.95 424
11	1.04 139	31	1.49 136	51	1.70 757	71	1.85 126	91	1.95 904
12	1.07 918	32	1.50 515	52	1.71 600	72	1.85 733	92	1.96 379
13	1.11 394	33	1.51 851	53	1.72 428	73	1.86 332	93	1.96 848
14	1.14 613	34	1.53 148	54	1.73 239	74	1.86 923	94	1.97 313
15	1.17 609	35	1.54 407	55	1.74 036	75	1.87 506	95	1.97 772
16	1.20 412	36	1.55 630	56	1.74 819	76	1.88 081	96	1.98 227
17	1.23 045	37	1.56 820	57	1.75 587	77	1.88 649	97	1.98 677
18	1.25 527	38	1.57 978	58	1.76 343	78	1.89 209	98	1.99 123
19	1.27 875	39	1.59 106	59	1.77 085	79	1.89 763	99	1.99 564
20	1.30 103	40	1.60 206	60	1.77 815	80	1.90 309	100	2.00 000

Common Logarithms (Five-Place) of the Natural Numbers 1 to 10,000

N	0	1	2	3	4	5	6	7	8	9
100	00 000	043	087	130	173	217	260	303	346	389
101	00 432	475	518	561	604	647	689	732	775	817
102	00 860	903	945	988	*030	*072	*115	*157	*199	*242
103	01 284	326	368	410	452	494	536	578	620	662
104	01 703	745	787	828	870	912	953	995	*036	*078
105	02 119	160	202	243	284	325	366	407	449	490
106	02 531	572	612	653	694	735	776	816	857	898
107	02 938	979	*019	*060	*100	*141	*181	*222	*262	*302
108	03 342	383	423	463	503	543	583	623	663	703
109	03 743	782	822	862	902	941	981	*021	*060	*100
110	04 139	179	218	258	297	336	376	415	454	493
111	04 532	571	610	650	689	727	766	805	844	883
112	04 922	961	999	*038	*077	*115	*154	*192	*231	*269
113	05 308	346	385	423	461	500	538	576	614	652
114	05 690	729	767	805	843	881	918	956	994	*032
115	06 070	108	145	183	221	258	296	333	371	408
116	06 446	483	521	558	595	633	670	707	744	781
117	06 819	856	893	930	967	*004	*041	*078	*115	*151
118	07 188	225	262	298	335	372	408	445	482	518
119	07 555	591	628	664	700	737	773	809	846	882
120	07 918	954	990	*027	*063	*099	*135	*171	*207	*243
121	08 279	314	350	386	422	458	493	529	565	600
122	08 636	672	707	743	778	814	849	884	920	955
123	08 991	*026	*061	*096	*132	*167	*202	*237	*272	*307
124	09 342	377	412	447	482	517	552	587	621	656
125	09 691	726	760	795	830	864	899	934	968	*003
126	10 037	072	106	140	175	209	243	278	312	346
127	10 380	415	449	483	517	551	585	619	653	687
128	10 721	755	789	823	857	890	924	958	992	*025
129	11 059	093	126	160	193	227	261	294	327	361
130	11 394	428	461	494	528	561	594	628	661	694
131	11 727	760	793	826	860	893	926	959	992	*024
132	12 057	090	123	156	189	222	254	287	320	352
133	12 385	418	450	483	516	548	581	613	646	678
134	12 710	743	775	808	840	872	905	937	969	*001
135	13 033	066	098	130	162	194	226	258	290	322
136	13 354	386	418	450	481	513	545	577	609	640
137	13 672	704	735	767	799	830	862	893	925	956
138	13 988	*019	*051	*082	*114	*145	*176	*208	*239	*270
139	14 301	333	364	395	426	457	489	520	551	582
140	14 613	644	675	706	737	768	799	829	860	891
141	14 922	953	983	*014	*045	*076	*106	*137	*168	*198
142	15 229	259	290	320	351	381	412	442	473	503
143	15 534	564	594	625	655	685	715	746	776	806
144	15 836	866	897	927	957	987	*017	*047	*077	*107
145	16 137	167	197	227	256	286	316	346	376	406
146	16 435	465	495	524	554	584	613	643	673	702
147	16 732	761	791	820	850	879	909	938	967	997
148	17 026	056	085	114	143	173	202	231	260	289
149	17 319	348	377	406	435	464	493	522	551	580
150	17 609	638	667	696	725	754	782	811	840	869
N	0	1	2	3	4	5	6	7	8	9

Prop. Parts

	44	43	42
1	4.4	4.3	4.2
2	8.8	8.6	8.4
3	13.2	12.9	12.6
4	17.6	17.2	16.8
5	22.0	21.5	21.0
6	26.4	25.8	25.2
7	30.8	30.1	29.4
8	35.2	34.4	33.6
9	39.6	38.7	37.8

	41	40	39
1	4.1	4.0	3.9
2	8.2	8.0	7.8
3	12.3	12.0	11.7
4	16.4	16.0	15.6
5	20.5	20.0	19.5
6	24.6	24.0	23.4
7	28.7	28.0	27.3
8	32.8	32.0	31.2
9	36.9	36.0	35.1

	38	37	36
1	3.8	3.7	3.6
2	7.6	7.4	7.2
3	11.4	11.1	10.8
4	15.2	14.8	14.4
5	19.0	18.5	18.0
6	22.8	22.2	21.6
7	26.6	25.9	25.2
8	30.4	29.6	28.8
9	34.2	33.3	32.4

	35	34	33
1	3.5	3.4	3.3
2	7.0	6.8	6.6
3	10.5	10.2	9.9
4	14.0	13.6	13.2
5	17.5	17.0	16.5
6	21.0	20.4	19.8
7	24.5	23.8	23.1
8	28.0	27.2	26.4
9	31.5	30.6	29.7

	32	31	30
1	3.2	3.1	3.0
2	6.4	6.2	6.0
3	9.6	9.3	9.0
4	12.8	12.4	12.0
5	16.0	15.5	15.0
6	19.2	18.6	18.0
7	22.4	21.7	21.0
8	25.6	24.8	24.0
9	28.8	27.9	27.0

Prop. Parts

Common Logarithms (Five-Place) of the Natural Numbers 1 to 10,000

N	0	1	2	3	4	5	6	7	8	9
150	17 609	638	667	696	725	754	782	811	840	869
151	17 898	926	955	984	*013	*041	*070	*099	*127	*156
152	18 184	213	241	270	298	327	355	384	412	441
153	18 469	498	526	554	583	611	639	667	696	724
154	18 752	780	808	837	865	893	921	949	977	*005
155	19 033	061	089	117	145	173	201	229	257	285
156	19 312	340	368	396	424	451	479	507	535	562
157	19 590	618	645	673	700	728	756	783	811	838
158	19 866	893	921	948	976	*003	*030	*058	*085	*112
159	20 140	167	194	222	249	276	303	330	358	385
160	20 412	439	466	493	520	548	575	602	629	656
161	20 683	710	737	763	790	817	844	871	898	925
162	20 952	978	*005	*032	*059	*085	*112	*139	*165	*192
163	21 219	245	272	299	325	352	378	405	431	458
164	21 484	511	537	564	590	617	643	669	696	722
165	21 748	775	801	827	854	880	906	932	958	985
166	22 011	037	063	089	115	141	167	194	220	246
167	22 272	298	324	350	376	401	427	453	479	505
168	22 531	557	583	608	634	660	686	712	737	763
169	22 789	814	840	866	891	917	943	968	994	*019
170	23 045	070	096	121	147	172	198	223	249	274
171	23 300	325	350	376	401	426	452	477	502	528
172	23 553	578	603	629	654	679	704	729	754	779
173	23 805	830	855	880	905	930	955	980	*005	*030
174	24 055	080	105	130	155	180	204	229	254	279
175	24 304	329	353	378	403	428	452	477	502	527
176	24 551	576	601	625	650	674	699	724	748	773
177	24 797	822	846	871	895	920	944	969	993	*018
178	25 042	066	091	115	139	164	188	212	237	261
179	25 285	310	334	358	382	406	431	455	479	503
180	25 527	551	575	600	624	648	672	696	720	744
181	25 768	792	816	840	864	888	912	935	959	983
182	26 007	031	055	079	102	126	150	174	198	221
183	26 245	269	293	316	340	364	387	411	435	458
184	26 482	505	529	553	576	600	623	647	670	694
185	26 717	741	764	788	811	834	858	881	905	928
186	26 951	975	998	*021	*045	*068	*091	*114	*138	*161
187	27 184	207	231	254	277	300	323	346	370	393
188	27 416	439	462	485	508	531	554	577	600	623
189	27 646	669	692	715	738	761	784	807	830	852
190	27 875	898	921	944	967	989	*012	*035	*058	*081
191	28 103	126	149	171	194	217	240	262	285	307
192	28 330	353	375	398	421	443	466	488	511	533
193	28 556	578	601	623	646	668	691	713	735	758
194	28 780	803	825	847	870	892	914	937	959	981
195	29 003	026	048	070	092	115	137	159	181	203
196	29 226	248	270	292	314	336	358	380	403	425
197	29 447	469	491	513	535	557	579	601	623	645
198	29 667	688	710	732	754	776	798	820	842	863
199	29 885	907	929	951	973	994	*016	*038	*060	*081
200	30 103	125	146	168	190	211	233	255	276	298

Prop. Parts

	29	28
1	2.9	2.8
2	5.8	5.6
3	8.7	8.4
4	11.6	11.2
5	14.5	14.0
6	17.4	16.8
7	20.3	19.6
8	23.2	22.4
9	26.1	25.2

	27	26
1	2.7	2.6
2	5.4	5.2
3	8.1	7.8
4	10.8	10.4
5	13.5	13.0
6	16.2	15.6
7	18.9	18.2
8	21.6	20.8
9	24.3	23.4

	25
1	2.5
2	5.0
3	7.5
4	10.0
5	12.5
6	15.0
7	17.5
8	20.0
9	22.5

	24	23
1	2.4	2.3
2	4.8	4.6
3	7.2	6.9
4	9.6	9.2
5	12.0	11.5
6	14.4	13.8
7	16.8	16.1
8	19.2	18.4
9	21.6	20.7

	22	21
1	2.2	2.1
2	4.4	4.2
3	6.6	6.3
4	8.8	8.4
5	11.0	10.5
6	13.2	12.6
7	15.4	14.7
8	17.6	16.8
9	19.8	18.9

Prop. Parts	N	0	1	2	3	4	5	6	7	8	9

Common Logarithms (Five-Place) of the Natural Numbers 1 to 10,000

N	0	1	2	3	4	5	6	7	8	9	Prop. Parts
200	30 103	125	146	168	190	211	233	255	276	298	
201	30 320	341	363	384	406	428	449	471	492	514	
202	30 535	557	578	600	621	643	664	685	707	728	
203	30 750	771	792	814	835	856	878	899	920	942	
204	30 963	984	*006	*027	*048	*069	*091	*112	*133	*154	
205	31 175	197	218	239	260	281	302	323	345	366	
206	31 387	408	429	450	471	492	513	534	555	576	
207	31 597	618	639	660	681	702	723	744	765	785	
208	31 806	827	848	869	890	911	931	952	973	994	
209	32 015	035	056	077	098	118	139	160	181	201	
210	32 222	243	263	284	305	325	346	366	387	408	
211	32 428	449	469	490	510	531	552	572	593	613	
212	32 634	654	675	695	715	736	756	777	797	818	
213	32 838	858	879	899	919	940	960	980	*001	*021	
214	33 041	062	082	102	122	143	163	183	203	224	
215	33 244	264	284	304	325	345	365	385	405	425	
216	33 445	465	486	506	526	546	566	586	606	626	
217	33 646	666	686	706	726	746	766	786	806	826	
218	33 846	866	885	905	925	945	965	985	*005	*025	
219	34 044	064	084	104	124	143	163	183	203	223	
220	34 242	262	282	301	321	341	361	380	400	420	
221	34 439	459	479	498	518	537	557	577	596	616	
222	34 635	655	674	694	713	733	753	772	792	811	
223	34 830	850	869	889	908	928	947	967	986	*005	
224	35 025	044	064	083	102	122	141	160	180	199	
225	35 218	238	257	276	295	315	334	353	372	392	
226	35 411	430	449	468	488	507	526	545	564	583	
227	35 603	622	641	660	679	698	717	736	755	774	
228	35 793	813	832	851	870	889	908	927	946	965	
229	35 984	*003	*021	*040	*059	*078	*097	*116	*135	*154	
230	36 173	192	211	229	248	267	286	305	324	342	
231	36 361	380	399	418	436	455	474	493	511	530	
232	36 549	568	586	605	624	642	661	680	698	717	
233	36 736	754	773	791	810	829	847	866	884	903	
234	36 922	940	959	977	996	*014	*033	*051	*070	*088	
235	37 107	125	144	162	181	199	218	236	254	273	
236	37 291	310	328	346	365	383	401	420	438	457	
237	37 475	493	511	530	548	566	585	603	621	639	
238	37 658	676	694	712	731	749	767	785	803	822	
239	37 840	858	876	894	912	931	949	967	985	*003	
240	38 021	039	057	075	093	112	130	148	166	184	
241	38 202	220	238	256	274	292	310	328	346	364	
242	38 382	399	417	435	453	471	489	507	525	543	
243	38 561	578	596	614	632	650	668	686	703	721	
244	38 739	757	775	792	810	828	846	863	881	899	
245	38 917	934	952	970	987	*005	*023	*041	*058	*076	
246	39 094	111	129	146	164	182	199	217	235	252	
247	39 270	287	305	322	340	358	375	393	410	428	
248	39 445	463	480	498	515	533	550	568	585	602	
249	39 620	637	655	672	690	707	724	742	759	777	
250	39 794	811	829	846	863	881	898	915	933	950	
N	0	1	2	3	4	5	6	7	8	9	Prop. Parts

Prop. Parts

	22	21
1	2.2	2.1
2	4.4	4.2
3	6.6	6.3
4	8.8	8.4
5	11.0	10.5
6	13.2	12.6
7	15.4	14.7
8	17.6	16.8
9	19.8	18.9

	20
1	2.0
2	4.0
3	6.0
4	8.0
5	10.0
6	12.0
7	14.0
8	16.0
9	18.0

	19
1	1.9
2	3.8
3	5.7
4	7.6
5	9.5
6	11.4
7	13.3
8	15.2
9	17.1

	18
1	1.8
2	3.6
3	5.4
4	7.2
5	9.0
6	10.8
7	12.6
8	14.4
9	16.2

	17
1	1.7
2	3.4
3	5.1
4	6.8
5	8.5
6	10.2
7	11.9
8	13.6
9	15.3

Common Logarithms (Five-Place) of the Natural Numbers 1 to 10,000

N	0	1	2	3	4	5	6	7	8	9
250	39 794	811	829	846	863	881	898	915	933	950
251	39 967	985	*002	*019	*037	*054	*071	*088	*106	*123
252	40 140	157	175	192	209	226	243	261	278	295
253	40 312	329	346	364	381	398	415	432	449	466
254	40 483	500	518	535	552	569	586	603	620	637
255	40 654	671	688	705	722	739	756	773	790	807
256	40 824	841	858	875	892	909	926	943	960	976
257	40 993	*010	*027	*044	*061	*078	*095	*111	*128	*145
258	41 162	179	196	212	229	246	263	280	296	313
259	41 330	347	363	380	397	414	430	447	464	481
260	41 497	514	531	547	564	581	597	614	631	647
261	41 664	681	697	714	731	747	764	780	797	814
262	41 830	847	863	880	896	913	929	946	963	979
263	41 996	*012	*029	*045	*062	*078	*095	*111	*127	*144
264	42 160	177	193	210	226	243	259	275	292	308
265	42 325	341	357	374	390	406	423	439	455	472
266	42 488	504	521	537	553	570	586	602	619	635
267	42 651	667	684	700	716	732	749	765	781	797
268	42 813	830	846	862	878	894	911	927	943	959
269	42 975	991	*008	*024	*040	*056	*072	*088	*104	*120
270	43 136	152	169	185	201	217	233	249	265	281
271	43 297	313	329	345	361	377	393	409	425	441
272	43 457	473	489	505	521	537	553	569	584	600
273	43 616	632	648	664	680	696	712	727	743	759
274	43 775	791	807	823	838	854	870	886	902	917
275	43 933	949	965	981	996	*012	*028	*044	*059	*075
276	44 091	107	122	138	154	170	185	201	217	232
277	44 248	264	279	295	311	326	342	358	373	389
278	44 404	420	436	451	467	483	498	514	529	545
279	44 560	576	592	607	623	638	654	669	685	700
280	44 716	731	747	762	778	793	809	824	840	855
281	44 871	886	902	917	932	948	963	979	994	*010
282	45 025	040	056	071	086	102	117	133	148	163
283	45 179	194	209	225	240	255	271	286	301	317
284	45 332	347	362	378	393	408	423	439	454	469
285	45 484	500	515	530	545	561	576	591	606	621
286	45 637	652	667	682	697	712	728	743	758	773
287	45 788	803	818	834	849	864	879	894	909	924
288	45 939	954	969	984	*000	*015	*030	*045	*060	*075
289	46 090	105	120	135	150	165	180	195	210	225
290	46 240	255	270	285	300	315	330	345	359	374
291	46 389	404	419	434	449	464	479	494	509	523
292	46 538	553	568	583	598	613	627	642	657	672
293	46 687	702	716	731	746	761	776	790	805	820
294	46 835	850	864	879	894	909	923	938	953	967
295	46 982	997	*012	*026	*041	*056	*070	*085	*100	*114
296	47 129	144	159	173	188	202	217	232	246	261
297	47 276	290	305	319	334	349	363	378	392	407
298	47 422	436	451	465	480	494	509	524	538	553
299	47 567	582	596	611	625	640	654	669	683	698
300	47 712	727	741	756	770	784	799	813	828	842

Prop. Parts

18	17	16	15	14
1 1.8	1 1.7	1 1.6	1 1.5	1 1.4
2 3.6	2 3.4	2 3.2	2 3.0	2 2.8
3 5.4	3 5.1	3 4.8	3 4.5	3 4.2
4 7.2	4 6.8	4 6.4	4 6.0	4 5.6
5 9.0	5 8.5	5 8.0	5 7.5	5 7.0
6 10.8	6 10.2	6 9.6	6 9.0	6 8.4
7 12.6	7 11.9	7 11.2	7 10.5	7 9.8
8 14.4	8 13.6	8 12.8	8 12.0	8 11.2
9 16.2	9 15.3	9 14.4	9 13.5	9 12.6

Common Logarithms (Five-Place) of the Natural Numbers 1 to 10,000

N	0	1	2	3	4	5	6	7	8	9	Prop. Parts
300	47 712	727	741	756	770	784	799	813	828	842	
301	47 857	871	885	900	914	929	943	958	972	986	
302	48 001	015	029	044	058	073	087	101	116	130	
303	48 144	159	173	187	202	216	230	244	259	273	
304	48 287	302	316	330	344	359	373	387	401	416	**15**
305	48 430	444	458	473	487	501	515	530	544	558	1 — 1.5
306	48 572	586	601	615	629	643	657	671	686	700	2 — 3.0 3 — 4.5
307	48 714	728	742	756	770	785	799	813	827	841	4 — 6.0
308	48 855	869	883	897	911	926	940	954	968	982	5 — 7.5
309	48 996	*010	*024	*038	*052	*066	*080	*094	*108	*122	6 — 9.0 7 — 10.5
310	49 136	150	164	178	192	206	220	234	248	262	8 — 12.0
311	49 276	290	304	318	332	346	360	374	388	402	9 — 13.5
312	49 415	429	443	457	471	485	499	513	527	541	
313	49 554	568	582	596	610	624	638	651	665	679	
314	49 693	707	721	734	748	762	776	790	803	817	
315	49 831	845	859	872	886	900	914	927	941	955	
316	49 969	982	996	*010	*024	*037	*051	*065	*079	*092	**14**
317	50 106	120	133	147	161	174	188	202	215	229	1 — 1.4
318	50 243	256	270	284	297	311	325	338	352	365	2 — 2.8 3 — 4.2
319	50 379	393	406	420	433	447	461	474	488	501	4 — 5.6
320	50 515	529	542	556	569	583	596	610	623	637	5 — 7.0 6 — 8.4
321	50 651	664	678	691	705	718	732	745	759	772	7 — 9.8
322	50 786	799	813	826	840	853	866	880	893	907	8 — 11.2
323	50 920	934	947	961	974	987	*001	*014	*028	*041	9 — 12.6
324	51 055	068	081	095	108	121	135	148	162	175	
325	51 188	202	215	228	242	255	268	282	295	308	
326	51 322	335	348	362	375	388	402	415	428	441	
327	51 455	468	481	495	508	521	534	548	561	574	**13**
328	51 587	601	614	627	640	654	667	680	693	706	1 — 1.3
329	51 720	733	746	759	772	786	799	812	825	838	2 — 2.6
330	51 851	865	878	891	904	917	930	943	957	970	3 — 3.9 4 — 5.2
331	51 983	996	*009	*022	*035	*048	*061	*075	*088	*101	5 — 6.5
332	52 114	127	140	153	166	179	192	205	218	231	6 — 7.8
333	52 244	257	270	284	297	310	323	336	349	362	7 — 9.1 8 — 10.4
334	52 375	388	401	414	427	440	453	466	479	492	9 — 11.7
335	52 504	517	530	543	556	569	582	595	608	621	
336	52 634	647	660	673	686	699	711	724	737	750	
337	52 763	776	789	802	815	827	840	853	866	879	
338	52 892	905	917	930	943	956	969	982	994	*007	
339	53 020	033	046	058	071	084	097	110	122	135	
340	53 148	161	173	186	199	212	224	237	250	263	**12**
341	53 275	288	301	314	326	339	352	364	377	390	1 — 1.2
342	53 403	415	428	441	453	466	479	491	504	517	2 — 2.4 3 — 3.6
343	53 529	542	555	567	580	593	605	618	631	643	4 — 4.8
344	53 656	668	681	694	706	719	732	744	757	769	5 — 6.0 6 — 7.2
345	53 782	794	807	820	832	845	857	870	882	895	7 — 8.4
346	53 908	920	933	945	958	970	983	995	*008	*020	8 — 9.6
347	54 033	045	058	070	083	095	108	120	133	145	9 — 10.8
348	54 158	170	183	195	208	220	233	245	258	270	
349	54 283	295	307	320	332	345	357	370	382	394	
350	54 407	419	432	444	456	469	481	494	506	518	
N	0	1	2	3	4	5	6	7	8	9	Prop. Parts

Common Logarithms (Five-Place) of the Natural Numbers 1 to 10,000

Prop. Parts	N	0	1	2	3	4	5	6	7	8	9
	350	54 407	419	432	444	456	469	481	494	506	518
	351	54 531	543	555	568	580	593	605	617	630	642
	352	54 654	667	679	691	704	716	728	741	753	765
	353	54 777	790	802	814	827	839	851	864	876	888
	354	54 900	913	925	937	949	962	974	986	998	*011
	355	55 023	035	047	060	072	084	096	108	121	133
	356	55 145	157	169	182	194	206	218	230	242	255
	357	55 267	279	291	303	315	328	340	352	364	376
	358	55 388	400	413	425	437	449	461	473	485	497
	359	55 509	522	534	546	558	570	582	594	606	618
	360	55 630	642	654	666	678	691	703	715	727	739
	361	55 751	763	775	787	799	811	823	835	847	859
	362	55 871	883	895	907	919	931	943	955	967	979
	363	55 991	*003	*015	*027	*038	*050	*062	*074	*086	*098
	364	56 110	122	134	146	158	170	182	194	205	217
	365	56 229	241	253	265	277	289	301	312	324	336
	366	56 348	360	372	384	396	407	419	431	443	455
	367	56 467	478	490	502	514	526	538	549	561	573
	368	56 585	597	608	620	632	644	656	667	679	691
	369	56 703	714	726	738	750	761	773	785	797	808
	370	56 820	832	844	855	867	879	891	902	914	926
	371	56 937	949	961	972	984	996	*008	*019	*031	*043
	372	57 054	066	078	089	101	113	124	136	148	159
	373	57 171	183	194	206	217	229	241	252	264	276
	374	57 287	299	310	322	334	345	357	368	380	392
	375	57 403	415	426	438	449	461	473	484	496	507
	376	57 519	530	542	553	565	576	588	600	611	623
	377	57 634	646	657	669	680	692	703	715	726	738
	378	57 749	761	772	784	795	807	818	830	841	852
	379	57 864	875	887	898	910	921	933	944	955	967
	380	57 978	990	*001	*013	*024	*035	*047	*058	*070	*081
	381	58 092	104	115	127	138	149	161	172	184	195
	382	58 206	218	229	240	252	263	274	286	297	309
	383	58 320	331	343	354	365	377	388	399	410	422
	384	58 433	444	456	467	478	490	501	512	524	535
	385	58 546	557	569	580	591	602	614	625	636	647
	386	58 659	670	681	692	704	715	726	737	749	760
	387	58 771	782	794	805	816	827	838	850	861	872
	388	58 883	894	906	917	928	939	950	961	973	984
	389	58 995	*006	*017	*028	*040	*051	*062	*073	*084	*095
	390	59 106	118	129	140	151	162	173	184	195	207
	391	59 218	229	240	251	262	273	284	295	306	318
	392	59 329	340	351	362	373	384	395	406	417	428
	393	59 439	450	461	472	483	494	506	517	528	539
	394	59 550	561	572	583	594	605	616	627	638	649
	395	59 660	671	682	693	704	715	726	737	748	759
	396	59 770	780	791	802	813	824	835	846	857	868
	397	59 879	890	901	912	923	934	945	956	966	977
	398	59 988	999	*010	*021	*032	*043	*054	*065	*076	*086
	399	60 097	108	119	130	141	152	163	173	184	195
	400	60 206	217	228	239	249	260	271	282	293	304
Prop. Parts	N	0	1	2	3	4	5	6	7	8	9

Prop. Parts

13		12		11		10	
1	1.3	1	1.2	1	1.1	1	1.0
2	2.6	2	2.4	2	2.2	2	2.0
3	3.9	3	3.6	3	3.3	3	3.0
4	5.2	4	4.8	4	4.4	4	4.0
5	6.5	5	6.0	5	5.5	5	5.0
6	7.8	6	7.2	6	6.6	6	6.0
7	9.1	7	8.4	7	7.7	7	7.0
8	10.4	8	9.6	8	8.8	8	8.0
9	11.7	9	10.8	9	9.9	9	9.0

Common Logarithms (Five-Place) of the Natural Numbers 1 to 10,000

N	0	1	2	3	4	5	6	7	8	9
400	60 206	217	228	239	249	260	271	282	293	304
401	60 314	325	336	347	358	369	379	390	401	412
402	60 423	433	444	455	466	477	487	498	509	520
403	60 531	541	552	563	574	584	595	606	617	627
404	60 638	649	660	670	681	692	703	713	724	735
405	60 746	756	767	778	788	799	810	821	831	842
406	60 853	863	874	885	895	906	917	927	938	949
407	60 959	970	981	991	*002	*013	*023	*034	*045	*055
408	61 066	077	087	098	109	119	130	140	151	162
409	61 172	183	194	204	215	225	236	247	257	268
410	61 278	289	300	310	321	331	342	352	363	374
411	61 384	395	405	416	426	437	448	458	469	479
412	61 490	500	511	521	532	542	553	563	574	584
413	61 595	606	616	627	637	648	658	669	679	690
414	61 700	711	721	731	742	752	763	773	784	794
415	61 805	815	826	836	847	857	868	878	888	899
416	61 909	920	930	941	951	962	972	982	993	*003
417	62 014	024	034	045	055	066	076	086	097	107
418	62 118	128	138	149	159	170	180	190	201	211
419	62 221	232	242	252	263	273	284	294	304	315
420	62 325	335	346	356	366	377	387	397	408	418
421	62 428	439	449	459	469	480	490	500	511	521
422	62 531	542	552	562	572	583	593	603	613	624
423	62 634	644	655	665	675	685	696	706	716	726
424	62 737	747	757	767	778	788	798	808	818	829
425	62 839	849	859	870	880	890	900	910	921	931
426	62 941	951	961	972	982	992	*002	*012	*022	*033
427	63 043	053	063	073	083	094	104	114	124	134
428	63 144	155	165	175	185	195	205	215	225	236
429	63 246	256	266	276	286	296	306	317	327	337
430	63 347	357	367	377	387	397	407	417	428	438
431	63 448	458	468	478	488	498	508	518	528	538
432	63 548	558	568	579	589	599	609	619	629	639
433	63 649	659	669	679	689	699	709	719	729	739
434	63 749	759	769	779	789	799	809	819	829	839
435	63 849	859	869	879	889	899	909	919	929	939
436	63 949	959	969	979	988	998	*008	*018	*028	*038
437	64 048	058	068	078	088	098	108	118	128	137
438	64 147	157	167	177	187	197	207	217	227	237
439	64 246	256	266	276	286	296	306	316	326	335
440	64 345	355	365	375	385	395	404	414	424	434
441	64 444	454	464	473	483	493	503	513	523	532
442	64 542	552	562	572	582	591	601	611	621	631
443	64 640	650	660	670	680	689	699	709	719	729
444	64 738	748	758	768	777	787	797	807	816	826
445	64 836	846	856	865	875	885	895	904	914	924
446	64 933	943	953	963	972	982	992	*002	*011	*021
447	65 031	040	050	060	070	079	089	099	108	118
448	65 128	137	147	157	167	176	186	196	205	215
449	65 225	234	244	254	263	273	283	292	302	312
450	65 321	331	341	350	360	369	379	389	398	408
N	0	1	2	3	4	5	6	7	8	9

Prop. Parts

11		10		9	
1	1.1	1	1.0	1	0.9
2	2.2	2	2.0	2	1.8
3	3.3	3	3.0	3	2.7
4	4.4	4	4.0	4	3.6
5	5.5	5	5.0	5	4.5
6	6.6	6	6.0	6	5.4
7	7.7	7	7.0	7	6.3
8	8.8	8	8.0	8	7.2
9	9.9	9	9.0	9	8.1

Common Logarithms (Five-Place) of the Natural Numbers 1 to 10,000

N	0	1	2	3	4	5	6	7	8	9
450	65 321	331	341	350	360	369	379	389	398	408
451	65 418	427	437	447	456	466	475	485	495	504
452	65 514	523	533	543	552	562	571	581	591	600
453	65 610	619	629	639	648	658	667	677	686	696
454	65 706	715	725	734	744	753	763	772	782	792
455	65 801	811	820	830	839	849	858	868	877	887
456	65 896	906	916	925	935	944	954	963	973	982
457	65 992	*001	*011	*020	*030	*039	*049	*058	*068	*077
458	66 087	096	106	115	124	134	143	153	162	172
459	66 181	191	200	210	219	229	238	247	257	266
460	66 276	285	295	304	314	323	332	342	351	361
461	66 370	380	389	398	408	417	427	436	445	455
462	66 464	474	483	492	502	511	521	530	539	549
463	66 558	567	577	586	596	605	614	624	633	642
464	66 652	661	671	680	689	699	708	717	727	736
465	66 745	755	764	773	783	792	801	811	820	829
466	66 839	848	857	867	876	885	894	904	913	922
467	66 932	941	950	960	969	978	987	997	*006	*015
468	67 025	034	043	052	062	071	080	089	099	108
469	67 117	127	136	145	154	164	173	182	191	201
470	67 210	219	228	237	247	256	265	274	284	293
471	67 302	311	321	330	339	348	357	367	376	385
472	67 394	403	413	422	431	440	449	459	468	477
473	67 486	495	504	514	523	532	541	550	560	569
474	67 578	587	596	605	614	624	633	642	651	660
475	67 669	679	688	697	706	715	724	733	742	752
476	67 761	770	779	788	797	806	815	825	834	843
477	67 852	861	870	879	888	897	906	916	925	934
478	67 943	952	961	970	979	988	997	*006	*015	*024
479	68 034	043	052	061	070	079	088	097	106	115
480	68 124	133	142	151	160	169	178	187	196	205
481	68 215	224	233	242	251	260	269	278	287	296
482	68 305	314	323	332	341	350	359	368	377	386
483	68 395	404	413	422	431	440	449	458	467	476
484	68 485	494	502	511	520	529	538	547	556	565
485	68 574	583	592	601	610	619	628	637	646	655
486	68 664	673	681	690	699	708	717	726	735	744
487	68 753	762	771	780	789	797	806	815	824	833
488	68 842	851	860	869	878	886	895	904	913	922
489	68 931	940	949	958	966	975	984	993	*002	*011
490	69 020	028	037	046	055	064	073	082	090	099
491	69 108	117	126	135	144	152	161	170	179	188
492	69 197	205	214	223	232	241	249	258	267	276
493	69 285	294	302	311	320	329	338	346	355	364
494	69 373	381	390	399	408	417	425	434	443	452
495	69 461	469	478	487	496	504	513	522	531	539
496	69 548	557	566	574	583	592	601	609	618	627
497	69 636	644	653	662	671	679	688	697	705	714
498	69 723	732	740	749	758	767	775	784	793	801
499	69 810	819	827	836	845	854	862	871	880	888
500	69 897	906	914	923	932	940	949	958	966	975

Prop. Parts

	10		9		8
1	1.0	1	0.9	1	0.8
2	2.0	2	1.8	2	1.6
3	3.0	3	2.7	3	2.4
4	4.0	4	3.6	4	3.2
5	5.0	5	4.5	5	4.0
6	6.0	6	5.4	6	4.8
7	7.0	7	6.3	7	5.6
8	8.0	8	7.2	8	6.4
9	9.0	9	8.1	9	7.2

Common Logarithms (Five-Place) of the Natural Numbers 1 to 10,000

N	0	1	2	3	4	5	6	7	8	9
500	69 897	906	914	923	932	940	949	958	966	975
501	69 984	992	*001	*010	*018	*027	*036	*044	*053	*062
502	70 070	079	088	096	105	114	122	131	140	148
503	70 157	165	174	183	191	200	209	217	226	234
504	70 243	252	260	269	278	286	295	303	312	321
505	70 329	338	346	355	364	372	381	389	398	406
506	70 415	424	432	441	449	458	467	475	484	492
507	70 501	509	518	526	535	544	552	561	569	578
508	70 586	595	603	612	621	629	638	646	655	663
509	70 672	680	689	697	706	714	723	731	740	749
510	70 757	766	774	783	791	800	808	817	825	834
511	70 842	851	859	868	876	885	893	902	910	919
512	70 927	935	944	952	961	969	978	986	995	*003
513	71 012	020	029	037	046	054	063	071	079	088
514	71 096	105	113	122	130	139	147	155	164	172
515	71 181	189	198	206	214	223	231	240	248	257
516	71 265	273	282	290	299	307	315	324	332	341
517	71 349	357	366	374	383	391	399	408	416	425
518	71 433	441	450	458	466	475	483	492	500	508
519	71 517	525	533	542	550	559	567	575	584	592
520	71 600	609	617	625	634	642	650	659	667	675
521	71 684	692	700	709	717	725	734	742	750	759
522	71 767	775	784	792	800	809	817	825	834	842
523	71 850	858	867	875	883	892	900	908	917	925
524	71 933	941	950	958	966	975	983	991	999	*008
525	72 016	024	032	041	049	057	066	074	082	090
526	72 099	107	115	123	132	140	148	156	165	173
527	72 181	189	198	206	214	222	230	239	247	255
528	72 263	272	280	288	296	304	313	321	329	337
529	72 346	354	362	370	378	387	395	403	411	419
530	72 428	436	444	452	460	469	477	485	493	501
531	72 509	518	526	534	542	550	558	567	575	583
532	72 591	599	607	616	624	632	640	648	656	665
533	72 673	681	689	697	705	713	722	730	738	746
534	72 754	762	770	779	787	979	803	811	819	827
535	72 835	843	852	860	868	876	884	892	900	908
536	72 916	925	933	941	949	957	965	973	981	989
537	72 997	*006	*014	*022	*030	*038	*046	*054	*062	*070
538	73 078	086	094	102	111	119	127	135	143	151
539	73 159	167	175	183	191	199	207	215	223	231
540	73 239	247	255	263	272	280	288	296	304	312
541	73 320	328	336	344	352	360	368	376	384	392
542	73 400	408	416	424	432	440	448	456	464	472
543	73 480	488	496	504	512	520	528	536	544	552
544	73 560	568	576	584	592	600	608	616	624	632
545	73 640	648	656	664	672	679	687	695	703	711
546	73 719	727	735	743	751	759	767	775	783	791
547	73 799	807	815	823	830	838	846	854	862	870
548	73 878	886	894	902	910	918	926	933	941	949
549	73 957	965	973	981	989	997	*005	*013	*020	*028
550	74 036	044	052	060	068	076	084	092	099	107
N	**0**	**1**	**2**	**3**	**4**	**5**	**6**	**7**	**8**	**9**

Prop. Parts

	9		**8**		**7**
1	0.9		0.8		0.7
2	1.8		1.6		1.4
3	2.7		2.4		2.1
4	3.6		3.2		2.8
5	4.5		4.0		3.5
6	5.4		4.8		4.2
7	6.3		5.6		4.9
8	7.2		6.4		5.6
9	8.1		7.2		6.3

Common Logarithms (Five-Place) of the Natural Numbers 1 to 10,000

N	0	1	2	3	4	5	6	7	8	9
550	74 036	044	052	060	068	076	084	092	099	107
551	74 115	123	131	139	147	155	162	170	178	186
552	74 194	202	210	218	225	233	241	249	257	265
553	74 273	280	288	296	304	312	320	327	335	343
554	74 351	359	367	374	382	390	398	406	414	421
555	74 429	437	445	453	461	468	476	484	492	500
556	74 507	515	523	531	539	547	554	562	570	578
557	74 586	593	601	609	617	624	632	640	648	656
558	74 663	671	679	687	695	702	710	718	726	733
559	74 741	749	757	764	772	780	788	796	803	811
560	74 819	827	834	842	850	858	865	873	881	889
561	74 896	904	912	920	927	935	943	950	958	966
562	74 974	981	989	997	*005	*012	*020	*028	*035	*043
563	75 051	059	066	074	082	089	097	105	113	120
564	75 128	136	143	151	159	166	174	182	189	197
565	75 205	213	220	228	236	243	251	259	266	274
566	75 282	289	297	305	312	320	328	335	343	351
567	75 358	366	374	381	389	397	404	412	420	427
568	75 435	442	450	458	465	473	481	488	496	504
569	75 511	519	526	534	542	549	557	565	572	580
570	75 587	595	603	610	618	626	633	641	648	656
571	75 664	671	679	686	694	702	709	717	724	732
572	75 740	747	755	762	770	778	785	793	800	808
573	75 815	823	831	838	846	853	861	868	876	884
574	75 891	899	906	914	921	929	937	944	952	959
575	75 967	974	982	989	997	*005	*012	*020	*027	*035
576	76 042	050	057	065	072	080	087	095	103	110
577	76 118	125	133	140	148	155	163	170	178	185
578	76 193	200	208	215	223	230	238	245	253	260
579	76 268	275	283	290	298	305	313	320	328	335
580	76 343	350	358	365	373	380	388	395	403	410
581	76 418	425	433	440	448	455	462	470	477	485
582	76 492	500	507	515	522	530	537	545	552	559
583	76 567	574	582	589	597	604	612	619	626	634
584	76 641	649	656	664	671	678	686	693	701	708
585	76 716	723	730	738	745	753	760	768	775	782
586	76 790	797	805	812	819	827	834	842	849	856
587	76 864	871	879	886	893	901	908	916	923	930
588	76 938	945	953	960	967	975	982	989	997	*004
589	77 012	019	026	034	041	048	056	063	070	078
590	77 085	093	100	107	115	122	129	137	144	151
591	77 159	166	173	181	188	195	203	210	217	225
592	77 232	240	247	254	262	269	276	283	291	298
593	77 305	313	320	327	335	342	349	357	364	371
594	77 379	386	393	401	408	415	422	430	437	444
595	77 452	459	466	474	481	488	495	503	510	517
596	77 525	532	539	546	554	561	568	576	583	590
597	77 597	605	612	619	627	634	641	648	656	663
598	77 670	677	685	692	699	706	714	721	728	735
599	77 743	750	757	764	772	779	786	793	801	808
600	77 815	822	830	837	844	851	859	866	873	880

Prop. Parts

8	
1	0.8
2	1.6
3	2.4
4	3.2
5	4.0
6	4.8
7	5.6
8	6.4
9	7.2

7	
1	0.7
2	1.4
3	2.1
4	2.8
5	3.5
6	4.2
7	4.9
8	5.6
9	6.3

Common Logarithms (Five-Place) of the Natural Numbers 1 to 10,000

N	0	1	2	3	4	5	6	7	8	9	Prop. Parts
600	77 815	822	830	837	844	851	859	866	873	880	
601	77 887	895	902	909	916	924	931	938	945	952	
602	77 960	967	974	981	988	996	*003	*010	*017	*025	
603	78 032	039	046	053	061	068	075	082	089	097	
604	78 104	111	118	125	132	140	147	154	161	168	
605	78 176	183	190	197	204	211	219	226	233	240	
606	78 247	254	262	269	276	283	290	297	305	312	
607	78 319	326	333	340	347	355	362	369	376	383	
608	78 390	398	405	412	419	426	433	440	447	455	**8**
609	78 462	469	476	483	490	497	504	512	519	526	1 0.8
610	78 533	540	547	554	561	569	576	583	590	597	2 1.6 / 3 2.4
611	78 604	611	618	625	633	640	647	654	661	668	4 3.2
612	78 675	682	689	696	704	711	718	725	732	739	5 4.0 / 6 4.8
613	78 746	753	760	767	774	781	789	796	803	810	7 5.6
614	78 817	824	831	838	845	852	859	866	873	880	8 6.4
615	78 888	895	902	909	916	923	930	937	944	951	9 7.2
616	78 958	965	972	979	986	993	*000	*007	*014	*021	
617	79 029	036	043	050	057	064	071	078	085	092	
618	79 099	106	113	120	127	134	141	148	155	162	
619	79 169	176	183	190	197	204	211	218	225	232	
620	79 239	246	253	260	267	274	281	288	295	302	
621	79 309	316	323	330	337	344	351	358	365	372	**7**
622	79 379	386	393	400	407	414	421	428	435	442	1 0.7
623	79 449	456	463	470	477	484	491	498	505	511	2 1.4 / 3 2.1
624	79 518	525	532	539	546	553	560	567	574	581	4 2.8
625	79 588	595	602	609	616	623	630	637	644	650	5 3.5 / 6 4.2
626	79 657	664	671	678	685	692	699	706	713	720	7 4.9
627	79 727	734	741	748	754	761	768	775	782	789	8 5.6
628	79 796	803	810	817	824	831	837	844	851	858	9 6.3
629	79 865	872	879	886	893	900	906	913	920	927	
630	79 934	941	948	955	962	969	975	982	989	996	
631	80 003	010	017	024	030	037	044	051	058	065	
632	80 072	079	085	092	099	106	113	120	127	134	
633	80 140	147	154	161	168	175	182	188	195	202	
634	80 209	216	223	229	236	243	250	257	264	271	
635	80 277	284	291	298	305	312	318	325	332	339	
636	80 346	353	359	366	373	380	387	393	400	407	**6**
637	80 414	421	428	434	441	448	455	462	468	475	1 0.6
638	80 482	489	496	502	509	516	523	530	536	543	2 1.2 / 3 1.8
639	80 550	557	564	570	577	584	591	598	604	611	4 2.4
640	80 618	625	632	638	645	652	659	665	672	679	5 3.0 / 6 3.6
641	80 686	693	699	706	713	720	726	733	740	747	7 4.2
642	80 754	760	767	774	781	787	794	801	808	814	8 4.8
643	80 821	828	835	841	848	855	862	868	875	882	9 5.4
644	80 889	895	902	909	916	922	929	936	943	949	
645	80 956	963	969	976	983	990	996	*003	*010	*017	
646	81 023	030	037	043	050	057	064	070	077	084	
647	81 090	097	104	111	117	124	131	137	144	151	
648	81 158	164	171	178	184	191	198	204	211	218	
649	81 224	231	238	245	251	258	265	271	278	285	
650	81 291	298	305	311	318	325	331	338	345	351	
N	0	1	2	3	4	5	6	7	8	9	Prop. Parts

Common Logarithms (Five-Place) of the Natural Numbers 1 to 10,000

Prop. Parts

7
1	0.7
2	1.4
3	2.1
4	2.8
5	3.5
6	4.2
7	4.9
8	5.6
9	6.3

6
1	0.6
2	1.2
3	1.8
4	2.4
5	3.0
6	3.6
7	4.2
8	4.8
9	5.4

N	0	1	2	3	4	5	6	7	8	9
650	81 291	298	305	311	318	325	331	338	345	351
651	81 358	365	371	378	385	391	398	405	411	418
652	81 425	431	438	445	451	458	465	471	478	485
653	81 491	498	505	511	518	525	531	538	544	551
654	81 558	564	571	578	584	591	598	604	611	617
655	81 624	631	637	644	651	657	664	671	677	684
656	81 690	697	704	710	717	723	730	737	743	750
657	81 757	763	770	776	703	790	796	803	809	816
658	81 823	829	836	842	849	856	862	869	875	882
659	81 889	895	902	908	915	921	928	935	941	948
660	81 954	961	968	974	981	987	994	*000	*007	*014
661	82 020	027	033	040	046	053	060	066	073	079
662	82 086	092	099	105	112	119	125	132	138	145
663	82 151	158	164	171	178	184	191	197	204	210
664	82 217	223	230	236	243	249	256	263	269	276
665	82 282	289	295	302	308	315	321	328	334	341
666	82 347	354	360	367	373	380	387	393	400	406
667	82 413	419	426	432	439	445	452	458	465	471
668	82 478	484	491	497	504	510	517	523	530	536
669	82 543	549	556	562	569	575	582	588	595	601
670	82 607	614	620	627	633	640	646	653	659	666
671	82 672	679	685	692	698	705	711	718	724	730
672	82 737	743	750	756	763	769	776	782	789	795
673	82 802	808	814	821	827	834	840	847	853	860
674	82 866	872	879	885	892	898	905	911	918	924
675	82 930	937	943	950	956	963	969	975	982	988
676	82 995	*001	*008	*014	*020	*027	*033	*040	*046	*052
677	83 059	065	072	078	085	091	097	104	110	117
678	83 123	129	136	142	149	155	161	168	174	181
679	83 187	193	200	206	213	219	225	232	238	245
680	83 251	257	264	270	276	283	289	296	302	308
681	83 315	321	327	334	340	347	353	359	366	372
682	83 378	385	391	398	404	410	417	423	429	436
683	83 442	448	455	461	467	474	480	487	493	499
684	83 506	512	518	525	531	537	544	550	556	563
685	83 569	575	582	588	594	601	607	613	620	626
686	83 632	639	645	651	658	664	670	677	683	689
687	83 696	702	708	715	721	727	734	740	746	753
688	83 759	765	771	778	784	790	797	803	809	816
689	83 822	828	835	841	847	853	860	866	872	879
690	83 885	891	897	904	910	916	923	929	935	942
691	83 948	954	960	967	973	979	985	992	998	*004
692	84 011	017	023	029	036	042	048	055	061	067
693	84 073	080	086	092	098	105	111	117	123	130
694	84 136	142	148	155	161	167	173	180	186	192
695	84 198	205	211	217	223	230	236	242	248	255
696	84 261	267	273	280	286	292	298	305	311	317
697	84 323	330	336	342	348	354	361	367	373	379
698	84 386	392	398	404	410	417	423	429	435	442
699	84 448	454	460	466	473	479	485	491	497	504
700	84 510	516	522	528	535	541	547	553	559	566

Prop. Parts	N	0	1	2	3	4	5	6	7	8	9

APPENDIX TABLE XII — Continued

Common Logarithms (Five-Place) of the Natural Numbers 1 to 10,000

N	0	1	2	3	4	5	6	7	8	9	Prop. Parts
700	84 510	516	522	528	535	541	547	553	559	566	
701	84 572	578	584	590	597	603	609	615	621	628	
702	84 634	640	646	652	658	665	671	677	683	689	
703	84 696	702	708	714	720	726	733	739	745	751	
704	84 757	763	770	776	782	788	794	800	807	813	
705	84 819	825	831	837	844	850	856	862	868	874	
706	84 880	887	893	899	905	911	917	924	930	936	
707	84 942	948	954	960	967	973	979	985	991	997	**7**
708	85 003	009	016	022	028	034	040	046	052	058	1　0.7
709	85 065	071	077	083	089	095	101	107	114	120	2　1.4
710	85 126	132	138	144	150	156	163	169	175	181	3　2.1 　4　2.8
711	85 187	193	199	205	211	217	224	230	236	242	5　3.5
712	85 248	254	260	266	272	278	285	291	297	303	6　4.2
713	85 309	315	321	327	333	339	345	352	358	364	7　4.9 　8　5.6
714	85 370	376	382	388	394	400	406	412	418	425	9　6.3
715	85 431	437	443	449	455	461	467	473	479	485	
716	85 491	497	503	509	516	522	528	534	540	546	
717	85 552	558	564	570	576	582	588	594	600	606	
718	85 612	618	625	631	637	643	649	655	661	667	
719	85 673	679	685	691	697	703	709	715	721	727	
720	85 733	739	745	751	757	763	769	775	781	788	
721	85 794	800	806	812	818	824	830	836	842	848	
722	85 854	860	866	872	878	884	890	896	902	908	**6**
723	85 914	920	926	932	938	944	950	956	962	968	1　0.6 　2　1.2
724	85 974	980	986	992	998	*004	*010	*016	*022	*028	3　1.8
725	86 034	040	046	052	058	064	070	076	082	088	4　2.4 　5　3.0
726	86 094	100	106	112	118	124	130	136	141	147	6　3.6
727	86 153	159	165	171	177	183	189	195	201	207	7　4.2 　8　4.8
728	86 213	219	225	231	237	243	249	255	261	267	9　5.4
729	86 273	279	285	291	297	303	308	314	320	326	
730	86 332	338	344	350	356	362	368	374	380	386	
731	86 392	398	404	410	415	421	427	433	439	445	
732	86 451	457	463	469	475	481	487	493	499	504	
733	86 510	516	522	528	534	540	546	552	558	564	
734	86 570	576	581	587	593	599	605	611	617	623	
735	86 629	635	641	646	652	658	664	670	676	682	
736	86 688	694	700	705	711	717	723	729	735	741	**5**
737	86 747	753	759	764	770	776	782	788	794	800	1　0.5 　2　1.0
738	86 806	812	817	823	829	835	841	847	853	859	3　1.5
739	86 864	870	876	882	888	894	900	906	911	917	4　2.0 　5　2.5
740	86 923	929	935	941	947	953	958	964	970	976	6　3.0
741	86 982	988	994	999	*005	*011	*017	*023	*029	*035	7　3.5 　8　4.0
742	87 040	046	052	058	064	070	075	081	087	093	9　4.5
743	87 099	105	111	116	122	128	134	140	146	151	
744	87 157	163	169	175	181	186	192	198	204	210	
745	87 216	221	227	233	239	245	251	256	262	268	
746	87 274	280	286	291	297	303	309	315	320	326	
747	87 332	338	344	349	355	361	367	373	379	384	
748	87 390	396	402	408	413	419	425	431	437	442	
749	87 448	454	460	466	471	477	483	489	495	500	
750	87 506	512	518	523	529	535	541	547	552	558	
N	0	1	2	3	4	5	6	7	8	9	Prop. Parts

Common Logarithms (Five-Place) of the Natural Numbers 1 to 10,000

Prop. Parts	N	0	1	2	3	4	5	6	7	8	9
	750	87 506	512	518	523	529	535	541	547	552	558
	751	87 564	570	576	581	587	593	599	604	610	616
	752	87 622	628	633	639	645	651	656	662	668	674
	753	87 679	685	691	697	703	708	714	720	726	731
	754	87 737	743	749	754	760	766	772	777	783	789
	755	87 795	800	806	812	818	823	829	835	841	846
	756	87 852	858	864	869	875	881	887	892	898	904
	757	87 910	915	921	927	933	938	944	950	955	961
	758	87 967	973	978	984	990	996	*001	*007	*013	*018
	759	88 024	030	036	041	047	053	058	064	070	076
	760	88 081	087	093	098	104	110	116	121	127	133
	761	88 138	144	150	156	161	167	173	178	184	190
	762	88 195	201	207	213	218	224	230	235	241	247
	763	88 252	258	264	270	275	281	287	292	298	304
	764	88 309	315	321	326	332	338	343	349	355	360
	765	88 366	372	377	383	389	395	400	406	412	417
	766	88 423	429	434	440	446	451	457	463	468	474
	767	88 480	485	491	497	502	508	513	519	525	530
	768	88 536	542	547	553	559	564	570	576	581	587
	769	88 593	598	604	610	615	621	627	632	638	643
	770	88 649	655	660	666	672	677	683	689	694	700
	771	88 705	711	717	722	728	734	739	745	750	756
	772	88 762	767	773	779	784	790	795	801	807	812
	773	88 818	824	829	835	840	846	852	857	863	868
	774	88 874	880	885	891	897	902	908	913	919	925
	775	88 930	936	941	947	953	958	964	969	975	981
	776	88 986	992	997	*003	*009	*014	*020	*025	*031	*037
	777	89 042	048	053	059	064	070	076	081	087	092
	778	89 098	104	109	115	120	126	131	137	143	148
	779	89 154	159	165	170	176	182	187	193	198	204
	780	89 209	215	221	226	232	237	243	248	254	260
	781	89 265	271	276	282	287	293	298	304	310	315
	782	89 321	326	332	337	343	348	354	360	365	371
	783	89 376	382	387	393	398	404	409	415	421	426
	784	89 432	437	443	448	454	459	465	470	476	481
	785	89 487	492	498	504	509	515	520	526	531	537
	786	89 542	548	553	559	564	570	575	581	586	592
	787	89 597	603	609	614	620	625	631	636	642	647
	788	89 653	658	664	669	675	680	686	691	697	702
	789	89 708	713	719	724	730	735	741	746	752	757
	790	89 763	768	774	779	785	790	796	801	807	812
	791	89 818	823	829	834	840	845	851	856	862	867
	792	89 873	878	883	889	894	900	905	911	916	922
	793	89 927	933	938	944	949	955	960	966	971	977
	794	89 982	988	993	998	*004	*009	*015	*020	*026	*031
	795	90 037	042	048	053	059	064	069	075	080	086
	796	90 091	097	102	108	113	119	124	129	135	140
	797	90 146	151	157	162	168	173	179	184	189	195
	798	90 200	206	211	217	222	227	233	238	244	249
	799	90 255	260	266	271	276	282	287	293	298	304
	800	90 309	314	320	325	331	336	342	347	352	358
Prop. Parts	N	0	1	2	3	4	5	6	7	8	9

Prop. Parts box (6):

	6
1	0.6
2	1.2
3	1.8
4	2.4
5	3.0
6	3.6
7	4.2
8	4.8
9	5.4

Prop. Parts box (5):

	5
1	0.5
2	1.0
3	1.5
4	2.0
5	2.5
6	3.0
7	3.5
8	4.0
9	4.5

Common Logarithms (Five-Place) of the Natural Numbers 1 to 10,000

N	0	1	2	3	4	5	6	7	8	9
800	90 309	314	320	325	331	336	342	347	352	358
801	90 363	369	374	380	385	390	396	401	407	412
802	90 417	423	428	434	439	445	450	455	461	466
803	90 472	477	482	488	493	499	504	509	515	520
804	90 526	531	536	542	547	553	558	563	569	574
805	90 580	585	590	596	601	607	612	617	623	628
806	90 634	639	644	650	655	660	666	671	677	682
807	90 687	693	698	703	709	714	720	725	730	736
808	90 741	747	752	757	763	768	773	779	784	789
809	90 795	800	806	811	816	822	827	832	838	843
810	90 849	854	859	865	870	875	881	886	891	897
811	90 902	907	913	918	924	929	934	940	945	950
812	90 956	961	966	972	977	982	988	993	998	*004
813	91 009	014	020	025	030	036	041	046	052	057
814	91 062	068	073	078	084	089	094	100	105	110
815	91 116	121	126	132	137	142	148	153	158	164
816	91 169	174	180	185	190	196	201	206	212	217
817	91 222	228	233	238	243	249	254	259	265	270
818	91 275	281	286	291	297	302	307	312	318	323
819	91 328	334	339	344	350	355	360	365	371	376
820	91 381	387	392	397	403	408	413	418	424	429
821	91 434	440	445	450	455	461	466	471	477	482
822	91 487	492	498	503	508	514	519	524	529	535
823	91 540	545	551	556	561	566	572	577	582	587
824	91 593	598	603	609	614	619	624	630	635	640
825	91 645	651	656	661	666	672	677	682	687	693
826	91 698	703	709	714	719	724	730	735	740	745
827	91 751	756	761	766	772	777	782	787	793	798
828	91 803	808	814	819	824	829	834	840	845	850
829	91 855	861	866	871	876	882	887	892	897	903
830	91 908	913	918	924	929	934	939	944	950	955
831	91 960	965	971	976	981	986	991	997	*002	*007
832	92 012	018	023	028	033	038	044	049	054	059
833	92 065	070	075	080	085	091	096	101	106	111
834	92 117	122	127	132	137	143	148	153	158	163
835	92 169	174	179	184	189	195	200	205	210	215
836	92 221	226	231	236	241	247	252	257	262	267
837	92 273	278	283	288	293	298	304	309	314	319
838	92 324	330	335	340	345	350	355	361	366	371
839	92 376	381	387	392	397	402	407	412	418	423
840	92 428	433	438	443	449	454	459	464	469	474
841	92 480	485	490	495	500	505	511	516	521	526
842	92 531	536	542	547	552	557	562	567	572	578
843	92 583	588	593	598	603	609	614	619	624	629
844	92 634	639	645	650	655	660	665	670	675	681
845	92 686	691	696	701	706	711	716	722	727	732
846	92 737	742	747	752	758	763	768	773	778	783
847	92 788	793	799	804	809	814	819	824	829	834
848	92 840	845	850	855	860	865	870	875	881	886
849	92 891	896	901	906	911	916	921	927	932	937
850	92 942	947	952	957	962	967	973	978	983	988
N	0	1	2	3	4	5	6	7	8	9

Prop. Parts

	6			5
1	0.6		1	0.5
2	1.2		2	1.0
3	1.8		3	1.5
4	2.4		4	2.0
5	3.0		5	2.5
6	3.6		6	3.0
7	4.2		7	3.5
8	4.8		8	4.0
9	5.4		9	4.5

Common Logarithms (Five-Place) of the Natural Numbers 1 to 10,000

Prop. Parts	N	0	1	2	3	4	5	6	7	8	9
	850	92 942	947	952	957	962	967	973	978	983	988
	851	92 993	998	*003	*008	*013	*018	*024	*029	*034	*039
	852	93 044	049	054	059	064	069	075	080	085	090
	853	93 095	100	105	110	115	120	125	131	136	141
	854	93 146	151	156	161	166	171	176	181	186	192
	855	93 197	202	207	212	217	222	227	232	237	242
	856	93 247	252	258	263	268	273	278	283	288	293
6	857	93 298	303	308	313	318	323	328	334	339	344
1 0.6	858	93 349	354	359	364	369	374	379	384	389	394
2 1.2	859	93 399	404	409	414	420	425	430	435	440	445
3 1.8											
4 2.4	860	93 450	455	460	465	470	475	480	485	490	495
5 3.0	861	93 500	505	510	515	520	526	531	536	541	546
6 3.6	862	93 551	556	561	566	571	576	581	586	591	596
7 4.2	863	93 601	606	611	616	621	626	631	636	641	646
8 4.8	864	93 651	656	661	666	671	676	682	687	692	697
9 5.4	865	93 702	707	712	717	722	727	732	737	742	747
	866	93 752	757	762	767	772	777	782	787	792	797
	867	93 802	807	812	817	822	827	832	837	842	847
	868	93 852	857	862	867	872	877	882	887	892	897
	869	93 902	907	912	917	922	927	932	937	942	947
	870	93 952	957	962	967	972	977	982	987	992	997
	871	94 002	007	012	017	022	027	032	037	042	047
	872	94 052	057	062	067	072	077	082	086	091	096
5	873	94 101	106	111	116	121	126	131	136	141	146
1 0.5	874	94 151	156	161	166	171	176	181	186	191	196
2 1.0	875	94 201	206	211	216	221	226	231	236	240	245
3 1.5	876	94 250	255	260	265	270	275	280	285	290	295
4 2.0	877	94 300	305	310	315	320	325	330	335	340	345
5 2.5	878	94 349	354	359	364	369	374	379	384	389	394
6 3.0	879	94 399	404	409	414	419	424	429	433	438	443
7 3.5	880	94 448	453	458	463	468	473	478	483	488	493
8 4.0	881	94 498	503	507	512	517	522	527	532	537	542
9 4.5	882	94 547	552	557	562	567	571	576	581	586	591
	883	94 596	601	606	611	616	621	626	630	635	640
	884	94 645	650	655	660	665	670	675	680	685	689
	885	94 694	699	704	709	714	719	724	729	734	738
	886	94 743	748	753	758	763	768	773	778	783	787
4	887	94 792	797	802	807	812	817	822	827	832	836
1 0.4	888	94 841	846	851	856	861	866	871	876	880	885
2 0.8	889	94 890	895	900	905	910	915	919	924	929	934
3 1.2	890	94 939	944	949	954	959	963	968	973	978	983
4 1.6	891	94 988	993	998	*002	*007	*012	*017	*022	*027	*032
5 2.0	892	95 036	041	046	051	056	061	066	071	075	080
6 2.4	893	95 085	090	095	100	105	109	114	119	124	129
7 2.8	894	95 134	139	143	148	153	158	163	168	173	177
8 3.2	895	95 182	187	192	197	202	207	211	216	221	226
9 3.6	896	95 231	236	240	245	250	255	260	265	270	274
	897	95 279	284	289	294	299	303	308	313	318	323
	898	95 328	332	337	342	347	352	357	361	366	371
	899	95 376	381	386	390	395	400	405	410	415	419
	900	95 424	429	434	439	444	448	453	458	463	468
Prop. Parts	N	0	1	2	3	4	5	6	7	8	9

Common Logarithms (Five-Place) of the Natural Numbers 1 to 10,000

N	0	1	2	3	4	5	6	7	8	9	Prop. Parts
900	95 424	429	434	439	444	448	453	458	463	468	
901	95 472	477	482	487	492	497	501	506	511	516	
902	95 521	525	530	535	540	545	550	554	559	564	
903	95 569	574	578	583	588	593	598	602	607	612	
904	95 617	622	626	631	636	641	646	650	655	660	
905	95 665	670	674	679	684	689	694	698	703	708	
906	95 713	718	722	727	732	737	742	746	751	756	
907	95 761	766	770	775	780	785	789	794	799	804	
908	95 809	813	818	823	828	832	837	842	847	852	
909	95 856	861	866	871	875	880	885	890	895	899	
910	95 904	909	914	018	923	928	933	938	942	947	
911	95 952	957	961	966	971	976	980	985	990	995	
912	95 999	*004	*009	*014	*019	*023	*028	*033	*038	*042	**5**
913	96 047	052	057	061	066	071	076	080	085	090	1 0.5
914	96 095	099	104	109	114	118	123	128	133	137	2 1.0
915	96 142	147	152	156	161	166	171	175	180	185	3 1.5
916	96 190	194	199	204	209	213	218	223	227	232	4 2.0
917	96 237	242	246	251	256	261	265	270	275	280	5 2.5
918	96 284	289	294	298	303	308	313	317	322	327	6 3.0
919	96 332	336	341	346	350	355	360	365	369	374	7 3.5
920	96 379	384	388	393	398	402	407	412	417	421	8 4.0
921	96 426	431	435	440	445	450	454	459	464	468	9 4.5
922	96 473	478	483	487	492	497	501	506	511	515	
923	96 520	525	530	534	539	544	548	553	558	562	
924	96 567	572	577	581	586	591	595	600	605	609	
925	96 614	619	624	628	633	638	642	647	652	656	
926	96 661	666	670	675	680	685	689	694	699	703	
927	96 708	713	717	722	727	731	736	741	745	750	
928	96 755	759	764	769	774	778	783	788	792	797	
929	96 802	806	811	816	820	825	830	834	839	844	
930	96 848	853	858	862	867	872	876	881	886	890	
931	96 895	900	904	909	914	918	923	928	932	937	**4**
932	96 942	946	951	956	960	965	970	974	979	984	1 0.4
933	96 988	993	997	*002	*007	*011	*016	*021	*025	*030	2 0.8
934	97 035	039	044	049	053	058	063	067	072	077	3 1.2
935	97 081	086	090	095	100	104	109	114	118	123	4 1.6
936	97 128	132	137	142	146	151	155	160	165	169	5 2.0
937	97 174	179	183	188	192	197	202	206	211	216	6 2.4
938	97 220	225	230	234	239	243	248	253	257	262	7 2.8
939	97 267	271	276	280	285	290	294	299	304	308	8 3.2
940	97 313	317	322	327	331	336	340	345	350	354	9 3.6
941	97 359	364	368	373	377	382	387	391	396	400	
942	97 405	410	414	419	424	428	433	437	442	447	
943	97 451	456	460	465	470	474	479	483	488	493	
944	97 497	502	506	511	516	520	525	529	534	539	
945	97 543	548	552	557	562	566	571	575	580	585	
946	97 589	594	598	603	607	612	617	621	626	630	
947	97 635	640	644	649	653	658	663	667	672	676	
948	97 681	685	690	695	699	704	708	713	717	722	
949	97 727	731	736	740	745	749	754	759	763	768	
950	97 772	777	782	786	791	795	800	804	809	813	
N	0	1	2	3	4	5	6	7	8	9	Prop. Parts

Common Logarithms (Five-Place) of the Natural Numbers 1 to 10,000

Prop. Parts	N	0	1	2	3	4	5	6	7	8	9
	950	97 772	777	782	786	791	795	800	804	809	813
	951	97 818	823	827	832	836	841	845	850	855	859
	952	97 864	868	873	877	882	886	891	896	900	905
	953	97 909	914	918	923	928	932	937	941	946	950
	954	97 955	959	964	968	973	978	982	987	991	996
	955	98 000	005	009	014	019	023	028	032	037	041
	956	98 046	050	055	059	064	068	073	078	082	087
	957	98 091	096	100	105	109	114	118	123	127	132
	958	98 137	141	146	150	155	159	164	168	173	177
	959	98 182	186	191	195	200	204	209	214	218	223
	960	98 227	232	236	241	245	250	254	259	263	268
	961	98 272	277	281	286	290	295	299	304	308	313
5	962	98 318	322	327	331	336	340	345	349	354	358
1 0.5	963	98 363	367	372	376	381	385	390	394	399	403
2 1.0	964	98 408	412	417	421	426	430	435	439	444	448
3 1.5	965	98 453	457	462	466	471	475	480	484	489	493
4 2.0	966	98 498	502	507	511	516	520	525	529	534	538
5 2.5	967	98 543	547	552	556	561	565	570	574	579	583
6 3.0	968	98 588	592	597	601	605	610	614	619	623	628
7 3.5	969	98 632	637	641	646	650	655	659	664	668	673
8 4.0	**970**	98 677	682	686	691	695	700	704	709	713	717
9 4.5	971	98 722	726	731	735	740	744	749	753	758	762
	972	98 767	771	776	780	784	789	793	798	802	807
	973	98 811	816	820	825	829	834	838	843	847	851
	974	98 856	860	865	869	874	878	883	887	892	896
	975	98 900	905	909	914	918	923	927	932	936	941
	976	98 945	949	954	958	963	967	972	976	981	985
	977	98 989	994	998	*003	*007	*012	*016	*021	*025	*029
	978	99 034	038	043	047	052	056	061	065	069	074
	979	99 078	083	087	092	096	100	105	109	114	118
	980	99 123	127	131	136	140	145	149	154	158	162
	981	99 167	171	176	180	185	189	193	198	202	207
4	982	99 211	216	220	224	229	233	238	242	247	251
1 0.4	983	99 255	260	264	269	273	277	282	286	291	295
2 0.8	984	99 300	304	308	313	317	322	326	330	335	339
3 1.2	985	99 344	348	352	357	361	366	370	374	379	383
4 1.6	986	99 388	392	396	401	405	410	414	419	423	427
5 2.0	987	99 432	436	441	445	449	454	458	463	467	471
6 2.4	988	99 476	480	484	489	493	498	502	506	511	515
7 2.8	989	99 520	524	528	533	537	542	546	550	555	559
8 3.2	**990**	99 564	568	572	577	581	585	590	594	599	603
9 3.6	991	99 607	612	616	621	625	629	634	638	642	647
	992	99 651	656	660	664	669	673	677	682	686	691
	993	99 695	699	704	708	712	717	721	726	730	734
	994	99 739	743	747	752	756	760	765	769	774	778
	995	99 782	787	791	795	800	804	808	813	817	822
	996	99 826	830	835	839	843	848	852	856	861	865
	997	99 870	874	878	883	887	891	896	900	904	909
	998	99 913	917	922	926	930	935	939	944	948	952
	999	99 957	961	965	970	974	978	983	987	991	996
	1000	00 000	004	009	013	017	022	026	030	035	039
Prop. Parts	N	0	1	2	3	4	5	6	7	8	9

List of References

1. Adler, F., "Yates' Correction and the Statisticians," *Journal of the American Statistical Association*, Dec., 1951.
2. Allen, R. G. D., *Mathematical Analysis for Economists*, London, Macmillan, 1942.
3. Allen, R. G. D., *Statistics for Economists*, London, Hutchinson, 1949.
4. Anderson, R. L. and Bancroft, T. A., *Statistical Theory in Research*, New York, McGraw-Hill, 1952.
5. Anglo-American Council on Productivity, *Final Report*, London (also U.S. Department of Commerce, Washington, D.C.), 1952.
6. Barger, H., *The Transportation Industries, 1889–1946: A Study of Output, Employment and Productivity*, New York, National Bureau of Economic Research, 1951.
7. Barger, H. and Schurr, S. H., *The Mining Industries: A Study of Output, Employment and Productivity*, New York, National Bureau of Economic Research, 1944.
8. Bartlett, M. S., "Properties of Sufficiency and Statistical Tests," *Proceedings of the Royal Society of London*, A, Vol. 160, 1937.
9. Bartlett, M. S., "The Use of Transformations," *Biometrics*, of the Biometrics Section of the American Statistical Association, March, 1947.
10. Beckett, S. H. and Robertson, R. D., "The Economical Irrigation of Alfalfa in the Sacramento Valley," Univ. of California Agricultural Experiment Station, *Bulletin* 280, 1917.
11. Burns, A. F., "Frickey on the Decomposition of Time Series," *Review of Economic Statistics*, August, 1944.
12. Burns, A. F., *Production Trends in the United States Since 1870*, New York, National Bureau of Economic Research, 1934.
13. Burns, A. F. and Mitchell, W. C., *Measuring Business Cycles*, New York, National Bureau of Economic Research, 1946.
14. Carter, C. F., Reddaway, W. B. and Stone, R., *The Measurement of Production Movements*, Cambridge University Press, 1948.
15. Churchman, C. W., *Theory of Experimental Inference*, New York, Macmillan, 1948.
16. Clark, C. E., *An Introduction to Statistics*, New York, Wiley, 1953.
17. Cochran, W. G., *Sampling Techniques*, New York, Wiley, 1953.
18. Cochran, W. G., "Some Consequences when the Assumptions for the

Analysis of Variance are not Satisfied," *Biometrics*, of the Biometrics Section of the American Statistical Association, March, 1947.

19. Cohen, Morris R., "The Statistical View of Nature," *Journal of the American Statistical Association*, June, 1936.

20. Committee on Graphics, *A Guide for Preparing Technical Illustrations for Publication and Projection*, American Standards Association and American Society of Mechanical Engineers, New York, 1953.

21. Committee on Standards for Graphic Presentation, "Time Series Charts, A Manual of Design and Construction," American Standards Association and American Society of Mechanical Engineers, New York, 1938.

22. Cramér, H., *The Elements of Probability Theory and Some of its Applications*, New York, Wiley, 1954.

23. Cramér, H., *Mathematical Methods of Statistics*, Princeton University Press, 1951.

24. Croxton, F. E. and Cowden, D. J., *Applied General Statistics*, New York, Prentice-Hall, 1946.

25. David, F. N., *Probability Theory for Statistical Methods*, Cambridge University Press, 1949.

26. David, F. N., *Tables of the Correlation Coefficient*, Cambridge University Press, 1938.

27. Dean, J., "The Relation of Cost to Output for a Leather Belt Shop," *Technical Paper* 2, New York, National Bureau of Economic Research, 1941.

28. Dean, J., *Statistical Cost Functions of a Hosiery Mill*, University of Chicago Press, 1941.

29. Deming, W. Edwards, *Some Theory of Sampling*, New York, Wiley, 1950.

30. Deming, W. Edwards, *Statistical Adjustment of Data*, New York, Wiley, 1943.

31. Deming, W. E. and Birge, R. T., "On the Statistical Theory of Errors," *Reviews of Modern Physics*, July, 1934.

32. Dixon, W. J. and Massey, F. J. Jr., *Introduction to Statistical Analysis*, New York, McGraw-Hill, 1951.

33. Eisenhart, C., "Some Assumptions Underlying the Analysis of Variance," *Biometrics*, of the Biometrics Section of the American Statistical Association, March, 1947.

34. Eisenhart, C., Hastay, M. W. and Wallis, W. A., (editors for Statistical Research Group, Columbia University), *Selected Techniques of Statistical Analysis*, New York, McGraw-Hill, 1947.

35. Elderton, W. P., *Frequency Curves and Correlation*, 4th ed., Washington, D.C., Harren Press, 1953.

36. Ezekiel, M., "A Method of Handling Curvilinear Correlation for Any Number of Variables," *Journal of the American Statistical Association*, Dec., 1924.

37. Ezekiel, M., *Methods of Correlation Analysis*, 2nd ed., New York, Wiley, 1941.
38. Fabricant, S., *Employment in Manufacturing, 1899–1939*, New York, National Bureau of Economic Research, 1942.
39. Fabricant, S., *The Output of Manufacturing Industries, 1890–1937*, New York, National Bureau of Economic Research, 1940.
40. Federal Reserve System, Board of Governors, *Charts on Money, Bank Credit, Money Rates and Business*, Washington, D.C.
41. Federal Reserve System, Board of Governors, "1954 Survey of Consumer Finances," *Federal Reserve Bulletin*, March, June, July, 1954.
42. Federal Reserve System, Board of Governors, "The Revised Federal Reserve Index of Industrial Production," *Federal Reserve Bulletin*, Dec., 1953.
43. Feller, W., *An Introduction to Probability Theory and its Applications*, Vol. I, New York, Wiley, 1950.
44. Ferber, R., "A Study of Aggregate Consumption Functions," *Technical Paper 8*, New York, National Bureau of Economic Research, 1953.
45. Festinger, L. and Katz, D. ed., *Research Methods in the Behavioral Sciences*, New York, The Dryden Press, 1953.
46. Fisher, Irving, *The Making of Index Numbers*, Boston, Houghton Mifflin, 1922.
47. Fisher, Sir Ronald (R.A.), *Contributions to Mathematical Statistics*, New York, Wiley, 1950.
48. Fisher, Sir Ronald (R.A.), *The Design of Experiments*, 4th ed., Edinburgh and London, Oliver and Boyd, Ltd., 1942.
49. Fisher, Sir Ronald (R.A.), "Frequency Distribution of the Values of the Correlation Coefficient in Samples from an Indefinitely Large Population," *Biometrika*, Vol. 10, 1915.
50. Fisher, Sir Ronald (R.A.), *Statistical Methods for Research Workers*, 11th ed., New York, Hafner, 1950.
51. Fisher, Sir Ronald (R.A.) and Yates, F., *Statistical Tables for Biological, Agricultural and Medical Research*, 3rd ed., New York, Hafner, 1948.
52. Florence, P. S., *The Statistical Method in Economics and Political Science*, New York, Harcourt, Brace, 1929.
53. Fowler, C. B., Griffin, J. I., Cohen, J. B., Cropsey, J., Greenwald, W. I. and Sethur, F., *Economic Handbook, A Visual Survey*, New York, Crowell, 1955.
54. Freeman, H. A., *Industrial Statistics*, New York, Wiley, 1942.
55. Freund, J. E., *Modern Elementary Statistics*, New York, Prentice-Hall, 1952.
56. Frickey, E., *Economic Fluctuations in the United States*, Harvard Economic Studies 73, Cambridge, 1942.

57. Friedman, Milton, "The Use of Ranks to Avoid the Assumption of Normality Implicit in the Analysis of Variance," *Journal of the American Statistical Association*, Dec., 1937.

58. Frisch, R., "Annual Survey of Economic Theory: The Problem of Index Numbers," *Econometrica*, January, 1936.

59. Frisch, R., "Some Basic Principles of Price of Living Measurements," *Econometrica*, Oct., 1954.

60. Frisch, R., *Statistical Confluence Analysis by Means of Complete Regression Systems*, Oslo, Universitetets Økonomiske Institutt, 1934.

61. Fryer, H. C., *Elements of Statistics*, New York, Wiley, 1954.

62. Geary, R. C., "The Concept of Net Volume of Output with Special Reference to Irish Data," *Journal of the Royal Statistical Society*, Vol. 107, 1944.

63. Gould, J. M., *Output and Productivity in the Electric and Gas Utilities*, New York, National Bureau of Economic Research, 1946.

64. Goulden, C. H., *Methods of Statistical Analysis*, 2nd ed., New York, Wiley, 1952.

65. Greenwood, E. R. Jr., *A Detailed Proof of the Chi-Square Test of Goodness of Fit*, Harvard University Press, 1940.

66. Hald, A., *The Decomposition of a Series of Observations Composed of a Trend, a Periodic Movement, and a Stochastic Variable*, Copenhagen, G. E. C. Gads, 1948.

67. Hansen, M. H., Hurwitz, W. N. and Madow, W. G., *Sample Survey Methods and Theories*, Vol. I, Methods and Applications; Vol. II, Theory, New York, Wiley, 1953.

68. Hartley, H. O., "The Maximum F-Ratio as a Short-cut Test for Heterogeneity of Variance," *Biometrika*, Vol. 37, 1950.

69. Hoel, P. G., *Introduction to Mathematical Statistics*, 2nd ed., New York, Wiley, 1954.

70. Hotelling, H., "New Light on the Correlation Coefficient and its Transforms," *Journal of the Royal Statistical Society*, Series B, Vol. 15, No. 2, 1953.

71. International Labor Office, "Methods of Labor Productivity Statistics," *Studies and Reports, New Series*, No. 18, Geneva, 1951.

72. Johnson, P. O., *Statistical Methods in Research*, New York, Prentice-Hall, 1949.

73. Joy, A. and Thomas, W., "The Use of Moving Averages in the Measurement of Seasonal Variations," *Journal of the American Statistical Association*, Sept., 1928.

74. Juliber, G. S., "Relation Between Seasonal Amplitudes and the Level of Production — An Application to the Production of Steel Ingots," *Journal of the American Statistical Association*, Dec., 1941.

75. Katona, G. and Mueller, E., *Consumer Attitudes and Demand*, Survey

Research Center, Institute for Social Research, University of Michigan, 1953.

76. Kelley, Truman L., *Fundamentals of Statistics*, Cambridge, Harvard University Press, 1947.

77. Kelley, Truman L., *The Kelley Statistical Tables*, rev. ed., Harvard University Press, 1948.

78. Kendall, M. G., *The Advanced Theory of Statistics*, 3rd ed., London, Griffin, 1947.

79. Kendall, M. G., *Contributions to the Study of Oscillatory Time Series*, Cambridge University Press, 1946.

80. Kendall, M. G., *Rank Correlation Methods*, London, Griffin, 1948.

81. Kendall, M. G., "The Statistical Approach," *Economica*, May, 1950.

82. Keynes, J. M., *A Treatise on Probability*, New York, Macmillan, 1921.

83. Klein, Lawrence R., *Contributions of Survey Methods to Economics*, New York, Columbia University Press, 1954.

84. Konus, A. A., "The Problem of the True Index of the Cost of Living," *Econometrica*, January, 1939.

85. Koopmans, T. C., "Measurement without Theory," *Review of Economic Statistics*, Aug., 1947.

86. Koopmans, T. C., ed., *Statistical Inference in Dynamic Economic Models*, New York, Wiley, 1950.

87. Kuznets, S., *Seasonal Variations in Industry and Trade*, New York, National Bureau of Economic Research, 1933.

88. Kuznets, S., *Secular Movements in Production and Prices*, Boston, Houghton Mifflin, 1930.

89. Lazarsfeld, P. F., ed., *Mathematical Thinking in the Social Sciences*, Glencoe, Ill., The Free Press, 1954.

90. Lewis, D. and Burke, C. J., "Further Discussion of the Use and Misuse of the Chi-Square Test," *The Psychological Bulletin*, July, 1950.

91. Lewis, D. and Burke, C. J., "The Use and Misuse of the Chi-Square Test," *The Psychological Bulletin*, Nov., 1949.

92. Lewis, E. E., *Methods of Statistical Analysis in Economics and Business*, Boston, Houghton Mifflin, 1953.

93. Livingston, J. A., "Charts Should Tell a Story," *Journal of the American Statistical Association*, Sept., 1945.

94. Lutz, R. R., *Graphic Presentation Simplified*, New York, Funk and Wagnalls, 1949.

95. Macaulay, F. R., *The Smoothing of Time Series*, New York, National Bureau of Economic Research, 1931.

96. Mather, K., *Statistical Analysis in Biology*, 2nd ed., New York, Interscience Publishers, Inc., 1947.

97. Mendershausen, H., "Methods of Computing and Eliminating Changing Seasonal Fluctuations," *Econometrica*, July, 1937.

98. Merriman, Mansfield, *The Method of Least Squares*, New York, Wiley, 1897.

99. Merz, J. T., *A History of European Thought in the Nineteenth Century*, Edinburgh and London, Blackwood, 1904, Vol. II, Chapter 12, "The Statistical View of Nature."

100. Mills, F. C., *The Behavior of Prices*, New York, National Bureau of Economic Research, 1927.

101. Mills, F. C., *Economic Tendencies in the United States*, New York, National Bureau of Economic Research, 1932.

102. Mills, F. C., "The Measurement of Correlation and the Problem of Estimation," *Journal of the American Statistical Association*, Sept., 1924.

103. Mills, F. C., "Productivity and Economic Progress," *Occasional Paper* 38, New York, National Bureau of Economic Research, 1952.

104. Miner, J. R., *Tables of $\sqrt{1 - r^2}$ and $1 - r^2$ for Use in Partial Correlation and in Trigonometry*, Baltimore, Johns Hopkins Press, 1922.

105. Mitchell, W. C., *Business Cycles*, University of California Press, 1913.

106. Mitchell, W. C., "The Making and Using of Index Numbers," *Bulletin* 656, U.S. Bureau of Labor Statistics.

107. Mitchell, W. C., *What Happens During Business Cycles*, New York, National Bureau of Economic Research, 1951.

108. Mitchell, W. C., King, W. I., Macaulay, F. R. and Knauth, O., *Income in the United States*, Vol. I, New York, Harcourt, Brace and Co. (for National Bureau of Economic Research), 1921.

109. Mood, A. M., *Introduction to the Theory of Statistics*, New York, McGraw-Hill, 1950.

110. Moore, G. H., "Statistical Indicators of Cyclical Revivals and Recessions," *Occasional Paper* 31, New York, National Bureau of Economic Research, 1950.

111. Moore, G. H. and Wallis, W. A., "Time Series Significance Tests Based on Signs of Differences," *Journal of the American Statistical Association*, 38 (1943).

112. Mosteller, F., and others, "The Pre-Election Polls of 1948," Social Science Research Council, *Bulletin* 60, 1949.

113. Mudgett, Bruce D., *Index Numbers*, New York, Wiley, 1951.

114. Mudgett, Bruce D., *Statistical Tables and Graphs*, Boston, Houghton Mifflin, 1930.

115. National Bureau of Standards, *Tables of the Binomial Probability Distribution*, Applied Mathematical Series 6, Washington, D.C., U.S. Government Printing Office, 1950.

116. Neyman, Jerzy, "Basic Ideas and Some Recent Results of the Theory of Testing Statistical Hypotheses," *Journal of the Royal Statistical Society*, Vol. 105, 1942.

117. Neyman, Jerzy, "Fiducial Argument and the Theory of Confidence In-

tervals," *Biometrika*, Vol. 32, 1941. (Also in Neyman, J., *Lectures and Conferences on Mathematical Statistics and Probability*, 2nd ed.)

118. Neyman, Jerzy, *First Course in Probability and Statistics*, New York, Henry Holt, 1950.

119. Neyman, Jerzy, *Lectures and Conferences on Mathematical Statistics and Probability*, 2nd ed., Washington, Graduate School, U.S. Department of Agriculture, 1952.

120. Neyman, Jerzy, "On the Two Different Aspects of the Representative Method," *Journal of the Royal Statistical Society*, Vol. 97, 1934.

121. Neyman, Jerzy, "Outline of a Theory of Statistical Estimation Based on the Classical Theory of Probability," *Philosophical Transactions of the Royal Society*, 1937.

122. Neyman, J. and Pearson, E. S., "Contributions to the Theory of Testing Statistical Hypotheses," *Statistical Research Memoirs*, Vol. 1, 1936; Vol. 2, 1938.

123. Neyman, J. and Pearson, E. S., "On the Problem of the Most Efficient Tests of Statistical Hypotheses," *Philosophical Transactions of the Royal Society*, Vol. 231, 1933.

124. Parten, M. B., *Surveys, Polls, and Samples*, New York, Harper, 1950.

125. Peake, E. G., *An Academic Study of Some Money Market and Other Statistics*, London, King, 1923.

126. Pearson, E. S. and Hartley, H. O., *Biometrika Tables for Statisticians*, Vol. I, Cambridge University Press, 1954.

127. Persons, W. M., "Indices of Business Conditions," *Review of Economic Statistics*, Preliminary Vol. 1, 1919.

128. Peters, C. C. and Van Voorhis, W. R., *Statistical Procedures and their Mathematical Bases*, New York, McGraw-Hill, 1940.

129. Reiersöl, O., *Confluence Analysis by Means of Instrumental Sets of Variables*, Stockholm, Almqvist and Wiksells, 1945.

130. Rider, Paul R., *An Introduction to Modern Statistical Methods*, New York, Wiley, 1939.

131. Riggleman, J. R. and Frisbee, I. N., *Business Statistics*, 3rd ed., New York, McGraw-Hill, 1951.

132. Rosander, A. C., *Elementary Principles of Statistics*, New York, Van Nostrand, 1951.

133. Royce, Josiah, "The Mechanical, the Historical and the Statistical," *Science*, April 17, 1914.

134. Sasuly, Max, *Trend Analysis of Statistics: Theory and Technique*, Washington, Brookings Institution, 1934.

135. Schultz, Henry, *Statistical Laws of Demand and Supply*, University of Chicago Press, 1928.

136. Schultz, Henry, *The Theory and Measurement of Demand*, University of Chicago Press, 1938.

137. Schumpeter, J. A., *Business Cycles*, New York, McGraw-Hill, 1939.

138. Sheppard, W. F., "The Calculation of Moments of a Frequency Distribution," *Biometrika*, Vol. 5, 1907.

139. Sheppard, W. F., "On the Calculation of the Most Probable Values of Frequency Constants for Data Arranged According to Equi-Distant Divisions of a Scale," *Proceedings of the London Mathematical Society*, Vol. 29, 1898.

140. Shewhart, W. A., *Economic Control of Quality of Manufactured Product*, New York, Van Nostrand, 1931.

141. Shewhart, W. A., *Statistical Method from the Viewpoint of Quality Control*, Washington, U.S. Dept. of Agriculture, 1939.

142. Siegel, I., *Concepts and Measurement of Production and Productivity*, Washington, U.S. Bureau of Labor Statistics, 1952.

143. Simpson, G. and Kafka, F., *Basic Statistics*, New York, Norton, 1952.

144. Smart, L. E. and Arnold, S., *Practical Rules for Graphic Presentation of Business Statistics*, Bureau of Business Research, The Ohio State University, 1947.

145. Smith, C. D., "On Generalized Tchebycheff Inequalities in Mathematical Statistics," *American Journal of Mathematics*, Vol. 52, No. 1, 1930.

146. Snedecor, G. W., *Analysis of Variance*, Ames, Iowa State College Press, 1934.

147. Snedecor, G. W., *Statistical Methods*, 4th ed., Iowa State College Press, 1946.

148. Social Science Research Council, "The Pre-Election Polls of 1948," *Bulletin* 60, New York, 1949.

149. Spear, Mary E., *Charting Statistics*, New York, McGraw-Hill, 1952.

150. Spurr, W. A., Kellogg, L. S. and Smith, J. H., *Business and Economic Statistics*, Homewood, Ill., Irwin, 1945.

151. Staehle, H., "A Development of the Economic Theory of Price Index Numbers," *The Review of Economic Studies*, June, 1935.

152. Stauber, B. R., Koffsky, N. M. and Randall, C. K., "The Revised Price Indexes," *Agricultural Economics Research*, April, 1950.

153. "Student," "The Probable Error of a Mean," *Biometrika*, Vol. 6, 1908.

154. Sturges, H. A., "The Choice of a Class Interval," *Journal of the American Statistical Association*, March, 1926.

155. Sukhatme, P. V., *Sampling Theory of Surveys*, Iowa State College Press, 1954.

156. Thompson, C. M. and Merrington, M., "Tables for Testing the Homogeneity of a Set of Estimated Variances," *Biometrika*, Vol. 33, 1946.

157. Thorp, Willard L., *Business Annals*, New York, National Bureau of Economic Research, 1926.

158. Tintner, G., *Mathematics and Statistics for Economists*, New York, Rinehart, 1953.

159. Tintner, G., *The Variate Difference Method*, Bloomington, Indiana, 1940.

160. Tippett, L. H. C., *The Methods of Statistics*, 4th ed., New York, Wiley, 1952.

161. Tippett, L. H. C., *Technological Applications of Statistics*, New York, Wiley, 1950.

162. Treloar, A. E., *Elements of Statistical Reasoning*, New York, Wiley, 1939.

163. Tugwell, R. G., ed., *The Trend of Economics*, New York, Knopf, 1924.

164. Ulmer, M. J., *The Economic Theory of Cost of Living Index Numbers*, New York, Columbia University Press, 1949.

165. United Nations, Economic Commission for Europe, *Economic Survey of Europe Since the War*, Geneva, 1953.

166. United Nations Statistical Office, "Index Numbers of Industrial Production," *Studies in Methods*, No. 1, New York, 1950.

167. United Nations Statistical Office, "International Standard Industrial Classification of all Economic Activities," *Statistical Papers Series M*, No. 4, New York.

168. United Nations Statistical Office, "The Preparation of Sampling Survey Reports," *Statistical Papers Series C*, No. 1 (revised), Feb., 1950.

169. U.S. Bureau of the Census, "Concepts and Methods Used in the Current Labor Force Statistics Prepared by the Bureau of the Census," *Current Population Reports*, Series P—23, No. 2, July 30, 1954.

170. U.S. Bureau of the Census, *Current Population Survey, Labor Force*, Series P—57.

171. U.S. Bureau of Labor Statistics, "The Consumer Price Index," *Bulletin* 1140, Washington, 1953.

172. U.S. Bureau of Labor Statistics, "A Description of the Revised Wholesale Price Index," *Monthly Labor Review*, Feb., 1952.

173. U.S. Bureau of Labor Statistics, "The Productivity Measurement Program of the Bureau of Labor Statistics," Washington, 1950.

174. U.S. Bureau of Labor Statistics, "Productivity Trends in Selected Industries Through 1950," *Bulletin* 1046, Washington, Oct., 1951.

175. U.S. Bureau of Labor Statistics, "The Revised Consumer Price Index," *Monthly Labor Review*, Feb., 1952.

176. U.S. Bureau of Labor Statistics, *Technical Note on the Measurement of Trends in Output per Man-Hour*, Washington, April, 1954.

177. U.S. Bureau of Labor Statistics, "Trends in Man-Hours Expended per Unit, Selected Machine Tools, 1939 to 1945," Washington, 1947; ". . . 1947 to 1948," Washington, 1950; ". . . 1949 to 1950," Washington, 1952.

178. U.S. Interstate Commerce Commission, Bureau of Transport Economics and Statistics, "Table of 105,000 Random Decimal Digits," Washington, D.C., May, 1949.

179. U.S. Office of Statistical Standards, Bureau of the Budget, "Standard Industrial Classification Manual."

180. U.S. Office of Statistical Standards, Bureau of the Budget, "Univac Seasonal Computations, Method No. 1," *Statistical Reporter*, January, 1955.

181. Vining, R., "Methodological Issues in Quantitative Economics: Koopmans on the Choice of Variables to be Studied and on Methods of Measurement," *The Review of Economics and Statistics*, May, 1949.

182. von Mises, R., *Probability, Statistics and Truth*, New York, Macmillan, 1939.

183. Wald, A., *Sequential Analysis*, New York, Wiley, 1947.

184. Wald, A., *Statistical Decision Functions*, New York, Wiley, 1950.

185. Walker, Helen M., *Mathematics Essential for Elementary Statistics*, 2nd ed., New York, Holt, 1951.

186. Walker, H. M. and Lev, J., *Statistical Inference*, New York, Holt, 1953.

187. Walsh, C. M., *The Problem of Estimation*, London, King, 1921.

188. Waugh, Albert E., *Elements of Statistical Method*, 3rd ed., New York, McGraw-Hill, 1952.

189. Wendt, Paul F., *Classification and Financial Experience of the Customers of a Typical New York Stock Exchange Firm from 1933 to 1938*, Maryville, Tennessee, 1941 (privately printed).

190. Whittaker, E. T. and Robinson, G., *The Calculus of Observations*, London, Blackie & Son, 1924.

191. Wilks, S. S., *Elementary Statistical Analysis*, Princeton University Press, 1949.

192. Wilks, S. S., *Mathematical Statistics*, Princeton University Press, 1943.

193. Wirth, Louis, ed., *Eleven Twenty Six: A Decade of Social Science Research*, Univ. of Chicago Press, 1940. Section on "Quantification: The Quest for Precision."

194. Wold, H., *A Study in the Analysis of Stationary Time Series*, Upsala, Almqvist, 1938.

195. Yates, F., "The Analysis of Multiple Classifications with Unequal Numbers in Different Classes," *Journal of the American Statistical Association*, March, 1934.

196. Yates, F., "Contingency Tables Involving Small Numbers and the χ^2 Test," *Supplement to the Journal of the Royal Statistical Society*, 1, 1934.

197. Yates, F., *Sampling Methods for Censuses and Surveys*, 2nd ed., New York, Hafner, 1953.

198. Youngdahl, R., "The Structure of Interest Rates on Business Loans at Member Banks," *Federal Reserve Bulletin*, July, 1947.

199. Yule, G. U. and Kendall, M. G., *An Introduction to the Theory of Statistics*, 14th ed., New York, Hafner, 1950.

Index

Index

(The index and the list of references are complementary. In general, the index does not include references to books named in the bibliography, unless the references are to specific sections of these books.)